PHYSICS

By

ERICH HAUSMANN, E.E., Sc.D.

THOMAS POTTS PROFESSOR OF PHYSICS AND DEAN OF THE COLLEGE
POLYTECHNIC INSTITUTE OF BROOKLYN

AND

EDGAR P. SLACK, S.B., M.S.

PROFESSOR OF PHYSICS
POLYTECHNIC INSTITUTE OF BROOKLYN

THIRD EDITION, THIRD PRINTING

D. VAN NOSTRAND COMPANY, Inc.

TORONTO   NEW YORK   LONDON

NEW YORK

D. Van Nostrand Company, Inc., 250 Fourth Avenue, New York 3

TORONTO

D. Van Nostrand Company (Canada), Ltd., 228 Bloor Street, Toronto

LONDON

Macmillan & Company, Ltd., St. Martin's Street, London, W.C. 2

———

First Published September 1935

Seven Reprintings

———

Second Edition, August 1939

Twenty-seven Reprintings

———

Third Edition, August 1948

Reprinted November 1948, April 1949

PRINTED IN THE UNITED STATES OF AMERICA

Preface

This third edition of *Physics* incorporates a number of changes through-out; these have been made for greater clarity, improved expression, and better coordination. There have been a few rearrangements of subject matter for more effective teaching; for example, merging the chapters on Calorimetry and Change of State, interchanging the chapters on Statics and Mechanical Energy, recasting the material on electrical communication to emphasize Electronics, and advancing the presentation of the properties and constitution of matter, of impulse and momentum, and of Coulomb's Law in Electrostatics.

Additions have been made to include recent developments in Physics as well as important practical applications of its principles. Some of the new topics are: effects at supersonic speeds, electron accelerators, nuclear reactions, and atomic energy. A chapter on the Mks. System of units has been added at the end of the section on Electricity and Magnetism, where its advantages can be appreciated by the student.

The level of the book is substantially the same as before and the same emphasis is placed upon analytical methods. More space is given to so-called Modern Physics, although, as before, this material is included at appropriate places throughout the text, reserving for the last chapter the more advanced phases which entail a background that spreads across the major divisions of the book.

The problems have been replaced practically in their entirety; there are over eight hundred of them arranged sequentially at the ends of chapters. The answers to the odd-numbered problems are given at the end of the book.

The text aims to present the essentials of Physics to college students who major particularly in science, technology, or engineering. It is intended to give a gradual and logical approach to the subject, to develop and illustrate the fundamental concepts clearly, and to afford a mastery of the basic principles of this fascinating branch of natural philosophy. To those who study Physics for its cultural value, the text should aid in developing a power of analysis that will be useful in any career.

Many years of teaching and professional experience have led the authors to devote considerable space to the subject of Mechanics, so that this initial part of the book may be found clear and understandable even by the student without previous training in Physics. The subsequent parts have been treated with more and more conciseness in keeping with the increased comprehension of the well-grounded student. This policy has been carried out also in connection with the handling of units, the inclusion of worked-out problems, and the mathematical steps in formulating the results.

The book should be found suitable for courses in which all parts of the subject are covered in one year, or for individual courses in Mechanics, Heat, Electricity and Magnetism, and Sound and Light that extend in the aggregate over longer periods. A number of the more advanced sections in the various chapters have been starred; these may be omitted in the shorter courses, but may well be used as additional assignments for the gifted student. Problems that apply to the material covered in starred sections have been similarly marked. It is expected that class work will be supplemented by demonstration lectures and laboratory experiments.

In presenting derivations of physical laws and relationships, the purpose of the proof and the course to be followed are stated before embarking upon the detailed description and mathematical processes. In working out the illustrative examples, attention is given to the units of measurement involved, and in the early part of the text the units are carried through the various steps and balanced. These details of presentation will aid the student in acquiring clarity and definiteness of thought, and should enable him to analyze and solve original problems with confidence.

Thanks are expressed to the many users of the earlier editions who have offered suggestions for the betterment of the text, and also to several professors who have read the present manuscript critically and have given advice in further improvement. Largely because of this help, the authors feel that this completely reworked edition is a more useful and teachable book.

ERICH HAUSMANN
EDGAR P. SLACK

August 1, 1948

Contents

Mechanics

Fundamental Quantities

Chapter I

1. Measurement.—Physics takes its place among the physical sciences with astronomy, chemistry, and geology, in dealing with natural phenomena concerning the behavior of inanimate objects, and some of its principles apply to living things as well. The fields of knowledge of these sciences overlap considerably and give rise to such branches as astrophysics, physical chemistry, geophysics, and biophysics. The laws and facts of Physics are concerned broadly with matter and energy, together with such related quantities as force and motion. These concepts and their interrelations are fundamental to all parts of the subject, comprising mechanics of solids and fluids, heat, electricity and magnetism, sound, and light.

A definite knowledge of natural phenomena, and of the precise relations between them, is based upon experimental information concerning the quantities involved. If this information were indefinite or ambiguous it would be subject to different interpretations, and naturally the conclusions drawn therefrom would be open to speculation. Clearly, the evidence obtained must be quantitative in order that it may have definite meaning. Evidence of this type is obtained by *measurement*, one of the most important elements in all scientific work.

The usual way to measure a quantity is to compare it with some other quantity of the same kind which is used as a basis of comparison. Everyone is familiar with the process of measuring the length of an object by laying a foot-rule alongside of it and expressing the result in feet and inches. A statement that a pole is 15 feet in length will enable anyone having a foot-rule to form a correct conception of that length by laying off a distance equal to 15 one-foot distances. The length of the pole can also be expressed as 180 inches. This illustration shows that *the measurement of a quantity involves two things: a number and a unit*. To say that the pole measures 15 or 180 is an incomplete statement; it is necessary to say 15 feet or 180 inches. The unit shows how large a quantity is used as the basis of comparison, and the number shows how many of these units are contained in the quantity being measured.

Some statements based on physical measurements are given below to indicate the necessity for both number and unit: The rating of a certain automobile engine is 65 horsepower. The speed of a large steamship was found to be 25.3 knots. Comfortable room temperature is 68 degrees fahrenheit. Atmospheric pressure is about 14.7 pounds per square inch. The angular speed of a particular motor is 1800 revolutions per minute. The wavelength of yellow light is 0.0000589 centimeter. The weight of an electron is 9.11×10^{-28} gram.

Physics is called an exact science because the quantities with which it is concerned are capable of accurate measurement. Accuracy in a measurement requires a knowledge of the correctness of the standard of comparison, the use of a measuring device of adequate sensitiveness, and the exercise of care by the operator in manipulation and computation.

Among the quantities with which Physics deals, three are generally regarded as fundamental, namely, *length*, *mass*, and *time*. These fundamental quantities and their measurement are considered in this chapter, together with some computations involving their use.

2. Standards and Units of Length.—The units of length commonly employed belong to two groups, namely the *British System of Units* and the *Metric System of Units*, and these are based upon definite distances on bars that are preserved as standards. The *yard* is the standard of length in the British group of units. The Imperial yard

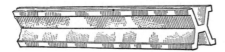

Fig. 1. Standard meter bar. The defining lines are engraved on the center rib

is the distance at 62 degrees fahrenheit (°F.) between two fine lines engraved on gold plugs in a bronze bar kept at the Standards Office in Westminster, London. The *meter* is the standard of length in the Metric group and is the distance at 0 degrees centigrade (°C.) between the centers of two lines traced on a platinum-iridium bar kept in a subterranean vault of the International Bureau of Weights and Measures at Sèvres, France.

Several standards of length are kept at the Bureau of Standards in Washington, D. C. Because of difficulty in marking and because of variations in length due to shrinkage and expansion since construction, the distance between marks on any one meter bar is not precisely 1 meter; for example, the length of Meter Bar No. 27 is

1.6 ± 0.1 microns short as certified by several recent comparisons with the standard meter bar at Sèvres. Fig. 1 shows a portion of a standard bar.

The multiples and submultiples of the yard and of the meter in common use, together with their equivalents, are given below for reference purposes:

Units of Length

British	Metric
1 mile (mi.) = 1760 yards	1 kilometer (km.) = 1000 meters
1 yard (yd.) = 3 feet	1 meter = 100 centimeters
1 mile (mi.) = 5280 feet	1 centimeter (cm.) = 10 millimeters
1 foot (ft.) = 12 inches	1 meter = 1000 millimeters
1 inch (in.) = 1000 mils	1 millimeter (mm.) = 1000 microns

It is often necessary to convert expressions of length in one group to corresponding ones in the other group. The fundamental relationship between the U. S. yard and the meter, as fixed by an Act of Congress in 1866, is: 1 yard = $\frac{3600}{3937}$ meter. In consequence, the following relations hold with sufficient exactness for most purposes; at least the last two relationships should be remembered.

Conversion Factors for Lengths

1 mile	=	1.6093 kilometers
1 kilometer	=	0.6214 mile
1 foot	= 30.48	centimeters
1 meter	=	3.281 feet
1 meter	= 39.37	inches
1 inch	=	2.540 centimeters

3. Handling of Units.—In carrying out computations involving lengths or other physical quantities, *the units should be included throughout*; they may be cancelled, multiplied, or divided as though they were numbers. For example, transfer to centimeters a reading of $\frac{1}{8}$ inch on a measuring scale, by using the fact that 1 inch = 2.54

centimeters. The specified reading can be multiplied by the factor $\dfrac{2.54 \text{ centimeters}}{1 \text{ inch}}$ without altering its value; thus,

$$\frac{1}{8} \text{ inch} = \frac{1}{8} \text{ inch} \times \frac{2.54 \text{ centimeters}}{1 \text{ inch}} = \frac{2.54 \text{ cm.}}{8} = 0.318 \text{ cm.}$$

Again, find the number of kilometers in a mile, by using the fact that 1 meter = 39.37 inches. Since 5280 feet = 1 mile, the fraction $\dfrac{5280 \text{ feet}}{1 \text{ mile}}$ will have a value of unity, and the distance of 1 mile can be converted to feet by using this fraction as a multiplier. The result is then converted to inches, subsequently to meters, and finally to kilometers by using appropriate fractions, each having a value of unity. The entire solution is given by

$$1 \text{ mile} = 1 \text{ mile} \times \frac{5280 \text{ feet}}{1 \text{ mile}} \times \frac{12 \text{ inches}}{1 \text{ foot}} \times \frac{1 \text{ meter}}{39.37 \text{ inches}} \times \frac{1 \text{ kilometer}}{1000 \text{ meters}}$$

$$= \frac{5280 \times 12}{39.37 \times 1000} \text{ kilometers} = 1.609 \text{ km.}$$

This procedure may seem laborious for such a simple computation, but in the more involved calculations which will be met with further on in this subject there is a distinct advantage in carrying all units through to avoid ambiguity and error.

4. Aids in Measuring Length.—In making careful measurements with a rule, the user generally desires a reading to the nearest fifth or tenth of a scale division. Fractional parts of divisions may be estimated by the eye, but can be obtained more accurately if an auxiliary scale called a *vernier* is provided. This device, named after Pierre Vernier, can be applied to straight and circular scales.

A vernier of simple design is shown in Fig. 2, applied to a caliper. The scale of the caliper is divided into millimeters, and the vernier has 10 divisions. These 10 divisions correspond in length to 9 scale divisions and, therefore, each vernier division is $\frac{1}{10}$ mm. shorter than a scale division. When the two jaws of the vernier caliper touch as shown at the left, the zero division of the vernier matches the zero division of the scale. When the jaws are separated $\frac{1}{10}$ of a scale division, that is, 0.1 mm., the first division of the vernier will match the first scale division, because the vernier division is $\frac{1}{10}$ mm. shorter than the other. When the jaws are separated by $\frac{7}{10}$ scale division, the seventh vernier division will match a scale division. Hence, the reading of the vernier at coincidence gives the number of tenths of a scale division by which the jaws are separated. When the jaws are

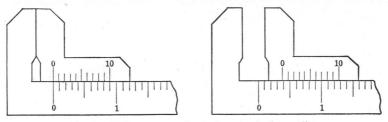

FIG. 2. Enlargement of vernier attached to caliper

separated farther than one scale division, the reading of the scale in full divisions up to the zero mark of the vernier is first taken, and to this is added the fractional part of a division as given by the vernier. Thus, the setting shown at the right in Fig. 2 is 3.7 mm.

The vernier aids the observer only in reading the fractional parts of a scale division; the smallest part to which it can be read directly by the vernier is called the *least count*. In the example chosen the least count of the instrument is 0.1 mm.

The *micrometer screw* is another device that is used in many instruments for precise measurement; it consists of an accurately threaded screw with a head that is divided into an integral number of divisions on its rim. Fig. 3 shows a micrometer caliper for measuring the

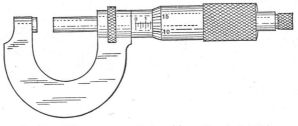

FIG. 3. Micrometer caliper; the reading is 0.163 in.

size of small objects. The screw has 40 threads to the inch and the head has 25 divisions, consequently a movement of the screw through one division on the head changes the distance between the screw end and the fixed jaw by $\frac{1}{25}$ of $\frac{1}{40}$ in., or 0.001 in. Estimation of tenths of the head divisions permits measurements to be made to 0.0001 in. The whole number of revolutions of the screw can be read on a fixed scale uncovered by the head as it moves away from the fixed jaw.

5. Angular Measure.—Where two lines lie along different directions, the angle between them is usually expressed in *degrees* (°). The total angle about a point is composed of 360°, and a right angle is equal to 90°. A degree has 60 *minutes* of arc ('), and a minute has 60 *seconds* of arc (").

Another unit for measuring angles is based upon the relative dimensions of a sector of a circle. In Fig. 4, the ratio of the arc s_1 to its radius r_1 is the same as that of any other arc s_2 to its radius r_2. This ratio of the arc length to the radius is not affected by the size of the circle but depends only upon the central angle θ (theta).

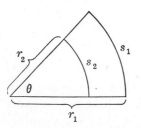

The angle subtended at the center of a circle by an arc equal in length to the radius is called a radian. Since the circumference of a circle is 2π (that is, 2×3.1416) times its radius, the total angle around the central point is 2π

FIG. 4. Illustrating radian measure

radians. A right angle is one-fourth as large, or $\pi/2$ radians. In general,

$$\text{Angle in radians} = \frac{\text{arc length}}{\text{radius}}$$

or in symbols

$$\theta = \frac{s}{r} \tag{1}$$

The angle θ is a ratio of two lengths; the arc length s must be expressed in the same unit as the radius r, consequently the angle in radians will be a numeric.

Conversion from degrees to radians, or vice versa, must often be made. Since 2π radians about a point equal 360°, 1 radian $= 360/2\pi = 57° \ 17' \ 45''$, or 57.3° approximately.

Conversion Factors for Angles

1 radian	= 57.3	degrees
1 degree	= 0.0175	radian
1 revolution	= 6.283	radians

Angles are usually measured by moving an arm over a plate that has a divided circular scale. Fig. 5 illustrates a small portion of a scale and the vernier used on a spectrometer intended for optical measurements; the least count of the instrument is 1 minute of arc.

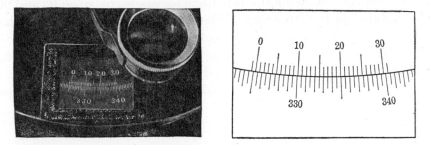

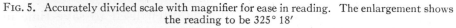

FIG. 5. Accurately divided scale with magnifier for ease in reading. The enlargement shows the reading to be 325° 18′

6. Trigonometric Functions of an Angle.—In many physical calculations it is necessary to deal with lengths so located as to form sides of a triangle, some of the sides and angles being known and others unknown. The determination of the unknown elements is generally made by applying the methods of trigonometry.

The trigonometric functions most often used are the sine, cosine and tangent; their definitions are reviewed below in connection with the right-angled triangle ABC of Fig. 6. The sine of either acute angle is the ratio of the length of the side opposite that angle to the length of the hypotenuse. The cosine of either acute angle is the ratio of the side adjacent to that angle to the hypotenuse. The

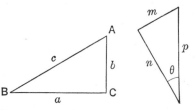

FIG. 6. Illustrating the trigonometric functions

tangent of either acute angle is the ratio of the side opposite that angle to the side adjacent to that angle. These statements are symbolized as follows:

Function:	For angle A:	For angle B:
$\sin = \dfrac{\text{opposite side}}{\text{hypotenuse}}$	$\sin A = \dfrac{a}{c}$	$\sin B = \dfrac{b}{c}$
$\cos = \dfrac{\text{adjacent side}}{\text{hypotenuse}}$	$\cos A = \dfrac{b}{c}$	$\cos B = \dfrac{a}{c}$
$\tan = \dfrac{\text{opposite side}}{\text{adjacent side}}$	$\tan A = \dfrac{a}{b}$	$\tan B = \dfrac{b}{a}$

$$(2)$$

It will be observed that $\sin A = \cos B$; that is, the sine of an angle is equal to the cosine of its complementary angle.

Values of the trigonometric functions for angles between 0° and 90° are tabulated in the Appendix. The functions for angles larger than 90° are obtained by applying the rules at the end of the table.

Experience should be acquired in handling these functions so that upon an inspection of a right-angled triangle such as $p\,m\,n$ in Fig. 6, the following can be written promptly without first writing the ratios expressing the foregoing functions:

$$m = p \sin \theta \qquad n = p \cos \theta \qquad m = n \tan \theta$$

For small angles an approximation is often used to save time in computations, to the effect that

$$\sin \theta = \theta \text{ (in radians)} = \tan \theta \tag{3}$$

As shown in the following table, these quantities are almost identical to the third decimal place for angles up to 10° and for most purposes may be used interchangeably.

Functions of Some Small Angles

Degrees	Radians	Sine	Tangent
0	0	0	0
5	0.087	0.087	0.088
10	0.175	0.174	0.176
15	0.262	0.259	0.268

The *Law of Sines* expresses the relation between the sides of a triangle and the sines of the angles opposite them. This law is given mathematically for the triangles of Fig. 7 by the statement

$$\frac{a}{\sin A} = \frac{b}{\sin B} = \frac{c}{\sin C} \tag{4}$$

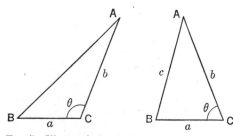

FIG. 7. Illustrating some laws of trigonometry

which shows that in any triangle the ratio of any side to the sine of the opposite angle is a constant.

This law applies to a right-angled triangle or to an oblique triangle as in the figure.

The *Law of Cosines* is used in the solution of an oblique triangle when two sides and the included angle are known, and the length of the other side is required. This law states that in any triangle, the square of any side is equal to the sum of the squares of the other two sides minus twice the product of these two sides and the cosine of the angle included between them. For example, in Fig. 7,

$$c^2 = a^2 + b^2 - 2ab \cos \theta \tag{5}$$

where θ is the angle between sides a and b, and c is the side opposite this angle. When $\theta = 90°$, the last term disappears, and the expression reduces to the form $c^2 = a^2 + b^2$, which is the familiar Theorem of Pythagoras for a right triangle.

7. Triangulation.—The principles of trigonometry may be used in determining distances which cannot be measured directly. Such measurements are made by indirect methods which usually require the calculation of one side of a triangle of which the other sides or the angles have been measured. These indirect processes are spoken of as *triangulation*. The angles are frequently measured with a surveying instrument called a *transit*. This consists essentially of a telescope suitably mounted on a tripod and so arranged that its angular position can be read on two graduated circles, one horizontal and the other vertical. To measure either the horizontal or the vertical angle between two objects, the telescope is sighted first upon one object and then upon the other, and the angle through which it is turned can be read by a vernier on the corresponding graduated circle.

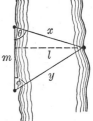

An example of triangulation is the measurement of the width of a river from one river bank. A known distance m is laid off with a tape along the bank parallel to the river; from its two extremities

Fig. 8. Determining the width of a stream by triangulation

some spot on the opposite river edge is sighted, and the angles which these lines of sight make with the known length m are measured. The information may be plotted on a diagram to scale, and the width of the river determined. Analytically the problem is solved by reference to Fig. 8, in which the measured angles are marked θ and ϕ (phi). From the Law of Sines, equation (4):

$$\frac{y}{\sin \theta} = \frac{m}{\sin (180 - \theta - \phi)} = \frac{m}{\sin (\theta + \phi)}$$

This expression is solved for y, and the width l of the river is obtained at once from the relation $l = y \sin \phi$.

*8. Latitude and Longitude.—For purposes of navigation and cartography the surface of the earth is considered to be marked off by two sets of circles at right angles to each other, so that the location of all places can be described with reference to them. One set of circles is formed on the surface by planes passed perpendicular to the earth's axis. These are called *parallels of latitude*. The largest of these, the great circle called the *equator*, has zero latitude, and from it latitude is reckoned northward and southward up to the value 90° at the poles. The other set of circles is formed by planes which include the earth's axis, each plane intersecting the surface in a great circle passing through the poles. These circles are called *meridians of longitude*. The circle through

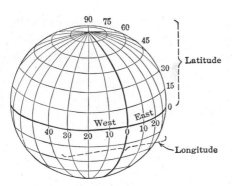

Fig. 9. Parallels of latitude and meridians of longitude

Greenwich, England, is taken as the starting line and from it longitude is reckoned eastward and westward as far as 180° each way. Fig. 9 shows the marking of the globe in this manner.

The average radius of the earth is 3958 miles, which makes the length of arc for each degree of latitude $2\pi\ 3958 \div 360 = 69.1$ mi. This is also the length of a degree of longitude at the equator, but elsewhere a degree of longitude is less, depending upon the latitude. A distance subtending one minute of latitude is called a nautical mile; its value is $69.1 \div 60 = 1.152$ (land) miles.

In measuring astronomical distances it is often necessary to have stations at widely different latitudes or longitudes in order to provide adequate base lines for triangulation. To measure the distance to the moon, for example, observations are taken on some point of the moon from two stations that are quite far apart. For simplicity assume these stations to be on the same meridian of longitude, as shown in Fig. 10, and the points A, B, O and M to lie in the same plane. At station A the angle of depression α (alpha) of the telescope away from the zenith Z_a is measured when the reference point on the moon is in the center of the field of view. The corresponding angle β (beta) from OZ_b is measured by a telescope at station B. From the known latitudes of the two stations, the angle γ (gamma) subtended by them at the center of the earth O becomes known, and the distance AB can be computed by the Law of Cosines applied to the isosceles triangle OAB, having the radius of the earth, namely 3958 mi., for two of its sides. Thereafter,

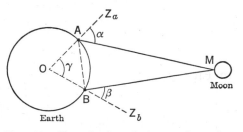

FIG. 10. Use of triangulation to determine distance to the moon

the distances AM and BM can be determined by applying the Law of Sines to the triangle ABM, and finally the distance OM is ascertained. The distance from the earth to the moon (center to center) varies from 225,000 to 252,000 mi.

9. Area and Bulk.—The areas and volumes of regular geometric figures are often found by calculation, based upon measurements of their linear dimensions. A few formulas which are frequently used for this purpose in physical calculations are given herewith:

Areas and Volumes

Figure	Area	Figure	Volume
Triangle of altitude h and base b	$\frac{1}{2}hb$	Right cylinder of altitude h and base of area B	hB
Triangle of sides a, b, and c, and semi-perimeter s, that is $s = \frac{1}{2}(a + b + c)$	$\sqrt{s(s-a)(s-b)(s-c)}$	Pyramid or cone of altitude h and base of area B	$\frac{1}{3}hB$
Trapezium of altitude h and bases b and b'	$\frac{h}{2}(b + b')$	Sphere of radius r	$\frac{4}{3}\pi r^3$
Circle of radius r	πr^2		
Sphere of radius r, surface area	$4\pi r^2$		

The units in which areas and volumes are expressed are usually the squares and cubes respectively of the regular linear dimensions; for example, square feet (abbreviated sq. ft. or ft.²), square centimeters (sq. cm. or cm.²), cubic yards (yd.³), and cubic meters. Other units met with and their equivalents appear in the following table:

Some Units of Area and Volume

Circular mil	= area of circle 1 mil in diameter
Acre	= 43,560 sq. ft. = $\frac{1}{640}$ square mile
Gallon	= 4 quarts (liquid measure) = 231 cu. in. = 3.785 liters
Liter	= 1000 cu. cm. = 61.02 cu. in. = 1.057 quarts (liquid measure)
Bushel	= 32 quarts (dry measure) = 2150.4 cu. in.

*10. The Planimeter.—For measuring small areas, such as indicator cards and map areas, an instrument called the *planimeter* is used. The usual form consists of two arms hinged together as shown in Fig. 11; the far end of one arm is provided with a stylus to be

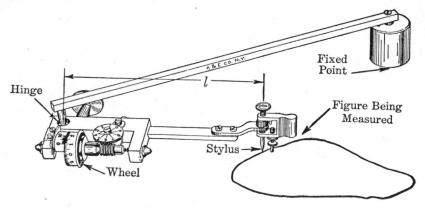

Fig. 11.   Planimeter set up to measure an area
(*Courtesy of Keuffel & Esser Company*)

moved clockwise around the perimeter of the figure under measurement, while the other arm has a weight or a pin point for anchoring the instrument to some point outside of the figure. The arm with the stylus carries a graduated wheel; the axis is parallel to that arm, and the wheel rolls and slides along the paper on which the figure is drawn. It can be shown by mathematical analysis that the area of the figure is

Area = arm length × wheel radius × wheel rotation

or

$$A = lr\phi \tag{6}$$

where l is the length of the arm carrying the wheel, r is the radius of the wheel, and ϕ is the angle through which the wheel turns while the stylus traces completely around the figure. The wheel is calibrated to read directly in square inches, square centimeters, or the like, and the calibration can be verified by tracing the perimeter of some geometric figure of which the area can be computed readily.

11. Matter.—Anything which occupies space is called *matter*, and all substances are included in this comprehensive term. Matter may be recognized in three states, namely as solids, liquids, or gases. Water, for example, is matter in the liquid state; when the temperature is lowered sufficiently it will freeze and become ice, and when the temperature is raised sufficiently it will vaporize and become steam. Whether water has changed to the solid or to the gaseous state, its chemical composition remains the same.

Everyone is familiar with many kinds of matter, and each kind is distinguished from the others by certain *properties*. Such properties include the obvious characteristics of color and smell, as well as a host of physical and chemical properties which are determined by measurement. A knowledge of the various properties of a substance determines its suitability for any particular experimental or industrial use.

The various substances known to man may be classified broadly into *elements* and *compounds*, elements being basic substances and compounds being formed of two or more elements in definite proportions. Each element is composed of *atoms*, and the atom is regarded as the smallest particle into which matter may be divided by purely chemical means. The atoms of any one element differ from those of the other elements. Atoms of all the elements are much too small to be seen, but despite their minuteness many things are definitely known about them. In fact, effects produced by individual atoms can actually be observed. A compound is composed of *molecules*, all alike, and the molecules of one compound differ from those of another. The number of compounds that can be formed from the ninety-two natural elements is almost limitless.

A few examples of elements and compounds in the various states of matter at ordinary temperatures are given below:

Elements and Compounds

Solids		Liquids		Gases	
Elements	Compounds	Elements	Compounds	Elements	Compounds
Aluminum	Copper	Bromine	Alcohol	Helium	Acetylene
Carbon	sulfate	Mercury	Gasoline	Hydrogen	Carbon
Copper	Lead dioxide	Gallium	Sulfuric acid	Nitrogen	dioxide
Zinc	Quartz	(melts in	Water	Oxygen	Hydrogen
	Table salt	the palm of			sulfide
		the hand)			Methane

Some kinds of matter are recognized as *mixtures* and others as *alloys*. For example, the atmosphere is a mixture of a number of gases, mostly oxygen and nitrogen in the proportion of about one to four, and contains among the other elements small quantities of helium, argon, and neon. An alloy is a mixture, usually of metals, produced by melting them together. For example, brass is formed by the fusion of copper and zinc, and bronze by the fusion of copper and tin. Steel is essentially an alloy of iron and carbon, the carbon ranging from a few hundredths of 1 per cent to about 1.6 per cent depending on the type of steel.

Even though atoms are extremely small, they are known to be made up of still smaller particles, some of which have electric charges, § 205. The actual structure of an atom is naturally subject to conjecture, but there is ample theoretical and experimental evidence to conclude that it comprises three types of particles, called electrons, protons, and neutrons. The *electron* has a tiny but definite charge and it is designated as negative. The *proton* has a weight about 1800 times that of the electron, and its charge is just the same as that of the electron in amount but is opposite in its effect and is therefore positive. The *neutron* weighs about the same as the proton but possesses no charge.

Research with cosmic rays has demonstrated the existence of two short-lived particles of matter, named the *positron* and the *meson*.

The weight and electric charge of the positron are about the same as those of an electron, but the charge is positive. The meson may be positive or negative, with charges equal to that of the electron, but the weight is from 20 to 300 times as much.

The atom may be pictured as consisting of a central nucleus together with electrons whirling about it in the same way that the planets revolve about the sun, most of the region "occupied" by the atom being empty space, as in the solar system. The atom of one element differs from that of another by the number of protons in the nucleus as well as by the number of electrons that surround it. When the atom is in an electrically neutral or "uncharged" condition, the number of electrons equals the number of protons.

An important fact about an atom is the quantity of electric charge on its nucleus; this is expressed as the number of protons in the nucleus and is called the *atomic number*. The atoms of any one element are not all alike, for some are heavier than others. Elements containing atoms that have the same atomic number but different weights are called *isotopes;* they differ in the number of neutrons in the atomic nucleus. The total number of protons and neutrons in the nucleus is called the *atomic mass*.

The *average* weight of the atoms of any one element is always the same and is called its *atomic weight*. That for oxygen is taken as 16, and the atomic weights of all the other elements are expressed relative to this value.

12. Mass and Its Measurement.—Any particular object is composed of a definite quantity of matter determined by the number of molecules it contains and by the structure of the molecules themselves. The term *mass* will be used for the present as a measure of the quantity of matter in the object. Mass is a fundamental concept and a broader definition will be given in § 39. The British and Metric standards of mass are the *pound* and the *kilogram*.

The Imperial pound of mass is defined as the mass of a particular block of platinum which is kept at the Standards Office in Westminster, London.

The kilogram of mass is defined as the mass of a certain block of platinum preserved at the International Bureau of Weights and Measures and known as the standard kilogram. The U. S. pound is defined to five places as 0.45359 kilogram.

Other units of mass and the relations between them appear in the following table:

Units of Mass

British	Metric
1 ton = 2000 pounds 1 pound (lb.) = 16 ounces (oz.) 1 pound = 453.6 grams	1 kilogram (kg.) = 1000 grams 1 gram (gm.) = 1000 milligrams (mg.) 1 kilogram = 2.2046 pounds

The measurement of mass is usually accomplished with an equal-arm balance such as shown in Fig. 12. A mass to be measured is placed on one of its scale-pans, and known masses on the other, and the latter are varied until a balance is obtained. The operating principle is in reality the balancing of two forces, the earth's attraction for the mass on one pan being just counteracted by the earth's attraction for the known masses on the other.

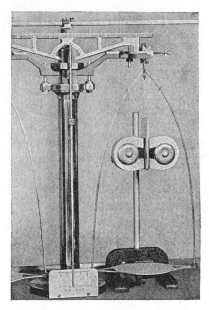

Fig. 12. Portion of analytical balance with magnetic damping device (*Courtesy of Christian Becker, Inc. and Central Scientific Company*)

The mass of a substance per unit volume is known as the *density* of that substance. For example, the mass of 1 cubic centimeter of water is 1 gram, therefore the density of water is 1 gm. per cu. cm. In British units the density of water is not such a prime number. Since a gallon of water has a mass of 8.34 lb. and a volume of 231 cu. in. = 0.1337 cu. ft., the density of water is

$$\frac{8.34 \text{ lb.}}{0.1337 \text{ cu. ft.}} = 62.4 \text{ lb. per cu. ft.}$$

13. Measurement of Time.—The regularity of the earth's motion around the sun serves as the basis for measurements of time. The earth revolves about the sun once a year (about $365\frac{1}{4}$ days). Its orbit or ecliptic is strictly an ellipse with the sun at one focus, but it may be considered approximately as a circle having a radius of

92,900,000 mi. The speed of the earth along this path varies slightly on account of the eccentricity of the orbit, the speed being greater where the earth is nearer the sun. The earth also rotates uniformly on its axis once a day. The axis passes through the north and south geographic poles, and is not perpendicular to the plane of the ecliptic but is inclined about 23.5° from a perpendicular position. The direction of the axis remains almost fixed in space as the earth rotates, and points almost directly toward the North Star, Polaris.

The stars are tremendously distant, the nearest star being many thousand times as far away as the sun. For this reason, the stars appear almost like fixed points in space, occupying virtually the same positions regardless of the position of the earth in its orbit. To us it appears that the earth is stationary and that the sun and stars move; and when one of the celestial bodies appears to pass through the plane of a given meridian it is said to cross the meridian.

If the instants that a given *star* crosses the meridian are recorded on two successive nights, the elapsed interval will be the time required for one complete rotation of the earth with reference to a star. This is called a *sidereal* day, and this constant interval is used in astronomical measurements. On the other hand, if the instants that the *sun* crosses the meridian are recorded on two successive days, the elapsed interval will be the time required for an apparent rotation of the earth with respect to the sun, and this is called a *solar* day. The solar days vary somewhat in length, the average throughout the year being known as the *mean solar day*. Through the course of a year, a given point on the earth in facing the sun 365 times must face a fixed point in space (i.e., a star) 366 times, and owing to this fact the mean solar day is about $\frac{366}{365}$ of a sidereal day; that is, the mean solar day is about 4 min. longer than the sidereal day.

The mean solar day is subdivided into 24 hours, each hour being further divided into 60 minutes, and each minute into 60 seconds. Thus the mean solar day is composed of 86,400 mean solar seconds. This *mean solar second* is the unit of time which is in general use for physical and engineering work, as well as for everyday purposes.

In most clocks or watches a spring-driven gear train is allowed to run down at a slow and uniform rate under the action of an escapement, controlled either by a pendulum or a balance wheel, and the gear train turns the hands of the instrument in front of a dial or faceplate. In the synchronous electric clock, the hands are driven by a small motor which is connected to an alternating-current circuit. The motor runs in synchronism with the generators at the power station, and the speed of these machines is controlled accurately.

For the recording of official time, a *precision clock* is used, the accuracy of which is checked at regular intervals with a meridian telescope. Precision clocks are designed and constructed with the utmost care, and are kept in constant-temperature rooms to insure uniform operation. The mechanism is enclosed in a glass case from which most of the air is removed. They are the most accurate time-keepers available.

In scientific and engineering work, it is usually desired to measure the *duration of an interval of time* rather than to determine the correct time at a certain instant. For this purpose the familiar stop watch is widely used. In laboratory work, clocks are used in which each sweep of the pendulum operates an electrical contact in a sounder circuit, the audible clicks of the sounder making the intervals easy to count. Short time intervals can be measured accurately by indirect methods that make use of tuning forks, chronographs, oscillographs, and crystals exhibiting the piezoelectric effect.

14. Numerical Computations.—The solution of numerical problems is an essential part of any serviceable course in physics, and the observance of a few rules will make the work easier and more meaningful. Computations should be carried out to a number of places consistent with the data provided and the nature of the problem. Results should usually be stated to three or four significant figures, and such precision can be obtained directly from a standard slide rule. In stating problems in this text, numerical quantities are often given to only one or two digits, such as 7 ft. or 0.12 mm. This is done to lessen mathematical work and to avoid distraction from the physical concepts involved; these figures should be regarded as precise to three or four places.

Where data are supplied to many places, as in dealing with the wavelength of light, or where the effect under observation is very small, as in the expansion caused by heat, the number of figures to be kept in the computations and result should be correspondingly increased. Care should be taken, however, not to express results to more figures than are justified by the data. For example, in computing the area of a rectangle that is measured as 2.26 in. long and 1.89 in. wide, it should be noted that these dimensions are expressed to the nearest 0.01 in., and are precise to about 1 part in 200, or $\frac{1}{2}$ of 1 per cent. Since the area was not ascertained more precisely than this, the result should be expressed as 2.26 in. $\times$ 1.89 in. = 4.27 sq. in. It is needless and incorrect to express it with more figures, as *these would imply a precision not obtainable from the data provided.*

PROBLEMS

1. The greatest depth in the Atlantic Ocean is 30,246 ft. and is found north of Puerto Rico. Express this depth in meters.

2. The length of the Amazon River in South America is 6270 km. Convert this distance to miles.

3. Given 1 meter = 39.37 in. Show that 1 kilometer = 0.6214 mile by carrying all the units through the computation.

4. A scale having divisions $\frac{1}{8}$ in. long is equipped with a vernier by which readings may be made to the nearest $\frac{1}{64}$ in. Compute (*a*) the length of each vernier division, and (*b*) the number of vernier divisions required.

5. The angle subtended by the moon's diameter at a place on the surface of the earth is 31′ 5.16″. Determine the approximate diameter of the moon based on an average distance of 235,000 miles from that place on the earth's surface.

6. The mil is an angle used in gunnery; one mil is $\frac{1}{6400}$ of a complete revolution. Determine the angle in mils subtended by a bull's-eye 0.150 in. in diameter at the marksman's position 50 ft. away from the target.

7. It is convenient to measure astronomical distances in terms of the distance that light travels in one year; this distance, known as a light-year, is equal to 588×10^{10} mi. The parsec is also used in astronomical measurements; it is defined as that distance at which the radius of the earth's orbit (92.9×10^6 mi.) subtends an angle of one second of arc. Express the light-year as a fractional part of a parsec.

8. A camera with a wide-angle lens embraces a field of view of 40°. What is the width of the field covered by the camera at a distance of 100 ft.?

9. Three towns, *A*, *B*, and *C*, are connected by straight roads of the following lengths: $AB = 6$ mi., $BC = 4$ mi., and $AC = 5$ mi. Find the angle between roads AB and AC.

10. An airplane travels at an elevation of 20,000 ft. How far away is the horizon from an observer in the plane?

11. A church spire casts a shadow on level ground and the angular elevation of the tip is 25° as measured from its shadow. At a point 250 ft. nearer the spire the angular elevation of the tip is 55°. Compute the height of the spire.

12. A datum line 75 ft. long is measured along the bank of a stream and from its ends an intermediate point on the opposite bank is sighted. The angles which these lines of sight make with the datum line are 60° and 50° respectively. Calculate the width of the stream.

13. Directions by radio bearings are commonly given in degrees reckoned in a clockwise direction from due north as zero; thus, due east = 90° and due west = 270°. Radio signals are picked up by two shore stations *A* and *B* from a ship which desires to know its location. Station *A* reports that the

bearing of the ship is 100° and Station B reports the bearing as 25°. Station B is known to be 200 mi. south and 70 mi. east of Station A; how far is the ship from each station?

14. A piece of wire 5 meters long is wound into a round coil of 4 turns. Find the radius and the area of the coil.

15. The area of Manhattan Island in New York is 22.24 square miles. How many gallons of water fall on the island during a 0.1-in. rainfall?

16. Calculate the volumetric piston displacement in the nine cylinders of an airplane engine which has a cylinder bore of $6\frac{1}{8}$ in. and a piston stroke of $6\frac{7}{8}$ in.

17. In surveying, directions are given by departures from north or south; for example, northeast = N 45° E, and southwest = S 45° W. Compute the area of a closed field having boundary lines as indicated by the following surveyor's notes:

Line	Bearing	Length
AB	N 37° 20′ E	425.3 ft.
BC	S 54° 25′ E	310.2 ft.
CD	S 37° 20′ W	472.7 ft.
DA	N 45° 40′ W	312.4 ft.

18. A cylindrical fuel-oil tank, having a volume of 550 gal. and an internal diameter of 4 ft., is installed with its axis horizontal. The depth of oil in the tank, as measured by inserting a stick vertically through an opening in the top, is found to be 1 ft. (*a*) What is the length of the tank? (*b*) How many gallons of oil are in the tank?

19. A planimeter has an arm 7.08 in. long and a wheel 0.90 in. in diameter. There are 100 divisions on the wheel. Determine the value of each division.

20. The uncharged atom of helium has 2 protons and 2 neutrons in the nucleus and has also 2 electrons, while that of oxygen has 8 protons and 8 neutrons in the nucleus and has also 8 electrons. (*a*) What is the atomic mass of oxygen? (*b*) What is the atomic number of helium?

21. The U. S. gold dollar was proclaimed in 1934 to be $15\frac{5}{21}$ grains of gold, nine-tenths fine. There are 480 grains in a troy ounce. What is the equivalent value of a troy ounce of fine (pure) gold?

22. (*a*) What is the mass of 1 cu. in. of water? (*b*) What is the mass of a column of water 1 ft. high and 1 sq. in. in sectional area?

23. A 16-lb. bowling ball has a circumference of 27.2 in. Consider the ball as a uniform sphere and compute the density of the material of which it is made.

24. How many cubic inches of metal are there in a 10-ft. length of "half-inch" electric conduit, which has an internal diameter of 0.622 in. and a wall thickness of 0.109 in.?

25. Howard Hughes took less than 4 days in his eastward flight around the world in 1938, yet reported that he had witnessed the sun rise on 5 mornings. Explain.

Vectors

Chapter II

15. Addition of Directed Quantities.—Many quantities that are involved in physical measurements or calculations can be added by simple arithmetic. Thus, a 100-gm. mass placed on the scale-pan of a balance in addition to 500 gm. already there makes a total mass of 600 gm.; again, a 4-min. interval followed without pause by one of 8 min. makes a total elapsed time of 12 min. Additions can be carried out in this manner when the quantities do not involve the idea of direction. Physical quantities that have directions can also be added; the process is more involved but not difficult.

Changes of position, called *displacements*, can be added even though these displacements are not in the same direction. Such an addition is necessary, for example, when a man walks a certain distance in one direction, another distance in a different direction, and so on, and desires to know his position with respect to the starting point. His entire journey may be mapped out as a series of displacements, one after another, each represented by an arrow of appropriate length and direction. An arrow drawn from the beginning to the end of such a diagram shows the man's final position with respect to the starting point and represents the "sum" of the separate displacements when their directions are taken into account; this sum is also known as the *resultant* displacement.

In solving such a problem *graphically*, the diagram is made carefully to scale, and the resultant is measured with rule and protractor to determine its length and direction. To solve the problem *analytically*, a rough diagram will suffice as a guide, and the length and direction of the resultant are calculated by mathematics. Both procedures will be illustrated by a specific problem.

Consider a pedestrian to walk 2 mi. due east and then 3 mi. in a direction 60° north of east. How far is he from the starting point and in what direction is he from that point? To solve the problem graphically, lay off the arrows representing the displacements accurately to suitable scale and at the exact inclinations, with the tail-end of the second arrow placed at the head-end of the first, thereby forming two sides of a triangle, as in the plan view of Fig. 13. Draw the closing side of the triangle, and measure its length carefully to the same scale. This will give the numerical value of the distance sought as $R = 4.4$ mi. Measure the direction that this closing side of the triangle makes with the east direction with a protractor; this angle is marked θ in the diagram. The result shows that side R is

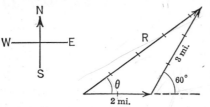

north of east by an angle $\theta = 37°$. It will be observed that both R and θ are accurate to only two significant figures.

Fig. 13. Addition of two displacements

The accuracy of a graphical result depends not only upon care in using the correct lengths and directions, but also upon making the drawing of adequate size. If a directed quantity were represented as an arrow 6 in. long, an error of $\frac{1}{32}$ in. in its length would mean an inaccuracy of one part in 6×32 or 192, that is, an error of $\frac{1}{2}$ per cent. Graphical solutions like the foregoing can be depended upon for an accuracy of one per cent if care is exercised. Much greater accuracy may be attained by analytical solutions since these do not require the making of drawings to scale.

To solve the foregoing problem analytically, make a rough sketch to resemble Fig. 13, and figure out the unknown parts of the triangle by trigonometry. First, use the Law of Cosines to determine the magnitude of the resultant R, the angle between the two known sides of the triangle being 120°. Thus

$$R^2 = (2)^2 + (3)^2 - 2 \times 2 \times 3 \cos 120°$$
$$= 4 + 9 - 12(- \sin 30°) = 13 + 12 \times 0.500 = 19.00$$

whence $R = 4.36$ mi. Next, apply the Law of Sines to find the direction of R:

$$\frac{3 \text{ mi.}}{\sin \theta} = \frac{4.36 \text{ mi.}}{\sin 120°}$$

whence $\sin \theta = (3/4.36) \sin 120° = 0.688 \times 0.866 = 0.596$. From trigonometric tables, the angle having this value for its sine is $\theta = 36.6°$.

It is apparent from this illustration that an analytical solution is inherently more precise than a graphical one since it does not depend upon the accuracy of a diagram, but only upon the precision of the data given and the number of places to which the computation is carried out.

16. Parallelogram Method of Combining Displacements.—In adding displacements, or other directed quantities, several methods may be used. These are described in this and the following sections.

In the first method, two displacements *a* and *b* are laid off graphically to scale in the proper directions *from a common starting point S*, so as to form two adjacent sides of a parallelogram, as shown in Fig. 14. The parallelogram is then completed by drawing the sides *a'* and *b'* parallel to *a* and *b* respectively and intersecting at *T*. The diagonal *R* drawn from the starting point, called the *concurrent diagonal*, gives the resultant both in length and direction. This method of finding the distance and direction from the starting point *S* to the terminating point *T* is called the Parallelogram Method of adding displacements. Since lengths *b* and *b'*

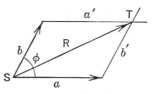

are equal, the resultant *R* is the same as though distance *b'* were added to distance *a* by the method described in the preceding section. Consequently the same mathematical steps used in the solution of the oblique triangle may be used to obtain an analytical solution by the Parallelogram Method. In this case it will be convenient to use the

Fig. 14. Adding two displacements by the Parallelogram Method

Law of Cosines, § 6, in a modified form. Applied to a parallelogram having adjacent sides *a* and *b* at an angle ϕ with each other, this law gives the length of the concurrent diagonal *R* from the expression

$$R^2 = a^2 + b^2 + 2ab \cos \phi \qquad (7)$$

The Parallelogram Method may be used for the addition of any number of displacements, by first finding the resultant of two of them, then adding another displacement to this resultant in the same way, and continuing this process until all are included.

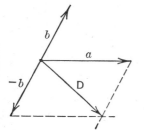

FIG. 15. Subtracting one displacement from another

The process of addition just described applies also to the reverse operation of *subtraction* with but a slight modification. Thus, to subtract one displacement, or other directed quantity, from another, *reverse its direction and proceed as in addition*. For example, to subtract the displacement *b* from displacement *a* in Fig. 14, first reverse *b* by shifting it through 180° to the position −*b* as in Fig. 15, and then add *a* and −*b* by the Parallelogram Method to get the difference *D*, as shown.

17. Polygon Method.—In adding three or more displacements, the Parallelogram Method is somewhat unwieldy, and it will be more convenient to proceed by the so-called Polygon Method. From a chosen starting point lay off one of the displacements to appropriate scale and in proper direction; *from its terminal* or head-end lay off another of the displacements similarly; from the terminal of the latter lay off the third distance; and so on until all are included. Lastly, draw the line that will close the figure and form a polygon;

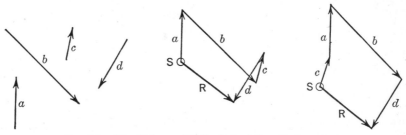

Fig. 16.   The Polygon Method of adding displacements

this is the resultant. This method is illustrated in Fig. 16, wherein the four displacements *a*, *b*, *c*, and *d* shown at the left are to be added. At the center of the figure the order of addition, starting at *S*, is *a*, *b*, *c*, *d*, and at the right is *c*, *a*, *b*, *d*; the resultant *R* is, of course, the same in magnitude and direction whatever the order followed in the additive process. It is to be noted that the resultant is directed away from the starting point.

The Polygon Method is an extension of that used in the problem of § 15 in which only two displacements were added; in that case the polygon had the simpler form of a triangle.

18. Resolution of Directed Quantities.—In the preceding sections, attention was focused upon two methods by which displacements

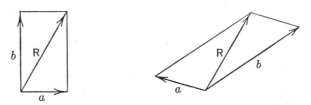

Fig. 17.   Resolution of a displacement into components

could be added to form a resultant. From the reverse point of view, the resultant displacement may be regarded as composed of *components*. Thus, in either diagram of Fig. 17, *R* is the resultant of *a* and *b*, and therefore *a* and *b* may be considered the components of *R*.

The diagram at the left illustrates the most frequent case, in which the components are at right angles to each other and hence are termed *rectangular components*. The process of breaking up a directed quantity into components is called *resolution*.

To resolve a displacement into two components it is desirable to follow a definite procedure. This is illustrated in Fig. 18, where the displacement L to be resolved and the two direction lines 1 and 2, along which the desired components shall lie, are shown at I. Draw the displacement L and the two direction lines from a common point S as depicted in II. From the head-end of length L draw lines parallel

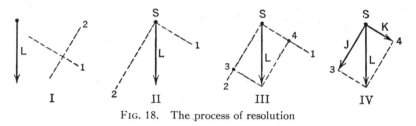

Fig. 18. The process of resolution

to the two direction lines 1 and 2, meeting those lines at points 3 and 4, as in III. Finally, replace the intercepts of these direction lines by the desired components J and K, and locate their head-ends at the intersecting points 3 and 4, as illustrated in IV. Naturally J and K must be measured to the same scale that is used in constructing L. This procedure is the same whatever the directions of the displacement to be resolved or the direction lines may be.

19. Addition by the Resolution Method.—The process of resolution just described is extremely useful when applied to the addition of displacements analytically, particularly where there are more than two such quantities to be added. Under these circumstances, each of the displacements concerned is resolved into rectangular components, usually in the horizontal and vertical directions, then the horizontal and vertical components of all displacements are added separately, and finally these results are combined at right angles to form the resultant. The diagrams need not be drawn to scale, since the lengths are determined accurately by trigonometric methods.

The following numerical example will clarify the procedure: Add the five displacements shown in elevation in Fig. 19 by the Resolution Method. Displacement a is 13.5 ft. vertically up, and has no horizontal component. Displacement e is 3.4 ft. horizontally to the right, and has no vertical component. The other three displacements must be resolved into their horizontal and vertical components. This resolution is shown in Fig. 20, where the perpendiculars dropped from the head-ends of the displacements upon

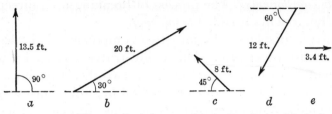

FIG. 19. Addition of displacements by the Resolution Method

the horizontal and vertical direction lines fix the terminals of the components. Thus, the displacement b of 20 ft. at an angle 30° up from the horizontal is replaced in the addition by a component 20 cos 30° = 17.32 ft.

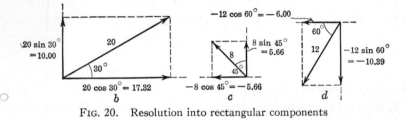

FIG. 20. Resolution into rectangular components

horizontally to the right and another component 20 sin 30° = 10.00 ft. vertically up.

The addition of the components is tabulated below:

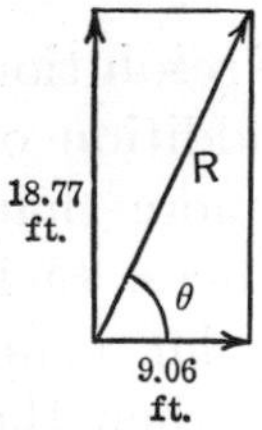

		Components		
Displace-ment	Up	Down	Right	Left
a	13.50	0	0	0
b	10.00	0	17.32	0
c	5.66	0	0	5.66
d	0	10.39	0	6.00
e	0	0	3.40	0
Totals	29.16	10.39	20.72	11.66
	10.39		11.66	
	18.77		9.06	

FIG. 21. Composition of rectangular components to form resultant

Consequently the result of the addition is a displacement 9.06 ft. horizontally to the right and 18.77 ft. vertically up. The resultant R of these components is obtained in Fig. 21; its magnitude is $\sqrt{(18.77)^2 + (9.06)^2} = $ 20.84 ft., and its direction is upward from the horizontal datum by an angle θ of which the tangent is 18.77/9.06 = 2.072, namely 64.2°.

20. Vector and Scalar Quantities.—It will be observed upon reviewing the quantities discussed so far that some have direction as well as numerical value or *magnitude*, while others are completely expressed by magnitude alone. *The term vector is applied to quantities which have both direction and magnitude* and which can be added by the procedures already given in this chapter. Any vector quantity may be represented by an arrow drawn in the appropriate direction and having a length which represents, to some convenient scale, the numerical value of the quantity which it represents. The displacement of a box along a chute, the velocity of an airplane, and the force used in stretching a spring, are examples of vector quantities. *The term scalar refers to quantities which have magnitude only.* As illustrations of scalar quantities, the mass of a pendulum bob, the density of platinum, or the horsepower of a motor, may be mentioned.

21. Vector Addition Applied to Forces.—The widest application of the addition of vectors deals with the action of forces. There are innumerable cases where an object is acted upon by several forces in different directions at the same time, and it is necessary to determine what single force is equivalent to all of them acting together. For this reason, the methods described ahead will be illustrated further by reference to forces.

A force is a push or a pull exerted upon an object, and is described subjectively as muscular effort. Forces produce a variety of effects. Sometimes a force is applied to set an object into motion, as in pushing a stalled automobile; sometimes it acts to retard a body already moving, as in a machine slowing down because of the backward drag of friction. Again, a force may produce distortion, as in stretching or compressing a spring. Such effects are described and analyzed in Chapter V, and from these effects, precise statements of the units of force are derived. It will suffice here in illustrating the addition of forces to use just one unit of force, the *pound*, and to define it as the pull which the earth exerts upon a 1-pound mass. This is the unit familiar alike to the engineer, physicist and layman.

If the forces acting on a body have the same or opposite directions, their resultant is found by direct addition or subtraction. Thus, if two locomotives are pulling a train up a grade and each exerts a force of 50,000 lb., the resultant of these forces is twice 50,000 lb., or 100,000 lb. acting in the same direction as the separate forces. Again, if a boy is pulling a sled over level snow with a horizontal force of 15 lb., and the snow exerts a backward force of friction of

2 lb. on it, the resultant force is 13 lb. in the direction of the boy's pull. When a number of forces act on a body in different directions, the resultant is found by vector addition as previously used with displacements.

For example, two forces are exerted at a point by pulling on spring balances in the directions shown at I in Fig. 22. The forces, *a* of 10 lb. and *b* of 7 lb., are actually exerted upon a knot in the strings fastened to the balances, and the knot is kept steady in position by a suitable force along the dotted line. To find the resultant of *a* and *b* graphically, draw them to scale as in part II of the figure, so as to form two sides of a parallelogram;

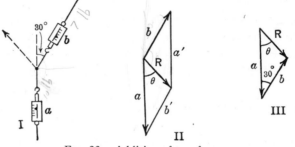

FIG. 22.   Addition of two forces

next, complete the parallelogram; and finally draw in the concurrent diagonal *R*. This diagonal represents the resultant of the two forces and its length and direction are measured. It is found to have a magnitude of 5.3 lb., and to make an angle of $\theta = 41°$ with *a*.

The resultant force may be found analytically from a diagram of the general form shown in part III of the figure, not necessarily to scale. From such a figure, the Law of Cosines shows that

$$R^2 = a^2 + b^2 - 2ab \cos 30° = (10)^2 + (7)^2 - 2 \times 10 \times 7 \times 0.866 = 27.8,$$

whence $R = 5.27$ lb. Since the upper angle is θ, it follows from the Law of Sines that $\dfrac{b}{\sin \theta} = \dfrac{R}{\sin 30°}$; whence

$$\sin \theta = \frac{b \sin 30°}{R} = \frac{7 \text{ lb.} \times 0.500}{5.27 \text{ lb.}} = 0.664$$

and $\theta = 41.3°$.

The Resolution Method, applied to the addition of displacements in § 19, is equally useful with forces, when the resultant of several of them is desired. The procedure is, first, to resolve each of the forces into components along two lines at right angles to each other; next, to combine the components along each of these lines into a single force by simple addition or subtraction; and finally, from the two rectangular forces thus found, to calculate the resultant.

To illustrate this procedure, suppose that it is desired to find the resultant of four forces acting on a single body. These are shown in Fig. 23, where A = 50 lb., acting upward and to the right, at an angle of 20° with

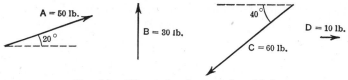

FIG. 23.   Illustrating forces to be added

the horizontal; B = 30 lb., acting directly upward; C = 60 lb., acting downward and to the left at an angle of 40° with the horizontal; and D = 10 lb. acting toward the right.   In resolving these forces, the horizontal and vertical directions will be used for the components, since two of the forces already have these directions, and so will require no resolution.   Thus A (50 lb.) is composed of a horizontal component 50 cos 20° and a vertical component 50 sin 20°, as shown in Fig. 24; B (30 lb.) is vertical; C (60 lb.)

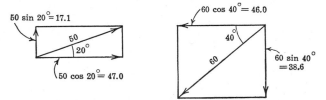

FIG. 24.   Forces resolved into rectangular components

consists of a horizontal component 60 cos 40° and a vertical component 60 sin 40° as shown; and D (10 lb.) is horizontal.   The components are evaluated and tabulated as follows:

Force	Components			
	Up	Down	Right	Left
A	17.1	0	47.0	0
B	30.0	0	0	0
C	0	38.6	0	46.0
D	0	0	10.0	0
Totals	47.1	38.6	57.0	46.0
	38.6		46.0	
	8.5		11.0	

The result of the addition is consequently a force of 8.5 lb. upward and one of 11.0 lb. to the right; these are combined at right angles and give the resultant of the four forces A, B, C and D as $R = \sqrt{(8.5)^2 + (11.0)^2} = 13.9$ lb., directed upward and toward the right at an angle $\theta = \tan^{-1} 8.5/11.0 = \tan^{-1} 0.773 = 37.7°$ with the horizontal.

22. Vector Addition in More Than One Plane.

—The methods used in the preceding sections for determining the resultant of vector quantities can be extended to more than one plane.

In the diagram of Fig. 25, the axes OX, OY, and OZ represent the intersections of three planes at right angles to one another, with the XZ plane horizontal; and a, b, and c represent forces acting along the directions of these axes. The resultant of any two of them is found exactly as before; for example, the resultant of b and c is R_1 and lies in the YZ plane at an angle $\theta = \tan^{-1} \dfrac{b}{c}$ with the horizontal XZ plane.

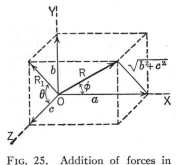

Fig. 25. Addition of forces in more than one plane

The force R_1 is next combined with the third force a; the final resultant of the three forces a, b, and c is $R = \sqrt{a^2 + b^2 + c^2}$; its plane is inclined at the angle θ with the horizontal, and in this plane it makes an angle $\phi = \tan^{-1} \dfrac{\sqrt{b^2 + c^2}}{a}$ with the axis OX.

In more involved problems, where the quantities to be added do not lie along mutually perpendicular axes, they can be resolved into components that do have these directions and the solution then carried forward in the same manner.

23. Moment of a Force; Torque.

—The rotation of a wheel or the twisting of a bolt may be described as either clockwise or counterclockwise. This statement implies direction, but direction in quite a different sense from the previous use of the term. It will be of interest to note how a rotational or angular quantity can be represented by a vector.

A force applied to a body may produce rotation about some axis. The rotational effect depends upon the direction of the force and also upon the place where it is applied with respect to the axis of rotation. The truth of this statement can be verified readily by opening a heavy door. If the hand exerts a force upon the door knob in the various directions shown from 1 to 4 in part I of Fig. 26, it will be observed that a smaller force is needed in direction 2 to open the door than in direction 3. A force along direction 4, parallel to the door, will produce no rotational effect, no matter how large the force may be. The most favorable direction is that along direction 1, perpendicular to the door, for the least force is required along this line.

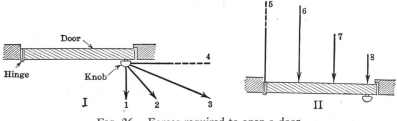

FIG. 26.   Forces required to open a door

Again, if the door is pushed at various places along its width in a direction at right angles to the door, as in part II, it will be observed that the least force is needed at position 8, along the edge farthest from the hinges, to open it; that more and more force must be exerted in approaching the hinges, positions 7 and 6; and that a force applied at the hinges, position 5, will not produce rotation, no matter how great it may be.

Experience in turning a door, together with a variety of similar experiences, shows the need of expressing definitely the effectiveness of a force in setting a body into rotation. The rotational effect is known as the *moment* of force, or *torque*, and is measured by *the product of the force and the perpendicular distance from the axis of rotation to the line of action of the force.* This perpendicular distance is called the *lever arm;* consequently

$$\text{Torque} = \text{force} \times \text{lever arm}$$

In symbols, the force is represented by F and the lever arm by L, and the torque becomes

$$T = FL \tag{8}$$

For example, in the crank shown in Fig. 27, the moment of force F tending to turn the crank clockwise about an axis O, is equal to $F \times OB$ for the position shown, where OB is the lever arm. Note that the lever arm L is not the length l of the crank, but is the perpendicular distance from the axis at O to the line of action of the force at point B. The lever arm can, of course, be expressed in terms of l by replacing L by its equal, $l \sin \theta$, thus making the torque $T =$

$Fl \sin \theta$. Another way to obtain this result is to resolve the force F into two components, namely: $F \cos \theta$ along the crank, and $F \sin \theta$ at right angles to the crank. The latter component multiplied by the length l of the crank yields the correct value of the torque.

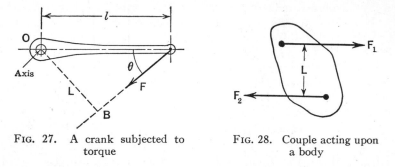

FIG. 27.   A crank subjected to torque   FIG. 28.   Couple acting upon a body

Another example illustrating torque is shown in Fig. 28, which represents a pair of forces acting upon a body to set it into rotation. Two equal and opposite forces that do not act along the same line constitute a *couple*. The torque exerted by a couple is equal to the product of one of the forces, F, and the perpendicular distance, L, between their lines of action; equation (8) applies to this example also.

The units of torque depend on the units selected for the force and for the lever arm: such units as pound-inches (lb-in.) and pound-feet (lb-ft.) are commonly used.

Torque is represented vectorially by an arrow drawn parallel to the axis about which it could by itself produce rotation. The arrow

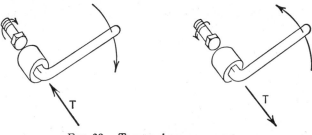

FIG. 29.   Torque shown as a vector

has a length which indicates the numerical value of the torque to some suitable scale, and points in the direction in which the torque would advance a bolt having the usual right-handed thread. This mode of vector representation is shown in Fig. 29 and will be used in Chapter VI in the study of the gyroscope.

PROBLEMS

1. A ship steams in still water 100 mi. due west and then 45 mi. due north. How far is the ship from its starting point, and in what direction is it from that point? Solve both graphically and analytically.

2. An airplane in still air travels 200 km. north and then 300 km. northwest. Determine graphically and analytically how far the airplane is from its starting point and in what direction it is from that point.

3. A yacht sails 24 mi. due east and then sails 12 mi. southwest. How far is the yacht from its starting point, and in what direction is it from that point? Solve both graphically and analytically.

4. A displacement of 80 ft. has a direction 60° east of north. Resolve it into two components one of which is directed north and the other east.

5. Resolve a displacement of 700 cm. into two components along direction lines that lie on opposite sides of the displacement and each of which makes an angle of 30° with the displacement.

6. Find the resultant of the following displacements by the resolution method: A, 4 km. due north; B, 2 km. 40° east of north; and C, 7 km. 60° west of north.

7. A person walks 3 mi. northeast, then 1 mi. east, and finally 4 mi. south. Calculate the distance from the starting point to the finishing point of the walk by using the polygon and resolution methods.

8. A vertically downward force of 100 lb. is combined with a force of unknown magnitude which is directed upward and toward the right at an angle of 30° from the horizontal, producing a resultant which is known to be directed toward the right at an angle of 30° below the horizontal. Compute the magnitude of the resultant.

9. A vertically downward force of 5 lb. is to be added to a force directed upward 50° from the horizontal, it being known that their resultant is horizontal. Find the numerical value of the resultant force.

10. A 200-lb. force is directed upward at an angle of 40° from the horizontal. Resolve this force into horizontal and vertical components.

11. Resolve a horizontal force of 75 lb. into two components, one of which is vertically downward and the other directed upward at an angle of 30° from the vertical.

12. Find the resultant of the following forces by the resolution method: A, 45 lb. vertically downward; B, 25 lb. upward and toward the right, making an angle of 40° with the vertical; C, 60 lb. downward and toward the right at an angle of 30° with the horizontal; and D, 20 lb. horizontally to the left.

13. A body makes three displacements of 5 ft. each in mutually perpendicular directions. How far is it from the starting point?

14. To open a certain door requires a force of 5 lb. at the knob when the force is at right angles to the door. How large a force would be needed when it makes an angle of 60° with the door?

15. A yard stick is pivoted at its midpoint so that it can rotate in a vertical plane. The stick is placed in a horizontal position and a 10-lb.

force is applied at one end. Compute the value of the torque tending to rotate the stick about the pivot when the applied force is (*a*) vertical, (*b*) horizontal, and (*c*) along a direction 35° from the horizontal and in a vertical plane.

16. Two shafts are coupled by means of a belt around two pulleys. The driving shaft has a 24-in. pulley and the driven shaft has an 18-in. pulley. The taut and slack sides of the belt are under tensions of 80 lb. and 10 lb. respectively. Find the torque exerted at each pulley.

Uniform Motion *Chapter III*

24. Uniform Linear Motion.—There are many examples which illustrate the motion of a body from one place to another along some sort of path. Thus, a crate hoisted by a rope moves directly upward, a stone whirled around at the end of a string describes a circle, and a train traveling between two cities follows the line of track. In each of these cases the body moves along a line, and therefore its motion is said to be *linear*.

The motion of such a body may be studied by observing the body carefully for a period of time, and measuring how far it moves during every second. If the motion of the body is *uniform*, these distances will be found to be equal. For example, if a trolley car having uniform motion passes a certain point at a given instant and passes another point 30 ft. away at the end of one second, it will pass a third point 30 ft. still farther away at the end of the next second, and so on, covering the same distance (namely, 30 ft.) during each second. If shorter time intervals are chosen, the same equality of displacement will be observed. In general, a body is said to have uniform linear motion if it traverses equal distances during equal intervals of time, however brief these intervals may be.

Motion that is both linear and uniform is easy to imagine and is the simplest of all motions to study. Often motion that is linear is not uniform; for example, a falling body is known to travel faster and faster as it approaches the earth. Also, the trolley car above mentioned, after starting from rest, had to acquire the uniform motion referred to, and later will lose that uniform motion when the brakes are applied. Many other cases will doubtless suggest themselves in which uniform motion is preceded and followed by periods of non-uniform motion. Such cases of non-uniform motion are treated in later chapters; for the present, in dealing with uniform motion, it will be assumed that the body has already started from rest and reached a state of uniform motion before any consideration of its motion is begun.

The *speed* of a body having uniform linear motion is defined as *the length of path which the body traverses divided by the time required to traverse this distance*. In equation form,

$$\text{Speed} = \frac{\text{length of path}}{\text{time needed}}$$

or, in symbols,

$$v = \frac{s}{t} \tag{9}$$

where v is the speed of the body, s is the space or distance covered, and t is the time required to travel this distance, these being the symbols commonly used for these quantities. The distance s is measured along the line of motion and is therefore linear; hence v

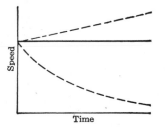

is called the *linear speed*. From the fact that equal distances are covered in equal intervals of time, it is seen that the ratio of s to t in this equation remains constant; hence, if a body has uniform linear motion, it has a constant linear speed.

All kinds of motion can be represented on a graph by plotting speed as ordinates and time as abscissas. On such a graph uniform motion would be a straight line drawn hori-

FIG. 30. Comparison of uniform and non-uniform motion

zontally through the appropriate speed value on the ordinate scale; this is shown by the heavy line in Fig. 30. Non-uniform motion may be represented by inclined or curved lines; the straight dotted one in the figure shows a uniformly increasing speed and the curved one a gradually decreasing speed.

The unit in which linear speed is expressed depends upon the units which are used in designating distance and time. If the distance is stated in miles and the time in hours, the speed, from equation (9), will be given in miles per hour; if instead, the distance is expressed in meters and the time in minutes, the speed will be given in meters per minute. Any given speed may thus be stated in many different ways, depending on the units selected for distance and for time. Although all of these may be correct, there are two particular units for linear speed which are used quite generally in scientific and technological work, namely, *feet per second* in British units, and *centimeters per second* in metric units. In expressing speeds of steamships the term *knot* is commonly used; the knot is 1 nautical mile per hour.

Suppose that a racing boat after getting under way crosses the starting line and travels with uniform motion over a 2-mi. course in exactly 4 min. Find the speed of the boat in miles per hour. Since the boat travels 2 mi. in 4 min., that is, in $\frac{1}{15}$ hr., it would travel 30 mi. in 1 hr. if it continued at the same rate. The speed of the boat is therefore 30 mi. per hr. The same result is found from equation (9) as follows:

$$v = \frac{s}{t} = \frac{2 \text{ mi.}}{\frac{1}{15} \text{ hr.}} = 30 \frac{\text{mi.}}{\text{hr.}}$$

A speed expressed in miles per hour may be converted to feet per second by multiplying it by suitable conversion factors, each of which is equal to unity, as in § 3. Thus,

$$30 \frac{\text{mi.}}{\text{hr.}} = \frac{30 \text{ mi.}}{\text{hr.}} \times \frac{5280 \text{ ft.}}{1 \text{ mi.}} \times \frac{1 \text{ hr.}}{60 \text{ min.}} \times \frac{1 \text{ min.}}{60 \text{ sec.}}$$

$$= \frac{30 \times 5280 \text{ ft.}}{3600 \text{ sec.}} = 44 \frac{\text{ft.}}{\text{sec.}}$$

It will be convenient to remember that a speed of 30 mi. per hr. is exactly equal to 44 ft. per sec. in converting from one of these units to the other.

25. Distinction Between Speed and Velocity.—In defining the speed of a body that has uniform motion as the distance which it traverses divided by the time required to traverse this distance, no reference was made to the direction in which the body moves. The *velocity* of a body is a vector quantity having the same magnitude as its *speed*, but including also the *direction* of motion. Thus, in stating the velocity of a body, both the speed and the direction of motion must be included. If either the speed or the direction is changed, the velocity of the body will be altered.

Consider, for example, a body which is moving with constantly increasing speed along a straight path; its velocity increases also, but the change is one of magnitude only, for there is no change of direction. Again a body may have uniform motion along a curved path; its speed is constant for the motion is specified as uniform, but its velocity nevertheless changes at each instant because of the continual change in direction. To be sure, the numerical value of its velocity remains unchanged, but the fact that its direction of motion keeps changing from instant to instant means that its velocity is also changing continuously. Equation (9) for the linear speed of a body also gives the numerical value of its linear velocity.

26. Uniform Angular Motion.—Consider a body spinning about a fixed axis, such as a flywheel rotating in stationary bearings, or a chuck turning in a lathe. The body as a whole, although in motion, does not move from one point to another along a line, and consequently its motion is not linear. The motion of such a rotating body can be studied most easily by referring to a radius drawn from the axis to any point on the body. As the body rotates, this radius sweeps through an angle; for instance, it sweeps through 2π radians or $360°$ in making one complete revolution. For this reason, a rotating body is said to have *angular motion*.

If the rotation of a body is *uniform*, measurements will show that it sweeps through the same angle during each second (or each minute, or other convenient interval of time). For example, if a flywheel having uniform angular motion revolves 40 times in one minute, it will revolve 40 times in the next minute, and so on. In general, a rotating body has uniform angular motion if it sweeps through equal angles in equal intervals of time, however short. The rotation of the earth and the motion of the hands of a clock are familiar examples of uniform angular motion. It is evident that a rotating body in starting from rest moves slowly at first, turning faster and faster, before it finally reaches a steady state of uniform angular motion. Such non-uniform angular motion will be discussed in Chapter VI; for the present, consideration will be given only to bodies that have already acquired a state of uniform rotation.

The *angular speed* of a body having uniform angular motion is defined as *the angle through which the body sweeps divided by the time required to sweep through this angle*, that is

$$\text{Angular speed} = \frac{\text{angle swept through}}{\text{time needed}}$$

or

$$\omega = \frac{\theta}{t} \tag{10}$$

where ω (omega) is the angular speed, θ is the angle swept through, and t is the time required to sweep through this angle. Since equal angles are swept through in equal intervals of time, it follows that the ratio of θ to t is a constant; hence, if a body has uniform angular motion, it has a constant angular speed.

The angular speed of a body can be expressed in several different ways. For instance, if the angle swept through is expressed in degrees and the time in seconds, the speed, from equation (10), will be given in degrees per second; again, if the angle is expressed in revolutions and the time in minutes, the speed will be given in revolutions per minute (rev. per min.), a unit which is often used by engineers. In scientific work it is customary to express the angle swept through in radians and the time in seconds, in which case the angular speed is given in radians per second. Since 1 rev. = 2π radians, it follows that 1 rev. per min. = $2\pi/60$ radians per sec.

Suppose it is desired to find the time required for a wheel to make 10 complete revolutions if it is turning at a constant speed of 80 radians per sec. From equation (10),

$$t = \frac{\theta}{\omega} = \frac{10 \times 2\pi \text{ radians}}{\dfrac{80 \text{ radians}}{\text{sec.}}} = 10 \times 2\pi \text{ radians} \times \frac{\text{sec.}}{80 \text{ radians}} = 0.785 \text{ sec.}$$

The distinction between speed and velocity, which was described in the preceding section for linear motion, applies equally to angular motion.

27. Relation Between Angular and Linear Speeds.—When a body is rotating about a fixed axis, the different points on the body describe concentric circles about that axis. Hence, while the body as a whole has angular motion, different points on it move along lines, and so these points have linear motion. A flywheel rotating about a fixed axis O, as shown in Fig. 31, has angular motion, and the points A and B on it have linear motion. The linear speed of point A, located near the rim of the wheel, is greater than that of point B, near the axis, since A moves through a larger circle than does B for each revolution of the wheel.

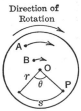

FIG. 31. Comparing linear and angular speeds

A simple relation exists between the angular speed of a rotating body and the linear speed of any point on it. To derive this relation, first find the angular speed of a body in uniform rotation; next find the linear speed of any point on it; and then compare the two speeds. Suppose that the body in Fig. 31 turns through an angle θ radians in

t sec.; its angular speed is $\omega = \dfrac{\theta}{t}$ radians per sec. In this time, any point P located at a distance r cm. from the axis travels a distance $s = \theta r$ cm., and consequently its linear speed is $v = \dfrac{s}{t} = \dfrac{\theta r}{t}$ cm. per sec. A comparison of these results shows that

$$v = \frac{\theta r}{t} = \frac{\theta}{t} \times r$$

or

$$v = \omega r \qquad\qquad (11)$$

Linear speed = angular speed × radius

In this equation, the angular speed ω must be expressed in *radians per unit time*, say radians per second, and the unit for the linear speed v will depend on that used for r. If r is expressed in centimeters, v will be given in centimeters per second, and if r is expressed in feet, v will be given in feet per second. In order to verify the correctness of these units, it will be helpful to recall that a radian is merely the ratio of an arc to a radius; so the term "radians" can be written as $\dfrac{\text{ft.}}{\text{ft.}}$ or $\dfrac{\text{cm.}}{\text{cm.}}$, and cancelled. Typical units in equation (11) are as follows for the metric system:

$$v = \omega r = \frac{\text{radians}}{\text{sec.}} \times \text{cm.} = \frac{1}{\text{sec.}} \times \text{cm.} = \frac{\text{cm.}}{\text{sec.}}$$

in which the term "radians" is replaced by unity.

As an example, determine the maximum allowable diameter of a cast-iron flywheel which is to rotate at 90 rev. per min., if the speed of the rim is not to exceed 6000 ft. per min. From equation (11),

$$r = \frac{v}{\omega} = \frac{6000\,\dfrac{\text{ft.}}{\text{min.}}}{\dfrac{90 \times 2\pi \text{ radians}}{\text{min.}}} = 6000\,\frac{\text{ft.}}{\text{min.}} \times \frac{\text{min.}}{90 \times 2\pi \text{ radians}} = 10.6 \text{ ft.}$$

whence the diameter = 2 × 10.6 ft. = 21.2 ft.

28. Average and Instantaneous Speeds in Non-Uniform Motion.—
The speeds of moving bodies often change from moment to moment. Thus, a motor bus is repeatedly started from rest, speeded up, slowed down, and stopped; its speed along a highway may be 30 miles an hour at one moment and 50 at another. Such instantaneous speeds are indicated by the speedometer and are often controlled by driving

conditions. Another aspect of motion is the average speed main-tained over a given period; in the operation of the bus mentioned, the average speed is of importance in establishing and maintaining sched-ules.

The *average speed* of a body is the total length of path covered divided by the time required to traverse it, or

$$\text{Average speed} = \frac{\text{total length of path}}{\text{total time needed}}$$

Symbolically

$$v_{av} = \frac{s}{t} \tag{12}$$

where v_{av} represents the average speed of a body which travels over a path of length s during a time interval t. As the length of path under consideration is taken shorter and shorter, the time needed becomes progressively less also, and the speed obtained by equation (12) would be restricted to only a short portion of the entire path. If the time required by the bus to travel a block is 5 sec., its average speed over that block, say a distance of $\frac{1}{20}$ mile, is that distance divided by the corresponding time, $\frac{1}{720}$ hr., or a speed of 36 mi. per hr. When the distance covered and the time interval are taken as in-finitesimals, then the speed reduces to a value called the instanta-neous speed.

Strictly, the *instantaneous speed* of a body is the limiting value of the ratio of the length of path covered to the time needed to traverse it, as the time approaches zero. The symbol Δ (delta) is commonly used as a prefix to represent an increment of a quantity; thus, Δs is an increment of space and Δt is one of time. If the short distance Δs is covered in the short time Δt, then the instantaneous speed is the limit of the ratio $\dfrac{\Delta s}{\Delta t}$ as Δt approaches zero. In the limit, the ratio is represented by $\dfrac{ds}{dt}$, so that

$$\frac{ds}{dt} = \mathop{\text{Limit}}_{\Delta t \,=\, 0} \frac{\Delta s}{\Delta t}$$

Hence the limiting ratio of space to time becomes

$$\text{Instantaneous speed} = \frac{\text{infinitesimal length of path}}{\text{infinitesimal time needed}}$$

for the particular instant under consideration. If the instantaneous speed is symbolized as v (without subscript) then

$$v = \frac{ds}{dt} \tag{13}$$

In the special case where a body moves uniformly, it has the same instantaneous speed at every instant, and its average speed is the same as its constant speed.

The same principles apply in the case of rotation. When a body is rotating, whether uniformly or not, its *average angular speed* over a given period can be found by dividing the total angle θ through which it sweeps by the total time t required to sweep through this angle. In symbols, the average angular speed is

$$\omega_{av} = \frac{\theta}{t} \tag{14}$$

The *instantaneous angular speed* of a rotating body is defined as the ratio of an infinitesimal angle $d\theta$ swept through to the infinitesimal time dt required to sweep through this angle. That is, the instantaneous angular speed is

$$\omega = \frac{d\theta}{dt} \tag{15}$$

In the special case where a body is rotating uniformly, its instantaneous angular speed stays constant at the average value.

29. Relative Motion of Two Bodies.—It is difficult for a person to conceive of absolute motion or of absolute rest, since he can observe only relative motion; that is, the motion of bodies with respect to each other. A person seated in a train at a railroad station and looking out of the window at another train nearby, is often unable to tell whether the train in which he is seated or the other train is in motion when one of them starts; he can observe only that one of them is moving relative to the other. Again, one may say that a house is stationary, a statement which means, of course, that the house does not move with respect to the earth; nevertheless the house is in rapid motion relative to the sun, for it is carried along with the earth as it rotates on its axis and as it moves in its orbit. Moreover, the sun and the whole solar system are not at rest; measurements show that the system is moving through space at about 700 mi. per min. relative to the constellation Hercules.

In ordinary usage the term "velocity of a body" means its velocity with respect to the earth, and the expression "condition of rest" refers to a state of rest with respect to the earth.

Suppose that while a railroad train is moving northward at 20 mi. per hr. a man walks forward through the train at 4 mi. per hr. The man's velocity relative to the train is 4 mi. per hr. northward, *as though the train had been at rest*. Meanwhile the train is moving relative to the earth at 20 mi. per hr., also northward. These velocities have the same direction, and the velocity of the man relative to the earth is 24 mi. per hr. northward. If he walks toward the rear of the train at the same rate, the two velocities have opposite directions and his resultant velocity with respect to the earth is only 16 mi. per hr. northward. If he walks in any other direction, the resultant velocity can also be determined, but the methods of adding vectors described in Chapter II must be applied.

Consider, for definiteness, that an object, No. 1, is moving relative to a second object (or medium), No. 2, with a velocity $v_{1\to2}$, while the second object is moving relative to a third object, No. 3, with a velocity $v_{2\to3}$. Then, the velocity of object No. 1 relative to object No. 3, $v_{1\to3}$, will be the vector sum of $v_{1\to2}$ and $v_{2\to3}$, or symbolically,

$$v_{1\to3} = v_{1\to2} + v_{2\to3} \tag{16}$$

It must be remembered that this expression is only a shorthand statement of a vectorial addition and is not intended in general to represent an arithmetical addition.

To illustrate, consider a traveling crane such as used in power plants and factories for moving heavy machinery from place to place within a building. The crane extends across the width of the building and rolls on tracks supported along the side walls near the eaves, as shown in Fig. 32. A machine can be moved along the crane, crosswise of the building, at the same time that the crane is moving lengthwise of the building. The velocity of the machine with respect to the floor will then be the resultant or vector sum of two separate velocities, that of the machine with respect to the crane, and that of the crane with respect to the floor. In subscript notation, v_{MF} will represent the velocity of the machine with respect to the floor, v_{MC} the velocity of the machine with respect to the crane, and v_{CF} the velocity of the crane with respect to the floor; then as a *vector addition*,

$$v_{MF} = v_{MC} + v_{CF}$$

Attention is drawn again to the fact that vector addition takes account of the *directions* of the quantities involved; the equation just stated is true *vectorially* but not *arithmetically*. To evaluate the resultant velocity v_{MF} the separate velocities v_{MC} and v_{CF} must be shown

FIG. 32.   A traveling crane for hand operation
(*Courtesy of Industrial Brownhoist Corporation*)

in their proper directions, and may then be added vectorially by the procedures described in the preceding chapter.

As a numerical example, suppose the machine just mentioned to be moved along the crane with a velocity $v_{MC} = 3$ ft. per sec., while at the same time the crane is moving at right angles to this direction, its velocity with respect to the floor being $v_{CF} = 5$ ft. per sec. The resultant velocity of the machine with respect to the floor, v_{MF}, is found graphically by the Parallelogram Method in Fig. 33 and by the Polygon (Triangle) Method

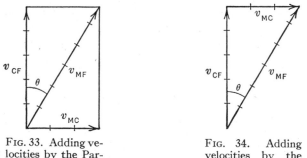

FIG. 33. Adding velocities by the Parallelogram Method

FIG. 34.   Adding velocities by the Polygon Method

in Fig. 34. By the use of a scale and a protractor, the velocity of the machine with respect to the floor is found to be 5.8 ft. per sec. at an angle $\theta = 31°$ with the side walls as shown.

To solve this problem analytically,

$$v_{MF} = \sqrt{v_{MC}{}^2 + v_{CF}{}^2} = \sqrt{3^2 + 5^2} = \sqrt{34} = 5.83 \text{ ft. per sec.}$$

and

$$\theta = \tan^{-1} \tfrac{3}{5} = \tan^{-1} 0.600 = 30.96°$$

This gives the velocity of the machine with respect to the floor as 5.83 ft. per sec., in the direction shown, making an angle of 30.96° with the side walls.

When the paths of moving objects are parallel, the relation stated in equation (16) is simplified because no angles need be considered. The procedure to follow will be illustrated by a problem in which one automobile passes another, and it will be assumed that one car is passing the other so long as a point on it is opposite any point on the other.

An automobile 17 ft. long driven at 50 mi. per hr. overtakes and passes a 28 ft. truck moving at 30 mi. per hr. Compute the time required in passing and the distance traveled by each vehicle during this time. The velocity of the automobile relative to the ground, v_{AG}, is 50 mi. per hr. and that of the truck relative to the ground, v_{TG}, is 30 mi. per hr. The velocity of the automobile relative to the truck, v_{AT}, is found from the relation $v_{AG} = v_{AT} + v_{TG}$ to be $50 - 30 = 20$ mi. per hr., or $73.3 - 44.0 = 29.3$ ft. per sec. The distance that the automobile travels relative to the truck while passing it is $17 + 28 = 45$ ft., as though the truck had been at rest. Hence the time occupied in passing is $t = s/v = 45$ ft. $\div$ (29.3 ft./sec.) = 1.535 sec. During this time the distance traveled by the automobile is $s = vt = 73.3$ ft/sec. $\times$ 1.535 sec. = 112.5 ft., and that traveled by the truck is 44 ft/sec. $\times$ 1.535 sec. = 67.5 ft.

★30. Motion of Craft in a Moving Medium.—The principles of relative velocity are applied wherever an object travels through a medium which is itself in motion, for example, the motion of a projectile on a windy day, the flight of an airplane in moving air currents, and the motion of a ship in flowing water. By way of illustration, three problems will be given dealing with the motion of a ship in a stream. Each problem is analyzed, but the numerical solution by the Parallelogram or Polygon Method is left to the student. The term "steered" in these problems denotes the direction in which the ship moves with respect to the water.

I. A ship is steered due west across a stream in which the current is 8 mi. per hr. south. If the ship is moving through the water at 20 mi. per hr., find its velocity with respect to the land.

The velocity of the ship with respect to the water, v_{SW}, is 20 mi. per hr. toward the west, and that of the water with respect to the land, v_{WL}, is 8 mi. per hr. south. The desired velocity of the ship with respect to the land, v_{SL}, is the vector sum of these two; thus, following equation (16),

$$v_{SL} = v_{SW} + v_{WL}$$

and is shown in diagram I of Fig. 35.

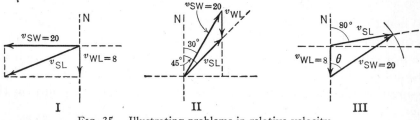

FIG. 35. Illustrating problems in relative velocity

II. A ship moving through the water at 20 mi. per hr. is steered 30° east of north, but is carried by the current so that it actually moves in a direction 45° east of north. Find the speed of the current if its direction is toward the south.

The velocity of the ship with respect to the water, v_{SW}, is 20 mi. per hr. 30° east of north; that of the ship with respect to the land, v_{SL}, is known in direction only, being 45° east of north; and that of the water with respect to the land, v_{WL}, is also known in direction only, being south. The relation between these velocities is represented by the vector addition $v_{SL} = v_{SW} + v_{WL}$, as before. The addition of v_{SW} and v_{WL} must lie somewhere along the direction of v_{SL}. This vector addition is performed in diagram II of Fig. 35 by drawing v_{SW} and then dropping a line in the direction of v_{WL} until it intersects a line drawn in the direction of v_{SL}. The intersection of these two lines determines both v_{WL} and v_{SL}. The desired speed of the current can be determined by evaluating the vector v_{WL}.

III. In what direction should a ship be steered in order to reach a destination 80° east of north from the ship's position, if it steams through the water at 20 mi. per hr. while the water is flowing due south at 8 mi. per hr.?

The velocity of the ship with respect to the land, v_{SL}, is along the direction 80° east of north; that of the ship with respect to the water, v_{SW}, is 20 mi. per hr. in an unknown direction; and that of the water with respect to the land, v_{WL}, is 8 mi. per hr. south. As before, $v_{SL} = v_{SW} + v_{WL}$. This problem is represented in diagram III of Fig. 35. First, v_{WL} and the direction line of v_{SL} are drawn. Next, since v_{SW} is known to have a value of 20 mi. per hr., an arc is drawn with a radius of 20 units to scale about the head of the vector representing v_{WL} as a center. Then the intersection of this arc with the line of direction v_{SL} determines the direction of v_{SW}. Connect the intersection with the center of construction and measure the angle θ. This direction, reckoned from north, shows the direction in which the ship should be steered.

PROBLEMS

1. How long does it take light, traveling at 186,000 mi. per sec., to reach the earth from the sun, 92×10^6 mi. away?

2. How much longer would it take to travel a distance of 5 mi. at a speed of 45 mi. per hr. than it would at a speed of 60 mi. per hr.?

3. Two runners, A and B, start at the same instant over a 2-mi. course. Runner A covers the entire course at 10 mi. per hr. Runner B runs 1 mi. at 11 mi. per hr. and the other mile at 9 mi. per hr. Which runner wins the race, and by what time does he beat his opponent?

4. The speed of a train can be estimated by a passenger by counting the number of rail clicks heard in a definite period of time. On a certain railroad the speed in miles per hour is numerically equal to the number of clicks heard in 22.5 seconds. What is the length of rails used on this railroad?

5. A body has three component velocities: 25 km. per hr. toward the north, 30 km. per hr. toward the east, and 20 km. per hr. toward the southwest. Find the resultant velocity of the body by the resolution method.

6. Compute the speed in radians per second (a) of an airport beacon that makes 1 rev. in 10 sec., and (b) of an ultra-centrifuge that rotates at 17,400 rev. per min.

7. To measure the speed of a bullet, two cardboard disks mounted on a long axle are rotated at a constant speed and the bullet is fired through them parallel to the axle. In a given test, the disks were 36 in. apart and were driven at 1720 rev. per min., and the holes left by the bullet were displaced 20°. Find the speed of the bullet.

8. A flywheel on a steam engine is to be driven at 400 rev. per min. What is the largest radius that the wheel can have without allowing a point on the rim to exceed a speed of 100 ft. per sec.?

9. A drum having a circumference of 500 mm. rotates upon a stationary axle. How many revolutions should it make per minute in order to have a rim speed of 50 mm. per sec.?

10. A belt is used to drive a pulley 12 in. in diameter from another 8 in. in diameter which revolves 108 times a minute. If the belt does not slip on either pulley, what is (a) the linear speed of the belt? and (b) the speed of the 12-in. pulley in revolutions per minute?

11. A mandrel $\frac{3}{4}$ in. in diameter is being turned down in a lathe by means of a cutting tool, while revolving at a speed of 240 rev. per min. What is the linear speed of cutting?

12. An outboard motor is started by pulling on a rope wound upon a drum 10 in. in diameter. With what speed must the rope be pulled in order to give the drum a speed of 300 rev. per min.?

13. The shortest time taken for the mile run is 4 min., 1.4 sec. This record was established by Gunder Haegg at Stockholm in 1945. Express the average speed of this run in meters per sec.

14. Robert Fulton's steamboat, the "Clermont," made its trip from New York to Albany in August, 1807. It covered the distance of 145 mi. in 32 hr. What average speed was maintained?

15. A record parachute jump of 40,200 ft. was made by Col. William R. Lovelace on June 30, 1943. The time of descent was 23 min., 51 sec. Compute the average velocity during the drop.

16. In a solo flight around the world in 1947, William P. Odom covered a 19,645-mi. course around the northern hemisphere in an overall time of 73 hr., 5 min., 11 sec. He made eight stops to refuel, totaling 9 hr., 50 min. What was his average speed in flight?

17. A train from New York City to Miami, Fla., is scheduled to cover the 340-mi. distance to Richmond, Va., in 7 hr., 15 min. and to make the entire run of 1387 mi. in 26 hr., 35 min. On a particular trip the train was 2 hr. late at Richmond and 3 hr. late at Miami. Calculate the average speeds of the train over the two parts of the run.

18. A man walking at 4 mi. per hr. beside a railroad track is overtaken and passed by a freight train 1300 ft. long traveling at 40 mi. per hr. Compute the time which is taken for the train to pass the man.

19. A piece of pipe rolls crosswise in a freight car with a speed of 12 ft. per sec., while the car is traveling forward with a speed of 30 mi. per hr. Find the speed of the pipe with respect to the ground.

20. An automobile having tires 30 in. in diameter travels along a straight road at 45 mi. per hr. (*a*) Compute the angular speed of the wheels in revolutions per minute. (*b*) Compute the linear speed of a point on the periphery of the tire with respect to the axle.

★21. An airplane has a speed of 300 km. per hr. in still air. In what direction should the pilot steer the plane in order to reach a point 20° north of east from his present position if the wind is blowing toward the southeast with a speed of 75 km. per hr.? How long will it take him to reach his destination if it is 800 km. away?

★22. The current in a river 1 mi. wide is due south at 4 mi. per hr. A boat leaves the west bank and crosses this river diagonally to a point on the opposite shore ½ mi. downstream from the starting point. If the trip requires 15 min., find how fast the boat moves through the water and in what direction it is steered.

★23. An aircraft carrier is steaming due east at a speed of 25 knots. To an observer on the carrier the wind appears to come from a direction 30° south of east and its apparent speed is 24 knots. Find the value and direction of the true wind velocity.

Accelerated Motion *Chapter IV*

31. Acceleration and Its Units.—Every automobilist speaks of pick-up as one of the requisites of a good motor car. By this he means the rapidity with which the car gains velocity. If the car starting from rest acquires a velocity along a straight highway of 4 ft. per sec. by the end of one second, gains an additional velocity of 4 ft. per sec. during the next second, and so on, the car is said to have a pick-up, or an *acceleration*, of 4 ft. per sec. in each second. By the end of three seconds the car will have a velocity of 12 ft. per sec., and so on, as long as it can maintain the same acceleration. During this period of increasing velocity every conceivable value of velocity, from zero up to the maximum reached by the car, is passed through at some instant. The instantaneous velocity values would fall along a curve such as in Fig. 36. The curve is straight from O to A, showing that during the first ten seconds the car gains velocity at a uniform rate; that is, the acceleration is constant.

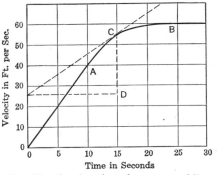

Fig. 36.   Acceleration of an automobile

The curve slopes off beyond A, showing that the acceleration is reduced, and becomes horizontal at B, the acceleration then being zero.

The acceleration of a body is defined as the change of its velocity during any interval of time divided by the duration of that interval. Observe that the definition is based not on distance traveled but rather on change of velocity. It may be stated in the form of an equation by supposing the motion of a body to be observed for some stated time interval. Take v_o as its initial velocity at the beginning of this period and v_f as its final velocity at the end of the period, then the change in velocity is $v_f - v_o$, and if this change occurs in a time interval t, the average acceleration of the body over that interval is

$$a_{av} = \frac{v_f - v_o}{t}$$

or

$$\text{Average acceleration} = \frac{\text{final velocity} - \text{original velocity}}{\text{time interval}}$$

The performance represented in Fig. 36 will now be analyzed in greater detail. The velocity of the car under consideration increases from 40 to 60 ft. per sec. during the time interval from 10 to 25 sec. after starting, but during this period the velocity does not increase uniformly, and therefore the acceleration varies from instant to instant. The *average acceleration* over any time interval can be found, however, by dividing the change of velocity during that interval by the duration of that interval. Thus, the average acceleration over the time interval from the tenth to the twenty-fifth second is

$$\left(60 \, \frac{\text{ft.}}{\text{sec.}} - 40 \, \frac{\text{ft.}}{\text{sec.}}\right) \div (25 \text{ sec.} - 10 \text{ sec.}) = 1.33 \, \frac{\text{ft.}}{\text{sec.}^2}$$

As the time interval becomes shorter and shorter, the average acceleration approaches nearer and nearer to the *instantaneous acceleration*. In the limit, for an infinitesimal change of velocity dv occurring in an infinitesimal time interval dt, the instantaneous acceleration a is expressed as

$$a = \frac{dv}{dt} \tag{17}$$

Defined tersely, *acceleration is the time rate of change of velocity.* Its value at any particular instant is represented graphically by the slope of the velocity-time curve at the corresponding point. Thus, in Fig. 36, to find the instantaneous acceleration 15 sec. after starting the car, draw a tangent to the curve at point C where it crosses the 15-second ordinate and determine the slope of the tangent. Since $CD = 55 \, \frac{\text{ft.}}{\text{sec.}} - 26 \, \frac{\text{ft.}}{\text{sec.}} = 29 \, \frac{\text{ft.}}{\text{sec.}}$, the slope is $29 \, \frac{\text{ft.}}{\text{sec.}} \div 15$ sec. $= 1.93 \, \frac{\text{ft.}}{\text{sec.}^2}$ and this value is the instantaneous acceleration at that particular moment.

When the acceleration is constant, its successive instantaneous values are all alike and the same as the average acceleration. In this chapter attention is directed only to motion in which the acceleration is constant.

From the form in which acceleration is expressed, it is clear that any velocity unit divided by any time unit would therefore be an acceleration unit. The most usual acceleration units are:

feet per second per second, written $\dfrac{\text{ft.}}{\text{sec.}^2}$

centimeters per second per second, written $\dfrac{\text{cm.}}{\text{sec.}^2}$

and some other acceleration units used in scientific and engineering work are:

miles per hour per second, written $\dfrac{\text{mi.}}{\text{hr.} \times \text{sec.}}$

kilometers per hour per second, written $\dfrac{\text{km.}}{\text{hr.} \times \text{sec.}}$

To say that a body has an acceleration of one mile per hour per second means that during every second the velocity of the body increases by one mile per hour. An acceleration of 10 cm. per sec. per sec. means that during each second the velocity of the body concerned increases by 10 cm. per sec.

32. Equations of Motion with Constant Acceleration.—The relations which exist between the initial velocity, final velocity, distance covered, acceleration, and time, in motion having constant acceleration along a straight path, may be expressed mathematically by three equations.

I. One of these equations follows from the definition of acceleration, as given in the last section, namely:

$$a = \frac{v_f - v_o}{t} \tag{18}$$

or by rearrangement,

$$v_f = v_o + at \tag{19}$$

wherein v_o = initial velocity, that is, the velocity of the body at the moment the consideration of its motion begins,

v_f = final velocity, that is, the velocity of the body at the moment the consideration of its motion ends,

t = time interval between the two moments mentioned, and

a = acceleration, assumed constant.

The following problems will serve as illustrations:

The speedometer on an automobile was observed to read 25 mi. per hr. at a certain instant, and 8 sec. later was observed to read 49 mi. per hr. Find the acceleration (assumed constant) of the car during this interval. By equation (18), the acceleration is

$$a = \frac{49\frac{\text{mi.}}{\text{hr.}} - 25\frac{\text{mi.}}{\text{hr.}}}{8\text{ sec.}} = \frac{24\frac{\text{mi.}}{\text{hr.}}}{8\text{ sec.}} = 3\text{ mi. per hr. per sec.}$$

A train which is accelerating at 5 km. per hr. per sec. will acquire what velocity in 8 sec., starting from rest? By equation (19), since $v_o = 0$, the speed is

$$v_f = 0 + 5\frac{\text{km.}}{\text{hr.} \times \text{sec.}} \times 8\text{ sec.} = 40\text{ km. per hr.}$$

II. The second equation of accelerated motion expresses the distance traveled by a body having constant acceleration. It is necessary first to ascertain the average velocity of the moving body during the interval desired. Since the change in velocity during the time interval t is uniform, the average velocity is the mean of the velocities at the beginning and end of the interval, these being v_o and v_f respectively; therefore the average velocity is $v_{av} = \frac{v_o + v_f}{2}$. Then the distance s traversed during the interval is the product of the average velocity and the duration of the interval as mentioned in § 28, namely

$$s = v_{av}\, t = \frac{v_o + v_f}{2}\, t \tag{20}$$

When the value of v_f from equation (19) is substituted in this expression, the distance traversed becomes

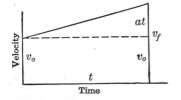

$$s = \frac{v_o + (v_o + at)}{2} \times t$$

or

$$s = v_o t + \tfrac{1}{2}at^2 \tag{21}$$

FIG. 37. Representing constant acceleration

The inclined line in Fig. 37 represents graphically the motion of a body in which the velocity increases uniformly with time; that is, motion with constant acceleration. By comparing the figure with equation (21) it will be evident that the area below the line represents the distance that the body travels.

The equation also shows that when a body starts from rest ($v_o = 0$) the distance covered by it in accelerated motion is proportional to the square of the elapsed time. Thus, if the acceleration is 2 ft. per sec. per sec., the distances in feet covered will be given by

$$s = \frac{1}{2} \times 2 \frac{\text{ft.}}{\text{sec.}^2} (t \text{ sec.})^2 = t^2;$$ these distances for $t = 1$ sec., $\cdots$ 5 sec.

are marked off to scale in Fig. 38 and show how much farther the object moves each second.

FIG. 38. Displacements of an object moving with constant acceleration

Suppose it is desired to know how far an object having constant acceleration moves during the fifth second after starting from rest, if its acceleration is 2 ft. per sec. per sec. Since the object has no initial velocity, the distances traversed in 5 and in 4 sec. are respectively

$$s = \frac{1}{2}\left(2\frac{\text{ft.}}{\text{sec.}^2}\right)(5 \text{ sec.})^2 = 25 \text{ ft.}, \qquad s = \frac{1}{2}\left(2\frac{\text{ft.}}{\text{sec.}^2}\right)(4 \text{ sec.})^2 = 16 \text{ ft.}$$

Consequently, the distance traversed during the fifth second is $25 - 16 = 9$ ft.

The foregoing equation for the distance traversed assumes that the motion of the body continues in one direction. When such is not the case as, for example, when a body is projected upward and falls back part way along its path during the interval t, the distance s should be interpreted as the displacement of the body; that is, the distance between its initial and final positions, without regard to the distance actually traversed in moving from one position to the other.

III. The third equation of motion with constant acceleration is derived from the other two by eliminating the time interval t. This is accomplished by multiplying equations (18) and (20) member by member, as follows:

$$as = \frac{v_f - v_o}{t} \times \frac{v_o + v_f}{2} t = \frac{1}{2}(v_f - v_o)(v_f + v_o)$$

from which

$$v_f{}^2 = v_o{}^2 + 2as \qquad (22)$$

As an example, the velocity of an automobile as it passes a given point is observed to be 20 mi. per hr., and its velocity as it passes a point 200 ft.

farther along is 50 mi. per hr. What is the average acceleration of the car? The speeds expressed in miles per hour must first be reduced to feet per second; 20 mi/hr. = 29.3 ft/sec. = v_o, and 50 mi/hr. = 73.3 ft/sec. = v_f. Then from equation (22):

$$a = \frac{v_f{}^2 - v_o{}^2}{2s} = \frac{\left(73.3\,\frac{\text{ft.}}{\text{sec.}}\right)^2 - \left(29.3\,\frac{\text{ft.}}{\text{sec.}}\right)^2}{2 \times 200\ \text{ft.}} = 11.3\,\frac{\text{ft.}}{\text{sec.}^2}$$

The three equations for linear motion with constant acceleration are collected herewith for ease of reference:

$$v_f = v_o + at$$

$$s = v_o t + \tfrac{1}{2}at^2$$

$$v_f{}^2 = v_o{}^2 + 2as$$

These equations should be thoroughly understood and experience should be acquired in applying them to the solution of practical

FIG. 39. Electropult showing jet plane bridled to shuttle car
(*Courtesy of Westinghouse Electric Corporation*)

problems. Care should be exercised that the units employed are consistent. It will be noted that the first of these equations has no distance term, the second has no final velocity, and the third has no time factor; therefore the choice of which equation to use in a particular example is apparent.

High accelerations are needed in launching airplanes from short runways on shipboard or ashore, and catapults of various types have been designed for this purpose. One of these, called an "electropult," consists of a runway that is essentially the rotor of an induction motor, § 311, laid out flat, and a low shuttle car that travels along the runway. In operation, the plane is hitched to the car by a bridle cable and is towed along the track on its own wheels as shown in Fig. 39; when flying speed is reached the car is stopped, the bridle falls off, and the plane takes to the air.

33. Acceleration Due to Gravity.—Bodies fall to the ground because the earth exerts a pull upon them. This pull, called the force of gravity, causes a body to accelerate while falling. Moreover, all bodies fall with the same acceleration, regardless of their masses, as was first shown experimentally at the Leaning Tower of Pisa by Galileo Galilei (1564–1642), the Italian philosopher and astronomer.

The force of gravity exerted upon a body, and consequently the acceleration due to the earth's attraction, depends upon the distance of the body from the center of the earth, and decreases as this distance increases. The acceleration of a falling body if measured at points above the earth's surface would be found to diminish as the elevation becomes greater. All over the surface of the earth this acceleration is nearly the same. It is slightly greater at the poles than at the equator because the earth is flattened at the poles, its polar radius being 13 miles shorter than its equatorial radius. The rotation of the earth also makes the acceleration of a falling body less at the equator than at the poles because of centrifugal force, § 50. Actual values of the acceleration due to gravity at a few places are given below:

Acceleration due to Gravity

	$\dfrac{\text{ft.}}{\text{sec.}^2}$	$\dfrac{\text{cm.}}{\text{sec.}^2}$		$\dfrac{\text{ft.}}{\text{sec.}^2}$	$\dfrac{\text{cm.}}{\text{sec.}^2}$
Equator at sea level...	32.086	977.99	New York City, N. Y..	32.160	980.23
Paris, France.........	32.184	980.96	Rome, Italy..........	32.163	980.32
Berlin, Germany......	32.193	981.26	San Francisco, Cal.....	32.150	979.94
North Pole...........	32.258	983.21	London, England......	32.191	981.19
New Orleans, La.......	32.129	979.31	Madison, Wis.........	32.164	980.35

The symbol generally used for the acceleration imparted by the earth is g and its numerical value in integral numbers is

$$g = 32 \text{ ft. per sec. per sec.}$$

or

$$g = 980 \text{ cm. per sec. per sec.}$$

These values may be used in problems unless other values or particular places are specified.

34. Falling Bodies.—The laws of falling bodies may be expressed by the same equations as used for motion having constant acceleration, except that the acceleration due to gravity g is used instead of any acceleration a. The equations are:

$$v_f = v_o + gt \tag{23}$$

$$s = v_o t + \tfrac{1}{2}gt^2 \tag{24}$$

$$v_f{}^2 = v_o{}^2 + 2gs \tag{25}$$

where v_o is the velocity at the moment consideration of the motion begins, t is the time interval, v_f is the velocity at the end of the interval, and s is the distance between the initial and final positions of the body in motion. Some direction may arbitrarily be taken as positive, and the opposite direction as negative; $+$ and $-$ signs will be given accordingly to displacement, velocity, and acceleration.

A few problems will illustrate the laws of falling bodies. In these air friction will be neglected, and the downward direction will be regarded as positive.

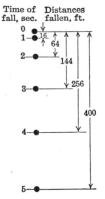

Time of Distances
fall, sec. fallen, ft.

Fig. 40. Distances traveled by falling object

I. A ball is dropped and allowed to fall freely; compute the distances it will travel in 1 sec., $\cdots$ 5 sec. The ball has no initial velocity, making $v_o = 0$, and its displacements are given by equation (24) as $s_1 = \dfrac{1}{2}\left(32\,\dfrac{\text{ft.}}{\text{sec.}^2}\right)(1\text{ sec.})^2 = 16\text{ ft.}; s_2 = \dfrac{1}{2}\left(32\,\dfrac{\text{ft.}}{\text{sec.}^2}\right)(2\text{ sec.})^2$ = 64 ft.; and so on as shown in Fig. 40.

II. Suppose a ball to be thrown vertically downward with a velocity of 12.4 meters per sec. from a cliff 110 meters high. With what velocity will it strike? and how long will it take to reach the ground? In this problem the initial velocity $v_o = 1240$ cm/sec., and the displacement $s = 11,000$ cm.

The velocity at impact is found from equation (25) as follows:

$$v_f^2 = v_o^2 + 2gs = \left(1240 \frac{\text{cm.}}{\text{sec.}}\right)^2 + 2\left(980 \frac{\text{cm.}}{\text{sec.}^2}\right) \times 11{,}000 \text{ cm.}$$

$$= (1{,}537{,}600 + 21{,}560{,}000) \frac{\text{cm.}^2}{\text{sec.}^2}$$

whence

$$v_f = 4806 \text{ cm. per sec.}$$

Then, from equation (23), the time of flight is

$$t = \frac{v_f - v_o}{g} = \frac{4806 \dfrac{\text{cm.}}{\text{sec.}} - 1240 \dfrac{\text{cm.}}{\text{sec.}}}{980 \dfrac{\text{cm.}}{\text{sec.}^2}} = 3.64 \text{ sec.}$$

Consequently the ball will strike the ground in 3.64 sec. with a velocity of 48.06 meters per sec.

III. Imagine a bullet to be fired vertically upward with a velocity of 280 ft. per sec. from the top of a tower of the George Washington Bridge at New York City which is 600 ft. above the water, as indicated in Fig. 41.

(*a*) How high does the bullet travel?

(*b*) With what velocity does the bullet pass the roadway of the bridge in its downward motion, the roadway at that part of the bridge being 240 ft. above the water?

(*c*) What is the velocity of the bullet on reaching the water?

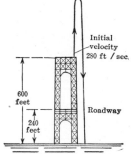

Fig. 41. Illustrating problem on the flight of a bullet

In order to find how far up the bullet will travel, place the final velocity $v_f = 0$ and the initial velocity $v_o = -280$ ft/sec. in equation (25), and solve for s. Thus

$$s = \frac{v_f^2 - v_o^2}{2g} = \frac{0 - \left(-280 \dfrac{\text{ft.}}{\text{sec.}}\right)^2}{2 \times 32 \dfrac{\text{ft.}}{\text{sec.}^2}} = -1225 \text{ ft.}$$

Hence the bullet will travel up 1225 ft. beyond the top of the tower and reach an elevation of 1825 ft. above the water. In descending, the bullet will cover a distance of $1825 - 240 = 1585$ ft. to reach the level of the roadway, and its velocity at that place is obtained from equation (25) by placing the initial velocity $v_o = 0$ and solving for v_f. Thus

$$v_f{}^2 = 0 + 2 \times 32 \frac{\text{ft.}}{\text{sec.}^2} \times 1585 \text{ ft.} = 101{,}440 \frac{\text{ft.}^2}{\text{sec.}^2}$$

from which the velocity of the bullet as it passes the roadway is $v_f = 319$ ft. per sec. The same equation is used to obtain the velocity with which the bullet strikes the water, but this time $s = 1825$ ft. Thus

$$v_f{}^2 = 0 + 2 \times 32 \frac{\text{ft.}}{\text{sec.}^2} \times 1825 \text{ ft.}$$

from which $v_f = 342$ ft. per sec. It will be noted that the other two equations of falling bodies were not used because they involve the time of flight, and this factor was not called for in the problem.

The acceleration due to gravity is so great that difficulty is experienced in measuring its value directly. However, mechanical means may be employed to lessen the effect of gravity on a particular body by partially counterbalancing it, thereby making it possible to measure the resulting acceleration more accurately. The Atwood's machine makes use of this principle by having two equal masses connected by a tape and hung over a large pulley, Fig. 42, and putting a rider upon one of them to set the tape in motion. By marking the tape at equal time intervals, the experimenter can find the distances traversed by the moving system during known intervals of time, and in this way can verify the laws of accelerated motion, and determine the acceleration due to gravity.

35. Combination of Uniform and Accelerated Motions.—An experiment commonly used in the lecture room makes use of two metal balls supported at the same level near the ceiling, one having a compressed spring behind it, and the other

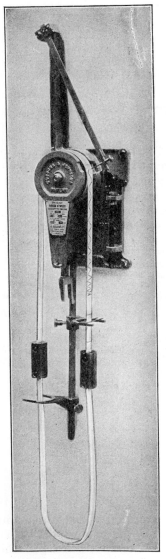

Fig. 42. Atwood's machine
(*Courtesy of G. Cussons, Ltd.*)

having a trap door beneath it. By closing an electric circuit controlling both spring and door, both are released simultaneously; the spring strikes one ball horizontally and the door opens to allow the other ball to fall freely. It is found that the two balls strike the floor at the same instant, showing that the horizontal motion imparted to the one ball by the spring did not affect its motion in the vertical direction.

The ball which is projected horizontally follows a curved path, moving both horizontally and vertically at the same time. *The horizontal motion* of the ball is *uniform*, there being nothing either to speed it up or slow it down along this direction, and is entirely unaffected by the fact that it is falling at the same time. *The vertical motion is accelerated*, like that of any falling body, and is neither helped nor hindered by the fact that the ball is moving horizontally while falling. Consequently, the motion of such an object will be studied by regarding it as made up of two parts, one horizontal and the other vertical, and by recognizing the fact that these motions occur *independently* of each other.

To illustrate numerically, suppose that a ball is thrown horizontally from the top of a high building with a velocity of 50 ft. per sec. The horizontal motion will be uniform and will be determined by equation (9), namely $s = vt$; that is, the distance covered will be equal to the product of the constant velocity and the time of flight. The vertical motion will be accelerated and will be determined by equations (23) to (25). During the first second of its flight it will move forward horizontally $50 \times 1 = 50$ ft., and it will fall $\frac{1}{2}g(1)^2 = 16$ ft. During a 2-second period after projection the ball will travel 100 ft. horizontally and will fall a total of $\frac{1}{2}g(2)^2 = 64$ ft. The horizontal motion with constant velocity and the vertical motion with constant acceleration result in the following displacements of the ball during the first few seconds:

Total time, sec.	1	2	3	4	5
Horizontal travel, ft.	50	100	150	200	250
Vertical drop, ft.	16	64	144	256	400

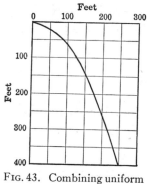

These values are coordinated in Fig. 43, and the resulting parabola shows the trajectory of the ball. If the building were just 400 ft. high, the ball would strike the ground at a point 250 ft. from the building. In the foregoing illustration, air friction was ignored, as heretofore. The actual distance traversed by the ball, that is, the length of the curve in the figure, has not been determined and is of little interest.

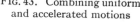

Fig. 43. Combining uniform and accelerated motions

36. Motion of Projectiles.—The composition of two motions, one uniform and the other accelerated, is of constant occurrence in the study of ballistics to determine the range of projectiles and to trace their paths. Two illustrations will explain the procedure; air friction is neglected.

I. A gun fires a projectile at a speed v in a direction θ degrees upward from the horizontal. How far from the gun will the projectile strike the ground? In this problem the first step is to resolve the projection velocity into a vertical and a horizontal component. The time of flight is determined by the vertical component of the projection velocity and the acceleration due to gravity, and can be found by application of the expressions for accelerated motion, § 34. After this time interval has been found, the horizontal range of the projectile is ascertained from the horizontal component of the projection velocity by means of the equation for uniform motion.

The vertical component of the projection velocity is $v \sin \theta$ and its horizontal component is $v \cos \theta$, as shown in Fig. 44. If t is the time of flight, as yet unknown, the horizontal distance traversed will be the range $X = vt \cos \theta$. To find the time of flight, use equation (23)

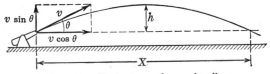

FIG. 44.   Trajectory of a projectile

selecting some direction, say upward, as positive. First, find the time t_1 in which the projectile reaches the top point of its flight, where its vertical velocity is zero, from the expression $v \sin \theta = gt_1$. During this period t_1 the projectile rises to a height given by equation (24) as $h = (v \sin \theta)t_1 - \frac{1}{2}gt_1^2$, which can be written $h = gt_1^2 - \frac{1}{2}gt_1^2$, or

$$h = \tfrac{1}{2}gt_1^2$$

The time t_2 required for the projectile to return to ground is found from

$$-h = -\tfrac{1}{2}gt_2^2$$

and since h in the last two equations represents the same height, it follows that $t_1 = t_2$, or the time of flight to reach the maximum elevation is the same as the time to drop from that level to the datum plane. The total time of flight is therefore $t = 2t_1$. Next, combine this result with the first two equations of this derivation, and obtain as the horizontal range

$$X = vt \cos \theta = 2vt_1 \cos \theta = 2v \left(\frac{v \sin \theta}{g} \right) \cos \theta$$

and since $2 \sin \theta \cos \theta = \sin 2\theta$,

$$X = \frac{v^2}{g} \sin 2\theta$$

Further, by eliminating t_1 from the equations $v \sin \theta = gt_1$ and $h = \frac{1}{2}gt_1{}^2$, the maximum elevation of the projectile is found to be

$$h = \frac{v^2}{2g} \sin^2 \theta$$

It is interesting to note from the foregoing that both the range and the maximum elevation depend upon the square of the projection speed and upon the angle of elevation. In this solution, air friction is neglected and the trajectory is a parabola, as shown in the figure. If air friction were taken into account, the path of the projectile would be noticeably altered, particularly during the latter part of the flight.

II. Consider a bombing airplane flying with constant velocity v at an elevation s, and suppose that it is moving horizontally toward its objective shown at O in Fig. 45. At what angle of sight ϕ with respect to the vertical should the observer release a bomb so that it will strike the objective? At the instant the bomb is released it has the same forward velocity as the airplane, and as a result the bomb travels horizontally with constant velocity independently of its accelerated motion toward the earth. In consequence, the bomb will not strike a point on the ground which was directly below the airplane at the moment of release, but will strike beyond that point in

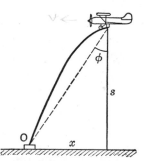

FIG. 45. Path of a bomb dropped from an airplane

the direction of flight by an amount which depends upon the velocity and height of the airplane. This distance subtends an angle ϕ at the observer's position, and is the angle of sight to be solved for. Let t be the time of flight reckoned from the release of the bomb and x the horizontal distance between the plane and the objective O. Then the following relations hold:

$$x = s \tan \phi \qquad s = \tfrac{1}{2}gt^2 \qquad x = vt$$

It is necessary to eliminate both x and t from these expressions, for the angle of sight ϕ should depend only on the elevation s of the airplane and its velocity v. Consequently the angle is such that

$$\tan \phi = v \sqrt{\frac{2}{gs}}$$

The substitution of numerical values in this equation will result in data from which curves may be plotted showing the proper angle of sight for any definite altitude and speed.

37. Angular Acceleration.—When a wheel is set into rotation about a fixed axis, it gains angular velocity and ultimately assumes some desired speed. If this final speed is acquired in a short time the wheel is said to have a high *angular acceleration*, and if it takes the wheel a longer time to reach the same final speed the wheel is said to have a lower angular acceleration.

In general, if the angular velocity of a rotating body changes from ω_o to ω_f in a time interval t, then its average angular acceleration over this interval is

$$\alpha = \frac{\omega_f - \omega_o}{t} \tag{26}$$

where ω_o is spoken of as the initial angular velocity and ω_f as the final angular velocity. Following the procedure of § 31, the instantaneous angular velocity can be expressed as

$$\alpha = \frac{d\omega}{dt}$$

where $d\omega$ is the infinitesimal change of angular velocity occurring in the infinitesimal time interval dt. Hence *the angular acceleration of a body is defined as its time rate of change of angular velocity.*

Equation (26) corresponds to equation (18) for linear acceleration, namely $a = \dfrac{v_f - v_o}{t}$, and it will be observed that it has the same form exactly. In consequence, the equations for angular motion with constant acceleration may be written by analogy with those of § 32 as follows:

$$\omega_f = \omega_o + \alpha t \tag{27}$$

$$\theta = \omega_o t + \tfrac{1}{2}\alpha t^2 \tag{28}$$

$$\omega_f{}^2 = \omega_o{}^2 + 2\alpha\theta \tag{29}$$

Herein θ is the angular displacement in the time t, α is the angular acceleration, ω_o is the initial angular velocity, and ω_f is the final angular velocity. In applying these equations it is usual to convert revolutions to radians before substituting numerical values.

As an illustration, consider the flywheel of a metal punch-press to have slowed down from 80 rev. per min. to 50 rev. per min. during the 0.7 sec. that it took to punch the metal. What is the angular acceleration (in this case an angular retardation)? Herein

$$\omega_f - \omega_o = (50 - 80)\,\frac{\text{rev}}{\text{min}} \times \frac{2\pi \text{ radians}}{1\,\text{rev}} \times \frac{1\,\text{min}}{60 \text{ sec.}} = -\pi\,\frac{\text{radians}}{\text{sec.}}$$

whence the angular acceleration of the flywheel is given by equation (26) as

$$\alpha = \frac{-\pi\,\dfrac{\text{radians}}{\text{sec.}}}{0.7 \text{ sec.}} = -4.5 \text{ radians per sec. per sec.}$$

To find the angle turned through by the wheel during the punching operation, apply equation (28), in which $\omega_o = (80 \times 2\pi)/60 = 8.37$ radians per sec., $\alpha = -4.5$ radians per sec. per sec., and $t = 0.7$ sec. Then

$$\theta = 8.37\,\frac{\text{radians}}{\text{sec}} \times 0.7\,\text{sec} - \frac{1}{2}\,(4.5)\,\frac{\text{radians}}{\text{sec}^2} \times (0.7\,\text{sec})^2 = 4.76 \text{ radians}$$

This corresponds to 272° or about three-fourths of a revolution.

When a rotating body has angular acceleration, any point upon it has a corresponding linear acceleration along a circular path. The angular acceleration of the body may be expressed as $\alpha = \dfrac{\omega_f - \omega_o}{t}$ and the linear acceleration of the point as $a = \dfrac{v_f - v_o}{t}$, in accordance with equations (26) and (18). The relation between these quantities can be found by applying the expression $v = \omega r$ as given in equation (11), in which r is the distance from the axis of rotation to the point in question. It follows that

$$a = \frac{\omega_f r - \omega_o r}{t} = r\left(\frac{\omega_f - \omega_o}{t}\right)$$

or

$$a = r\alpha \tag{30}$$

which states that *the linear acceleration of any point on a rotating body along its circular path is equal to the product of the radius extending to that point and the angular acceleration of the rotating body.*

An examination of equations (1), (11), and (30), that associate linear and angular quantities, shows that in each case the linear quantity (displacement, velocity, or acceleration) is equal to the radius multiplied by the corresponding angular quantity.

PROBLEMS

1. Compute the acceleration of an autobus which acquires a speed of 60 km. per hr. in 15 sec., starting from rest.

2. The speed of a street car is observed to increase uniformly from 20 mi. per hr. to 40 mi. per hr. in 8 sec. Calculate the distance that the car travels in this time.

3. The speedometer of an automobile was observed to read 35 mi. per hr. just before the brakes were applied, and the car was brought to rest in 3.0 sec. How far did the car go in this interval?

4. In making a landing, an airplane touches the ground at a speed of 60 mi. per hr. and comes to standstill in traveling 350 ft. What is the average acceleration during this period?

5. A jet-propelled plane is accelerated by an electropult and takes off at a speed of 115 mi. per hr. in a run of 340 ft. What is the average acceleration of the plane, and how long did it take to acquire the stated speed from standstill?

6. An airplane, catapulted from a carrier, reaches a speed of 80 mi. per hr. along a 50-ft. runway. Compute the acceleration of the plane, and the duration of the accelerating period.

7. A trolley car starting from rest accelerates at 2 mi. per hr. per sec. for 15 sec., then it coasts for 20 sec. losing velocity because of friction at the rate of 0.3 mi. per hr. per sec., and finally is brought to rest by the brakes in 5 sec. How far did the car travel during the 40-sec. run?

8. An elevator rises a distance of 22 ft. in accelerating from rest to its maximum speed of 700 ft. per min., and then it travels upward 100 ft. at this speed. Thereafter the elevator is brought to a stop in traveling 15 ft. farther. How long did this run take?

9. A swimmer steps off a diving board that is mounted horizontally 10 meters above the water surface. With what velocity does the swimmer strike the water?

10. Compute the velocity acquired by water in going down Niagara Falls, a descent of 167 ft.

11. A player threw a ball vertically upward and caught it on its return. How long was the ball in flight if it rose a distance of 30 meters?

12. Suppose an object to be projected vertically upward with a velocity of 96 ft. per sec. In what direction will it be moving and how far will it be from the starting point at the end of 1, 2, 3, 4, 5, and 6 sec.?

13. A 150-lb. man jumping from an airplane with a parachute attains a steady speed of 25 ft. per sec. in descending. From what height would he acquire the same speed if he jumped without a parachute?

14. Derive an expression for the distance traveled by a freely falling body during any one second, calling it the nth second.

15. A cannon ball is fired horizontally with a muzzle velocity of 360 meters per sec. The cannon is located at an elevation of 10 meters above a level terrain. At what distance horizontally from the cannon will the ball strike the ground?

16. To find the velocity of water issuing from the nozzle of a garden hose, the nozzle is held horizontally and the stream is directed against a vertical wall. If the wall is 20 ft. from the nozzle and the water strikes it 2 ft. below the level of the nozzle, what is the velocity of the water?

17. In what time will a baseball, pitched horizontally with a speed of 130 ft. per sec., travel the distance of 60.5 ft. from the pitcher's mound to the batter's box? How far will it fall because of gravity in this time interval?

18. A batted baseball is caught by a player 5.5 sec. after it was hit. Assume the ball to be struck and caught in the same horizontal plane. How high did it rise in its flight?

19. With what speed must a ball be thrown in a direction 40° upward from level ground in order to be caught at a point on the ground 30 meters away?

20. A bomb is dropped from an airplane in level flight of 300 km. per hr. at an elevation of 2500 meters. Plot the trajectory of the bomb.

21. A projectile is fired from a gun at a speed of 1800 ft. per sec. to hit a target 3000 yd. away and placed at the same elevation as the gun. In what direction with respect to the horizontal should the gun be aimed?

22. If a projectile is fired with a velocity of 1200 ft. per sec. at an angle of 30° upward from a level plain, how far from the gun will it strike the ground?

23. A golf ball is projected with a velocity of 200 ft. per sec. at an angle of 40° upward from a level fairway. How far horizontally will the ball travel before it hits the ground?

24. Derive equations (27) to (29) by using the definition of angular acceleration and following the procedure of § 32.

25. Current is turned off a motor when it is revolving at 1200 rev. per min., and the machine comes to rest in 20 sec. Find its average angular

acceleration (retardation) and the number of revolutions which it makes while stopping.

26. An automobile with 30-in. wheels starts from rest and acquires a speed of 45 mi. per hr. in 15 sec. What is the angular acceleration of the wheels?

27. A pulley 10 in. in diameter is brought from rest to a speed of 1200 rev. per min. in 30 sec. Compute the average linear acceleration of a point on its rim during this interval.

Force   *Chapter V*

FUNDAMENTAL PRINCIPLES

38. Effect of Force on Motion.—In the preceding chapter, accelerated motion was studied without any mention of how the acceleration was brought about; the present chapter deals with the agency which produces it. Acceleration is always produced by a *force*. Whenever a body is accelerating, a force must be acting upon it to cause the acceleration. Thus, if a body at rest is to be set into motion, it must be accelerated, and a force must be exerted on it. Again, if a body is in motion, a force must be applied to it in order to speed it up, slow it down, change its direction, or bring it to rest; any change in the velocity of a body implies an acceleration, and this acceleration can be produced only by a force acting on the body.

A force has already been described as a push or a pull acting upon a body. A man pushing a lawn mower exerts a force on the lawn mower, a locomotive pulling a train exerts a force on the train, and a book resting on a table exerts a force on the table. In each of these cases it is necessary that the two bodies touch each other; for example, the man must be in contact with the lawn mower in order to exert a force on it. Moreover, as the lawn mower moves, the man must move along also and stay in contact with it if he is to continue to exert a force on it. When a person throws a ball, he exerts a force on it only so long as it stays in contact with his hand. There is, however, an exception continually met with in Mechanics to the principle that one body cannot exert a force on another body unless the two are in contact. This exception is gravitation, by means of which a body, say the earth, exerts a force of attraction on other bodies, whether they are in contact with it or not. This gravitational action was mentioned in Chapter IV, and will be considered more fully later, § 43.

If a body is accelerating a force must be acting upon it, but it does not necessarily follow that if a force is exerted on a body the body will accelerate. For example, a man may exert a force on a crate, while at the same time friction or some other agent exerts an equal force on it in the opposite direction, in which case the two forces balance each other, and the crate will not accelerate. If, however, all of the forces acting on a body are taken into account, and if these do not balance, then the *unbalanced force* will always cause acceleration. Whenever a body is accelerating, there must be an unbalanced force acting upon it; also, whenever an unbalanced force acts on a body, the body accelerates.

39. Generalizations on Motion; Newton's Laws.—The relation of force to motion has been set forth by Sir Isaac Newton (1642–1727), one of the most profound scientists of all time, who interpreted and correlated many diverse observations in Mechanics and combined the results into three fundamental laws, known as Newton's Laws of Motion. It is impossible to estimate how much these laws have simplified the science of Mechanics, or to state how complex and difficult this subject might be without them. In the following paragraphs, each of these laws is stated in terms of quantities already defined, and is supplemented by a brief discussion.

FIRST LAW OF MOTION.—*A body at rest remains at rest, and a body in motion continues to move at constant speed along a straight line, unless the body is acted upon in either case by an unbalanced force.*

The first part of this law is evident from everyday experience; for instance, a book placed on a table remains at rest. In explanation, one might be inclined to say that the book stays at rest simply because no force is being exerted upon it. Further thought shows that this reasoning is not true, since it is known that the force of gravity pulls it downward and it can be inferred that the table pushes it upward. The fact is that these two forces *on* the book are equal and opposite, one balancing the other, and the unbalanced or resultant force acting on it is zero. The book therefore stays at rest because there is no *unbalanced* force acting on it.

The second part of the law is more difficult to visualize; it states virtually that if a body is set into motion and left to itself, it will keep on moving without any further force being exerted on it. This statement is correct; the body would continue to move without any reduction of velocity if no force acted on it to bring it to rest. However, experience shows that a retarding force is always present in the nature of friction. A block of wood thrown along a rough road slides a short distance only, because the friction is large; along a floor it would slide farther, the friction being smaller; and along a sheet of ice it would slide much farther, since in this case the friction is still smaller. From examples like these, it is reasoned that if friction could be eliminated entirely, which cannot actually be done, a body once set into motion on a level surface would continue to move indefinitely with undiminished velocity. Thus, uniform motion is a natural condition, and maintains itself without the action of any unbalanced force.

An example of the first law of motion is an airplane traveling horizontally at constant speed. The forces acting on the plane are indicated in Fig. 46, wherein *T* is the propeller thrust acting forward

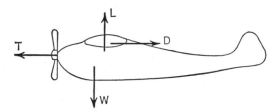

FIG. 46.   Forces on an airplane

along the propeller axis, *D* is the backward drag of air friction, *W* is the weight acting vertically downward, and *L* is the "lift" acting upward at right angles to the thrust of the propeller. When *T* equals *D*, and *L* equals *W*, there will be no unbalanced force on the plane and the velocity it has attained will continue without change as long as the propeller thrust can be maintained.

It is interesting to note that whether a body is at rest or moving with constant speed along a straight line, its acceleration in either case is zero. Hence the first law of motion means that a body will not have an acceleration unless an unbalanced force acts upon it.

SECOND LAW OF MOTION.—*An unbalanced force acting on a body causes the body to accelerate in the direction of the force, and the acceleration is directly proportional to the unbalanced force and inversely proportional to the mass of the body.*

Expressed mathematically, the law states that

$$a \propto \frac{F}{m}$$

where *a* is the acceleration of a body of mass *m* when acted upon by an unbalanced force *F*. A constant of proportionality *k* may be introduced to form an equation; thus,

$$ka = \frac{F}{m}$$

To illustrate the meaning of this law, suppose, for example, that two identical boxes are being drawn across the floor, and that more force is applied to one than to the other; experience shows that the box with the larger force will have the greater acceleration. Again, suppose that a full box and an empty box are being drawn across the floor, with exactly the same force acting on each; experience shows that the empty one will have the greater acceleration. In general, the greater the unbalanced force and the less the mass, the greater will be the acceleration.

If in the foregoing illustrations a box has been started in motion across the floor, and the applied force is then reduced until it is exactly equal to the backward force of friction which the floor exerts on the box, the box has one force pulling it forward and an equal force pulling it back, and therefore the unbalanced force acting upon it is zero. Hence, the acceleration of the box must be zero; that is, the box will neither speed up nor slow down, and so it will continue to slide with constant speed, as expressed in the First Law.

The opposition which a body offers to any change of motion, whereby an unbalanced force is needed to give it linear acceleration, is known as *inertia*. This property is common to all matter and leads to a broader conception of mass than is given by the definition in § 12. Mass may be considered as *that property of an object by virtue of which it possesses inertia*.

THIRD LAW OF MOTION.—*For every action, there is an equal and opposite reaction, and the two are along the same straight line.*

In stating this law, the term "action" means the force which one body exerts on a second body, and "reaction" means the force which the second body exerts on the first. A useful way to express this law is as follows: If body *A* exerts a force on body *B*, then body *B* must exert an equal and opposite force on body *A*.

Some illustrations will clarify the meaning of the law. If a book presses downward on a table with a force of 2 lb., then the table presses upward on the book with a force of 2 lb. Again, if a man pulls on a rope with a force of 50 lb., the rope pulls in the opposite direction on the man with a force of 50 lb. Evidently the ability to exert a force depends not only on the agent which is exerting the force, but also on the agent which is supplying the reaction. A truck striking a tree can exert only as much force on the tree as the tree is able to exert against the truck.

Note that two bodies are involved in each of these transactions, and that the action and reaction are never exerted on the same body. Thus *action and reaction, although equal and opposite, can never balance each other*, since in order for two equal and opposite forces to balance each other, they must be exerted on the same body.

The first and second laws deal with force actions on a single body; the third law deals with the mutual force actions between two bodies.

40. Absolute Units of Force.—Of the three laws of motion discussed in the preceding section, only the Second Law deals quantitatively with the relation between force, mass, and acceleration. The mathematical statement of the law can be written

$$F = kma$$

in which a is the acceleration produced in a mass m by an unbalanced force F, and k is a proportionality constant the value of which depends upon the units used in the expression. To make use of this relation in numerical calculations, it is necessary to establish units of force, such as the pound mentioned previously, which will be consistent with the units already adopted for mass and acceleration. Several systems of units are in common use, the force unit in each of them being such as to give a particular acceleration to a particular mass, in accordance with the Second Law.

In the absolute system, the unit of force is one of such magnitude as to impart unit acceleration to a unit of mass. It can be defined from the foregoing equation by making k equal to unity and writing

$$F = ma \qquad\qquad (31)$$

so that F will be unity when m and a are units of mass and acceleration respectively.

In British units, the unit mass is 1 lb. and the unit acceleration is $1\dfrac{\text{ft.}}{\text{sec.}^2}$; hence the absolute unit of force is $F = ma = 1 \text{ lb.} \times 1\dfrac{\text{ft.}}{\text{sec.}^2}$ $= 1\dfrac{\text{lb-ft.}}{\text{sec.}^2}$, and is read as "pound foot per second per second." This name is rather awkward to use and a simpler name, the *poundal*, has been assigned to it. *The poundal is that unbalanced force which acting on a mass of 1 lb. gives it an acceleration of 1 ft/sec.*^{2} The term "poundal" can always be replaced by its equivalent, $\dfrac{\text{lb-ft.}}{\text{sec.}^2}$.

Similarly, in metric units, the unit mass is 1 gm. and the unit acceleration is $1 \frac{\text{cm.}}{\text{sec.}^2}$, and hence the absolute unit of force is $1 \frac{\text{gm-cm.}}{\text{sec.}^2}$. This unit, the "gram centimeter per second per second," is called the *dyne*. *The dyne is that unbalanced force which acting on a mass of 1 gm. gives it an acceleration of 1 cm/sec.²* The term "dyne" can always be replaced by its equivalent, $\frac{\text{gm-cm.}}{\text{sec.}^2}$.

The poundal and dyne are called *absolute* units because their values are defined in terms of the fundamental quantities; they do not depend upon the acceleration due to gravity as do the gravitational units to be discussed in § 45. To conform to the foregoing definitions, the following groups of units will be found consistent in the expression $F = ma$. If the mass m is in pounds and the acceleration a is in feet per second per second, then the unbalanced force F must be in poundals; similarly, if m is in grams and a is in centimeters per second per second, then F must be in dynes. To illustrate the use of these units, two elementary problems will be considered in which objects are caused to slide along "smooth" surfaces, that is, surfaces on which friction may be ignored.

I. Suppose that a 100-lb. body resting on a smooth horizontal surface is acted upon by a horizontal force of 160 poundals, and that the resulting acceleration of this body is to be found. Since there is no backward force of friction, the applied force of 160 poundals acts as an unbalanced force on the body. The acceleration is calculated from equation (31) as follows:

$$a = \frac{F}{m} = \frac{160 \text{ poundals}}{100 \text{ lb.}} = \frac{160 \frac{\text{lb-ft.}}{\text{sec.}^2}}{100 \text{ lb.}} = 1.6 \frac{\text{ft.}}{\text{sec.}^2}$$

in which the term "poundals" is replaced by its equivalent, $\frac{\text{lb-ft.}}{\text{sec.}^2}$.

II. Find what horizontal force must be applied to a 140-gm. body resting on a smooth horizontal plane in order to give it an acceleration of $35 \frac{\text{cm.}}{\text{sec.}^2}$. From equation (31),

$$F = ma = 140 \text{ gm.} \times 35 \frac{\text{cm.}}{\text{sec.}^2} = 4900 \frac{\text{gm-cm.}}{\text{sec.}^2} = 4900 \text{ dynes}$$

41. Impulse and Momentum.—Newton's Second Law of Motion can be regarded from a different point of view, which is important because it introduces two concepts that are widely used in Physics; these are impulse and momentum. The action of a force for a definite time interval constitutes an *impulse*; quantitatively it is measured by the product of the force and the time during which it acts. The "quantity of motion" possessed by a body is called *momentum*; this is measured by the product of the mass of the body and its velocity. Both impulse and momentum are vector quantities, and there is a definite relation between them.

An unbalanced impulse acting upon a body will cause a change in the momentum of the body, and moreover, the change in momentum will be numerically equal to the impulse. Restated with symbols, an unbalanced force F acting for a time t upon a body of mass m will cause a change in the velocity of the body from v_o to v_f such that

$$Ft = mv_f - mv_o$$

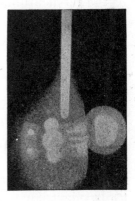

FIG. 47. Golf club and ball at impact. X-ray photograph taken in one-millionth of a second (*Courtesy of Westinghouse Electric Corporation*)

If this equation is divided through by t, the result will be identical with Newton's Second Law of Motion as expressed in equation (31).

The idea of impulse is particularly useful in instances where the force action is of short duration. This is the situation in impact or collision, for example, that between the golf club and ball in Fig. 47. When two bodies collide, the ensuing interaction follows from Newton's Third Law of Motion, namely that they exert equal and opposite forces on each other. Obviously the time intervals over which these forces act are also identical. Therefore, the colliding bodies are subjected to equal impulses and so they undergo equal changes in momentum. This illustration leads to a general principle in Mechanics known as the *Law of Conservation of Momentum*, which states that *for any collision, the vector sum of the momentums of the colliding bodies after collision equals the vector sum of their momentums before collision*. This subject is discussed further in § 110.

An impact is said to be *direct* when the colliding bodies strike head on, that is, when the striking surfaces are at right angles to the direction of motion, and it is *central* if the forces which the bodies exert upon each other act along the line joining their centers of mass,

§ 42. Imagine two colliding bodies having masses m_1 and m_2, and suppose their respective velocities are v_1 and v_2 before impact and v_1' and v_2' after impact. Then for direct central impact, by the Law of Conservation of Momentum,

$$m_1v_1 + m_2v_2 = m_1v_1' + m_2v_2' \tag{32}$$

the velocities being taken positive in one direction and negative in the opposite direction. If one of the bodies gains a certain amount of momentum, the other will lose the same amount.

When the impact is other than direct and central, the directions of the momentums must be taken into account, as with any vector quantities.

Consider an automobile to be struck by a truck at a road intersection despite attempts to stop both vehicles. Assume that at the moment of impact the automobile of 2 tons mass is moving north at a speed of 15 mi. per hr., the truck of 5 tons mass is moving east at 8 mi. per hr., and that the two become interlocked. The resulting momentum of the wreckage immediately after impact will be 2×15 ton-mi/hr. north and 5×8 ton-mi/hr. east, or a total of $\sqrt{30^2 + 40^2} = 50$ ton-mi/hr. in a direction making an angle of $\tan^{-1} \frac{30}{40}$ north of east.

42. Center of Mass.—A distinction is frequently made in Mechanics between particles and rigid bodies because they react differently to force action. A *particle* is a portion of matter, usually small, upon which all forces may be regarded as acting at a common point. A *rigid body* is an aggregation of particles which maintain their relative positions, and the forces do not, in general, act upon a common point of the body. The result of such force action upon a particle is then motion without rotation, which may be designated as translation, and on a rigid body is either translation or rotation, or both. To set the body into rotation, the forces acting upon it must form a couple, § 23.

For each body there is a point known as the *center of mass* which has an important bearing on the behavior of the body under the action of applied forces. In symmetrical objects of uniform density the center of mass is at the geometrical center; thus, for a sphere it is at the center, and for a parallelopiped it is at the intersection of the diagonals. Practically, the center of mass of a body coincides with the center of gravity, and its location can be calculated or measured as described in § 84.

If the various forces acting upon a body produce a resultant which passes through its center of mass, and if no couple acts upon it, the motion of the body will be the same as though its mass were concentrated at this center, with all of the forces applied there parallel to their actual directions. Such a body may be treated as if it were a particle, and its motion is pure translation. If the forces acting upon a body produce only an unbalanced couple, the body will then rotate about its center of mass if it is free to do so.

Generally the applied forces are equivalent to an unbalanced force plus a couple. For example, when a stick is picked up by one end and thrown, the center of mass of the stick will move as though the mass were concentrated at that point and as though the unbalanced force acted upon it there, while at the same time the stick will be set into rotation about its center of mass by the action of the couple. Throughout the present chapter the resultant force acting upon a body is assumed to pass through its center of mass.

The term center of mass is also applied to a combination of two or more interacting bodies. It is interesting to consider the behavior of such a "system" of bodies upon which there is no unbalanced force or couple. A man diving out of a canoe will serve as an illustration. The man and the canoe exert forces upon each other but these are merely internal forces which one part of the system exerts upon another part, and there is no external force applied to the system as a whole, if friction of the water may be neglected. Under these circumstances if the center of mass of the combination was initially at rest it will remain at rest. While the man moves through the air one way, the canoe will move through the water the other way, and the location of the center of mass of the combination will not change.

*43. Law of Universal Gravitation.—Newton's investigations in Mechanics were not limited to the facts now incorporated in his three Laws of Motion, but extended to the general subject of gravitation. He showed that every body in the universe attracts every other body, and was also able to show how this attraction is affected by the masses of the bodies and the distance separating them.

LAW OF UNIVERSAL GRAVITATION.—*Each particle of matter attracts every other particle with a force which is directly proportional to the product of their masses and inversely proportional to the square of the distance between them.* Expressed mathematically, the law states that the attractive force between two particles is

$$P = G \frac{m_1 m_2}{d^2} \tag{33}$$

where m_1 and m_2 are the masses of particles, d is the distance between them, P is the force with which either particle attracts the other, and G is known as the *gravitational constant*. Note that G does not represent the acceleration due to gravity, which is symbolized by g. When P is expressed in dynes, m_1 and m_2 in grams, and d in centimeters, G has the value $6.67 \times 10^{-8} \frac{\text{dyne-cm.}^2}{\text{gm.}^2}$; thus, two particles each having a mass of 1 gm. when 1 cm. apart attract each other with a force of 6.67×10^{-8} dyne.

The gravitational constant may be measured by means of two metal spheres mounted on a slender rod which is suspended horizontally by a thin wire, with the spheres close to a pair of massive lead globes. Upon moving the globes slightly, the spheres are seen to follow them. From the amount of twist in the suspension wire, and a knowledge of the masses and their separation, the value of the gravitational constant can be determined.

44. Pull of Gravity; Weight.—The most familiar illustration of universal gravitation is the force of attraction which the earth exerts upon objects near it, by virtue of which a body accelerates downward when it is released and allowed to fall freely. If the body is constrained so that it cannot fall when released, the earth exerts the same force on it, but in this case the pull of the earth is balanced by some equal and opposite force exerted by the restraining agent. Thus, a box resting on a table is pulled downward by the earth, but is pushed upward by the table, and so it stays at rest. If the table were incapable of pushing upward on the box as much as the earth pulls downward on it; that is, if it were not strong enough to support the box; there would then be an unbalanced force acting upon the box which would make it accelerate downward, and the table, being in the way of its motion, would collapse; a result that might be expected in the case of a very heavy box on a frail table. The force of attraction which the earth exerts on a body, that is, the pull of gravity on it, is called the *weight* of the body, and shows how heavy the body is. The weight of a body is therefore a force, and is treated in exactly the same way as any other force. Its direction is toward the center of the earth.

It was shown in § 33 that the acceleration due to gravity varies slightly from point to point on or near the earth's surface; thus if a body were dropped at the pole it would have a slightly greater acceleration than if it were dropped at the equator. The increased acceleration of the body dropped at the pole must be caused by an increased force of gravity acting on it there; in other words, the body must weigh slightly more at the pole than at the equator. This result follows at once from the Law of Universal Gravitation. Since the earth is flattened at the poles, a body located there is nearer the center of the earth than if it were at the equator, thus reducing the distance d in equation (33), and consequently increasing the attraction P.

It is a matter of everyday experience that bodies having different masses also have different weights. A full barrel not only has a larger mass than an empty one, but it also has the larger weight. This result is also to be expected from the Law of Universal Gravitation. If m_1 represents the mass of the earth and m_2 the mass of any other object, then, for any particular value of d, it follows that $P \propto m_2$. Hence, at any given location, the weights of bodies are directly proportional to their masses.

Weight or force is often measured with a spring balance, the essential parts of which are shown in Fig. 48. The body to be weighed is suspended by a spring; as it settles downward the spring stretches and exerts an increasing upward force upon it, and a balance is reached when the restoring force due to the spring equals the downward pull of gravity on the body.

FIG. 48. Illustrating the spring balance

Such a device is calibrated by hanging bodies of known weight on it and marking the corresponding extensions of the spring on a scale. The scale may then be used to furnish a direct reading of any weight or force within its range.

45. Gravitational Units of Force.—The principles set forth in § 40 show that the acceleration of a body is proportional to the unbalanced force that acts on it. This proportionality might be based on the mass of the body or its weight. Basically the distinction between the two lies in the units employed.

It is shown in the preceding section that the weights of bodies are directly proportional to their masses, a statement which is strictly true at any given location and approximately true at any place on

the earth's surface where the weights might be measured. This proportionality can be expressed as $m = k_1 W$, where k_1 is a constant. It
follows that Newton's Second Law of Motion, equation (31), can be
restated mathematically in the form

$$F = k_1 W a$$

in which a is the acceleration produced in a body of weight W by an
unbalanced force F. To evaluate the constant k_1, observe that if
an object were allowed to fall freely, the unbalanced force F acting
upon it would be its own weight W, and as a result its acceleration a
would necessarily be that due to gravity, namely g. Therefore,
when F becomes W, a becomes g, and the equation reduces to
$W = k_1 W g$. Hence $k_1 = \dfrac{1}{g}$, and the original equation becomes

$$F = \frac{W}{g} a \tag{34}$$

In this expression, a is the acceleration produced by an unbalanced
force F acting upon a body of weight W, and g is the acceleration due
to gravity.

The form of this equation shows that if the accelerations a and g
are expressed in the same units of acceleration, then the forces F
and W are to be expressed in the same units of force. In British
units, the accelerations are commonly stated in feet per second per
second, and the forces in pounds. In metric units, the accelerations
are usually stated in centimeters per second per second, and the forces
in grams. The pound of force and the gram of force are the so-called
gravitational force units.

The *pound of force is the force exerted by the earth on a 1-lb. mass;*
that is, it is the weight of a pound of mass. Inasmuch as the weight
of a body varies slightly at different places, it is necessary for exactness to specify the location where this weight is measured. The
pound of force is exactly defined as the weight of a pound of mass at
45° latitude and at sea level. For most practical engineering work,
slight variations in weight due to differences in location can be
neglected and, consequently, for ordinary purposes the pound of
force is defined simply as the weight of a pound of mass. For example, a cubic foot of water has a mass of approximately 62.4 lb.;
also it is attracted to the earth with a force of approximately 62.4 lb.,
which means that it weighs approximately 62.4 lb.

The *gram of force is the force exerted by the earth on a 1-gm. mass;* that is, it is the weight of a gram of mass. A cubic centimeter of water at 4° C. has a mass of 1 gm. and therefore also has a weight of 1 gm. of force.

It will be observed from the two paragraphs ahead that the words "pound" and "gram" each has two different meanings: in the absolute system they are units of mass, and in the gravitational system they are units of force or weight.

To establish the relation between the pound of force and the poundal, suppose a body of 1-lb. mass to be released and to fall freely. The unbalanced force acting upon the body is 1 lb. of force and, of course, its acceleration is $32 \dfrac{\text{ft.}}{\text{sec.}^2}$. Hence, a pound of unbalanced acting upon a mass of 1 lb. gives it an acceleration of $32 \dfrac{\text{ft.}}{\text{sec.}^2}$. Since this acceleration is 32 times as great as that produced in the same body by an unbalanced force of 1 poundal, it follows that *1 lb. of force = 32 poundals*. The ratio $\dfrac{32 \text{ poundals}}{1 \text{ lb.}}$ may be used as a unit factor to convert pounds of force to poundals.

Similarly, a gram of unbalanced force acting upon a mass of 1 gm. gives it an acceleration of $980 \dfrac{\text{cm.}}{\text{sec.}^2}$; consequently *1 gm. of force = 980 dynes*. The ratio $\dfrac{980 \text{ dynes}}{1 \text{ gm.}}$ may be used as a unit factor to convert grams of force to dynes.

To illustrate the use of the gravitational system, the problems that were worked out in § 40 will be solved again, this time in gravitational units. From the results it will be clear that either the absolute or the gravitational units may be used in calculations.

I. Suppose that a 100-lb. body resting on a smooth horizontal surface is acted upon by a horizontal force of 5 lb. (note that $5 \text{ lb.} \times \dfrac{32 \text{ poundals}}{1 \text{ lb.}} =$ 160 poundals, as before) and that the resulting acceleration of this body is to be found. The value 100 lb. is now taken as the weight of the body and the acceleration is found by rearranging equation (34) as follows:

$$a = \frac{F}{W} g = \frac{5 \text{ lb.}}{100 \text{ lb.}} \times 32 \frac{\text{ft.}}{\text{sec.}^2} = 1.6 \frac{\text{ft.}}{\text{sec.}^2}$$

II. Find what horizontal force must be applied to a 140-gm. body resting on a smooth horizontal plane in order to give it an acceleration of
$35 \frac{cm.}{sec.^2}$. From equation (34),

$$F = \frac{W}{g} a = \frac{140 \text{ gm.}}{980 \frac{cm.}{sec.^2}} \times 35 \frac{cm.}{sec.^2} = 5 \text{ gm.}$$

This result is equivalent to $5 \text{ gm.} \times \dfrac{980 \text{ dynes}}{1 \text{ gm.}} = 4900$ dynes.

46. Customary Units of Force.—Although the foregoing examples
show that either the absolute or the gravitational units may be used
in calculations, those most frequently used in practice will be the
ones more often employed in this text. These are:

Metric Absolute Units.—The acceleration is found from equation
(31), $F = ma$, in which the force is in dynes and the mass is in grams.
These are the units generally used for scientific purposes.

British Gravitational Units.—The acceleration is found from equation (34), $F = \frac{W}{g} a$, in which both force and weight are in pounds.
These are the units used for engineering work in this country.

47. Procedure in Problem Work.—In applying the foregoing principles to the solution of practical problems, experience has shown that
much difficulty can be avoided by following a definite procedure, at
least until a thorough familiarity with the subject has been attained.
In any problem involving force and acceleration, the following steps
are suggested:

1. Select some one body for consideration, usually the body which
is in motion.

2. Construct a force diagram, entirely separate from any "space"
diagram or picture that may be used to show the conditions of the
problem. On this force diagram, let a point represent the body which
has been selected, and represent *all* of the forces acting *on* this body
by suitable vectors. Be careful that no forces are omitted, and also
that only forces acting on the body are used (not forces which the
body may be exerting on other things). If any forces are unknown,
represent them also by vectors, but mark them as unknown quantities.

3. From the force diagram, find the resultant or unbalanced force acting on the body. When some of the forces are unknown, the expression for the unbalanced force will involve these unknown quantities.

4. Next, find the acceleration or force, whichever is unknown, by using either equation (31) or equation (34).

5. Finally, should the problem call for the distance traversed or the velocity acquired, then use the equations of accelerated motion to find the quantity required.

Several illustrations with their analyses follow:

I. Find the acceleration which a horizontal force of 25 lb. will produce in a 100-lb. body resting on a horizontal plane, which exerts a backward force of 10 lb. on the body because of friction.

The solution of this problem is visualized by constructing a simple diagram as indicated in Fig. 49. The body in part I is shown at O in part II and the two forces which act upon it are represented by lines drawn to scale,

I   II

FIG. 49. Calculating the acceleration produced by a force

pointing in the appropriate directions. Out of the 25-lb. force applied to the body, 10 lb. is balanced by friction because of the rough surface, and so the resultant or unbalanced force acting on the body is 15 lb. Equation (34), with the terms rearranged, gives the acceleration as

$$a = \frac{Fg}{W} = \frac{15 \text{ lb.} \times 32 \frac{\text{ft.}}{\text{sec.}^2}}{100 \text{ lb.}} = 4.8 \frac{\text{ft.}}{\text{sec.}^2}$$

II. A 50-gm. block starts from rest and slides along a smooth plane inclined 20° with the horizontal. Find its velocity after sliding a distance of 100 cm.

A diagram of block and plane is shown in part I of Fig. 50. The block is chosen as the body for consideration, and is represented at O in the force diagram shown as part II of the figure. Two forces only act on the block: the downward pull of gravity, W, and the outward push of the plane, P. Since the plane is smooth, it can exert no frictional drag on the block along the direction of the plane; the force P is therefore known to be at right angles to the plane, but its magnitude is unknown. The direction of the resultant of the two forces W and P is known to be downward along the incline, this being the direction in which the block accelerates. Hence, starting at the lower end of the vector W, construct a parallelogram having

W and P for its adjacent sides. The angle indicated in part II of the figure is 20°, its sides being mutually perpendicular to the incline and the base in part I, and the resultant of W and P, which is represented by the concur-

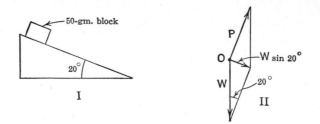

FIG. 50. Block sliding down smooth plane

rent diagonal of the parallelogram, is consequently W sin 20°. This is the unbalanced force F acting on the block. Since

$$W = 50 \text{ gm.} \times \frac{980 \text{ dynes}}{1 \text{ gm.}} = 49,000 \text{ dynes}$$

and $F = W$ sin 20° = 49,000 × 0.342 = 16,750 dynes; it follows from equation (31) that the acceleration is

$$a = \frac{F}{m} = \frac{16,750 \text{ dynes}}{50 \text{ gm.}} = \frac{16,750 \frac{\text{gm-cm.}}{\text{sec.}^2}}{50 \text{ gm.}} = 335 \frac{\text{cm.}}{\text{sec.}^2}$$

The velocity is obtained from equation (22), $v_f{}^2 = v_o{}^2 + 2as$, giving

$$v_f{}^2 = 0 + 2 \times 335 \frac{\text{cm.}}{\text{sec.}^2} \times 100 \text{ cm.} = 67,000 \frac{\text{cm.}^2}{\text{sec.}^2}$$

from which the velocity v_f is found to be 258 cm/sec. along the incline.

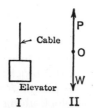

FIG. 51. Finding tension in elevator cable

III. What upward force must be applied to the cable of a 5-ton elevator in order that the car may have an upward acceleration of 4 ft/sec.² if friction is neglected?

The elevator, shown in part I of Fig. 51, is acted upon by two forces: the downward pull of gravity, W, and the unknown upward pull P of the cable. In part II of the figure, the elevator is indicated at O, and the forces W and P are represented by vectors pointing in the appropriate directions. Since the elevator is to accelerate upward, the upward force P must be greater than the downward force W; and the difference between them, $P - W$, must be the unbalanced force F acting upward on the elevator. Since $W = 5 \times 2000 = 10,000$ lb., $g = 32$ ft/sec.², and

$a = 4$ ft/sec.^{2}, it follows from equation (34) that

$$F = \frac{W}{g} a$$

$$P - 10,000 \text{ lb.} = \frac{10,000 \text{ lb.}}{32 \frac{\text{ft.}}{\text{sec.}^2}} \times 4 \frac{\text{ft.}}{\text{sec.}^2} = 1250 \text{ lb.}$$

hence the upward force on the elevator is $P = 10,000 + 1250 = 11,250$ lb.

IV. A cord with masses at the ends is hung over a pulley as in the Atwood's machine, § 34. Find the tension in the cord when it supports a 500-gm. mass at one end and a 400-gm. mass at the other. Assume that friction is absent and neglect the mass of the cord and that of the pulley.

The two masses are represented in part I of Fig. 52, and will be studied separately in solving the problem. The 500-gm. mass is acted upon by two forces: the downward pull of gravity, which equals $500 \text{ gm.} \times \frac{980 \text{ dynes}}{1 \text{ gm.}}$ = 490,000 dynes, and the unknown tension T in the cord pulling upward,

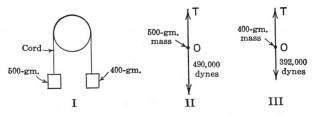

FIG. 52. Motion of two masses hanging from a pulley

as shown at O in part II of the figure. Since this mass accelerates downward, the downward force must be greater than the upward force, and the difference between them, namely 490,000 dynes $- T$, is the unbalanced force acting on the 500-gm. mass. The expression $F = ma$ is applied to this body alone, thus:

$$490,000 \text{ dynes} - T = 500 \text{ gm.} \times a$$

This equation cannot be solved by itself since it contains two unknown quantities, T and a.

Next, consider the 400-gm. body; it is acted on by a downward force of $400 \text{ gm.} \times \frac{980 \text{ dynes}}{1 \text{ gm.}} = 392,000$ dynes, and by an upward force T, as indicated in part III of the figure. The excess upward force acting upon this body is $T - 392,000$ dynes, and therefore,

$$T - 392,000 \text{ dynes} = 400 \text{ gm.} \times a$$

This provides another equation relating the tension in the cord and the acceleration of the moving system.

The two equations can be solved simultaneously, giving the tension T in the cord as 435,600 dynes, and the acceleration a of the moving system as 108.9 cm/sec.^{2}

FRICTION

48. Forces of Friction.—The surface of any solid if sufficiently magnified would be found rugged and uneven, and the irregularities cause it to oppose the sliding of another surface over it. This opposition is called *sliding friction*. A smooth (that is, frictionless) surface represents an ideal or limiting case which is never attained in practice. It must not be inferred that friction has no useful aspects; indeed, a person could not walk nor a wheel roll on the ground without friction.

It is found by experiment that the amount of friction depends upon the materials which are in contact, the condition of the sliding surfaces, and the force with which they are pressed together. Experiment also shows that the friction is virtually independent of the speed of sliding over a wide range of speeds, and that for any two given bodies, friction depends little, if any, upon the area of the sliding surfaces. As an illustration of the last-mentioned item, a slab of iron sliding along a wood plank will encounter practically the same friction when sliding on edge as when sliding on its face. The explanation probably lies in the fact that although there is less surface in contact when the slab is on edge, nevertheless, the whole weight of the slab is concentrated on this smaller surface, and the slab and plank are brought into more intimate contact. The amount of friction when a body is starting from rest is somewhat greater than while it is sliding, but for simplicity this effect will be neglected. The foregoing statements of experimental results are true only approximately, even for dry surfaces.

When a body slides over another body, a force acts upon it called the *force of friction*. Being a force, it is expressed in the same units, and has the same properties, as any force. Much can be learned about the force of friction by merely sliding a book around on a table top. It will be apparent that the force of friction always acts in the plane of sliding, and that its direction is always opposite to that of the motion. No matter which way the book is moved, the force of friction always acts on it in the opposite direction.

Suppose now that a person exerts a horizontal force of $\frac{1}{4}$ lb. on the book toward the right, but that on account of friction the book does not move. In this case, since the book stays at rest, the unbalanced force acting on it must be zero, and since the experimenter is then exerting a force on it of $\frac{1}{4}$ lb. toward the right, the surface of the table must be exerting a force of friction on it of $\frac{1}{4}$ lb. toward the left. A word of caution might be added at this point. It should not be thought that since the book stays at rest, the force of friction must be greater than $\frac{1}{4}$ lb. at this time, for if the force of friction could be greater than the applied force it would make the book move backward, and this result is absurd.

Next, suppose that the experimenter increases his force on the book from $\frac{1}{4}$ lb. to $\frac{1}{2}$ lb. and that still the book does not move; the force of friction must also have increased to $\frac{1}{2}$ lb. Imagine finally that by increasing the force little by little the book is set into motion, and that then a horizontal force of 1 lb. is found to be just sufficient to keep it moving with constant speed. For constant speed, the unbalanced force acting on a body is zero, and hence friction is now exerting a force of 1 lb. on the book. It is evident that in this case the force of sliding friction is as great as possible for these particular bodies, but is insufficient to hold the book at rest.

To give another illustration of friction, suppose that a man wishes to move a heavy packing case along the floor, the maximum force of friction between the case and the floor being 100 lb. If the man pushes horizontally with a force of 100 lb. on the case he will merely balance friction; he must push harder than this to start it from rest. Thus, if he were to push horizontally with a force of 125 lb., the result would be the same as if he had exerted only 25 lb. with friction absent.

The packing case could have been moved much more easily by rolling it along on two pieces of pipe, because rolling friction has a much lower value than sliding friction. Perhaps the maximum force of friction might be reduced to 30 lb., including the effects at both top and bottom of the rollers. Under these circumstances a horizontal push of 30 lb. would balance friction, and any harder push would start the case moving. Rolling friction is the opposition which occurs when one body rolls upon another, and is probably due to slight deformations of the bodies at the points of contact. In problems, rolling friction and sliding friction are treated in the same way.

49. Coefficient of Friction.—The maximum force of friction which one body is capable of exerting upon another is directly proportional to the normal or perpendicular force with which their surfaces are pressed together. Thus, if f is the maximum force of friction between two bodies which are pressed together with a force N perpendicular to their contacting surfaces, then $f \propto N$, or

$$f = \mu N$$

where the proportionality factor μ (mu) is a quantity which is called the *coefficient of friction* between the surfaces. This expression can be transposed to read

$$\mu = \frac{f}{N} \tag{35}$$

from which the coefficient of friction is defined as *the ratio of the maximum force of friction between two bodies to the normal force pressing the surfaces together.* It is evident from equation (35) that since f and N are both forces, they may be expressed in any desired force unit, so long as the same unit is used for both, and that μ is a pure numeric, having no unit.

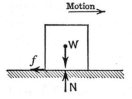

FIG. 53. Forces acting on block sliding to rest

Since the frictional force f is always in the plane of sliding, and the normal force N pressing the two surfaces into contact is perpendicular to this plane, it follows that f and N are always at right angles to each other. Fig. 53 shows the forces acting upon a block which had been set in motion toward the right and is now sliding to rest along a level plane. In this example, the supporting surface is horizontal, and so the normal reaction N of the plane is equal and opposite to the weight W of the block. The force of friction f is at right angles to N and opposite to the direction of motion.

The coefficient of sliding friction may be taken as a constant for any two surfaces; it depends only on the materials involved and the condition of the surfaces in contact. Some representative values for dry surfaces appear in the accompanying table.

Coefficients of Sliding Friction

Wood on wood..............	0.25 to 0.5
Metals on wood.............	0.2 to 0.6
Metals on metals............	0.15 to 0.2
Leather on oak..............	0.27 to 0.38
Leather on metals...........	0.56

For surfaces which are carefully machined and thoroughly lubricated, the coefficient of sliding friction is much smaller, 0.005 being a representative value.

As a typical problem involving sliding friction, consider a sled being drawn on level snow by a constant force of 10 lb. applied at an angle 25° upward from the horizontal. If the sled with its load weighs 60 lb. and if the coefficient of friction between the sled and the snow is 0.05, how much time is required to travel 100 ft., starting from rest?

In accordance with the procedure of § 47, the sled, shown in part I of Fig. 54, is chosen as the body to be considered, and is represented at O

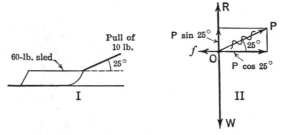

Fig. 54. Sled drawn along horizontal surface

in the force diagram forming part II of the figure. The forces acting on the sled are as follows: the downward pull of gravity, W (60 lb.); the pull P (10 lb.) applied in the direction shown; the upward reaction of the snow, R (unknown); and the backward force of friction, f (also unknown). The pull P is resolved into a horizontal component $P \cos 25° = 10 \times 0.906 = 9.06$ lb., which shows how much of the pull is effective in drawing the sled horizontally, and a vertical component $P \sin 25° = 10 \times 0.422 = 4.22$ lb., which shows how much the sled is being pulled up, reducing its force against the snow. The pull P may now be disregarded and is crossed out, since it is replaced by its components.

The net force which the sled exerts downward on the snow is $60 - 4.22 = 55.78$ lb., and hence the upward thrust R of the snow on the sled is also 55.78 lb., this being the normal force between the sliding surfaces. The frictional force is obtained from equation (35) as $f = \mu N = 0.05 \times 55.78 = 2.79$ lb. Since the vertical forces are balanced, the only unbalanced force acting on the sled is toward the right and amounts to $9.06 - 2.79$ or 6.27 lb. Consequently the acceleration of the sled, from equation (34), is

$$a = \frac{Fg}{W} = \frac{6.27 \text{ lb.} \times 32 \dfrac{\text{ft.}}{\text{sec.}^2}}{60 \text{ lb.}} = 3.35 \frac{\text{ft.}}{\text{sec.}^2}$$

Next this acceleration value is substituted in equation (21), which is

$$s = v_0 t + \tfrac{1}{2}at^2 = 0 + \tfrac{1}{2}at^2$$

and the time to travel 100 ft. is found to be

$$t = \sqrt{\frac{2s}{a}} = \sqrt{\frac{2 \times 100 \text{ ft.}}{3.35 \frac{\text{ft.}}{\text{sec.}^2}}} = \sqrt{59.8 \text{ sec.}^2} = 7.73 \text{ sec.}$$

Some typical values of the coefficients of rolling friction appear below.

Coefficients of Rolling Friction

Cast-iron wheels on rails................	0.004
Ball bearings in rolling contact.........	0.001 to 0.003
Roller bearings in rolling contact.......	0.002 to 0.007

It is because rolling friction is so small compared with sliding friction that wheels are used instead of runners on wagons, that casters are provided on heavy furniture, and that for many purposes ball bearings are preferred to those of the sliding, or sleeve, type. In the sleeve bearing the shaft slides, while in the ball bearing it rolls, and although the balls slide somewhat upon each other, the force of friction is much reduced.

In addition to sliding and rolling friction, retardation is also offered to the motion of an object by the air, and this is of particular importance in the propulsion of automobiles, trains, and aircraft. This retardation increases with velocity, and at relatively low speeds is often regarded as being proportional to the velocity. On this assumption, the retarding force will be expressed as $f \propto v$ or $f = Rv$, where v is the velocity of an object, and R is a proportionality factor which may be termed mechanical resistance. When this frictional force is included in equation (31) for accelerated motion, the total force required to produce an acceleration $a = \dfrac{dv}{dt}$ (§ 31) in a mass m is written as

$$P = ma + Rv = m\frac{dv}{dt} + Rv$$

In starting, $v = 0$ and the entire unbalanced force produces acceleration; when the body has accelerated to the maximum speed permitted by the frictional drag, $v = $ constant, $\dfrac{dv}{dt} = 0$, and the entire force is exerted in maintaining the speed acquired against the mechanical resistance. The foregoing equation is useful in studying motion at relatively low speeds; the behavior at high speeds is complicated by the fact that air resistance is then more nearly proportional to the square of the speed.

CIRCULAR MOTION

50. Force Involved in Circular Motion.—In accordance with Newton's First Law of Motion, a moving body left to itself will travel in a straight line; a body will not move around a curve unless a lateral force is exerted upon it. When a locomotive encounters a curve, its forward motion causes the flanges on the wheels to press outwardly against the edge of the outer rail, and consequently the rail presses inwardly against the flanges; the locomotive, under the action of this inward force, undergoes a change of direction and continues to follow the curved track.

There are many other examples that show the existence of this lateral force which is necessary for motion along a curve. If a stone is whirled around at the end of a cord, it pulls outwardly on the cord, whereupon the cord becomes taut and pulls inwardly upon the stone. In the same way, the earth, in moving along its orbit, it always being drawn inward by the gravitational attraction of the sun. A little thought will show why an automobile sometimes skids when the driver tries to make a sharp turn on a slippery street.

The motion of a body traveling around a circular curve with constant speed is of special interest, for in such circular motion the moving object acts upon the restraining agent with a constant force directed radially outward from the center; this outward push or pull is called the *centrifugal* force. Since for any action there is always an equal and opposite reaction, the restraining agent exerts an equal inward force upon the moving object, and this is called the *centripetal* force. In all motion on curves, the centrifugal and centripetal forces are equal and opposite, and both are exerted in the plane in which the curve lies. *Although equal, these forces cannot balance each other, because they are not exerted upon the same object.*

An unbalanced force always produces acceleration, and thus the centripetal force acting upon a body in circular motion continually accelerates it toward the center of the circle; in fact, it is this inward motion combined with the forward motion that makes the body move in a circle.

51. Centripetal and Centrifugal Force.—In studying the factors upon which centripetal force depends, emphasis is placed upon the fact that when a body traverses a circular path with constant speed its velocity changes continually, the change taking place in direction but not in magnitude.

Suppose that a body moves with constant speed v around a circle of radius r which is centered at O as indicated in part I of Fig. 55, and that in a time interval t it moves a distance $MN = vt$ as shown in part II. Its velocities at M and at N may be represented by vectors v_o and v_f, tangent to the circle at these points respectively and each

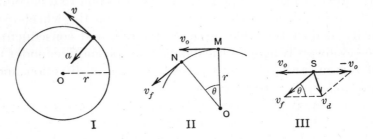

Fig. 55. Pertaining to centripetal acceleration

having the same magnitude as v. These velocities differ in direction, and thus some additional velocity must have been given to the body in moving from M to N in order to change its velocity from v_o to v_f. To find this additional velocity, draw v_o and v_f from a common point S as in part III of the figure, and subtract v_o from v_f. This result is accomplished by reversing the direction of v_o and proceeding as in addition, § 16; the desired change in velocity is found to be v_d. Since this velocity change occurs in a time interval t, the average accelera-

tion over this interval is $a = \dfrac{v_d}{t}$. To obtain the instantaneous accel-

eration, observe that the two angles marked θ are equal, and that as the time interval is taken shorter and shorter, approaching zero as a limit, the sector in part II becomes more and more nearly similar to the isosceles triangle in part III. Hence, in the limit,

$$\frac{v_d}{v_f} = \frac{MN}{OM} \quad \text{or} \quad \frac{at}{v_f} = \frac{vt}{r}$$

Numerically $v_f = v$, and hence the magnitude of the acceleration a is obtained from this equation as

$$a = \frac{v^2}{r} \qquad (36)$$

It is evident that acceleration is a vector quantity. In the present instance its direction may be found by observing that the shorter the time interval taken, the more nearly v_d becomes perpendicular to v_o and v_f; in the limit it is perpendicular to both of these vectors. Therefore, *the centripetal acceleration is directed toward the center of the circle.*

The force which must be exerted upon the body to produce the acceleration is given in British units by equation (34), $F = \dfrac{W}{g} a$; hence, the centripetal force acting upon a body of weight W lb. when moving with speed v ft. per sec. around a curve of radius r ft. is given in pounds by the expression

$$F = \frac{W}{g} \frac{v^2}{r} \qquad (37)$$

In metric units, the centripetal force in dynes acting upon a body of mass m gm., when moving with a speed v cm. per sec. around a curve of radius r cm., is found from equation (31), $F = ma$, to be

$$F = m \frac{v^2}{r} \qquad (38)$$

It will be observed that the centripetal force acting on a body moving in a circular path varies directly as the square of the speed, and inversely as the radius of the circle. In traveling around a given curve with doubled speed, for example, four times as much centripetal force is brought into play; again, when the same speed is maintained around a curve of half the radius, the centripetal force is doubled.

As an illustrative problem, calculate the centrifugal force exerted by a 30-ton railway car traveling at 75 ft. per sec. around a curve of 1000-ft. radius. From equation (37), the centrifugal force is found to be

$$F = \frac{60{,}000 \text{ lb.}}{32 \, \frac{\text{ft.}}{\text{sec.}^2}} \times \frac{(75)^2 \, \frac{\text{ft.}^2}{\text{sec.}^2}}{1000 \text{ ft.}} = 10{,}550 \text{ lb.}$$

Again, suppose it is desired to find the centripetal force exerted on a 200-gm. stone whirled in a vertical circle at the end of a string 50 cm. long, at the rate of 3 rev. per sec. In this example,

$$v = \frac{s}{t} = \frac{3 \times 2\pi \, 50 \text{ cm.}}{1 \text{ sec.}} = 300\pi \, \frac{\text{cm.}}{\text{sec.}}$$

The centripetal force, by equation (38), is therefore

$$F = 200 \text{ gm.} \times \frac{(300\pi)^2 \, \frac{\text{cm.}^2}{\text{sec.}^2}}{50 \text{ cm.}} = 3,552,000 \text{ dynes}$$

The rotation of the earth causes a reduction in the force with which a body is pulled toward the earth. The error due to this cause is greatest at the equator, where it amounts to about 7 lb. per ton, and is zero at the poles. This situation is somewhat like that of a passenger in an elevator which is accelerating downward: the floor of the car tends to recede from him and so he presses against it with less force than if the elevator were stationary.

52. Banking of Curves.—When an automobile rounds a curve at constant speed, it is accelerating toward the center of the curve, and so the resultant force acting upon it must also have this direction. If the highway is level, the only way to get such a force is by means of friction between tires and roadway. In such a case, the central force

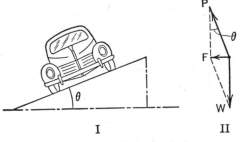

I   II

Fig. 56. Car rounding a banked curve

is likely to be small and uncertain, and the curve must be rounded slowly to avoid skidding. To overcome this difficulty, it is usual to bank curves, by sloping the roadbed upward from the inner to the outer edge; when the angle of banking is correct, a car can round the curve safely at a higher speed without depending upon friction. In Fig. 56, part I represents a car rounding a curve banked at an angle θ, the roadbed being shown in cross-section. Two forces act upon the car: the pull of gravity W downward, and the push P exerted by the road. The latter force is regarded as acting perpendicularly to the roadway in order not to count upon friction. The forces W and P are shown in part II of the figure acting in appropriate directions. These forces must be so proportioned that their resultant, F, is horizontal, this being the centripetal force needed for circular motion around a horizontal curve. Since the two angles marked θ are equal, it follows that

$$\tan \theta = \frac{F}{W} = \frac{\dfrac{Wv^2}{gr}}{W} = \frac{v^2}{gr}$$

and hence the banking angle is $\theta = \tan^{-1} \dfrac{v^2}{gr}$, where v is the speed of the car, g is the acceleration due to gravity, and r is the radius of the curve.

UNITS AND DIMENSIONS

53. Survey of Physical Units.—One of the most difficult matters encountered in beginning the study of Physics, but nevertheless one of the most important, is the subject of units. If there were a single unit for each kind of quantity, the work would be much simplified; but such is not the case, as will be evident when one considers, for example, the many units used for expressing area: square centimeters, circular mils, square feet, acres, square miles, and so on. Fortunately, not all of the possible units for the various quantities are used in scientific and engineering work.

The units that are used widely belong to four systems, with which the student should become familiar. These systems and some of their units are indicated in the accompanying table. In each system, the different units are so related to one another that any true equation will hold, provided the quantities which appear in it are all expressed in the units of that system.

Absolute Systems.—The *British absolute system* is based on three fundamental units: the foot as the unit of length, the pound as the unit of mass, and the second as the unit of time; for which reason this system is known as the *foot-pound-second* or *fps.* system. The remaining units in this system, including those for all other mechanical quantities, are derived from the three fundamental units. Thus, instead of arbitrarily choosing the square yard or the acre as the unit of area, recognition is given to the fact that area is fundamentally the square of a length, and since the foot has already been selected as the unit of length, the unit of area becomes the square foot. Similarly unit volume is the cubic foot; unit speed $(v = s/t)$ is the foot per second; unit acceleration $(a = [v_f - v_o]/t)$ is the foot per second per second; unit force $(F = ma)$ is the pound foot per second per second or poundal, and so on. Note that in solving any equation using this system of units, mass must always be expressed in pounds, accelera-

Systems of Units

Absolute units			Gravitational units		
Quantity	British (fps.)	Metric (cgs.)	Quantity	British	Metric
Fundamental			*Fundamental* •		
Length.....	ft.	cm.	Length.......	ft.	cm.
Mass.......	lb.	gm.	Force........	lb.	gm.
Time.......	sec.	sec.	Time........	sec.	sec.
Derived			*Derived*		
Area.......	ft.^{2}	cm.^{2}	Area.........	ft.^{2}	cm.^{2}
Volume.....	ft.^{3}	cm.^{3}	Volume.......	ft.^{3}	cm.^{3}
Speed......	ft/sec.	cm/sec.	Speed........	ft/sec.	cm/sec.
Acceleration	ft/sec.^{2}	cm/sec.^{2}	Acceleration...	ft/sec.^{2}	cm/sec.^{2}
Force.......	poundal	dyne	Mass.........	slug	no names
Density.....	lb/ft.^{3}	gm/cm.^{3}	Density......	slug/ft.^{3}	assigned
Energy.....	ft-poundal	erg	Energy.......	ft-lb.	cm-gm.
Power......	ft-poundal/sec.	erg/sec.	Power........	ft-lb/sec.	cm-gm/sec.

tion in feet per second per second, and force in poundals. For instance, if a force were given in pounds, it would be necessary to convert it to poundals before using it in connection with this system of units.

In a similar manner the *metric absolute system* is based on the three fundamental units of length, mass and time, these units being the centimeter, gram, and second respectively; whence this system is called the *centimeter-gram-second* or *cgs.* system. For scientific purposes, this system is used more than any other. The remaining units are derived from the fundamental units in the same way as previously described; thus, unit area is the square centimeter, unit volume is the cubic centimeter, unit force is the gram centimeter per second per second or dyne, and so on. In solving an equation using this system of units, mass must always be expressed in grams, acceleration in centimeters per second per second, and force in dynes.

Gravitational Systems.—An examination of the foregoing table shows that the gravitational systems of units differ from the absolute systems in that they employ *force* as a fundamental quantity instead of *mass*. They are called gravitational systems because in each of them the unit of force is defined as the attraction of gravity upon a certain mass.

The *British gravitational system* is based on the following fundamental units: the foot as the unit of length, the pound as the unit of force, and the second as the unit of time; and the remaining units are derived from these as already explained. This is the system commonly used in engineering work. The unit of mass in this system is not often used, and no name has been generally adopted for it. Actually, this unit of mass is a mass of 32 lb. (strictly speaking, g lb.), and is sometimes called a "slug." The slug is defined as the mass which will receive an acceleration of 1 foot per second per second when it is acted upon by an unbalanced force of 1 pound.

Finally, there is the *metric gravitational system*, which is based on the centimeter, gram, and second as the units of length, force, and time respectively, the remaining units being derived from these, as indicated in the table.

Other Systems.—A new metric system of units is coming into use, particularly in electrophysics, and is discussed in Chapter XXIX. It is based upon the meter as the unit of length, the kilogram as the unit of mass, and the second as the unit of time; it is known as the *meter-kilogram-second* or *mks.* system. The unit of force in this system is called the *newton;* it is that force which will give a 1-kilogram mass an acceleration of 1 meter per second per second.

Should occasion arise to apply the mks. units to problems in mechanics and to compare results so expressed with those in the cgs. system, it will be helpful to use the following conversion factors for density and force respectively:

1 kilogram per cubic meter $= 10^{-3}$ grams per cubic centimeter
1 newton $\qquad\qquad = 10^{5}$ dynes

*54. Dimensional Analysis.—The relations among physical quantities can be analyzed apart from the units in which these quantities may be expressed, by a method known as *dimensional analysis*. This method will be illustrated by reference to the absolute system.

The entities length, mass, and time are recognized as fundamental concepts, and are represented dimensionally as: length = $[L]$, mass = $[M]$, and time = $[T]$. Since area is essentially the product of two lengths its dimensions are $[L^2]$; similarly, those of volume are $[L^3]$. The dimensions of speed ($v = s/t$) are $[LT^{-1}]$; those of acceleration are similarly $[LT^{-2}]$; and those of force ($F = ma$) are $[LMT^{-2}]$. In this manner, *all mechanical quantities can be expressed in terms of the three fundamental quantities.*

One purpose for which dimensional analysis is useful is in verifying equations for correctness; an equation must have the same dimensions on both sides and thus reduce dimensionally to an identity if it is correct and complete. Thus, to determine whether an assumed "equation" $F = \dfrac{Wv^2}{2g}$ is valid, it would be written dimensionally as

$$[LMT^{-2}] = \frac{[LMT^{-2}][LT^{-1}]^2}{[LT^{-2}]}$$

the coefficient 2 being omitted because it has no dimensions. The dimensional statement reduces to $[LMT^{-2}] = [L^2MT^{-2}]$, and since this form is not an identity, the assumed equation is incorrect. The equation $F = \dfrac{Wv^2}{gr}$ similarly analyzed would be found correct dimensionally.

PROBLEMS

1. Find the acceleration which will be produced in a 100-gm. body when acted upon by an unbalanced force of 7500 dynes.

2. For test purposes, a 600-lb. object is to be brought from rest to a speed of 15 ft/sec. in moving a distance of 50 ft. What steady force must be exerted upon it, if friction is neglected?

3. What horizontal force must be applied continuously to a 20-kg. body in order to move it along a level surface with an acceleration of 50 cm/sec.², if friction exerts a backward drag of 500,000 dynes upon it?

4. A steady horizontal force of 22,000 poundals is applied to a 4-ton truck along a level road. If the truck, starting from rest, acquires a speed of 20 ft/sec. in 10 sec., what is the backward force of friction acting upon it?

5. What is the momentum of a bus weighing 8 tons when traveling at 40 mi. per hr.?

6. A billiard ball having a mass of 0.4 lb. and moving at a speed of 40 ft. per sec. strikes a similar ball that is at rest. After impact, the first ball is deflected 30° from its original direction and its speed is reduced to 34.6 ft. per sec. Describe the motion of the second ball just after impact.

*7. Compute the mass of the earth from the fact that at its surface, 6370 km. from the center, it attracts a mass of 1 gm. with a force of 980 dynes.

8. What horizontal force must a locomotive exert on a train weighing 200 tons in order to increase its speed from 10 mi. per hr. to 30 mi. per hr. in moving 350 ft. along a level track, if the backward force of friction amounts to 8 lb. per ton of weight?

9. A steady horizontal force of 10 lb. is applied to a 70-lb. sled resting on level snow. How far will the sled move in 5 sec., neglecting friction?

10. Suppose a paratrooper to drop from an airplane for 10 sec. before he opens his parachute. What is his downward speed at the end of this time if his weight with equipment is 220 lb. and if the air exerts an average retarding force of 90 lb. upon him?

11. An airplane is gliding in a direction 10° downward from the horizontal. Three forces act upon it: (A) its weight of 10,000 lb.; (B) the lift, perpendicular to the direction of motion; and (C) the drag of air friction, opposite to the direction of motion. Assume that the plane moves with constant speed, and compute the value of the lift.

12. An airplane is climbing in a direction 15° upward from the horizontal. Four forces act upon it: (A) its weight of 10,000 lb.; (B) the thrust of the propeller, along the direction of motion, amounting to 3000 lb.; (C) the lift, perpendicular to the propeller thrust; and (D) the drag of air friction, opposite to the direction of motion. Assume that the plane moves with constant speed, and compute the value of the lift.

13. The cable of a derrick exerts an upward pull of $5\frac{1}{2}$ tons on a 5-ton crate. Find the resulting acceleration of the crate, friction being neglected, and the time needed to raise it 15 ft., starting from rest.

14. An elevator which, with its load, weighs 8 tons, is descending with a speed of 700 ft. per min. If the load on the cables must not exceed 14 tons, what is the shortest distance in which the elevator should be stopped?

15. Find how much force a 160-lb. passenger will exert upon the floor of an elevator, when the elevator has (a) an upward acceleration of 3 ft/sec.^{2}, and (b) a downward acceleration of 3 ft/sec.^{2}

16. A 10-kg. block slides from rest down a smooth plane 250 cm. long inclined 25° with the horizontal. Find the velocity of the block at the bottom of the incline.

17. A 5-lb. weight and a 3-lb. weight are fastened to opposite ends of a string, and the string is placed over a frictionless pulley. Compute the acceleration of the moving system.

18. In a test on an Atwood's machine, § 34, the tape supported a 275-gm. body at one end and a 285-gm. body at the other. When released from rest, the moving system was found to move 35.0 cm. in 2.0 sec. Calculate the acceleration due to gravity at the place where the test was conducted. Also find the tension in the tape.

19. A 40-lb. block is placed on a level table and a rope is fastened to it which passes horizontally to a pulley at the edge of the table and thence

extends downward to a 1.5-lb. block suspended from its other end. Find the acceleration of the moving blocks neglecting friction.

20. A package thrown along a bench with an initial speed of 700 cm/sec. slides to rest in 1000 cm. Find the coefficient of friction between the package and the bench.

21. A horse pulls a 500-lb. wagon along a level road by means of traces which make an angle of 10° upward from the horizontal. How hard must the horse pull to maintain constant speed if the coefficient of friction is taken as 0.15?

22. If a block is placed on an inclined plane and the angle which the plane makes with the horizontal is varied, a limiting value will be found, called the limiting angle of repose, at which the block if at rest will remain at rest but if started will slide down the plane with constant speed. Show that the coefficient of friction between block and plane is equal to the tangent of the limiting angle of repose.

23. In moving a 1000-lb. safe upstairs a plank is placed over the steps at an angle of 30° with the floor, and the safe is drawn up this incline by pulling a rope in the direction of motion. How much pull must be exerted on the rope to move the safe at constant speed, if the coefficient of friction between safe and plank is 0.30?

24. A 30-kg. box slides from rest down a straight chute 15 meters long, one end of which is raised 9 meters above the other. What is the speed of the box at the bottom (a) if the chute is smooth? (b) if the chute is rough, the coefficient of friction between box and chute being 0.25?

25. Calculate the centrifugal force exerted by a 5-ton truck while rounding a curve of 300-ft. radius at 30 mi. per hr.

26. A stone is being whirled in a horizontal circle of 1-meter radius. If the stone weighs 500 gm. and makes 2 complete revolutions per second, how much centrifugal force does it exert?

27. A 1-lb. stone, at the end of a string 2 ft. long, is whirled in a vertical circle. Determine the tension in the string when the stone is at the bottom of the circle traveling at 20 ft/sec.

28. A ball attached to a cord 40 cm. long travels in a horizontal circle, the cord describing the surface of a cone. Find the speed of the ball in centimeters per second at which the string will swing around at an angle of 30° with the vertical.

29. The rotor of an air-driven ultra-centrifuge, made of duralumin, is driven at 60,000 rev. per min. and a specimen in the rotor moves in a circle of 6.5-cm. radius. Compare the centripetal force exerted on the specimen with the force of gravity acting upon it.

30. What is the highest speed at which a 3400-lb. automobile could travel around a curve of 400-ft. radius, if the roadway were level and if the coefficient of friction between the tires and the roadway were 0.125?

31. Compute the angle of banking of a curve 600 ft. in radius in order that traffic moving at 50 mi. per hr. may round the curve without depending upon friction.

Rotational Motion   *Chapter VI*

55. Relation Between Torque and Angular Acceleration.—The action of a force in producing acceleration was considered in the preceding chapter, and it was found that the acceleration imparted to a body was directly proportional to the unbalanced force acting upon it and inversely proportional to the mass of the body. This statement, which is Newton's Second Law of Motion, is expressed mathematically by

$$a = \frac{F}{m}$$

where a is the acceleration of the body, F is the unbalanced force upon it, and m is its mass.

Now suppose the mass m to be attached to the end of a crank (imagined to be weightless) pivoted at O, as in Fig. 57, and suppose the force F which acts upon it is a steady force so directed that it is always at right angles to the crank. Then as the mass moves, the crank pulls it toward the center and makes it travel in a circular path, and at the same time the tangential force F will cause it to move along the circle with increasing speed, giving it a linear acceleration along this path equal to

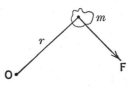

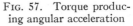

Fig. 57. Torque producing angular acceleration

$a = \dfrac{F}{m}$. In the meantime the crank will have an increasing angular velocity and if the crank has a length r, its angular acceleration can be expressed as

$$\alpha = \frac{a}{r}$$

according to § 37. The force F acting on the mass produces a torque about the axis O which amounts to

$$T = Fr$$

as in § 23. From the three foregoing equations, the torque may be expressed as

$$T = Fr = ma \times r = mr^2\alpha$$

where the product mr^2 is a constant for the particular combination of mass m and crank length r. The single letter I is used to designate this constant, whence the angular acceleration of the crank becomes

$$\alpha = \frac{T}{I} \qquad\qquad (39)$$

an expression similar in form to that expressing Newton's Law for linear acceleration at the beginning of this section. The constant I is called the *moment of inertia* of the rotating system; it depends not alone upon the mass m, but also upon its distance r from the center of rotation.

56. Units for Moment of Inertia.—It has been pointed out in the preceding section that a particle of mass m located at a distance r from an axis of rotation has a moment of inertia with respect to that axis of $I = mr^2$. This expression will later be applied to a body comprising many particles located at different distances from the axis, but it will suffice now to point out the fact that the moment of inertia of such a body depends not only upon the entire mass of that body but also upon the distribution of the many tiny masses of which it is composed. For example, the two wheels in Fig. 58 are solid disks composed in part of metal and in part of wood. Both wheels have the same radius, and are so designed as to have the same mass. The wheel with the heavy rim is found to require a larger torque than the other to start it spinning, and hence it has the larger moment of inertia. The constant I for a body is independent of the speed of the body and of the forces acting upon it.

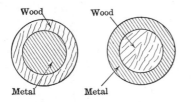

Fig. 58. Wheels of same size having different moments of inertia

Moment of inertia is generally expressed in units of the absolute systems, § 53. These units may be found by transposing equation (39) to read

$$I = \frac{T}{\alpha}$$

and substituting appropriate units for the torque T and the angular acceleration α. In metric (cgs.) units, T is in dyne-centimeters and α is in radians per second per second, and so the unit for moment of inertia will be

$$I = \frac{\text{dyne-cm.}}{\dfrac{\text{radians}}{\text{sec.}^2}} = \frac{\dfrac{\text{gm.} \times \text{cm.}}{\text{sec.}^2} \times \text{cm.}}{\dfrac{\text{radians}}{\text{sec.}^2}} = \text{gm-cm.}^2$$

In British (fps.) units, T must be in poundal-feet and α is in radians per second per second, whence the unit for moment of inertia will be

$$I = \frac{\text{poundal-ft.}}{\dfrac{\text{radians}}{\text{sec.}^2}} = \frac{\dfrac{\text{lb.} \times \text{ft.}}{\text{sec.}^2} \times \text{ft.}}{\dfrac{\text{radians}}{\text{sec.}^2}} = \text{lb-ft.}^2$$

If the torque is given in pound-feet it can be converted to poundal-feet by using the relation: 32 poundals = 1 lb.

The above-mentioned units in which I is expressed are those generally used; in both cases the unit is a mass unit multiplied by the square of a length unit, or dimensionally $[ML^2]$; see § 54. Two examples will illustrate the application of equation (39) to problems involving rotation.

I. A water turbine having a moment of inertia of 250 kg-meters^2 is brought to rest by friction from a speed of 180 rev. per min. in 26 min. after the gate-valve is closed. What is the frictional torque?

To convert the units to the cgs. system, moment of inertia will be expressed in gram-centimeters^2 and angular acceleration in radians per second per second. Thus

$$I = 250 \times 1000 \times (100)^2 = 25 \times 10^8 \text{ gm-cm.}^2$$

and

$$\alpha = \frac{0 - 180 \times 2\pi}{60 \times 26 \times 60} = -0.0121 \text{ radians per sec.}^2$$

Then

$$T = I\alpha = 25 \times 10^8 \text{ gm-cm.}^2 \times \left(-0.0121 \frac{\text{radians}}{\text{sec.}^2}\right)$$

$$= -303 \times 10^5 \frac{\text{gm-cm.}^2}{\text{sec.}^2} = -303 \times 10^5 \text{ dyne-cm.}$$

Since a force of 1 gm. = 980 dynes, the frictional torque that brings the turbine to rest may also be stated as 30,900 gm-cm. = 0.309 kg-meter.

II. A motor armature is brought from rest to its normal speed of 1200 rev. per min. in 3 sec.   The torque exerted between the current in the armature conductors and the magnetism of the field structure is 53 lb-ft., and the frictional drag is 3 lb-ft.   Determine the moment of inertia of the armature.

It took 3 sec. to acquire the normal speed of 1200 rev. per min., or 20 rev. per sec., or 40π radians per sec.; therefore the angular acceleration is $\dfrac{40\pi}{3} = 41.9$ radians per sec.^{2} The unbalanced torque is $53 - 3 = 50$ lb-ft. or $50 \times 32 = 1600$ poundal-ft.   Hence, by equation (39), the moment of inertia of the armature is

$$I = \frac{1600 \text{ poundal-ft.}}{41.9 \dfrac{\text{radians}}{\text{sec.}^2}} = \frac{1600 \dfrac{\text{lb-ft.}^2}{\text{sec.}^2}}{41.9 \dfrac{\text{radians}}{\text{sec.}^2}} = 38.2 \text{ lb-ft.}^2$$

57. Moments of Inertia of Rigid Bodies.

—In order to ascertain how the distribution of mass about the axis of a rotating body influences its moment of inertia, consider a body divided into a number of particles and subject to an unbalanced torque which produces rotation.   Imagine this torque to be transmitted from one particle to another through cohesion so that it is equivalent to a number of individual torques which act severally on the particles.   Investigate the torque on each particle and the acceleration which it produces, and then collect the results to find the effect upon the entire body.

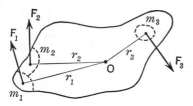

FIG. 59.   Determining the moment of inertia of a body

A body is shown in Fig. 59 pivoted at O, and several of its particles are indicated by dotted lines.   The masses of these particles are marked m_1, m_2, m_3, $\cdots$, their radial distances from the axis are designated as r_1, r_2, r_3, $\cdots$ respectively, and the forces acting perpendicularly to these distances are denoted by the vectors F_1, F_2, F_3, $\cdots$ respectively.   The torque produced by force F_1 acting on particle m_1 is given in § 55 as

$$T_1 = F_1 r_1 = m_1 a_1 r_1 = m_1 r_1{}^2 \alpha$$

where α, the angular acceleration of the rigid body, is the same for all of its particles, so that there is no need of subscripting it.   Similarly, for the other particles, the torques are

$$T_2 = m_2 r_2{}^2 \alpha \qquad T_3 = m_3 r_3{}^2 \alpha$$

The total unbalanced torque on the body, namely $T_1 + T_2 + T_3 + \cdots$, may be represented merely by T, and it follows that

$$T = m_1 r_1{}^2 \alpha + m_2 r_2{}^2 \alpha + m_3 r_3{}^2 \alpha + \cdots$$
$$= [m_1 r_1{}^2 + m_2 r_2{}^2 + m_3 r_3{}^2 + \cdots] \alpha = \Sigma m r^2 \times \alpha$$

where the bracketed expression containing a number of terms of the same type is replaced by the symbolic form $\Sigma m r^2$. The letter Σ (sigma) is used to represent "sum," consequently $\Sigma m r^2$ means the sum of a number of terms, each of which is a mass multiplied by the square of its distance from the axis of rotation. When this result is compared with equation (39), from which the torque is

$$T = I\alpha$$

it is clear that $\Sigma m r^2$ is the quantity previously called the moment of inertia. Consequently,

$$I = \Sigma m r^2 \qquad (40)$$

or in words, *the moment of inertia of a body is equal to the mass of one particle multiplied by the square of its distance from the axis of rotation, plus the mass of another particle multiplied by the square of its distance from the axis, plus $\cdots$ and so on, until all the particles of the body have been included.*

The moment of inertia of a single particle of mass m located at a distance r from the axis of rotation is merely mr^2, since there is but one particle and no need for summation as called for in equation (40). In a thin ring the mass is distributed all around the axis but the various particles have the same distance from the axis of rotation, making r constant; thus, the moment of inertia becomes $r^2 \Sigma m = M r^2$, where M is the total mass of the ring. While these values follow directly from the definition of moment of inertia, the application of the expression $I = \Sigma m r^2$ to most geometric shapes will require the methods of calculus, because the correct result is obtained only when the body is considered to be made up of a vast number of particles.

*58. Computing the Moment of Inertia of a Stick.—The moment of inertia of a body may often be approximated by supposing the body to be subdivided into relatively few particles, determining the moment of inertia of each, and adding the results. The procedure will be illustrated by determining the moment of inertia of a slim stick about a transverse axis through one end.

As a first approximation consider the entire uniform stick of length l to be just one particle of mass M, as shown in part I of Fig. 60. Then the equation for the moment of inertia reduces to $I = mr^2$, where

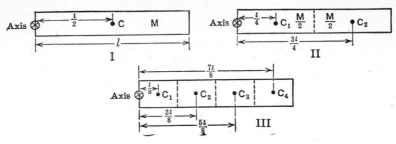

FIG. 60.   How monemts of inertia are calculated

m is equal to the entire mass M of the stick, and r is the distance $\frac{l}{2}$ from the axis of rotation to the center of mass C; this is at the center of the stick since it is uniform in cross-section. The moment of inertia of the stick on this assumption is, therefore,

$$I = M\left(\frac{l}{2}\right)^2 = \frac{1}{4}Ml^2 = 0.250Ml^2$$

As a second approximation, consider the stick to be divided into two particles of equal mass and centered at C_1 and C_2, as shown in part II of the same figure.   In this case $m_1 = m_2 = \frac{M}{2}$, $r_1 = \frac{l}{4}$, and $r_2 = \frac{3}{4}l$. The moment of inertia of the stick on this assumption is

$$I = m_1r_1{}^2 + m_2r_2{}^2 = \frac{M}{2}\left(\frac{l}{4}\right)^2 + \frac{M}{2}\left(\frac{3l}{4}\right)^2 = \frac{10}{32}Ml^2 = 0.313Ml^2$$

As a third approximation, assume the stick to be divided further, this time into four equal particles having their centers of mass located at C_1 to C_4 in part III of Fig. 60.   Here

$$m_1 = m_2 = m_3 = m_4 = \frac{M}{4} \qquad r_1 = \frac{l}{8} \quad \cdots \quad r_4 = \frac{7l}{8}$$

and the moment of inertia becomes

$$I = \frac{M}{4}\left(\frac{l}{8}\right)^2 + \frac{M}{4}\left(\frac{3l}{8}\right)^2 + \frac{M}{4}\left(\frac{5l}{8}\right)^2 + \frac{M}{4}\left(\frac{7l}{8}\right)^2 = \frac{21}{64}Ml^2 = 0.328Ml^2$$

Imagine this process of subdivision into smaller and smaller particles to be continued until the stick is divided into an infinitely large number of particles; the ultimate result for its moment of inertia as determined by calculus is

$$I = \tfrac{1}{3}Ml^2 = 0.333Ml^2 \; .$$

In the third approximation, in which the stick was divided into quarters, the result was less than 2 per cent below the correct value.

59. Moments of Inertia of Some Shapes.—Although the values of the moments of inertia of various geometric shapes will not be derived in this text, the results are easy to understand and to apply; accordingly some useful ones are given in the accompanying table for reference.

Moments of Inertia

Shape	I
Slim rod of mass M and length l, about a transverse axis through one end......................................	$\tfrac{1}{3}Ml^2$
Same, but transverse axis is through center............	$\tfrac{1}{12}Ml^2$
Hollow cylinder (thin wall) of mass M, radius r, and of any axial length, about its own axis................	Mr^2
Solid cylinder or disk of mass M, radius r, and of any axial length, about its own axis....................	$\tfrac{1}{2}Mr^2$
Solid disk of mass M and radius r about any diameter..	$\tfrac{1}{4}Mr^2$
Rectangular bar of mass M, length l, and width b, about an axis through its center and at right angles to dimensions b and l..	$\dfrac{M}{12}(b^2 + l^2)$
Solid sphere of mass M and radius r about any diameter	$\tfrac{2}{5}Mr^2$

Sometimes the moment of inertia of a body about a particular axis is known and it is desired to determine its moment of inertia about another axis parallel to the first. This can be done in a simple manner when one of the axes passes through the center of mass of the body. Analysis shows that if the moment of inertia of a body of mass M about an axis through its center of mass is I_G, then the moment of inertia about a parallel axis distant h from the first axis is

$$I = I_G + Mh^2 \tag{41}$$

For example, when a solid cylinder rolls on a flat surface it may be necessary to know the moment of inertia of the cylinder about its line of contact with the surface. The moment of inertia about its own axis is $I_G = \frac{1}{2}Mr^2$, and when the axis is shifted parallel to itself a distance r to the line of contact with the surface on which it rolls, the moment of inertia of the cylinder will be $I = \frac{1}{2}Mr^2 + Mr^2 = \frac{3}{2}Mr^2$.

60. Radius of Gyration.—The moment of inertia of an object embodies the masses of the particles that make up the object and the squares of the individual radii that extend from these particles to the axis. Moment of inertia is often expressed quite differently, however, in terms of the aggregate mass of the body and a single fictitious radius called the radius of gyration.

The radius of gyration of a body is the radius of a thin ring which has the same mass and same moment of inertia as the body when centered at the same axis. A rotating object of any shape may be imagined to have its mass compressed into a thin ring of such size that its moment of inertia remains unchanged. Then, if K is the radius of the ring it will also be the radius of gyration of the body about the same axis, and it follows that the moment of inertia of the body of mass M is

$$I = MK^2 \tag{42}$$

The moment of inertia of a meter stick about an axis through one end perpendicular to the stick can be calculated from the first equation in the table of the preceding section, namely $I = \frac{1}{3}Ml^2$, by taking $l = 100$ cm. From equation (42) it follows that

$$\tfrac{1}{3}Ml^2 = MK^2$$

whence the radius of gyration of the stick is

$$K = \frac{l}{\sqrt{3}} = \frac{100 \text{ cm.}}{1.732} = 57.7 \text{ cm.}$$

Manufacturers of rotating machinery, such as turbines and generators, indicate the radii of gyration of the rotating elements so that the users may readily compute the moments of inertia of these odd-shaped elements.

61. Typical Problems on Rotation.—The following problems will illustrate the action of torque on rotating bodies:

I. A steel wheel of a gyro-stabilizer is a solid disk 12.5 ft. in diameter and 7.5 in. thick, and a motor brings it up to its operating speed of 600 rev. per min. in 1.5 hr. What torque does the motor exert? In this problem it is necessary to compute the moment of inertia of the wheel knowing that steel weighs 490 lb. per ft.^{3}, and then to determine the angular acceleration during the starting period. From these data the required torque of the motor can be calculated by using equation (39).

The mass of the disk is

$$\pi \left(\frac{12.5}{2} \text{ ft.}\right)^2 \times \frac{7.5}{12} \text{ ft.} \times 490 \frac{\text{lb.}}{\text{ft.}^3} = 37{,}600 \text{ lb.}$$

and the moment of inertia about its axis is

$$I = \frac{1}{2} Mr^2 = \frac{1}{2} (37{,}600 \text{ lb.}) \times \left(\frac{12.5}{2} \text{ ft.}\right)^2 = 734{,}000 \text{ lb-ft.}^2$$

The angular velocity of the wheel at full speed is $\frac{600}{60} 2\pi = 20\pi$ radians per sec., and its angular acceleration during the 1.5-hr. starting period is $\frac{20\pi}{3600 \times 1.5} = 0.0116$ radian per sec. per sec. Therefore, from equation (39), the motor must exert a torque of

$$T = 734{,}000 \text{ lb-ft.}^2 \times 0.0116 \frac{\text{radians}}{\text{sec.}^2} = 8510 \text{ poundal-ft.}$$

which is the equivalent of 266 lb-ft.

II. A wheel and axle has a total weight of 4 kg. and is rotated by a 200-gm. weight fastened to a cord that is wrapped around the 6-cm. axle, as shown in Fig. 61. The weight is observed to fall a distance of 3 meters, starting from rest, in 5.2 sec. Find the radius of gyration of the wheel. In solving this problem, the first step is to determine the linear acceleration of the descending weight and then the tension in the cord. From these data the torque applied to the wheel and axle and its angular acceleration are computed. Finally, the moment of inertia and the radius of gyration of the wheel and axle are obtained.

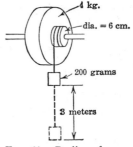

Fig. 61. Radius of gyration of a wheel and axle

Since the weight starts from rest and covers a distance of 3 meters with uniformly accelerated motion in 5.2 sec., its linear acceleration is

$$a = \frac{2s}{t^2} = \frac{2 \times 300 \text{ cm.}}{(5.2 \text{ sec.})^2} = 22.2 \frac{\text{cm.}}{\text{sec.}^2}$$

and the angular acceleration of the wheel having an axle of 3 cm. radius is

$$\alpha = \frac{a}{r} = \frac{22.2 \dfrac{\text{cm.}}{\text{sec.}^2}}{3 \text{ cm.}} = 7.4 \text{ radians/sec.}^2$$

The tension in the cord is ascertained by investigating the forces acting upon the 200-gm. mass. A force of gravity of 200 gm. or $200 \times 980 = 196{,}000$ dynes acts downward upon this body and the unknown tension P in the cord pulls upward upon it. The unbalanced force is 196,000 dynes $- P$, and produces the acceleration of $22.2 \dfrac{\text{cm.}}{\text{sec.}^2}$ in the 200-gm. body. From equation (31),

$$196{,}000 \text{ dynes} - P = 200 \text{ gm.} \times 22.2 \frac{\text{cm.}}{\text{sec.}^2} = 4440 \text{ dynes}$$

from which the tension is found to be $P = 191{,}560$ dynes, and thus the torque exerted by the cord is $3 \times 191{,}560 = 574{,}680$ dyne-cm. This is the unbalanced torque acting on the apparatus, assuming friction as absent, and therefore the moment of inertia of the wheel and axle must be

$$I = \frac{T}{\alpha} = \frac{574{,}680 \text{ dyne-cm.}}{7.4 \dfrac{\text{radians}}{\text{sec.}^2}} = 77{,}700 \text{ gm-cm.}^2$$

and its radius of gyration will be

$$K = \sqrt{\frac{I}{M}} = \sqrt{\frac{77{,}700 \text{ gm-cm.}^2}{4000 \text{ gm.}}} = 4.4 \text{ cm.}$$

III. Compute the moment of inertia of a flywheel which is brought from rest to a speed of 1800 rev. per min. in 30 sec. by the application of a torque of 20 lb-ft. Refer to § 53 and use gravitational units throughout. The desired result can be found from equation (39), $I = \dfrac{T}{\alpha}$. When the torque T is expressed in pound-feet and the angular acceleration α is in radians per second per second, the moment of inertia I will be in slug feet squared. The angular acceleration, from equation (26), is $\alpha = \dfrac{\omega_f - \omega_o}{t} = \dfrac{1800 \dfrac{\text{rev.}}{\text{min.}} - 0}{30 \text{ sec.}}$, which reduces to $2\pi \dfrac{\text{radians}}{\text{sec.}^2}$. Hence the moment of inertia of the flywheel is

$$I = \frac{T}{\alpha} = \frac{20 \text{ lb-ft.}}{2\pi \dfrac{\text{radians}}{\text{sec.}^2}} \times \frac{1 \text{ slug} \dfrac{\text{ft.}}{\text{sec.}^2}}{1 \text{ lb.}} = 3.19 \text{ slug-ft.}^2$$

*62. Motion of Precession.—Angular velocity can be represented vectorially by a line which is directed along the axis of the rotating

see page 35

body, as explained for torque in § 23. Thus, the angular velocity of a
wheel is represented by an axial line having a length which indicates
the numerical value of that velocity according to some suitable scale,
as shown by ω in Fig. 62. The direction of this vector is chosen as
that in which the usual right-
handed screw will advance when
turned by a screw driver in the
direction in which the body
rotates.

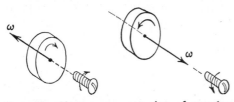

FIG. 62. Vector representation of angular
velocity

When a rotating body is given
an additional angular velocity
about the same axis, the result-
ing velocity will be their algebraic sum. Thus, if a body rotating at
20 radians per sec. in a clockwise direction were given an additional
angular velocity of 3 radians per sec. in a counter-clockwise direction,
then its resulting velocity would be 17 radians per sec. clockwise about
that axis. However, when the added velocity is about a different axis
from that of the original rotation the result must be obtained by vector
addition.

The addition of two angular velocities about separate axes gives
rise to an angular motion about a third axis, and this motion is called
precession. To explain this type of motion, consider a wheel to be
mounted loosely between collars on an axle *A,* as shown in Fig. 63,

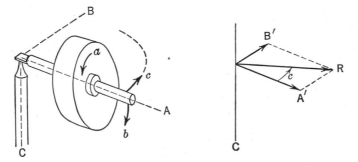

FIG. 63. Precession of a revolving wheel about one end of its axle

and to be set in rotation by some agency not illustrated. The shaft
does not rotate with the wheel and one end of it is set horizontally
upon a pivot on the vertical support *C,* the other end of the shaft
being free. If the wheel were not revolving, the free end of the shaft
would drop and the whole system would fall off the vertical support.

But with the wheel revolving, the tendency for the free end of the shaft to drop causes the wheel and shaft to describe horizontal circles about the pivot; that is, the wheel precesses in the horizontal plane.

The angular velocity of the wheel spinning in the direction *a* about axis *A* is represented by the vector *A'* parallel to shaft *A* in the perspective diagram at the right. The pull of the earth upon the wheel produces a torque which tends to turn the entire moving system about the axis *B* in the direction shown by arrow *b*. This torque sets up an angular acceleration and gives the body an additional angular velocity about axis *B* which is represented in the vector diagram as *B'*. If this velocity *B'* is added to the spin velocity *A'*, both being in the same horizontal plane, the resultant will be *R*. Accordingly the shaft will shift its position to point in the direction *R*, turning about the vertical axis *C* as shown by arrow *c*. This motion of precession occurs, therefore, about an axis that is perpendicular to both of the other axes *A* and *B*. This motion continues, for as soon as the wheel reaches position *R*, it is subject to another torque due to the tendency of the free end of the shaft to drop, the corresponding change in angular velocity is at right angles to *R*, and a new resultant is formed, to which position the shaft progresses; and so on. As described, it would appear that the shaft progresses in discrete steps, but the process is actually one of infinitesimally small angular shifts, thus producing a uniform velocity of precession.

It can be shown that the angular velocity of precession Ω (omega) of a wheel is equal to the torque T which tends to change the direction of its axis, divided by the product of the angular velocity ω of the wheel and its moment of inertia I, that is

$$\Omega = \frac{T}{\omega I} \tag{43}$$

*63. The Gyroscope.—A gyroscope is a wheel and axle supported in gimbal rings so that it can be set in rotation with its axis in any desired direction. When revolving, the wheel maintains its axis in the initial direction, even though the gyroscope as a whole is moved from one position to another, because the force exerted on the gyroscope is not transmitted through the gimbal rings to produce a torque on the wheel.

The action of the gyroscope as a compass is an application of the addition of two angular velocities in different directions. In Fig. 64, the earth is viewed from a point in space beyond the south pole, and is seen to revolve in a clockwise direction. The gyroscope is shown at the equator in various positions; that at G_3 is the ultimate one and the other two are disturbed positions used in explaining the action. The arrows on the wheel in positions G_1 and G_2 indicate the direction in which the rim of the wheel nearest the reader is moving. A weight is placed on the inner gimbal ring and is shown at w; this, of course, will always seek the position nearest the center of the earth because of the earth's attraction for it, no matter where the gyroscope is situated.

Suppose the gyroscope is placed at position G_1 with its axis directed arbitrarily from east to west. The angular velocity of the rotating wheel is represented by a vector directed axially toward the east; it is shown as A in the vector diagram. As the earth revolves and carries the gyroscope to position

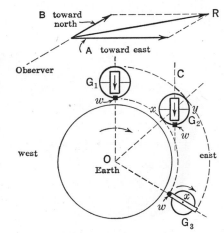

FIG. 64. The use of a gyroscope as a compass (The observer is looking northward toward the earth)

G_2, its axis will continue to point eastward, thereby bringing the weight w out of line with the earth's radius. The earth's attraction for this weight sets up a torque which tends to produce clockwise rotation of the gyroscope about an axis perpendicular to the page. The additional angular velocity produced by this torque is represented by a vector directed into the paper; it is shown in perspective as B in the vector diagram. The addition of A and B yields the resultant R as the direction toward which the axis of the wheel turns. Consequently the shaft-end y will move northward (into the paper) and the shaft-end x will move southward (out of the paper); this precessional motion occurs about the axis C. As the gyroscope is carried farther by the earth the precession continues until the shaft of the gyroscope becomes parallel to the axis O of the earth, with the shaft-end x pointing toward the reader as at G_3. When the gyroscope reaches this position the earth's pull on weight *w* will exert no further torque action and the gimbal ring will remain in a plane with the earth's axis.

Thus, the gyroscope wheel will seek a position so that its axis will point north and south, and thereafter maintain that position. This directive action of the earth upon the gyroscope permits this instrument to be used as a compass. Such a compass indicates on its scale the true geographic north-south direction, whereas the magnetic compass points along the magnetic meridian and is influenced by magnetic variations and magnetic materials nearby. Fig. 65 shows the assembly of a Sperry gyro-compass. The wheel is the rotating element of

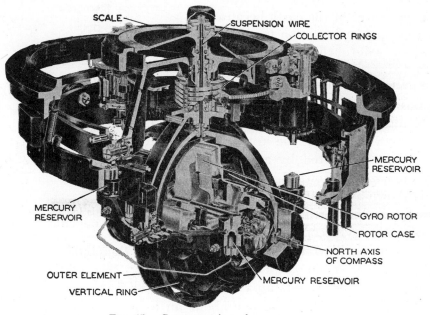

Fig. 65.   Cut-away view of gyro-compass
(*Courtesy of Sperry Gyroscope Company*)

an induction motor, § 311, which revolves upon a horizontal shaft inside a rotor case, the casing being supported on horizontal bearings within a vertical ring. This ring is hung by a suspension wire from the top point of the instrument, torsion in the wire being prevented by making the outer element follow all movements of the wheel about the vertical axis. The mass upon which the earth exerts its directive influence consists of four mercury reservoirs. Current is supplied to the stator of the motor through collector rings to drive the rotor at approximately 6000 rev. per min.

PROBLEMS

1. A torque of 20 lb-ft. is applied to a body. Of this, 4 lb-ft. opposes friction, and the remainder gives the body an angular acceleration of 80 radians per sec. per sec. When the applied torque is removed, with what angular acceleration will friction bring the body to rest?

2. What unbalanced torque must be applied to a cylindrical drum, having a moment of inertia of 6 kg-meters^2 about its axis, to give it an acceleration of 3 radians per sec. per sec. about that axis?

3. Calculate the moment of inertia of a meter stick, having a mass of 320 gm., about an axis at right angles to the stick and located at the 25-cm. mark.

4. Three slim rods, each having a length of 80 cm. and a mass of 200 gm., are fastened together at their ends to form a triangle. Determine the moment of inertia of the combination about an axis at one corner of the triangle and perpendicular to its plane.

5. A solid cylinder of steel is 12 in. in diameter and 3 in. thick. Take the density of steel as 490 lb. per cu. ft. and compute the moment of inertia of the cylinder about its geometric axis.

6. How large a hole might be bored axially through the cylinder described in Problem 5 without reducing its original moment of inertia by more than 1 per cent?

7. Compute the moment of inertia of the bowling ball described in Problem 23 of Chapter I (*a*) about an axis through its center, and (*b*) about an axis tangent to its surface.

8. A pendulum is formed of a disk and a slim rod in the same plane, the rim of the disk being firmly attached to one end of the rod. The disk has a mass of 5 lb. and a diameter of 6 in.; the rod has a mass of 0.5 lb. and a length of 30 in. Find the moment of inertia of the pendulum about an axis at the free end of the rod and perpendicular to the plane of the disk.

9. A thick-walled hollow cylinder has an inner radius r_1, an outer radius r_2, and a mass M. Refer to the data of § 59 and determine the moment of inertia of the cylinder about its geometric axis in terms of r_1, r_2, and M. *Hint:* first solve in terms of density and volume.

10. A cylindrical grindstone 20 in. in diameter weighs 120 lb.; it is turned by a handle fastened to a crank at a distance of 8 in. from the center of the grindstone. What steady force applied perpendicularly to the crank will bring the stone to a speed of 90 rev. per min. in 10 sec., ignoring friction?

11. A solid disk having a mass of 2 kg. and a diameter of 10 cm. is set in rotation in stationary bearings by the application of a tangential force of 50 gm. applied at the rim of the disk and perpendicular to the axis. What acceleration is produced if friction is disregarded?

12. How many revolutions will the disk of Problem 11 make in 1 sec. starting from rest? How many revolutions will it make in the next second?

13. Find the radius of gyration of a meter stick arranged to rotate about a transverse axis through its midpoint.

14. The armature of a certain motor has a mass of 90 lb. and a radius of gyration of 4 in. How much torque must be applied to this armature

in order to give it a speed of 1140 rev. per min. in 15 sec. starting from rest, if friction meanwhile exerts a retarding torque of 0.2 lb-ft. upon it?

15. A 100-lb. wheel 18 in. in diameter, which is turning at 150 rev. per min. in stationary bearings, is brought to rest by pressing a brake shoe radially against its rim with a force of 20 lb. If the radius of gyration of the wheel is 7 in., and if the coefficient of friction between the shoe and the rim has the steady value of 0.25, how many revolutions will the wheel make in coming to rest?

16. A pulley 15 cm. in diameter is mounted on a horizontal shaft in frictionless bearings, and around its rim is wound a light cord to which a 100-gm. mass is attached. When released, the mass is observed to descend 40 cm. in the first second, without slippage of the cord. Compute the moment of inertia of the pulley.

17. A constant torque is applied to a wheel having a moment of inertia of 12 slug-ft.^{2}, and its speed rises from standstill to 1200 rev. per min. in 1.5 min. Upon removal of this torque the wheel comes to rest in 10 min. What torque is applied during the acceleration period mentioned?

*18. A hand-type vacuum cleaner is driven by a motor with its shaft aligned in the general direction of the nozzle, and when the cleaner is used on a horizontal surface the shaft is also horizontal. The cleaner is then given a sharp clockwise twist as viewed from above, and the nozzle is observed to lift away from the surface. Which way does the motor revolve to account for this gyroscopic action?

*19. A wheel, mounted on an axle as shown in Fig. 63, has its center of mass 10 cm. from the pivot on the vertical support. The wheel is a solid disk 15 cm. in diameter and has a weight of 8 kg.; the weight of the axle is negligible. Determine the velocity of precession in a horizontal plane, when the wheel revolves at 960 rev. per min.

Mechanical Energy Chapter VII

WORK AND ENERGY

64. Work.—In popular language, the term "work" is applied to any form of labor, physical or mental, for producing any kind of result. In science and engineering, on the other hand, "work" has a definite technical meaning, which involves two physical concepts that have been developed in previous chapters. A few illustrations will make the meaning clear.

Suppose that a man moves a piano from one place to another meanwhile exerting a steady push on the instrument, or that he pulls an oar toward him in rowing, or that he lifts a weight from the floor to the top of a table. In each of these instances, two things should be noted: first, that the man exerts a *force*, and second, that he exerts it through a *distance* in the direction of that force. Under these conditions, the man is said to do *work*, the amount of work depending on the two factors: the force which he exerts, and the distance along the direction of the force through which he exerts it. The amount of work done is measured by the product of these two quantities. Suppose that the man moving the piano exerts a horizontal force of 50 lb. continuously through a horizontal distance of 10 ft.; in this action he does 50 lb. × 10 ft. = 500 ft-lb. of work. In general terms, when an agent exerts a steady force F upon a body, and exerts this force through a distance s along its own direction, then the amount of work done by the agent is

$$E = Fs \qquad (44)$$

The symbol E is used to represent work (rather than the initial letter of work), in order that W may continue to represent weight, as previously, without confusion. The product of force and distance was encountered in § 23, but these quantities were at right angles to each other to produce torque, instead of being in the same direction, as at present, to produce work.

117

Note that inanimate objects also can exert forces, and that any agent which exerts a force through a distance does work; hence a general statement may be made as follows: *Any agent does work on a body when it exerts a force on the body through a distance along the direction of the force.*

It frequently happens when work is being done, that the force exerted on the body is not in the same direction as the distance through which this force is exerted; that is, F is not in the same direction as s. In such cases the term F in equation (44) should be interpreted as that component of the force which is along the direction of s. Consider, for example, a boy pushing a sled a distance s along a level surface, with a force F which makes an angle θ with the horizontal plane, as shown in Fig. 66. Here F may be resolved into two components, $F \cos \theta$ along the direction of s, and $F \sin \theta$ at right angles to this direction. Only the first of these components is effective in doing work on the sled, while the other component increases the pressure of the sled against the snow and thereby causes the backward drag of friction to increase. The amount of work which the boy does on the sled is therefore

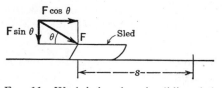

FIG. 66. Work being done in sliding sled

$$E = Fs \cos \theta \qquad\qquad 45)$$

This expression may be applied in general to give the amount of work E done on a body by an agent which exerts a force F on it through a distance s, the directions of F and s making an angle θ with each other. It might be remarked that F is the force applied by the agent which is doing the work, and is not, in general, the unbalanced force acting on the body.

As an illustrative problem, calculate the work done by a tractor in plowing a furrow 200 yd. long, if it exerts a steady force of 150 lb. on the plow at an angle of 15° with the ground. From equation (45), the work done is $E = Fs \cos \theta = 150$ lb. $\times$ 200 yd. $\times \cos 15° = 150$ lb. $\times$ 600 ft. $\times$ 0.966 $= 86,940$ ft-lb.

Since work is essentially the product of a force and a length, the unit for work is the product of a force unit and a length unit. In the cgs. system of units, the unit of work is called the erg. One *erg* of work is done on a body when a force of 1 dyne is exerted upon it

through a distance of 1 cm.   Lifting a half-dollar through a height of
1 meter requires the expenditure of 1,196,000 ergs of work.   Because
this unit is so small, a multiple of it called the *joule* is frequently used;
1 joule = 10^7 ergs.   This unit is named after the British experimenter,
James P. Joule (1818–1889).   In ordinary engineering work, where the
British gravitational system of units is used, the unit of work is the
foot-pound, being the amount of work done on a body when a force
of 1 lb. is exerted on the body through a distance of 1 ft.

65. Work Done in Rotation.—The amount of work done upon a
rotating body may also be calculated from the foregoing equations,
but usually can be obtained more directly when expressed in terms of
the angular quantities, torque and angle.   The desired expression is
found by supposing that a drum
of radius r has a cord fastened
to the rim, as represented in Fig.
67, and that the cord is pulled
with a force F for a distance s
along its length, so that an
amount of work $E = Fs$ is done
upon the drum.   The torque T
resulting from the force F is

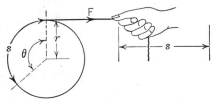

FIG. 67.   Work being done upon a rotating body

$T = Fr$, whence $F = T \div r$.   The angle through which the drum
turns is found by observing that as the cord is pulled, every point
on the rim of the drum travels through an arc of length s, and
therefore the drum rotates through an angle θ such that $s = r\theta$.
When these values are substituted for F and s, the expression for

work becomes $E = Fs = \dfrac{T}{r} \times r\theta$, whence

$$E = T\theta \tag{46}$$

where E is the work done upon a rotating body by an agent which
exerts a torque T upon the body through an angle of θ radians.

Sometimes bodies move in opposition to the efforts exerted upon
them; for instance, a rotating wheel may continue to turn in a certain
direction even after a brake is applied which exerts a torque upon it
in the opposite direction, or a heavy weight may slide down an incline in spite of attempts to pull it upward.   In such cases *the body
does work instead of having work done upon it;* equations (44) to (46)
may be used as before, but they will determine the amount of work
done *by* the body rather than the amount of work done *upon* it.

66. Energy.—An agent is said to possess *energy* if it is able to do work. For example, a man or a horse can do work and so possesses energy; steam possesses energy since it is able to push the piston within the cylinder of a steam engine; the mainspring of a watch possesses energy when wound, since it is able to drive the hands of the instrument. Moreover, *when an agent does work, its energy is reduced by an amount exactly equal to the work done.* Thus, if a raised weight does 1000 ft-lb. of work in falling, its energy is lessened by 1000 ft-lb. Work and energy are expressed in the same units.

There are many different forms of energy; thus, coal has chemical energy, a hot substance has internal energy, a stretched spring has mechanical energy, a charged capacitor has electrical energy, and so on.

In the study of Mechanics, mechanical energy is naturally the type which is of special interest. A body or a system of bodies may possess mechanical energy from either or both of two causes. First, whenever a body is in motion it will be able to exert a force and do work in coming to rest; a moving body always possesses energy by virtue of its motion; this is called *kinetic* energy. A moving hammer has kinetic energy, and this enables it to do work in driving a nail. Second, a body which has been moved to a new position is sometimes able to do work because of this fact; for example, a raised weight is commonly said to possess energy by virtue of its position; this is called *potential* energy. Strictly, it is not correct to regard potential energy as residing in a particular object, but rather as residing in a system which includes that object. Thus, while a weight is raised it is being separated from the earth against their mutual attraction; in the process work is done and the potential energy of the system, made up of the weight and the earth, is increased. Nevertheless, the potential energy is customarily ascribed to the weight since it is the tangible part of the system which makes that energy available.

A body is not necessarily given potential energy by displacing it, but only when it is able to do more work in its new position than it was originally. A weight which has been raised or a spring which has been wound is thereby given potential energy, but if a weight is merely moved along a level floor from one position to another its potential energy is not changed.

67. Conservation and Transformation of Energy.—Whenever a body does work, its capability of doing further work is lessened, and this means that it possesses less energy than before. This reduction must not be regarded as a loss of energy, for in doing work the body has imparted an equal amount of energy to some other body, which, together with the first, constitutes a system. Thus, when a man does 20 ft-lb. of work in throwing a ball he gives up this amount of energy, and the ball gains 20 ft-lb. of energy, since that amount of work was done upon it. The energy which is given up by a body is imparted to others without loss, and thus within the system, the total amount of energy remains unchanged. This illustrates a general law known as the *Law of Conservation of Energy* to the effect that *energy can neither be created nor destroyed.* Expressed differently, *the total amount of energy in the universe remains constant.*

Consider a body which is raised to the top of an inclined plane and is then allowed to slide down. A certain amount of work is done on the body in raising it, thereby increasing its potential energy. As the body slides down the incline, it gives up potential energy and gains kinetic energy; and if no work is done against friction, the increase of kinetic energy will equal the reduction of potential energy. If, however, part of the potential energy possessed by the body is expended in doing work against friction on the way down, then the kinetic energy of the body at the bottom will be less than before by this amount. This example shows that while energy can be transformed from one kind to another, it is not destroyed in the process. When energy is expended in work against friction, it is said to be wasted, that is, rendered unavailable for useful purposes; but it is not destroyed, for it is converted to heat, also recognized as a form of energy. When mechanical work is done on a body, it can be entirely accounted for by one or more of the following effects: (1) *increase in the kinetic energy of the body,* (2) *increase in its potential energy,* or (3) *production of heat due to friction.*

Although energy cannot be destroyed, it is sometimes wasted, as just pointed out. When a train is driven at constant speed along a level track there is no increase in either its kinetic energy or its potential energy, and hence all of the energy in the fuel burned is wasted in doing work against friction. With the exhaustion of natural fuels, the provision of energy in sufficient quantities to meet the future demands of mankind will be an engineering problem of utmost importance.

68. Kinetic Energy.—*Kinetic energy is the kind of energy that a body has by virtue of its motion.* It will be possible to derive an expression for kinetic energy by remembering that the only effects of doing

mechanical work on a body are to increase either its kinetic energy
or its potential energy or to produce heat through friction. The
expression, as applied to motion of translation, will be found by
calculating the amount of work done in sliding a body along a surface
under such conditions that there is no change in its potential energy
and that no energy is wasted by friction; then the work done will
appear entirely in the form of kinetic energy.

Suppose that a block of mass m is at rest on a smooth horizontal
plane and that a steady horizontal force F is exerted on it through a
distance s, in which case an amount of work Fs is performed on the
block. There being no friction, F acts as an unbalanced force and
gives the block a constant acceleration, in accordance with equation (31), $F = ma$. From the laws of accelerated motion, § 32, the
distance traversed by a body starting from rest with a constant
acceleration a and acquiring a velocity v is found to be $s = \dfrac{v^2}{2a}$.
The energy acquired by the block is obtained by substituting for F
and s the values found; it becomes $E_k = Fs = (ma)\left(\dfrac{v^2}{2a}\right)$, or

$$E_k = \frac{mv^2}{2} \tag{47}$$

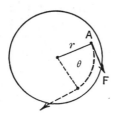

FIG. 68. Calculating
kinetic energy of ro-
tation

The expression involves the mass m of the body and is therefore
adapted to the absolute system of units. If the
mass is expressed in grams, and the velocity in
centimeters per second, it can easily be shown that
the kinetic energy will be in centimeter-dynes or
ergs.

To find an expression for kinetic energy due to
rotation, suppose that a body, initially at rest, is
free to turn in frictionless bearings, and that a
force F is applied to a pin A at the end of a radius
r, F being always at right angles to the radius, as
shown in Fig. 68. The force produces a torque $T = Fr$, causing the
body to accelerate in accordance with equation (39), $\alpha = \dfrac{T}{I}$, and in
sweeping through an angle θ it will acquire a velocity ω, such that
$\theta = \dfrac{\omega^2}{2\alpha}$. But the kinetic energy of the body equals the work performed upon it, which, from equation (46), is $T\theta$. Hence, in absolute

units, $E_k = T\theta = I\alpha \times \dfrac{\omega^2}{2\alpha}$, or

$$E_k = \frac{I\omega^2}{2} \qquad (48)$$

This expression gives the kinetic energy of a rotating body having a moment of inertia I and an angular velocity ω. The student should have no difficulty in showing that in metric units, with I expressed in gram-centimeters^2 and ω in radians per second, E_k will be in ergs.

A body that is undergoing both translation and rotation at the same time possesses an amount of energy $\dfrac{mv^2}{2}$ on account of its translation, and an amount $\dfrac{I\omega^2}{2}$ on account of its rotation. The total kinetic energy of such a body is, therefore,

$$E_k = \frac{mv^2}{2} + \frac{I\omega^2}{2}$$

69. Potential Energy.—*Potential energy is the kind of energy that a body has by virtue of its position.* When a body is raised to a higher level, it is able to do a certain amount of work in falling back again, and hence it was given this amount of potential energy in raising it. Although elevating a body is not the only way to give it potential energy, it is perhaps the most usual way. If the body is raised in such a manner that its kinetic energy is not increased, and without waste of energy on account of friction, the work done in raising it will all be expended in giving the body potential energy.

Suppose that a body of mass m is raised from one level to another at constant speed along a smooth plane, as represented in Fig. 69, the second level being a vertical distance h above the first. The plane has a

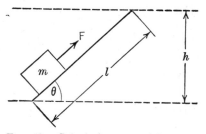

Fig. 69.   Calculating potential energy due to elevation

length l and makes an angle θ with the horizontal. The force F necessary to move the body along the plane with constant speed is $mg \sin \theta$, and since this force is exerted through a distance l, the work done on the body, and hence the potential energy given to it, is

$E_p = mg \sin \theta \times l = mg \dfrac{h}{l} \times l$.   Consequently, in absolute units,

$$E_p = mgh \tag{49}$$

which shows that the amount of potential energy given to a body by raising it from one level to another depends only on the weight mg of the body and the vertical distance h between the two levels. Since the result is independent of the value of θ, the path of the body may be inclined at any angle, it may have different inclinations at different points, or it may be a curved surface. The potential energy of the body is not affected by the path over which it is moved in reaching a fixed elevation.

70. Kinetic and Potential Energy in Gravitational Units.—The kinetic energy of a body due to motion of translation may be found in gravitational units by exactly the same method as used in § 68. The weight W of the body is used rather than its mass; the acceleration is obtained from the relation $F = \dfrac{W}{g} \times a$; and the expression for kinetic energy becomes

$$E_k = \frac{Wv^2}{2g} \tag{50}$$

If the weight of the body is expressed in pounds, its velocity in feet per second, and the acceleration due to gravity in feet per second per second, then the kinetic energy will be in foot-pounds.

Kinetic energy due to rotation can be found most simply by equation (48), $E_k = \dfrac{I\omega^2}{2}$, with I expressed in pound-feet^2 and ω in radians per second. Then E_k will be in foot-poundals and may be converted to foot-pounds by using the relation that 1 lb. of force is the equivalent of 32 poundals.

The potential energy of a body due to elevation may be expressed directly in foot-pounds by the relation

$$E_p = Wh \tag{51}$$

where W is the weight of the body in pounds and h is the vertical height in feet through which it is raised.

71. Energy Wasted in Friction.—*Whenever one body moves upon another, some work is done against friction which exists between them.* The amount of energy wasted in this manner can be found by supposing work to be done upon a body under such conditions that neither the kinetic energy nor the potential energy of the body is increased, since all the work done will then be expended against friction. Suppose, then, that a body, having been started from rest, is moved at constant speed along a rough horizontal surface; to give it this motion a force must be exerted upon it equal and opposite to the maximum force of friction f, and the work done in exerting this force through a distance s is equal to the product fs. Hence, the energy wasted through friction is

$$E_f = fs \qquad (52)$$

The method of calculating f was discussed in § 49.

The work done against friction is converted into heat and is usually wasted. Frequently the heating is so slight as to escape notice, but sometimes it is quite evident, such as the heating produced in an automobile brake, in an overheated bearing, or in striking a match.

72. Application of Energy Principles.—The principles of work and energy provide a method of procedure by means of which many problems may be solved with great simplicity. To illustrate how these principles are applied, three typical problems will be considered.

I. It is required to find the time taken by a solid cylinder, starting from rest, to roll without sliding down a plane 200 cm. long, one end of which is raised 80 cm. higher than the other. The conditions of the problem are represented in Fig. 70.

The cylinder will possess the same amount of energy when it reaches the bottom of the plane as it had at the top if any waste of energy due to rolling friction is ignored. At the top, this is entirely in the form of potential energy, but as the cylinder rolls down, its potential energy becomes transformed into kinetic energy, partly

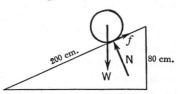

FIG. 70. Cylinder rolling down plane

of translation and partly of rotation. If the energies at the top and bottom of the incline are equated, the velocity of the cylinder upon reaching the bottom can be found, and the desired time follows at once from the laws of accelerated motion.

The reduction in potential energy from top to bottom of the plane is mgh, and the kinetic energy acquired upon reaching the bottom is $\dfrac{mv^2}{2} + \dfrac{I\omega^2}{2}$. These expressions are equated, thus:

$$mgh = \frac{mv^2}{2} + \frac{I\omega^2}{2}$$

where m is the mass of the cylinder, I is its moment of inertia about its own axis, v and ω are its linear and angular velocities respectively upon reaching the bottom of the incline, h is the elevation of the upper end of the plane, and g is the acceleration due to gravity. Since the moment of inertia of the cylinder about its own axis is $I = \dfrac{mr^2}{2}$, § 59, and its angular velocity is $\omega = \dfrac{v}{r}$, the last term can be replaced by $\dfrac{I\omega^2}{2} = \dfrac{1}{2}\left(\dfrac{mr^2}{2}\right)\left(\dfrac{v}{r}\right)^2 = \dfrac{mv^2}{4}$; whence $mgh = \dfrac{mv^2}{2} + \dfrac{mv^2}{4} = \dfrac{3mv^2}{4}$; and

$$v = \sqrt{\frac{4gh}{3}} = \sqrt{\frac{4 \times 980\,\dfrac{\text{cm.}}{\text{sec.}^2} \times 80\ \text{cm.}}{3}} = 324\,\frac{\text{cm.}}{\text{sec.}}$$

Hence from equation (20), the time of descent is

$$t = \frac{2s}{v} = \frac{400\ \text{cm.}}{324\,\dfrac{\text{cm.}}{\text{sec.}}} = 1.24\ \text{sec.}$$

This result may be verified by applying the dynamical methods of Chapter VI, using the forces represented by vectors W, N, and f in the figure.

II. A 2-ton weight in a pile driver is raised 12 ft. above the top of a pile and then released. What average force does it exert against the pile upon falling if it drives the pile 1 ft. into the ground?

In this problem, the potential energy given up by the weight is expended in work done upon the pile; these two quantities may be equated, and from this equation the desired force can be found. Since the weight finally comes to rest 13 ft. below its initial position, its potential energy is reduced by an amount $Wh = 4000$ lb. $\times$ 13 ft. $= 52,000$ ft-lb. The work done on the pile is $E = F \times s = F \times 1$ ft., where F is the average force exerted upon it. Therefore $F \times 1$ ft. $= 52,000$ ft-lb., or $F = 52,000$ lb.

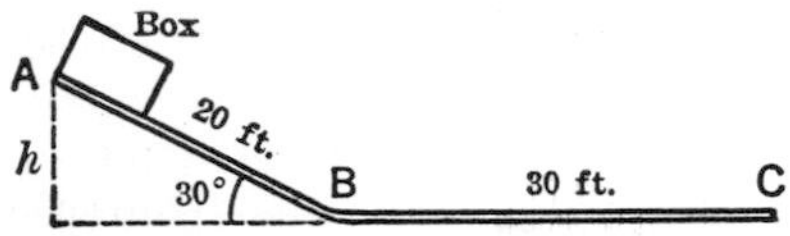

FIG. 71.   Box sliding down chute

III. A box is placed at the top of a chute 50 ft. long, the first 20 ft. of the chute being inclined downward at an angle of 30 deg. with the horizontal, as shown in Fig. 71. If the coefficient of friction between the box and the chute is 0.2, with what velocity will the box leave the chute at C?

In this problem, the potential energy which the box gives up as it moves from A is partly used in opposing friction from A to B and from B to C, and the remainder appears in the form of kinetic energy at C. The foregoing sentence will be written in the form of an equation, and from this the desired velocity can be found. The potential energy given up is *mgh*, where *m* is the mass of the box and *h* is its elevation. The energy used in opposing friction = (force of friction) × (distance) = (coefficient of friction) × (normal force between surfaces) × (distance). The box leaves the chute at *C* with a kinetic energy of $\frac{1}{2}mv^2$, where *v* is the terminating velocity. The energy equation becomes:

$$mgh = \mu(mg \cos 30°)(20 \text{ ft.}) + \mu(mg)(30 \text{ ft.}) + \frac{mv^2}{2}$$

When the common factor *m* is cancelled and the equation solved for *v*, it is found that the box leaves the end of the chute with a velocity of 5.9 ft/sec.

POWER

73. Rate of Doing Work.—In practice, where work is done upon a body, the amount of work is not the only item of importance; the time during which that work is done is of equal consequence. Suppose, for example, that a motor-driven hoist is to be selected for raising a certain load. If the load has to be raised quickly, a more powerful hoist and a larger driving motor must be provided than if more time is allowed. Usually the size of machinery is determined, not by the total amount of work to be done, but by the rate at which it must be done; that is, the amount of work required per unit of time. *The time rate of doing work is called power.*

When 1 foot-pound of work is done per second, the power is 1 *ft.-lb. per sec.* If a machine working steadily performs 150,000 ft-lb. of work in 10 min., it does work at the rate of 15,000 ft-lb. every minute, and its power output is therefore 15,000 ft-lb. per min. or 250 ft-lb. per sec. In general terms, the power *P* delivered by any agent which performs an amount of work *E* in a time interval *t* is given by the relation

$$P = \frac{E}{t} \tag{53}$$

If a machine operates steadily, performing the same amount of work every second, the power which it provides is constant. But if a machine works irregularly, doing more work during some intervals than in others, the power which it provides fluctuates from moment to moment. Under these circumstances equation (53) gives the *average value* of the power throughout the time interval considered.

Since power is the time rate of doing work, the unit for power in any system of units is found by dividing the work unit in that system by the time unit. Thus, in the cgs. system, power is expressed in ergs per second. In addition to the units which occur in the standard systems, there are other practical units for power which are much used in engineering work. *The horsepower* (hp.) *is the power provided by an agent while doing work at the rate of 550 ft-lb. per sec. or 33,000 ft-lb. per min.* The *watt* is a rate of doing work equal to 1 joule per second, and is named after the Scottish engineer, James Watt (1736–1819). The kilowatt (kw.) is a power unit used in rating electrical machines. The relations between some power units are given below:

Units of Power

$$1 \text{ watt} \qquad = 10^7 \frac{\text{ergs}}{\text{sec.}} = 1 \frac{\text{joule}}{\text{sec.}}$$

$$1 \text{ hp.} \qquad = 550 \frac{\text{ft-lb.}}{\text{sec.}} = 33,000 \frac{\text{ft-lb.}}{\text{min.}}$$

$$1 \text{ hp.} \qquad = 746 \text{ watts}$$

$$1 \text{ kw.} \qquad = 1000 \text{ watts} = 1.34 \text{ hp.}$$

$$1 \text{ ft-lb. per sec.} = 1.356 \text{ watts}$$

The use of power units will be illustrated by considering some practical examples.

I. A horse exerts a horizontal pull of 100 lb. on a wagon; how fast must he walk in order to develop exactly 1 hp.? Here the horse is to do 550 ft-lb. of work each second, meantime exerting a force of 100 lb., hence, from equation (44), he must travel each second a distance

$$s = \frac{E}{F} = \frac{550 \text{ ft-lb.}}{100 \text{ lb.}} = 5.5 \text{ ft.}$$

II. What power is represented by the friction loss in a sleeve bearing supporting a 2-in. shaft which turns at 480 rev. per min., if the shaft presses against the bearing with a force of 1 ton, and the coefficient of friction between the sliding surfaces is 0.005? The force of friction, from equation (35), is 0.005 × 2000 lb. = 10 lb. This force is tangent to the shaft at its rim, and is therefore exerted through a distance $\frac{2\pi}{12}$ ft. in each revolution. Hence the work done per minute because of friction is given by equation (52), as

$$E_f = fs = 10 \text{ lb.} \times \frac{2\pi}{12} \frac{\text{ft.}}{\text{rev.}} \times 480 \text{ rev.} = 2510 \text{ ft-lb.}$$

which is equivalent to $\dfrac{2510}{33,000} = 0.076$ hp.

The relation between work and power is emphasized by transposing equation (53) to read: $E = Pt$. In this form, the expression shows that if an agent provides an amount of power P continuously for a period of time t, the agent does an amount of work E which is equal to the product of P and t. This conception of work as the product of power and time values leads to some energy units which are widely used in engineering practice. The *horsepower-hour* (hp.-hr.) is thus a unit of work, being the amount of work performed when the rate is one horsepower over a period of one hour. Similarly, the *kilowatt-hour* (kw.-hr.), the unit upon which the cost of electrical energy is based, is the amount of work performed when the rate is one kilowatt over a period of one hour. If an engine delivers 60 hp. steadily for 5 hr., it does $60 \times 5 = 300$ hp.-hr. of work, and if a motor takes 12 kw. steadily for 4 hr., it receives $12 \times 4 = 48$ kw.-hr. of electrical energy.

*74. Measurement of Mechanical Power.—The mechanical output of a rotating machine can be measured by equipping the machine with a special form of brake which absorbs the output of the machine in friction and converts it into heat, and which at the same time measures the amount of power.

A simple style of brake used for small machines consists of a band of asbestos fabric which passes around the rotating pulley of the machine and is supported at the ends, as shown in Fig. 72. Two handwheels WW serve to tighten or loosen the band, thus regulating the output of the machine, and two spring balances show how much force is being exerted on the ends of the band. When arranged as in the figure, the band is dragged around in a clockwise direction by friction at the rim of the rotating pulley and remains slightly displaced. The band is in equilibrium under the action of three torques, as follows: one due to the drag of friction f at the rim of the pulley tending to twist the band clockwise, one due to the force F' which is counterclockwise, opposing the drag of friction, and one due to the force F, which is clockwise. For equilibrium, the clockwise torques must balance the counter-clockwise torques, thus $fr + Fr = F'r$, whence

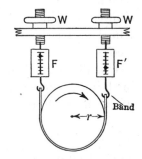

Fig. 72. Measuring power output with a band brake

$$f = F' - F$$

The force of friction acting on the band is, therefore, equal to the difference between the spring-balance readings. But the machine in opposing friction does an amount of work $f \times (2\pi r)$ during each revolution, or $f \times (2\pi rn)$ each minute, where n is the number of revolutions which it makes per minute. When the forces are expressed in pounds and the radius is in feet, the power output of the machine in foot-pounds per minute is $(2\pi rn) \times f$ or $2\pi rn \, (F' - F)$; or

$$\text{Output} = 2\pi rn(F' - F)\frac{\text{ft-lb.}}{\text{min.}} \times \frac{1 \text{ hp.}}{33,000\,\frac{\text{ft-lb.}}{\text{min.}}} = \frac{2\pi rn(F' - F)}{33,000}\,\text{hp.}$$

MACHINES

75. Simple Machines.—It is a matter of common experience that a stone firmly embedded in the ground can usually be dislodged easily with a crowbar, and that a heavy automobile can be raised with ease by means of a jack. The crowbar or jack serves as an intermediate device upon which work may be done, and which in turn will do work upon some other object. A device which accomplishes this result is technically called a *machine*. The complex machines used in industry are found upon analysis to be made up largely of certain elements which may be considered simple machines in themselves. These simple machines are generally considered as comprising the lever, the wheel and axle, the pulley, the inclined plane, the screw, and the wedge.

Usually a machine is employed in order to lessen the force required in doing a certain piece of work. Thus, if a 500-lb. weight is to be lifted, a machine may be used to exert this amount of upward force upon it while the person operating the machine exerts a smaller force, say only 50 lb. It is thus possible, and indeed usual, to obtain a larger force from a machine than that which is exerted upon it. Note that *this statement applies to force and not to energy;* for according to the law of conservation of energy *more work cannot be obtained from a machine than the energy that is supplied to it.* It is evident, since work = force × distance, that when the operator exerts a smaller force than does the machine, he must exert the smaller force through a correspondingly greater distance.

76. Efficiency.—On account of some waste due to friction in all moving machinery, however well designed, the energy given out by a machine is less than that supplied to it. More definitely, the principle of conservation of energy shows that

$$\text{Energy input} = \text{energy output} + \text{energy wasted}$$

if no energy is stored up in the machine. This statement is true over any period of time, and hence applies to unit time; and since energy per unit time is power, it can also be said that

$$\text{Power input} = \text{power output} + \text{power wasted}$$

The efficiency of a machine is defined as the ratio of its output to its input, both output and input being expressed in the same units of energy or power. This ratio is always less than unity; it is usually multiplied by 100 and expressed in per cent. Thus,

$$\text{Per cent efficiency} = \frac{\text{energy output}}{\text{energy input}} \times 100$$

or (54)

$$\text{Per cent efficiency} = \frac{\text{power output}}{\text{power input}} \times 100$$

High efficiency in a machine implies that a large part of the power supplied to it is given out by the machine to its load and only a small part wasted. The efficiency of a large electrical generator may be as high as 98 per cent. In some of the simple machines—a screw jack, for example—considerable friction is necessary to prevent the load from running down after it has been raised; because of the energy wasted in friction the efficiency of a screw jack is less than 50 per cent.

Suppose it is desired to calculate the power supplied to a 10-hp. motor which is delivering its full rated output at an efficiency of 85%. From equation (54),

$$\text{Power input} = \frac{\text{power output} \times 100}{\text{per cent efficiency}} = \frac{10 \text{ hp.} \times 100}{85} = 11.75 \text{ hp.}$$

Machines are rated in terms of their *output*; thus, a 10-hp. motor, such as that referred to in the foregoing problem, is one which is capable of *delivering* 10 hp. without exceeding its design limitations.

77. Mechanical Advantage.—The utility of a machine, as pointed out in § 75, is chiefly its capacity for enabling a person to lift a load or to do some similar mechanical work by the application of a comparatively small force. The ratio of the force W exerted by a machine on a load to the force F exerted by an operator on the machine,

is called the *mechanical advantage* of the machine. For example, if a
hoist has a mechanical advantage of 20, a force of 100 lb. exerted
upon it will enable the device to raise a load weighing 20 × 100 lb.
= 2000 lb. or 1 ton.

If it is assumed that the machine operates without friction, the
ratio of W to F is called the *ideal mechanical advantage* of that machine. Hence, if friction is neglected, the ideal mechanical advantage
is

$$A = \frac{W}{F} \tag{55}$$

Under this assumption the energy output would equal the energy
input, an ideal condition which cannot be attained in practice.
Suppose the machine to exert the force W through a distance h while
the operator exerts a force F through a distance s. The energy
output is Wh and the energy input is Fs; if these quantities are
equated, $Wh = Fs$; whence $\frac{W}{F} = \frac{s}{h}$. Therefore the ideal mechanical
advantage can also be expressed in terms of these distances, as follows:

$$A = \frac{s}{h} \tag{56}$$

If, on the other hand, friction is considered in calculating the mechanical advantage of a machine, or if the mechanical advantage is
found by actual test, in which case friction would be present and
produce a loss, the actual force ratio $\frac{W}{F}$ is called the *actual mechanical
advantage* of the machine.

78. Some Expressions for Mechanical Advantage.—The actual
mechanical advantage of a machine cannot be calculated with great
exactness, for such a calculation would involve a knowledge of the
frictional forces; these are uncertain because the coefficient of friction
is not very definite, § 49.

The ideal mechanical advantage, on the other hand, can be calculated without difficulty, since friction is assumed to be absent.
The general equations (55) and (56) will be applied in determining
the ideal mechanical advantage of the various simple machines mentioned. In finding these expressions, the procedure followed in each
case will be to assume that the machine exerts a force W through a

distance h while the operator exerts a force F through a distance s; the ratio $\dfrac{W}{F}$ or $\dfrac{s}{h}$ is then expressed in terms of the dimensions of the machine.

I. In the *lever*, one class of which is shown in Fig. 73, a bar of length AB is arranged with a fulcrum at X, dividing its length into two parts, l_1 and l_2, as shown. In order for the machine to raise a load W through a height h, the operator exerts a force F downward

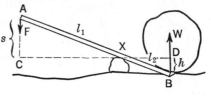

FIG. 73.   One class of lever

through a distance s. The triangles AXC and BXD are similar, and their corresponding sides are proportional; hence $\dfrac{s}{h} = \dfrac{l_1}{l_2}$, and the ideal mechanical advantage of the lever shown is

$$A = \frac{l_1}{l_2}$$

Other arrangements of the lever are frequently used, in which the fulcrum is differently located with respect to the forces F and W, but the ideal mechanical advantage is found in the same way.

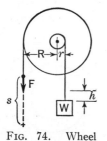

FIG. 74.   Wheel and axle

II. The *wheel and axle*, shown in Fig. 74, is a modified form of lever, consisting of a wheel of radius R fastened to an axle of radius r. A rope attached to the axle extends to the load W, and another rope attached to the wheel enables the operator to exert a force upon the machine. In order to raise the load through a height h, the operator exerts a force F through a distance s. During this process, the wheel and axle turn through an angle θ such that $\theta = \dfrac{h}{r}$ and also $\theta = \dfrac{s}{R}$.

Hence $\dfrac{s}{h} = \dfrac{R}{r}$, and the ideal mechanical advantage of the wheel and axle is

$$A = \frac{R}{r}$$

III. The *pulley* is used in a variety of ways. A single pulley merely produces a change in the direction of the force, and the mechanical advantage is unity. By using a combination of pulleys, a considerable mechanical advantage may be secured. In a typical pulley system, shown in Fig. 75, each block consists of two pulleys or sheaves encased in a frame or shell. The upper block is fixed and the lower one is attached to the load and moves with it, a rope fastened at one end passing around the several pulleys and thence to the operator. Part I of the figure represents a common type of construction, and part II shows the pulleys separated for clearness. Evidently, in order to raise the load through a height h, each of the four ropes A, B, C, and D must be shortened by this amount, and hence the operator must exert a force F through the distance $s = 4h$, making

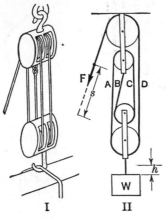

FIG. 75.　Block and tackle

$\frac{s}{h} = 4$. Therefore, the ideal mechanical advantage of the arrangement shown is 4, corresponding to the four ropes used to support W. For any pulley system arranged in the general manner shown, the ideal mechanical advantage is equal to the number of parallel ropes supporting the load.

IV. The *differential pulley* is an interesting modification of the simple pulley, in which an endless chain passes over toothed pulleys as represented in Fig. 76. At the top are two pulleys having nearly equal radii R and r and which are rigidly fastened together, turning in a block suspended from above. At the bottom a pulley of any convenient size turns in another block which is attached to the load and moves with it. In raising the weight, the operator exerts a downward force on the chain at D, while the portions A and B of the chain support the load, and the portion C remains slack. Suppose that in raising the load through a height h the operator exerts a force through the distance s. During this process the top pulleys ro-

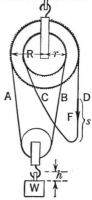

FIG. 76.　The differential pulley

tate clockwise through an angle θ such that $\theta = \frac{s}{R}$. This rotation shortens the chain at A by an amount θR and lengthens the chain at B

by an amount θr. As a result the loop AB is shortened a net amount $\theta R - \theta r = \theta(R - r)$, and the load is raised one-half of this distance, or $h = \frac{1}{2}\theta(R - r)$. But $s = \theta R$, and hence $\dfrac{s}{h} = \dfrac{\theta R}{\frac{1}{2}\theta(R - r)} = \dfrac{2R}{R - r}$; therefore the ideal mechanical advantage of the differential pulley is

$$A = \frac{2R}{R - r}$$

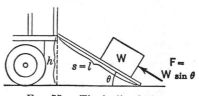

V. An *inclined plane*, Fig. 77, may also be used to reduce the force needed in raising an object. To push the ob-

FIG. 77. The inclined plane

ject up a smooth plane inclined at an angle θ with the horizontal requires a force $F = W \sin \theta$ along the plane, and in order to raise the object through a vertical height h, this force must be exerted through a distance $s = l$. The ratio of W to F or the ratio of s to h is equal to $\dfrac{1}{\sin \theta}$ or $\dfrac{l}{h}$. Therefore, the ideal mechanical advantage of an inclined plane, where the force is exerted along the direction of the incline, is

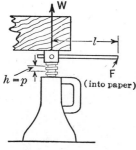

$$A = \frac{l}{h}$$

VI. The *screw* may be looked upon as an inclined plane wrapped around a cylinder. In a common form of screw jack, an upright screw threads into a stationary base and supports a load at the top, the screw being turned by means of a horizontal bar, as shown in Fig. 78.

FIG. 78. A screw jack

In order to raise the load W a distance h equal to the pitch p of the screw, the operator exerts a force F at the end of the bar through a circle of length $s = 2\pi l$, where l is the length of the bar. Hence $\dfrac{s}{h} = \dfrac{2\pi l}{p}$, and the ideal mechanical advantage of the screw jack is

$$A = \frac{2\pi l}{p}$$

VII. The *wedge*, Fig. 79, consists of a block having a base of length l and a thickness which varies from t at one end to zero at the other.

When placed under a load, it is caused to exert an upward force W through a distance h by driving it with a force F through a horizontal distance s. If the force F is parallel to the base, the ratio of s to h is easily found, for if the wedge is driven completely in, $s = l$ and $h = t$. Thus $\dfrac{s}{h} = \dfrac{l}{t}$, and therefore the ideal mechanical advantage of the wedge, where the applied force is parallel to the base, is

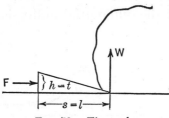

FIG. 79. The wedge

$$A = \frac{l}{t}$$

VIII. *Gear wheels* are used in rotating machinery not only to transmit motion from one point to another, but also for the mechanical advantage which they offer. Since in any machine the same time interval is used by the operator in exerting his force F through the distance s as is occupied by the machine in exerting the force W through the distance h, the ideal mechanical advantage may be expressed equally well by the ratio

$$A = \frac{\text{speed of operator}}{\text{speed of machine}}$$

This expression will be applied to angular motion in which one shaft drives another by means of gear wheels, as in Fig. 80. The angular speeds of these shafts are inversely proportional to the numbers of teeth on their respective gear wheels, and therefore, if the driving gear has n teeth and the driven gear has n' teeth, the ideal mechanical advantage of a pair of gear wheels is

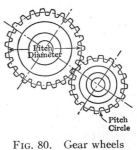

FIG. 80. Gear wheels

$$A = \frac{n'}{n}$$

If n' is larger than n, the driven gear having the larger number of teeth, the driven shaft turns slower than the driving shaft, and exerts a larger torque through a smaller angle. The same results may also be obtained where one shaft is driven from another by means of a chain or a belt.

Example.—A single problem will serve to coordinate the ideas of efficiency and mechanical advantage of a machine.

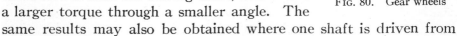

Suppose an operator to exert a force of 40 lb. in raising a load weighing 360 lb. with a wheel and axle having radii of 12 in. and 1 in. respectively. The actual mechanical advantage of the machine is $\dfrac{W}{F} = \dfrac{360 \text{ lb.}}{40 \text{ lb.}} = 9$, and the ideal mechanical advantage is $\dfrac{R}{r} = \dfrac{12 \text{ in.}}{1 \text{ in.}} = 12$. Since in raising the load 1 ft. the operator exerts a force through a distance of 12 ft., the energy output is 360 lb. × 1 ft. = 360 ft-lb., and the energy input is 40 lb. × 12 ft. = 480 ft-lb. The efficiency is therefore $\dfrac{360 \text{ ft-lb.}}{480 \text{ ft-lb.}} \times 100 = 75\%$.

Incidentally, it may be stated that the efficiency of a machine is always equal to the ratio of the actual mechanical advantage to the ideal mechanical advantage. This statement may be verified without difficulty from the results calculated in the foregoing illustration.

PROBLEMS

1. A 700-kg. crate is hoisted vertically through a height of 12 meters. How much work is done upon the crate?

2. A horizontal push is exerted on a 100-kg. box through a distance of 20 meters, causing the box to slide along a level floor at constant speed. If the coefficient of friction between the box and the floor is 0.3, how much work is done?

3. Compute the work done on a 3-ton elevator in accelerating it upward from rest at 2 ft. per sec. per sec. for a period of 5 sec.

4. A pull of 6 lb. is exerted upon a sled, drawing the sled 250 ft. along a level surface. If the direction of pull makes an angle of 20° upward from the horizontal, how much work is done?

5. Compute the work done in starting a 180-lb. sleigh and drawing it a distance of 100 ft. along a level snow surface, by a steady force of 25 lb. exerted on it in a horizontal direction. The coefficient of sliding friction between the sleigh and the snow is 0.08.

6. The work done in rotating a wheel is 1,000,000 ergs per revolution. What torque is being exerted on the wheel?

7. A grindstone 24 in. in diameter is driven at a constant speed of 90 rev. per min., and an axe is pressed perpendicularly against it with a force of 15 lb. for a period of 5 min. Take the coefficient of sliding friction between the axe and the stone as 0.3. Find how much energy was used in grinding the axe.

8. How much kinetic energy does the sleigh of Problem 5 possess after it has traveled 100 ft. from standstill?

9. A 750-lb. flywheel has a radius of gyration of $1\frac{1}{2}$ ft. What torque is needed to bring the wheel from rest to a speed of 150 rev. per min. in 1 min., and how much work is done in this interval?

10. The bowling ball described in Problem 23 of Chapter I is rolled

without sliding and moves at constant speed a distance of 60 ft. from the foul line to the head pin in 2 sec. Compute the kinetic energy of the ball.

11. A wheel of a trolley car has an overall diameter of 24 in., a radius of gyration of 9 in., and a mass of 260 lb. Calculate its kinetic energy when the trolley car has a speed of 25 mi. per hr.

12. An airplane having a mass of 3000 lb. travels at 120 mi. per hr. at an elevation of 5000 ft. What is the potential energy of the plane with respect to sea level and what is its kinetic energy?

13. A 75-gm. pendulum bob at the end of a 90-cm. cord sweeps through an angle of 60° as it vibrates to and fro. (a) How much is the potential energy of the bob increased as it moves from its midposition to the end of its travel? (b) With what velocity does it sweep through its midposition?

14. A thin-walled hollow cylinder, starting from rest, rolls down an incline that makes an angle of 20° with the horizontal. What is the velocity of the cylinder when its elevation is 1 meter lower than at the starting point?

15. Water is pumped at the rate of 80 cu. ft. per min. to an elevated tank, the average rise being 50 ft. At what rate is the pump doing work on the water?

16. A locomotive exerts a horizontal force of 18,700 lb. in drawing a train at a speed of 70 mi. per hr. on a level track. What power is exerted by the locomotive?

17. How heavy a load can a 25-hp. hoist lift at a steady speed of 360 ft. per min. without exceeding its rated output?

18. A steam engine develops 75 hp. when the piston moves forward and backward 90 times per min. with a stroke of 15 in. What average force does the steam exert on the piston?

19. What horsepower must be developed by the engine of an automobile running at 35 mi. per hr. while exerting a tractive pull of 400 lb., if 20 per cent of the power developed is wasted?

20. An automobile weighing 3800 lb. driven at 40 mi. per hr. is brought to rest by the brakes in 100 ft. Find (a) the time required in stopping, and (b) the number of horsepower expended in the brakes.

21. The shafting of a workshop is driven by belting through a 12-in. pulley on a motor revolving at 900 rev. per min. When the tension of the belt on one side of the pulley is 150 lb. and that on the other is 20 lb., what power is being supplied by the motor?

22. A motor drives a hoist which in turn lifts an 800-lb. load at constant speed a height of 125 ft. in 18 sec. If the hoist has an efficiency of 40% and the motor an efficiency of 80%, how many watts are supplied (a) to the load, (b) to the hoist, and (c) to the motor?

23. A 10-hp. motor operates at rated load for 8 hr. a day. Its efficiency is 87%. How much does it cost to operate it daily if electrical energy costs 3 cents per kw-hr.?

24. A screw jack has a screw with 4 threads to the inch which is turned by a bar extending 2 ft. from the center. What is the maximum load that could be lifted by a 30-lb. push at the end of the bar if friction were neglected?

25. A force of 300 gm. is required to raise a weight of 1600 gm. by means of a pulley system. If the weight is raised 10 cm. while the applied force is exerted through a distance of 80 cm., what is (a) the ideal mechanical advantage, (b) the actual mechanical advantage, and (c) the efficiency of the pulley system?

26. The two upper pulleys of a differential pulley hoist have diameters of $11\frac{1}{2}$ in. and 12 in. respectively. Upon testing this machine it is found necessary to apply a force of 54 lb. in raising a $\frac{1}{2}$-ton load. Calculate the ideal mechanical advantage, the actual mechanical advantage, and the efficiency of this machine.

Statics   *Chapter VIII*

79. Equilibrium.—In this chapter a study will be made of bodies which are at rest and of the requirements which must be fulfilled in order to maintain them in this condition. A body which continues in a state of rest is said to be in static *equilibrium*. A stone lying on the ground is at rest, and if it remains undisturbed it will continue in equilibrium.

It is known that a body initially at rest will be set into motion if it were acted on either by an unbalanced force or by an unbalanced torque; an unbalanced force would produce translation and an unbalanced torque would produce rotation. It follows, therefore, that two conditions must be satisfied if a body is to remain in equilibrium; first, the forces acting upon the body must balance each other to avoid translation, and second, the torques acting upon it must balance each other to avoid rotation. The forces referred to throughout this chapter are assumed to act in a single plane.

80. First Condition of Equilibrium.—The simplest case of equilibrium is that of a body acted upon by only two forces, for one of these must be equal and opposite to the other. A stationary ball suspended by a cord as in Fig. 81, for example, is acted on by only two forces. In the vector diagram at the right, these are shown acting upon the ball at O; the weight W of the ball is the attraction of the earth pulling downward upon it, and the force T is the tension in the cord pulling upward upon it. Since the ball is in equilibrium, the tension in the cord is equal to the weight of the ball and the forces T and W are equal.

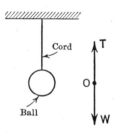

Fig. 81. Equilibrium under the action of two forces

When a body is in equilibrium under the action of three forces, it follows that the resultant of any two must be equal and opposite to the third force. Using this principle, the forces necessary to support a body in equilibrium can be found. Suppose, for example, that a ball of weight W is supported from the ceiling by two cords as shown at I in Fig. 82; the cords A and B make angles of θ and ϕ respectively with the ceiling, and are knotted at O to the vertical cord C. The tension in cord C is equal to the weight of the ball, as in the previous example, and the tensions in the other cords can be determined.

Each cord exerts a force on the knot O, and since the knot is at rest, it is in equilibrium under the action of three forces. The forces acting upon it are represented at II as follows: the weight of the ball, W, acts directly downward; the tension in cord A (unknown)

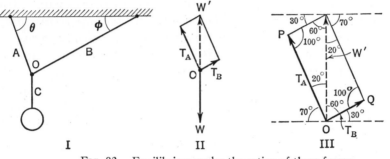

FIG. 82.   Equilibrium under the action of three forces

acts along the direction of A; and the tension in cord B (also unknown) acts along the direction of B. Since the forces must be balanced, the tensions in A and B, if known, would form a resultant W' equal and opposite to W; hence W' may be drawn and the parallelogram constructed, giving T_A as the tension in cord A and T_B as the tension in cord B. The values of T_A and T_B may be found graphically by constructing a diagram accurately to scale, as shown, and measuring the corresponding lengths, or they may be found analytically by means of the Law of Sines. It should not be thought that the shorter cord has the smaller tension; since this cord is more nearly vertical it naturally supports the greater part of the load.

To illustrate the analytical solution, suppose that in the foregoing example the weight of the ball is $W = 10$ lb. and that the angles which the cords make with the ceiling are $\theta = 70°$ and $\phi = 30°$. For clarity, the parallelogram shown at II in Fig. 82 is redrawn to large scale at III, and the angles are indicated. Those at P and Q are seen to be 100° each. From the Law of Sines, since W and W' are numerically equal, it follows that

$$\frac{T_A}{\sin 60°} = \frac{W}{\sin 100°}$$

whence the tension in cord A is

$$T_A = \frac{10 \text{ lb.} \times \sin 60°}{\cos 10°} = 8.79 \text{ lb.}$$

and similarly the tension in cord B is $T_B = 3.47$ lb. Thus, in supporting the 10-lb. weight in the manner described, the cords A and B are subjected to tensions of 8.79 lb. and 3.47 lb. respectively.

The illustrations point to a general conclusion about the equilibrium of a body under the action of forces that individually tend to produce translation in its position. To provide against translation, *the first condition of equilibrium requires that the vector sum of all the forces acting on a body along any direction must equal zero.*

81. Application to Components of Forces.—The study of the first condition of equilibrium may be simplified by resolving all of the forces which act upon the body into components, and considering the components rather than the forces themselves. The forces may be resolved along any directions desired, but are usually resolved along the horizontal and vertical axes. When a body is in equilibrium, it must be in equilibrium along the horizontal direction, which means that the horizontal components of the forces must balance. If components to the right are regarded as positive and those to the left negative, the algebraic sum of all the horizontal components must be zero. Similarly, the body must be in equilibrium along the vertical direction, which means that the sum of all the vertical components must be zero. Let the sum of the horizontal components be represented by ΣH, and the sum of the vertical components by ΣV; then the first condition of equilibrium may be symbolized as:

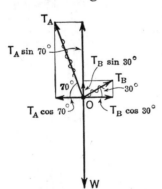

$$\left. \begin{array}{l} \Sigma H = 0 \\ \Sigma V = 0 \end{array} \right\} \qquad (57)$$

Fig. 83. Use of components in study of equilibrium

To illustrate this principle, the problem of the foregoing section will be worked out by resolving the forces exerted by the inclined cords in Fig. 82 into horizontal and vertical components, and applying equations (57). Fig. 83 shows the components of the tension T_A to be $T_A \cos 70°$ horizontally and $T_A \sin 70°$ vertically, and those of tension T_B to be $T_B \cos 30°$ horizontally and $T_B \sin 30°$ vertically, all acting at point O which represents the knot where the weight W is supported. Then

$$\Sigma H = T_B \cos 30° - T_A \cos 70° = 0$$

$$\Sigma V = T_A \sin 70° + T_B \sin 30° - W = 0$$

whence $0.866\ T_B = 0.342\ T_A$ and $0.940\ T_A + 0.500\ T_B = 10$.

When these equations are solved simultaneously, the tension in cord A is found to be $T_A = 8.79$ lb. while that in cord B is $T_B = 3.47$ lb.; these results agree with those previously found.

The foregoing principles may be extended to cases where a body is in equilibrium under the action of any number of forces, without change in method.

82. Second Condition of Equilibrium.—Even though the forces acting upon a body satisfy the first condition of equilibrium, it does not necessarily follow that the body will be at rest. The forces may be so directed as to produce *rotation* about an axis perpendicular to the plane of the forces. A body may be acted upon by a couple, § 23, a condition which satisfies equations (57) that $\Sigma H = 0$ and $\Sigma V = 0$, and yet this body will not be in equilibrium, for there is an unbalanced torque acting upon it which tends to produce rotation.

To overcome the tendency to rotate, another couple having an equal and opposite torque must be applied to the body. Hence, to provide against rotation, *the second condition of equilibrium requires that the torques acting upon a body shall be balanced, the clockwise torques being equal to the counter-clockwise torques.* If the clockwise torques be taken as positive and counter-clockwise torques as negative, the second condition of equilibrium requires that the sum of all the torques, ΣT, acting upon a body shall be zero, thus:

$$\Sigma T = 0 \tag{58}$$

When the forces which maintain equilibrium do not all pass through a common point, both conditions must be satisfied.

As a typical problem illustrating the two conditions of equilibrium, find the point at which a 12-ft. bar should be pivoted in order to remain at rest while supporting a load of 40 lb. at one end and a load of 8 lb. at the other end; assume that the weight of the bar itself is negligible. The bar is shown at AB in part I of Fig. 84, with the fulcrum C located a distance x ft. from the point where the 40-lb. load is applied. The forces acting on the bar are shown in part II of the figure. Since there are downward forces of 40 lb. at A and 8 lb. at B, the fulcrum must exert an upward force of $40 + 8 = 48$ lb. at C to satisfy the first condition of equilibrium. The moments of all the forces about the fulcrum will be determined and their algebraic sum equated to zero. Thus, the 40-lb. force produces a torque of −40 lb. × x ft., and the 8-lb. force produces a torque of 8 lb. × (12 − x) ft. The 48-lb. force produces no torque about this axis, its lever arm being zero. Hence, to satisfy the second condition of equilibrium

$$8 \text{ lb.} \times (12 - x) \text{ ft.} - 40 \text{ lb.} \times x \text{ ft.} = 0,$$

from which $x = 2$ ft. This is the distance from the 40-lb. load at which the fulcrum should be located to have the bar remain in balance.

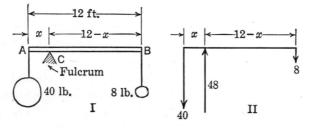

FIG. 84. Locating the fulcrum of a bar

Although it was natural in the foregoing problem to choose the fulcrum as the axis about which torques were taken, any other point might have been selected equally well, provided the same point were used throughout the calculation. The correctness of this statement may be verified by solving the problem again, taking torques about some other point.

A theorem of great value, based upon the second condition of equilibrium, states that *if three non-parallel forces acting upon a body produce equilibrium, their lines of action must pass through a common point.* This theorem will be demonstrated by taking moments of forces about the intersection of two of the lines of action and showing that the lever arm of the remaining force must be zero. Suppose a body to be in equilibrium under the action of three forces, as shown (incorrectly) in Fig. 85. Since their lines of action are not parallel, any two, if extended, will meet at some point. Thus, the lines of action of F_1 and F_2 meet at O. From this point draw a line OA perpendicular to the third force F_3, meeting its line of action at A. Apply the second condition of equilibrium, $\Sigma T = 0$, by taking the moments of all the forces about O, and placing their sum equal to zero. The moments of F_1 and F_2 are both zero, since the lines of action of these forces pass through O, and thus their

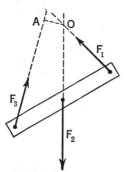

FIG. 85. Illustrating a theorem of equilibrium

lever arms are zero. Since the body is in equilibrium, the moment of the remaining force F_3 about O must be zero; and since the force F_3 is not zero, its lever arm OA must be zero; that is, the line of action of F_3 must pass through O. Hence the lines of action of three forces in equilibrium pass through a common point.

83. Resultant of Parallel Forces.—It was pointed out in § 80 that when a body is in equilibrium under the action of three forces, the resultant of any two of these forces is equal and opposite to the third force. This principle may be used in finding the resultant of two parallel forces. Suppose the body represented in Fig. 86 to be in equilibrium under the action of the three parallel forces F_1, F_2, and F_3. From the first condition of equilibrium, $F_3 = F_1 + F_2$; the resultant R of the forces F_1 and F_2 is equal and opposite to F_3. From the second condition of equilibrium $F_2 \times b - F_1 \times a = 0$, when moments are taken about O. This equation indicates an important relation between the forces and their lever arms, namely

$$\frac{F_2}{F_1} = \frac{a}{b} \tag{59}$$

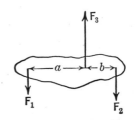

Fig. 86. Equilibrium under the action of parallel forces

Hence, the resultant of two parallel forces has the same direction as the forces and is equal to their sum, and its line of action divides the distance between them into two parts which are inversely proportional to the respective forces.

This principle can be extended to find the resultant of any number of parallel forces. First determine the force which, included with the forces given, will produce equilibrium; such a force is called the *equilibrant* of the given forces, and *the resultant is equal and opposite to the equilibrant and acts along the same line.*

Under certain conditions a body which is acted upon by several parallel forces is held in equilibrium by two or more forces instead of by a single equilibrant. These forces may also be found by applying the conditions of equilibrium.

As an illustration, consider a rod 12 ft. long supported by two cords, and carrying four loads aggregating 24 lb. The location of these loads is shown in Fig. 87 where the distances are indicated in feet. Find the tension T_A and T_B in the cords; assume that the weight of the rod is negligible. In solving problems of this type, the units are usually omitted for simplicity;

this practice is not likely to cause confusion if all units of distance are alike and all units of force are alike. For the first condition of equilibrium,

$$\Sigma V = T_A + T_B - 2 - 5 - 8 - 9 = 0$$

whence $T_A + T_B = 24$. For the second condition of equilibrium, with moments about the left end of the rod,

$$\Sigma T = 5 \times 3 + 8 \times 6 + 9 \times 12 - T_A \times 1 - T_B \times 11 = 0$$

or $T_A + 11T_B = 171$. When these equations are solved simultaneously, the tensions in the cords are found to be $T_A = 9.3$ lb. and $T_B = 14.7$ lb.

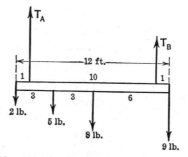

FIG. 87.   Weighted rod supported by two cords

It is interesting to note that this problem might have been solved by two applications of the condition $\Sigma T = 0$. When moments are taken about the left end of the rod, $T_A + 11T_B = 171$ as before, and when moments are taken about the right end

$$T_A \times 11 + T_B \times 1 - 2 \times 12 - 5 \times 9 - 8 \times 6 = 0$$

or

$$11T_A + T_B = 117$$

From these equations the tensions in the cords are found to be $T_A = 9.3$ lb. and $T_B = 14.7$ lb., as before.

It is clear that if the rod of the foregoing problem were supported by props instead of by cords, and if these were located at the same places as the cords, the props would divide the total load between them in the same way, each being under compression and exerting an upward force on the rod. Such upward forces are usually termed the *reactions* of the supports.

84. Center of Gravity.—The attraction which the earth exerts upon a body extends to each particle of matter which the object contains, and thus the weight of a body may be regarded as a system of parallel forces acting upon the individual particles of which the object is made. When these parallel forces are replaced by their resultant, this single force is exactly equivalent to them. For a given object there is a particular point through which the resultant of the weight forces will always pass, whatever the orientation of the object; this point is called the *center of gravity* of the body. Hence the weight of an object, although actually a system of parallel forces acting upon all of its component parts, can be correctly represented by a single force acting downward at the center of gravity.

As an illustrative problem, consider the forces on a truck having a 150-inch wheel base. The empty truck weighs 2600 lb. and its center of gravity is 90 in. in front of the rear axle. The truck carries a load of 3200 lb. which is placed centrally with its center of gravity 30 in. in front of the rear axle. What force does each tire exert upon the ground?

The conditions of the problem are indicated in part I of Fig. 88. The truck is represented by the line *AB* in part II of the figure, and the weights

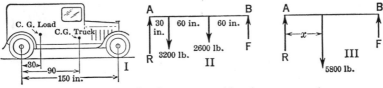

Fig. 88. Finding forces exerted by tires on ground

of truck and load are shown, each acting downward at its own center of gravity. The upward thrust of the ground on the two rear tires is represented as a single force R; and a similar thrust at the front tires is represented likewise as F. From the first condition of equilibrium, $R + F - 3200 - 2600 = 0$, whence $R = 5800$ lb. $- F$. Next, from the second condition of equilibrium, with moments about A, $3200 \times 30 + 2600 \times 90 - F \times 150 = 0$; from which $F = 2200$ lb. Finally, $R = 5800 - 2200 = 3600$ lb. But the forces exerted by the tires on the ground are equal to the reaction of the ground on the tires, and thus each front tire presses against the ground with a force of $F \div 2 = 1100$ lb., and also each rear tire presses with a force of $R \div 2 = 1800$ lb.

It may also be of interest in this problem to find the center of gravity of the loaded truck. This can be done by considering the combined weight of 5800 lb. to act downward at a single point distant x from the rear axle, as shown in part III. If moments are taken about A, then

$$5800 \times x - 2200 \times 150 = 0$$

and the center of gravity of the loaded truck is in front of the rear axle by a distance $x = 57$ in.

For bodies of simple shapes, the center of gravity can be located by inspection, being at the geometric center of the body, if the material is assumed to be of uniform density throughout. Thus the center of gravity of a rod, tube, or bar, whether of circular or rectangular cross-section, is located on the axis and midway between the ends; for a sphere it is at the center; for a cone it is on the axis at a point one-fourth of the way from the base to the vertex.

When a homogeneous body is in the form of a sheet, the center of gravity is the same as the center of area of the sheet. For a sheet of circular shape, the center of area is located at the center of the circle; for a rectangle it is at the intersection of the two diagonals; and for a triangle it is one-third of the distance from the middle point of any side to the opposite vertex.

Occasionally it is necessary to locate the center of gravity of a sheet from which a part has been removed. This is done by applying the second condition of equilibrium, as the following problem will show.

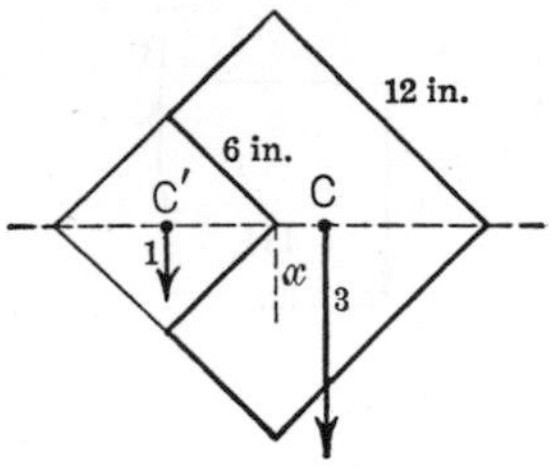

A 6-in. square is cut from one corner of a square sheet 12 in. on a side as shown in Fig. 89. To find the center of gravity of the piece that remains, let the removed square have a weight of 1 and be centered at C', and let the L-shaped remainder have a weight of 3 and be centered at C, at a distance x from the center of the initial square. Then

FIG. 89. Finding the center of gravity of an irregular sheet

$$3x = 1 \times \frac{12\sqrt{2}}{4} \quad \text{and} \quad x = \sqrt{2} = 1.41 \text{ in.}$$

Centers of gravity of irregular solids may be determined experimentally by suspending the body successively from three different points. In each test the body will come to rest with its center of gravity on a line directly beneath the point of suspension; the intersection of the three lines is the center of gravity. In Fig. 90 a sheet cut to represent the cross-section of a retaining wall is under test in this manner. This model is shown displaced from its position of rest and the forces W and W' constitute a counter-clockwise couple which will rotate it until its center of gravity CG is directly below the point of suspension S. After the vertical line through S is determined, the model is supported at another point and the test repeated. The intersection of the two lines fixes the center of gravity of the model and for the retaining wall.

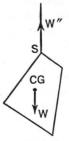

FIG. 90. Experiment to locate center of gravity

85. Conditions of Stability.—The way in which a body is supported with respect to its center of gravity has a great effect upon the stability of equilibrium of the body. If a cubical box rests on a level floor as shown in part I of Fig. 91, it is in *stable equilibrium* because if one edge is raised a little and then released, the box falls back again to its original position. The tilting of the box shifts the reaction R of the floor to the edge S, and the unbalanced torque set up by the weight W of the box acting at the center of gravity G produces rotation to restore the box to its initial position. The same effect is produced in a suspended body which is hung from a point above its center of gravity, as mentioned in the preceding section.

Again, consider a ball resting on a level surface, as in part II of the figure. No matter how the ball is moved, it shows no tendency

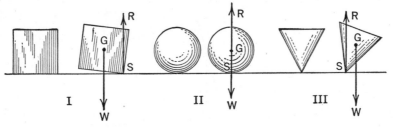

FIG. 91. Stable, neutral, and unstable equilibrium

either to return to its former position or to go the other way. Its weight W and the reaction R of the surface lie along a single line and therefore do not produce a couple; in consequence the ball is said to be in *neutral equilibrium*. So also is a cylinder lying on its side.

Sometimes an electrical galvanometer which is specially susceptible to jarring is supported in neutral equilibrium by attaching the instrument to a massive frame which in turn is suspended by long springs. Careful adjustment is made to bring the center of gravity of the entire system into coincidence with the point of suspension of the moving system of the instrument. This idea is also applied in supporting the engine of the automobile in such a manner that the plane of support includes the center of gravity of the engine, thus reducing vibration resulting from road shocks, and improving riding comfort.

The third part of Fig. 91 illustrates a condition of *unstable equilibrium*. Here a cone (not revolving) is shown while momentarily balanced upon the vertex. It is evident that if the cone is given a slight displacement its weight W will produce a torque about the vertex S which increases the displacement, and the cone will fall over.

*86. The Balance.—The equal-arm analytical balance offers an interesting study in equilibrium. In this instrument, which is shown pictorially in Fig. 12 and diagrammatically in Fig. 92, a long slender beam AB of length $2l$ supports a scale-pan at each end and is pivoted at its midpoint O. At this point it carries a downwardly projecting pointer OD, the lower end of which plays across a scale. The moving system has a weight W, and being symmetrical, has its center of gravity at some point C along the pointer, a distance d below the pivot O. This distance is of importance in the operation of the balance and is exaggerated in the figure for clearness. The broken lines represent the beam and pointer when not deflected, and the solid

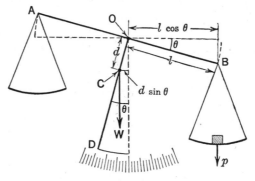

FIG. 92.   The equal-arm balance

lines show the result of adding a very small weight p to the right-hand scale-pan. This action sets up a deflecting torque about O equal to $p \times l \cos \theta$, which becomes smaller and smaller as θ increases. At the same time, the center of gravity is displaced, thus producing an opposing torque about the same axis equal to $Wd \sin \theta$ which becomes larger and larger as θ increases. The balance will evidently come to rest at some angle θ such that

$$pl \cos \theta = Wd \sin \theta$$

A sensitive balance is one which sweeps through a large angle when a very small weight is added to one scale-pan, the sensitivity of a balance usually being expressed as the amount of deflection in scale divisions produced by a weight of one milligram. Physically, however, the sensitivity of a balance is defined from the equation of balance that appears above. While the ratio of the deflection θ to the load p cannot be found directly from this equation, the ratio of $\tan \theta$ to p is seen to be

$$\frac{\tan \theta}{p} = \frac{\sin \theta}{p \cos \theta} = \frac{l}{Wd}$$

The expression for $\dfrac{\tan \theta}{p}$ thus gives the sensitivity of the balance in terms of its constants l, W, and d.

This equation shows that for a balance to have great sensitivity the arms should have considerable length l, the beam should have a small weight W, which usually implies a truss-like design to obtain the necessary rigidity, and the center of gravity of the moving system should be only a short distance d below the point of support. The moving system is sometimes provided with an adjustable weight near the pivot by means of which the center of gravity may be raised or lowered, thus adapting the balance to measurements requiring more or less sensitivity.

87. Application of the Principles of Equilibrium.—In applying the conditions of equilibrium to the solution of statical problems it is advisable to follow a definite procedure in order to avoid confusion and error. The procedure recommended is as follows:

1. Make a sketch of the device or structure; mark upon it all the known data; and assign symbols to the desired quantities.

2. Consider some member or point of the body and make a force diagram showing all the forces acting upon the portion considered.

3. Apply the conditions of equilibrium to this portion, by writing the equations expressing $\Sigma H = 0$, $\Sigma V = 0$, and $\Sigma T = 0$. The moments may be taken about any one axis.

4. Solve these equations for the quantities desired.

5. Follow the same procedure for the other points or members involved in the problem.

Two examples will illustrate the procedure.

I. A derrick consists of a uniform boom 24 ft. long weighing 700 lb., and a vertical mast to which the boom is hinged. A load of 5000 lb. is supported at the outer end of the boom. The directions are shown by the angles in part I of Fig. 93. Compute the tension in the cable which extends between the boom and the mast, and also the horizontal and vertical thrusts on the hinge-pin.

Select the boom as the body to be considered, and make a force diagram as shown

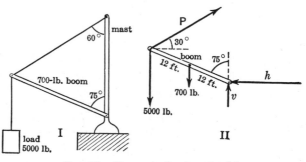

Fig. 93. Forces acting in a derrick

in part II, wherein the tension in the cable is called *P*, and the horizontal and vertical reactions on the boom due to the thrust of the hinge-pin are marked *h* and *v* respectively. The weight of the boom is considered as a single force acting at its center of gravity. When the conditions of equilibrium with respect to translation are applied, the equations become

$$\Sigma H = P \cos 30° - h = 0$$

$$\Sigma V = P \sin 30° - 5000 - 700 + v = 0$$

and when moments are taken about the hinge-pin, thereby eliminating both *h* and *v*, the torque equation in pound-feet becomes

$$\Sigma T = P\, 24 \sin 45° - 5000 \times 24 \sin 75° - 700 \times 12 \sin 75° = 0$$

These equations can be reduced to

$$h = P \cos 30° = 0.866P$$

$$v = 5700 - P \sin 30° = 5700 - 0.500P$$

$$P \sin 45° = 5350 \sin 75°$$

whence *P* = 7310, *h* = 6330, and *v* = 2045. That is, the tension in the cable is 7310 lb., and the horizontal and vertical thrusts on the hinge-pin are respectively 6330 and 2045 lb. Let *C* represent the resultant of these thrusts; then the force acting on the lower end of the boom becomes

$$C = \sqrt{(6330)^2 + (2045)^2} = 6660 \text{ lb.}$$

and its direction with respect to the vertical is given by

$$\tan \phi = \frac{h}{v} = \frac{6330}{2045} = 3.10 \quad \text{or} \quad \phi = 72°$$

Note that this force is not directed along the boom for the boom makes an angle of 75° with the vertical mast.

II. A uniform ladder, 18 ft. long and weighing 90 lb., leans against a smooth vertical wall at an angle of 70° with the ground. With what forces does the ladder press against the wall and ground?

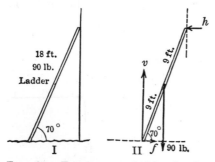

The ladder is shown in position in part I of Fig. 94, and the forces acting upon it are represented in part II. Herein *h* is the reaction by the wall upon the ladder and balances its push against the wall; it is perpendicular to the wall because that surface was assumed frictionless. Force *v* is the vertical reaction of the ground on the ladder and *f* is the frictional force of the ground and acts in opposition to the

Fig. 94. Forces on a ladder leaning against a smooth wall

direction in which the ladder tends to slide. Apply the conditions of equilibrium to find these three forces; then

$$\Sigma H = f - h = 0$$

$$\Sigma V = v - 90 = 0$$

ΣT (about foot of ladder) $= 90 \times 9 \cos 70° - h\, 18 \sin 70° = 0$

whence $f = h = \dfrac{90 \times 9}{18} \cot 70° = 16.4$ lb. and $v = 90$ lb. Hence, the ladder pushes against the wall with a normal force of 16.4 lb., and pushes against the ground with a force having a horizontal component of 16.4 lb. and a vertical component of 90 lb.

Next, assume that a 150-lb. man is standing two-thirds the way up on this ladder. The equations of equilibrium are then

$$\Sigma H = f - h = 0$$

$$\Sigma V = v - 90 - 150 = 0$$

$$\Sigma T = 90 \times 9 \cos 70° + 150 \times 12 \cos 70° - h \times 18 \sin 70° = 0$$

whence $f = h = 52.9$ lb. and $v = 240$ lb.

In the first case the frictional force is $\dfrac{16.4}{90} = 0.182$ of the normal force v at the base of the ladder, while in the latter case the frictional force is $\dfrac{52.9}{240}$ $= 0.22$ of that normal force. If the coefficient of friction between ladder and ground were just 0.22, the ladder would commence to slide when the man reached the position two-thirds of the way up.

*88. Elementary Structures.—The principles of equilibrium find a wide application in the design of structures of all kinds. When the forces have been determined in the various portions of a proposed structure, the designer will know how large to make the various sections in order to give the structure sufficient strength. The calculation of the forces acting in the members of an A-frame will serve as an elementary example.

The first step is to find the reactions of the supports upon the frame in its entirety, as though the structure were a simple rigid beam. Next, each member of the frame is considered by itself and all forces acting upon each are indicated. Instead of showing the actual forces themselves their horizontal and vertical components are indicated because often one component may be determined earlier in the computation than the other. Finally, the conditions of equilibrium are applied and the resulting equations solved for the forces desired.

Determine the forces acting on the three members of the A-frame shown in part I of Fig. 95, in which the lengths are marked in feet. The frame rests upon smooth horizontal surfaces and supports a load of 3000 lb. on its horizontal member at point *F*. The weight of the frame itself will be ignored.

Since the supporting surfaces are smooth, they can exert only vertically upward forces upon the frame. Call these reactions *A* and *B*. It is clear from the first condition of equilibrium that $A + B = 3000$ lb. The individual values are found from the second condition by taking moments about the two supports:

About *A* $\qquad$ $3000 \times 5.5 - 15B = 0$

About *B* $\qquad$ $15A - 3000 \times 9.5 = 0$

whence $A = 1900$ lb. and $B = 1100$ lb. The sum of these, 3000 lb., agrees with the result derived from the first condition of equilibrium.

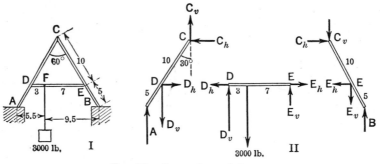

Fig. 95. Forces in an A-frame

Part II of the figure shows the three members considered separately, with force lines at each joint in the structure to indicate the horizontal and vertical components, these being differentiated by the subscripts h and v respectively. The conditions of equilibrium are applied first to the horizontal member *DE*, for there are as yet too many unknown forces on the others. The moments are:

About *D* $\qquad$ $3000 \times 3 - 10E_v = 0$

About *E* $\qquad$ $10D_v - 3000 \times 7 = 0$

whence $E_v = 900$ lb. and $D_v = 2100$ lb., a total of 3000 lb. These reactions are directed perpendicularly upward on member *DE* at its ends, and hence this member must exert corresponding downward forces on the inclined members, as shown. The horizontal components on *DE* cannot be determined from the forces on this member alone.

Next, consider the left-hand member *AC*. It is apparent that there must be a push against it at the top by the right-hand member *BC*; its magnitude and direction are unknown, but it will consist of two components C_h and C_v as represented, the vertical component being taken upward because D_v was found to be greater than the reaction A. For this member the equations of equilibrium are:

$$\Sigma H = D_h - C_h = 0$$

$$\Sigma V = A - D_v + C_v = 1900 - 2100 + C_v = 0$$

$$\Sigma T \text{ (about } C) = A15 \sin 30° - D_v 10 \sin 30° - D_h 10 \cos 30° = 0$$

$$= 1900 \times 7.5 - 2100 \times 5 - D_h \times 8.66 = 0$$

whence the forces on member AC are

$C_v = 200$ lb. upward
$C_h = 433$ lb. to the left
$D_h = 433$ lb. to the right (because C_h is to the left as above explained)

The horizontal forces on the tie-member DE are, therefore

$$D_h = 433 \text{ lb. to the left} \quad \text{and} \quad E_h = 433 \text{ lb. to the right}$$

It is apparent from the foregoing that the forces on the remaining member BC are as follows:

$E_h = 433$ lb. to the left
$C_h = 433$ lb. to the right
$C_v = 1100 - 900 = 200$ lb. downward

All of the force actions on the A-frame have been determined by computing their components; if the forces themselves are desired they may be calculated in the usual way.

PROBLEMS

1. Two ropes each 5 ft. long are attached to the ceiling at two points 8 ft. apart. The ropes are tied together at their lower ends, and jointly support a 60-lb. load. Calculate the tension in each rope.

2. A rope is stretched horizontally between fixed supports 30 ft. apart. When a 130-lb. tight-rope walker stands at its center the rope stretches farther and sags 1 ft. at that point. Compute the tension in the rope.

3. A 1-ton load supported from a derrick by a cable 13 ft. long must be pulled aside a horizontal distance of 5 ft. in order to clear an obstruction. How much force must be applied to this load in a horizontal direction in order to hold it at rest in its displaced position?

4. A thread 3 meters long is fastened to hooks in the ceiling 2 meters apart. Two 100-gm. weights are attached to the thread at points 1 meter apart, so that each weight is 1 meter from an end of the thread. Find the tension in the portion of the thread that extends between the weights.

5. Prove that the correct weight of a body may be determined with a balance that has unequal arms, by first weighing the body in the left scale-pan, then weighing it in the right scale-pan, and taking the square root of the product of the results of these weighings as the correct weight. Neglect the weights of the balance arms.

6. A meter stick is loaded with four weights, a 900-gm. weight at the 20-cm. mark, a 1000-gm. weight at the 30-cm. mark, a 500-gm. weight at the 60-cm. mark, and a 700-gm. weight at the 90-cm mark. At what mark should the stick be supported in order to balance, if its own weight is negligible?

7. A rectangular frame of negligible weight is subjected to four forces as specified in the diagram. The frame is held at rest in a vertical plane,

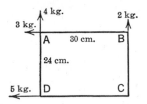

with the members AB and CD horizontal, by the application of one additional force at some point along CD. Find the magnitude and the point of application of this additional force.

8. A uniform beam having a length of 12 ft. and a weight of 10 lb. carries a 30-lb. load at one end and a 20-lb. load at the other. It is held horizontal while resting on a fulcrum 4 ft. from the larger load. What torque must be applied to keep it at rest in this position?

9. The gate across a street at a railroad crossing consists of a uniform bar 18 ft. long, pivoted to swing in a vertical circle about a fulcrum 2 ft. from one end. The bar weighs 3 lb. per foot of length. (*a*) What concentrated load applied as a counterbalance at the end of the short arm will produce equilibrium? (*b*) What torque acts on each side of the pivot when the counterbalanced gate is inclined 30° from the horizontal?

10. A uniform plank which is 12 ft. long and weighs 90 lb. rests on two props 1 ft. from each end. What is the reaction at each prop when a 160-lb. man stands on the plank 4 ft. from one end?

11. A yard stick which weighs 8 oz. is loaded with three weights, a 32-oz. weight at the 4-in. mark, a 24-oz. weight at the 10-in. mark, and a 16-oz. weight at the 30-in. mark. At what mark should the stick be supported in order to balance?

12. When the front wheels of a certain automobile are run on a platform scale, the scale balances at 1930 lb., and when the rear wheels are run on the scale, it balances at 1750 lb. The automobile has a 122-in. wheelbase; locate its center of gravity with respect to the rear axle.

13. A traveling crane, consisting essentially of a horizontal beam rolling along rails at its ends, is 20 ft. long and weighs 3 tons. When it is lifting a load at a point 12 ft. from the left end, the center of gravity of the crane with its hoisting machinery is located 8 ft. from the same end. If the load weighs 5 tons, what are the reactions at the supporting rails?

14. A shovel balances at a point 41 in. from its upper end, and when a 2-lb. weight is attached to that end, the point of balance is shifted 13 in. Find the weight of the shovel.

15. If a thin square sheet measuring 18 in. along each edge has its area

reduced 25 per cent by cutting out a piece along diagonals from the center to two adjacent corners, how far will the center of gravity of the sheet be shifted?

16. If a thin parallel-sided metal strip 2.0 meters long is folded back upon itself along a line 10 cm. from an end, how far will the center of gravity of the strip be shifted?

★17. An equal-arm balance deflects 1.5° when a 50-milligram weight is placed on one of its scale-pans. Determine the sensitivity of this balance.

18. A pole 12 ft. long weighs 200 lb. and its center of gravity is one-third of the way up from the base. While the pole is being raised, it rests momentarily at an angle of 30° from the horizontal with its base on the ground, being held in this position by a rope fastened to its upper end. If the rope is then at right angles to the pole, what is the tension in the rope?

19. A uniform ladder 12 ft. long and weighing 40 lb. is placed upon the ground with its upper end resting against a smooth vertical show window. Suppose that the ladder makes an angle of 75° with the ground, and that a 150-lb. man has climbed up the ladder a distance of 6 ft. Find the force that the ladder exerts upon the window and the horizontal and vertical components of the force that it exerts upon the ground.

20. A uniform ladder 18 ft. long stands on level concrete, with its upper end resting against a smooth vertical wall. The coefficient of friction between the ladder and the concrete is 0.3. How far can the bottom of the ladder be moved away from the wall before it starts to slip?

21. A 100-lb. sign is supported on an 8-ft. bar fastened to a wall as shown in the accompanying sketch, in which the distances indicated are in feet.

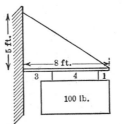

Find the tension in the guy and the thrust exerted by the bar against the wall. The bar is uniform and weighs 20 lb.

22. A derrick has a uniform boom 20 ft. long and weighing 400 lb., which is pivoted at the bottom of the vertical mast, and which is supported at the outer end by a cable extending to the top of the mast. A load of 5000 lb. hangs vertically from the outer end of the boom. When the boom makes an angle of 60° with the mast and 75° with the cable, what is the tension in the cable and the thrust of the boom against the mast?

★23. A ladder having the shape of the A-frame shown in Fig. 95 has two members 12 ft. long and a tie-rod 6 ft. long connecting the members at points 8 ft. from the hinged apex. Determine the tension in the tie-rod when a load of 400 lb. is placed at the apex of the ladder. Neglect the weight of the ladder and assume that it rests on a smooth surface.

*24. The bridge truss *AB–H* shown in the accompanying sketch has a span of 36 ft.   The truss is fixed at *A* and free to roll at *H*, and the members are hinged at the lettered joints.   A single load of 1000 lb. is placed at point *E*, this number being selected for simplicity, although such trusses

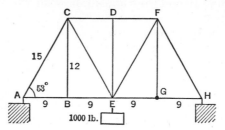

usually support loads hundreds of times greater.   The dimensions shown are in feet, and the weight of the truss itself is disregarded.   Calculate the forces in members *AB*, *AC*, *BC*, and *CD*.   *Hint.*   Consider the equilibrium of joints *A*, *B*, and *C* separately.

*25. The reel holder shown in the diagram consists of a rigid square frame *ABCD* and a back brace *BEFA*, which is hinged to the frame along the top *AB* and joined to it at the bottom by two chains *CE* and *DF*.   The

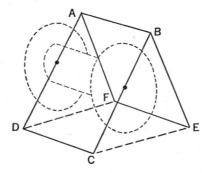

triangles *BCE* and *ADF* measure 4 ft. along each side and the shaft for the reel is half-way up the sides *AD* and *BC*.   The weight of the holder and the friction at the supporting surface may be disregarded.   If the reel weighs 500 lb., what is the tension in each chain?

89. Harmonic Motion Defined.—In addition to uniform motion and accelerated motion considered previously, there is another important type which is of common occurrence. It is a vibratory motion, in which the moving object sweeps back and forth repeatedly over the same path. Such motion may be illustrated by the oscillation of a weight hanging from the end of a coiled spring, the swinging of the bob of a long pendulum, or the vibration of the prongs of a tuning fork.

To investigate the characteristics of this type of motion, suppose that a weight fastened to a coiled spring is pulled down and released, so that it vibrates up and down about its original position as a central point. In pulling the weight down, if only a small force is applied, the spring stretches only slightly, and if more force is applied, it stretches more; provided that the force is not too large, the stretching force and the extension of the spring vary in direct proportion. This behavior is, indeed, characteristic of elastic substances, and the properties of these will be studied in Chapter X.

Whenever a force is applied to stretch the spring, there is set up within it an equal force in the opposite direction. It is this restoring force which causes the spring to pull the weight up when it is released. Since acceleration is proportional to the force which causes it, the acceleration of the weight is proportional to the restoring force and thus varies directly as the displacement of the weight from its central position of equilibrium. It may also be observed that when the displacement is downward, the restoring force and acceleration are directed upward, and vice versa. It is found, then, that in this vibratory motion, *the acceleration of the vibrating body and the restoring force acting upon it are proportional to its displacement from the midpoint of its path, and are directed toward that point.* Motion of this type is known as *harmonic motion.*

It might be remarked that all to-and-fro motion is not necessarily harmonic; in fact, it will not be harmonic unless it has the properties just described. There are many examples of machine parts in which the motion occurs back and forth repeatedly over the same path in equal time intervals but which does not conform to the foregoing definition. Such motion would be classed as periodic (recurring in equal periods) but it would not be harmonic.

90. Relation Between Circular and Harmonic Motion.—The study of harmonic motion is much simplified by the discovery of a relation that it bears to motion in a circle. If a body that is going around a circle at constant speed is viewed in the plane of the circle, it will

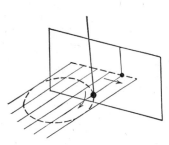

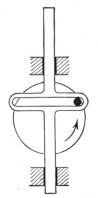

FIG. 96. Shadowgraph demonstration of harmonic motion

FIG. 97. Mechanical illustration of harmonic motion

be observed to vibrate to and fro along a line equal in length to the diameter of the circle, and this particular form of vibration is found to be harmonic. In brief, the projection of uniform circular motion in the plane of the circle, as in Fig. 96, is harmonic motion. It can be produced mechanically by a disk and a bar coupled by a pin-and-slot arrangement as shown in Fig. 97. The projecting pin near the rim of the disk engages the slot in the bar, the bar itself being supported in stationary guides to constrain its motion to the vertical direction. When the disk is driven at constant speed, the pin travels uniformly in a circle, but the bar receives only the vertical projection of this motion, and consequently slides up and down the diameter of the circle with harmonic motion.

91. Amplitude, Frequency, and Related Terms.—Usually when a body describes harmonic motion, there is no associated body which actually travels with circular motion as just described. It is then convenient to construct an artificial *reference circle*, and to imagine a body moving uniformly around it, as in Fig. 98. Here, if a body vibrates up and down harmonically along *CD*, its motion can always be considered as the projection of the motion of another body that is assumed to revolve uniformly around a reference circle of diameter *C'D'*. Thus, when the revolving body is at *M'*, the vibrating body is at the midpoint *M* of its path; as the revolving body moves to *P'*, the vibrating body moves to *P*; when the revolving body reaches *D'*, the vibrating body arrives at *D*, and so on. In this way the angle θ at the center *O* increases, sweeping out 2π radians in each revolution.

When the body in harmonic motion moves from *M* to *D*, then from *D* to *C*, and finally from *C* back to *M*, it has completed one *vibration*. In general terms, a vibration is a complete to-and-fro movement of the body over its entire path. It corresponds to a complete revolution of the body in the reference circle.

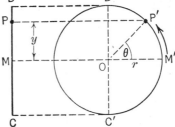

Fig. 98. The relation between harmonic and circular motion

The *displacement* of a body in harmonic motion at any instant is its distance from the midposition at that instant. In Fig. 98, when the body is at *P* its displacement is $y = MP$.

The *amplitude* of a vibration is the maximum displacement, and is represented in the figure by either *MC* or *MD*. The amplitude is equal to the radius *r* of the reference circle.

The *period* or *periodic time* is the time interval during which a vibrating body completes one vibration. In this time the body in the reference circle makes one revolution.

The *frequency* of vibratory motion is the number of vibrations completed per second, and is therefore the reciprocal of the period. If the frequency is denoted by *n* and the period by *T*, it follows that

$$n = \frac{1}{T}$$

The *equilibrium position* of a body in harmonic motion is the midpoint of its path. In the figure, point *M* represents the equilibrium position.

92. Sinusoidal Representation.—A body having harmonic motion continually traces the same path over and over, and this fact makes it difficult to indicate clearly the direction in which the body is moving at a particular instant. To overcome this difficulty, the path of the vibration may be spread out laterally to form a curve such as shown in Fig. 99. This curve combines the harmonic motion up and down with uniform linear motion sideways, the two motions being at right angles. Such a curve can be traced on a strip of paper by a body vibrating on the path *CD* if the paper is moved uniformly in a transverse direction. The starting point *M''* of the curve represents the vibrating body at an instant when it is at point *M* and moving upward, the corresponding body in the reference circle being at *M'*. As this body rotates through the angle θ to the position *P'*, the curve advances to *P''*, which therefore represents the

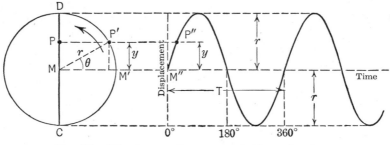

Fig. 99. Vibratory motion represented by a sine curve

vibrating body when at the point *P*. In a similar manner, the entire vibration may be mapped out, and the position of the vibrating body and the direction in which it is moving may be identified at any instant by a corresponding point on the curve.

The amplitude of the vibration is represented on the curve by the distance *r* between the extreme points and the axis; and the displacement at a particular instant is indicated by the distance *y*. The angle θ through which *P'* has rotated from its assumed datum position *M'* is called the *phase angle*. At the instant represented by *P*, *P'*, and *P''* in the figure, the phase of the vibration is 30° or $\frac{1}{12}$ period. Phase angles may also be indicated on the curve as shown, since in one period *T* the curve advances a complete cycle, while the phase angle increases from 0° to 360°. The displacement of the particle can be expressed in terms of the angular position, for the ratio of *y* to *r* is equal to sin θ. If *t* is the time reckoned from the instant when $\theta = 0$, the angular velocity of the radius *r* can be expressed as $\omega = \theta/t$, whence $\theta = \omega t$, and the displacement becomes

$$y = r \sin \theta = r \sin \omega t \tag{60}$$

This equation indicates why the curve is called a sine curve.

93. Velocity in Harmonic Motion.—In the foregoing sine curve representing the motion of a vibrating body, the slope at any point shows how rapidly the displacement is changing at the corresponding instant, and thus the slope of the curve at that point is an indication of the instantaneous velocity. The slope varies from zero at the extreme points to a maximum where the curve crosses the axis, consequently the velocity of the vibrating body shows these same variations.

In Fig. 100 a body having harmonic motion along *CD* is represented as the projection of a second body moving uniformly around a reference circle of radius $r = CD/2$.

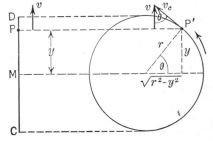

At a particular instant when the body in the circle is at point P', its velocity is represented by a vector v_c (the subscript referring to the *circle* as path); this vector is tangent to the circle at P' and represents a constant speed of $2\pi rn$, where n is the frequency. At the instant mentioned, the body hav-

Fig. 100. Velocity in harmonic motion

ing harmonic motion is at P, the projection of P' on the path *CD*, and its velocity is represented by v, the projection of v_c on that path. The angle between v_c and v is equal to the phase angle θ at the center, and hence $v = v_c \cos \theta$. But $v_c = 2\pi rn$ and $\cos \theta = \dfrac{\sqrt{r^2 - y^2}}{r}$, hence the instantaneous velocity of the body in harmonic motion when it is passing a point distant y from the equilibrium position is

$$v = 2\pi n \sqrt{r^2 - y^2} \tag{61}$$

The velocity has a maximum value of $v = 2\pi rn$ when the body is at the equilibrium position M for which $y = 0$, and is zero when the body is at the end points C and D for which $y = r$.

94. Acceleration and Restoring Force in Harmonic Motion.—The procedure used in the foregoing section will be followed again, and the acceleration of a body describing harmonic motion will be regarded as the projection of the acceleration of a body which is assumed to travel uniformly around a corresponding reference circle, as in Fig. 101. When the body in the circle is at P', its acceleration is directed toward the center and has the value $a_c = \dfrac{v_c^2}{r}$ exactly as in equation (36) except that the subscript is used here to designate the path as circular. At the same instant, the body describing harmonic motion is at P, and its acceleration is represented by a, which is the projection of a_c along the path CD; thus $a = -a_c \sin \theta$. But $v_c = 2\pi rn$ and $\sin \theta = y/r$, whence

$$a = -4\pi^2 n^2 y \tag{62}$$

The negative sign is introduced because the acceleration is opposite in direction to the displacement.

The acceleration is zero at the instant the vibrating body sweeps through the equilibrium position M for which $y = 0$, and has its maximum value at the end positions C and D, being then equal to the acceleration of the body in the reference circle, $4\pi^2 n^2 r$.

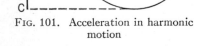

FIG. 101. Acceleration in harmonic motion

In deriving the expressions for velocity and acceleration in harmonic motion, a vertical vibration was used for illustration. However, the final equations involve only the frequency, displacement, and amplitude, and hence apply to vibrations along any direction.

Since a body describing harmonic motion is continually being accelerated toward its midposition, and since an unbalanced force is necessary to produce acceleration, it follows that such a body must be acted upon continually by an unbalanced restoring force. This force may be calculated in absolute units from equation (31), thus: $F = ma = m \times (-4\pi^2 n^2 y)$, from which the ratio of the force to the displacement is found to be

$$\frac{F}{y} = -4\pi^2 n^2 m \tag{63}$$

where m represents the mass of the vibrating body. Similarly, in gravitational units,

$$\frac{F}{y} = -4\pi^2 n^2 \frac{W}{g} \tag{64}$$

in which W is the weight of the vibrating body and g is the acceleration due to gravity.

Since $4\pi^2$ in the foregoing equations is a numerical constant, and n, W, g, and m are fixed for any one vibrating body under particular conditions, the expressions for acceleration and force may be written: $a \propto -y$ and $F \propto -y$, which show that both acceleration and force are proportional to the displacement of the body. These facts conform to the definition in § 89, and show that the projection of uniform circular motion upon a diameter of the circle is harmonic motion.

95. Illustrative Problem.—The foregoing principles may be illustrated by the behavior of a block attached to a flexible spring. The spring is elastic (see Chapter X) and sets up a restoring force when distorted, which force is proportional to the amount of distortion. When the block is released, it will vibrate with harmonic motion, and the foregoing expressions may be applied.

Suppose that a 15-lb. block, which originally hangs at the bottom of a long helical spring, is pulled down 1 ft., and that it takes a force of 5 lb. to hold it at this point. Calculate the frequency of vibration when it is released. Also determine the velocity and acceleration of the block at an instant when it is 3 in. above its original position.

The block upon release sweeps upward through its original position and vibrates above and below it with an amplitude $r = 1$ ft. which will remain the same if friction is ignored. Consider the downward direction as positive, and neglect the weight of the spring. Since a force of 5 lb. downward is needed to produce a displacement of 1 ft., the restoring force when $y = 1$ ft. is 5 lb. upward, so $F = -5$ lb. Also, the weight of the vibrating body is $W = 15$ lb. Therefore, by equation (64), the frequency is found to be

$$n = \frac{1}{2\pi} \sqrt{\frac{-F}{y} \times \frac{g}{W}} = \frac{1}{2\pi} \sqrt{\frac{5 \text{ lb.}}{1 \text{ ft.}} \times \frac{32 \frac{\text{ft.}}{\text{sec.}^2}}{15 \text{ lb.}}} = 0.52 \text{ per sec.}$$

At an instant when the block is 3 in. above the equilibrium position, $y = -3$ in. $= -\frac{1}{4}$ ft., and the velocity, from equation (61), is

$$v = 2\pi n \sqrt{r^2 - y^2} = 2\pi \times \frac{0.52}{\text{sec.}} \sqrt{(1 \text{ ft.})^2 - \left(-\frac{1}{4} \text{ ft.}\right)^2} = \pm 3.16 \frac{\text{ft.}}{\text{sec.}}$$

Similarly, the acceleration of the block at this instant is found from equation (62) as follows:

$$a = -4\pi^2 n^2 y = -4\pi^2 \left(\frac{0.52}{\text{sec.}}\right)^2 \left(-\frac{1}{4} \text{ ft.}\right) = 2.67 \frac{\text{ft.}}{\text{sec.}^2}$$

96. The Simple Pendulum.—The *simple pendulum* consists of a concentrated mass at the end of a cord of negligible weight. It is closely approximated by a small metal bob attached to a thin thread.

The time of vibration can be found by considering the bob to be displaced slightly and by studying the forces acting upon it; such analysis will show that the unbalanced force is proportional to the displacement and opposite in direction. It then follows that the vibration of the bob is harmonic, and the equations of harmonic motion can be applied to determine the period.

Consider a pendulum bob B which is suspended from a support S by a thin cord of length l and which has been shifted horizontally to the left a distance x (positive), as in Fig. 102. Two forces act upon the bob: the attraction of gravity, W, vertically downward, and the pull P in the cord acting toward S. The resultant or unbalanced force F acting on the bob is directed toward the right (negative) and can be found by completing a parallelogram as in the figure, from which it is seen that the angles marked β are equal. The force F acts at right angles to the cord, since this is the direction in which the bob will accelerate when released; so $F = -W \sin \beta = -\dfrac{Wx}{l}$.

FIG. 102. Finding the period of a simple pendulum

The displacement AB of the bob is toward the left and may be considered equal to x if β is small. Under this condition the equation shows that the restoring force F is directly proportional to the displacement and opposite in direction. Consequently the motion of the bob is harmonic. The restoring force corresponding to the displacement x is found from equation (64) to be $F = -4\pi^2 n^2 \dfrac{W}{g} x$.

The two values of F may be equated, thus:

$$-\frac{Wx}{l} = -4\pi^2 n^2 \frac{W}{g} x$$

from which $n = \dfrac{1}{2\pi} \sqrt{\dfrac{g}{l}}$, and hence the period $T = \dfrac{1}{n}$ is given by the expression

$$T = 2\pi \sqrt{\frac{l}{g}} \qquad (65)$$

The time of vibration of a pendulum is seen to be determined by its length l and by the acceleration due to gravity g at the point where the pendulum is located. By using a pendulum of known length and measuring its period of vibration, the value of g can be determined with accuracy. Equation (65) applies only to small values of the displacement angle β, which, however, need not be constant. As the vibration of a pendulum continues, the amplitude becomes smaller and smaller but the period remains practically unchanged. It is this property which makes the pendulum of value in controlling the escapements of timekeepers.

97. The Physical Pendulum.—Any body which vibrates in the manner of a pendulum but in which the mass is distributed and not concentrated as in the simple pendulum is called a *physical* or *compound pendulum*. A rod suspended at one end, or a hoop hung on a nail, would vibrate as a physical pendulum if displaced and released.

To determine the period of a physical pendulum, consider the motion of a pivoted body at an instant after it has been displaced slightly from its equilibrium position and released; then the restoring torque set up will produce a corresponding angular acceleration, from which the linear acceleration of some point can be determined. It will be found that this acceleration is proportional to the displacement, which makes the motion harmonic, and the period can be found from the laws of harmonic motion as in the simple pendulum.

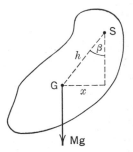

FIG. 103. Finding the period of a physical pendulum

A body of mass M vibrating about an axis S is shown in Fig. 103 at an instant when displaced from its equilibrium position by an angle β. The attraction of gravity acts upon the body as a downward force at the center of gravity G, and may be expressed in absolute units as Mg. The torque due to this force about the axis S is Mgx, being the product of the force Mg and the perpendicular distance x between its line of action and the axis. This torque tends to restore the body to its position of equilibrium. The angular acceleration which this torque produces is $\alpha = Mgx/I$, where I is the moment of inertia of the body about a transverse axis at the point of suspension. The linear acceleration of the point G follows from equation (30): $a = \alpha h = -\dfrac{Mgx}{I} \times h$, where h is the distance between the center of suspension S and the center of gravity G. If the displacement angle β is small, x may be taken as the displacement of G. Under this condition the equation shows that the acceleration of this point is proportional to its displacement; the negative sign is introduced because these quantities are opposite in direction. Hence G may be considered as having harmonic motion, and its acceleration is given by equation (62) as $a = -4\pi^2n^2x$. This is the type of motion for all points of the body. Hence, the period for the entire body is obtained by equating the foregoing values for acceleration, or

$$-\frac{Mgx}{I} \times h = -4\pi^2n^2x$$

Hence, $n = \dfrac{1}{2\pi}\sqrt{\dfrac{Mgh}{I}}$, and the period is

$$T = 2\pi\sqrt{\frac{I}{Mgh}} \tag{66}$$

where, as before, I is the moment of inertia of the pendulum about a transverse axis at the point of suspension and h is the distance between the axis of suspension and the center of gravity.

Suppose it is desired to find the time of vibration of a meter stick pivoted at one end, as pictured in Fig. 104. The moment of inertia of the stick

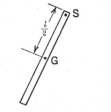

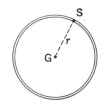

Fig. 104.   A vibrating stick   Fig. 105.   A vibrating hoop

about the axis of suspension is given in § 59 as $I = \frac{1}{3}Ml^2$, and the distance between the center of suspension S and the center of gravity G is $h = l/2$; whence the period is

$$T = 2\pi\sqrt{\frac{Ml^2/3}{Mgl/2}} = 2\pi\sqrt{\frac{2l}{3g}} = 2\pi\sqrt{\frac{2 \times 100 \text{ cm.}}{3 \times 980 \text{ cm/sec.}^2}} = 1.64 \text{ sec.}$$

As another example, find the time of vibration of a hoop 1 ft. in diameter about an axis S at its circumference, as shown in Fig. 105. The moment of inertia of the hoop about a transverse axis at G is $I_G = Mr^2$, and hence about a parallel axis at S its moment of inertia is

$$I = I_G + Mr^2 = Mr^2 + Mr^2 = 2Mr^2$$

where the distance h between S and G is replaced by r.   Therefore

$$T = 2\pi\sqrt{\frac{2Mr^2}{Mgr}} = 2\pi\sqrt{\frac{2r}{g}} = 2\pi\sqrt{\frac{2 \times \frac{1}{2} \text{ ft.}}{32 \text{ ft/sec.}^2}} = 1.11 \text{ sec.}$$

*98. Centers of Oscillation and Percussion.—The *center of oscillation* of a physical pendulum is that point at which the concentration of the whole mass of the pendulum would cause no change in its period of vibration. If the mass were so concentrated, the physical pendulum would reduce to a simple pendulum having the same period. The period is $2\pi\sqrt{\dfrac{l}{g}}$ for a simple pendulum and $2\pi\sqrt{\dfrac{I}{Mgh}}$ for a physical pendulum; if these are equated it follows that the length of the equivalent simple pendulum is

$$l = \frac{I}{Mh} \qquad\qquad (67)$$

The center of oscillation of a physical pendulum is therefore separated from the axis of suspension by the distance $\dfrac{I}{Mh}$, and this expression also shows the length of a simple pendulum which will have the same period as the physical pendulum. In this expression the symbols have the same meaning as previously.

The center of oscillation may be interchanged with the center of suspension without affecting the period. To prove this statement, it is merely necessary to compute the equivalent length of a physical pendulum when suspended (1) at its axis of suspension, and (2) at its center of oscillation, and to show that the two values found are equal.

The center of oscillation is also called the *center of percussion*, because it is a point at which the pendulum can be struck without jar on the axis, the only tendency produced by a blow at this point being to rotate the pendulum about its axis of suspension. When struck at any other point there is not only a tendency to rotate the pendulum but also to give the axis a motion of translation. The stinging sensation sometimes experienced in batting a ball is probably due to striking the ball with the bat at some point other than the center of percussion.

*99. The Torsion Pendulum.—When a weight attached to a vertical wire as shown in Fig. 106 is twisted and released, it will act as a *torsion pendulum*, describing a series of angular vibrations similar to the linear vibrations met with previously in harmonic motion. In the figure the forces FF acting at the distance R from the center O produce a torque $2RF$. The consequent twisting of the wire sets up within it an oppositely directed restoring torque which is proportional to the angular displacement, just as in linear harmonic motion a restoring force is set up which is proportional to the linear displacement. The two types of motion are closely analogous, and angular harmonic motion can be studied most simply by comparing it directly to linear harmonic motion.

Hence, in equation (63), $\dfrac{F}{x} = -4\pi^2 n^2 m$, which is a characteristic expression for linear harmonic motion, if each linear quantity is replaced by the corresponding angular quantity, there results as the

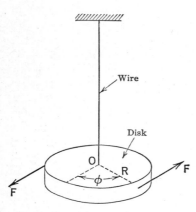

corresponding expression for angular harmonic motion:

$$\frac{T'}{\phi} = -4\pi^2 n^2 I \qquad (68)$$

wherein T' represents the restoring torque (this symbol being used to avoid confusion with the period T), ϕ is the corresponding angular displacement, n is the frequency, and I is the moment of inertia of the vibrating body about the axis of rotation. The ratio of the torque T' to the corresponding twist ϕ is a constant determined by the stiffness of the suspension wire and is essentially negative. When this ratio is replaced by $-\tau$ (tau) and the expression is rearranged, the frequency of angular vibration is found to be $n = \dfrac{1}{2\pi}\sqrt{\dfrac{\tau}{I}}$, and consequently the period is

Fig. 106. A torsion pendulum

$$T = 2\pi\sqrt{\frac{I}{\tau}} \qquad (69)$$

an expression which is analogous to equation (65) for the period of linear vibration.

The torsion principle may be used to determine the moment of inertia of a body; the body is supported as a torsion pendulum and measurements are made of its period and of the angle of twist produced by a measured torque. From the data thus obtained and the use of equation (69), the moment of inertia of the suspended body can be determined.

PROBLEMS

1. A pendulum is set in motion and has a frequency of 1.7 vibrations per sec. How long does it take to complete 100 vibrations?

2. A particle moves with harmonic motion in a vertical line between two points 20 cm. apart. How far does the particle move during the first $\frac{1}{8}$ period after passing through the midpoint of its path?

3. A bird cage is hung on a helical spring and extends it $\frac{3}{8}$ in. Calculate the frequency with which the cage will vibrate when it is displaced and released.

4. A ball travels with constant speed once per second around a horizontal circle 10 in. in diameter, its shadow moving with harmonic motion on a wall behind it. Find the velocity and the acceleration of the shadow (*a*) at the midpoint of its path, (*b*) at an end point, and (*c*) at a point half way between the midpoint and the end point.

5. A spring scale used for weighing ice has scale divisions $\frac{1}{8}$ in. long, each representing 1 lb. A 50-lb. cake of ice hung from this spring scale is set vibrating up and down with an amplitude of 2 in. Compute (*a*) the frequency of vibration, and (*b*) the maximum velocity of the vibrating weight.

6. A mass of 20 gm. is executing harmonic motion along a vertical line 10 cm. long, with a frequency of 2 vibrations per sec. Calculate the position and acceleration of the mass and the restoring force acting upon it at an instant 0.1 sec. after leaving the highest point in its path.

7. A block of wood floating on water is pushed down, and the downward displacement of the block is found to increase directly with the applied force until the block is completely submerged. A particular block required a force of 2 kg. when pushed down 1 cm. from its rest position, and when released vibrated up and down twice a second. Compute the mass of the block.

8. A 400-gm. weight is hung on a coiled spring and extends it 8 cm. The weight is then increased to 500 gm. and set into vibration with an amplitude of 4 cm. Calculate the frequency of vibration; also the velocity and acceleration of the weight and the restoring force acting upon it at an instant one-sixth of a period after passing through the midposition.

9. What is the approximate time of vibration of a child's swing, if the ropes supporting the seat are parallel and each is 12 ft. long?

10. A pendulum which would have a period of 2 sec. at sea level on the equator, where the acceleration due to gravity is 977.99 cm/sec.^{2}, makes 100 vibrations in 3 min., 20.2 sec. on a certain mountain top. Find the acceleration due to gravity at this location.

11. A simple pendulum is arranged to operate an electric contact when its bob sweeps through the midpoint of its path. How long should the pendulum be in order to operate the contact 100 times a minute?

12. A hole is bored transversely through a yard stick at the 6-in. mark and the stick is set into vibration about a horizontal nail through the hole. Find the period of vibration.

13. It can be shown that for a slim stick of length *l* vibrating about a transverse axis, the period of the stick is a minimum when the distance

between axis and center of gravity is equal to $l \div \sqrt{12}$. Compute the minimum period for a meter stick oscillating in this manner.

14. Find the length of a simple pendulum which will have the same period of vibration as that of a solid disk 8 in. in diameter when pivoted about a transverse axis at its rim.

★15. A method for comparing masses without recourse to gravity makes use of a torsion pendulum in which a slender horizontal rod of negligible mass is attached to the lower end of a vertical wire. With a pair of 4-lb. masses attached to the ends of the rod, the pendulum vibrates 18 times per min. When these masses are replaced by a different pair, the pendulum vibrates 12 times per min. What masses were used for the second pair?

★16. A bar supported horizontally by a wire at its center is twisted through an angle of 17.5° by a torque of 2.0×10^6 dyne-cm., and is then released. It vibrates 90 times a minute as a torsion pendulum. Find the moment of inertia of the bar.

★17. In most electrical galvanometers the moving element is a coil which is suspended at the end of a thin wire and which can oscillate as a torsion pendulum. If such a coil has a moment of inertia of 4 gm-cm.^{2} and a period of vibration of 15 sec., what torque is exerted upon it by the suspension wire when the coil is twisted through an angle of 20°?

Elasticity and Impact — *Chapter X*

MODULI OF ELASTICITY

100. Elastic Bodies.—Perhaps everyone has observed the bending of a piece of wood and its return to the original shape upon removal of the bending force, as well as the twisting of a wire or rod of metal and its return to the original shape upon removal of the twisting force. These effects are evidences of the *elasticity* of matter, and the substances are said to be *elastic*. More strictly, an elastic body is one which, having had its size or shape changed by the application of a distorting force, returns to its original condition upon the removal of that force.

In the foregoing chapters, it was assumed that bodies were rigid, and that under the action of applied forces the body would move as a whole, perhaps with translation, or rotation, or vibration, or combinations of these types of motion. Consideration is given here to the action of forces in distorting a body, the particles of the body moving relatively to each other through rather narrow ranges, and it is understood that the forces are applied in such a manner that the body in its entirety will not move.

101. Stress and Strain; Hooke's Law.—When a load is applied to an elastic body, the body becomes distorted; that is, some portion of the body is displaced with respect to some other portion which has not been disturbed. As a result of this displacement, a force action is developed between the molecules of the body which resists the change that the applied load has brought about, and tends to restore the body to its original condition. The aggregate of these molecular forces will just balance the applied load when the body has reached a stable condition (namely rest) under the action of these forces. The larger the load, the larger will be the deformation necessary to establish molecular restoring forces that balance the increased load. The relation between the deformation and the restoring force was investigated by Robert Hooke (1635–1703), English experimental physicist. He found that the force developed within an elastic body to withstand an outside load is proportional to the deformation of the body under that load.

The correctness of this statement can be verified by applying weights to a helical spring or a flat spring in the manner indicated in Fig. 107. If different weights W_1, W_2, W_3, etc., are placed in

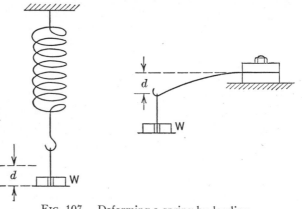

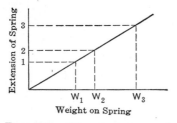

FIG. 107. Deforming a spring by loading

turn upon either spring, it will be found that the steady deflections produced by them, respectively d_1, d_2, d_3, etc., are proportional to the applied weights as shown by the straight line plotted in Fig. 108. The restoring force is, therefore, proportional to the deflection or deformation.

It is customary to express the restoring action set up in an elastic body when subject to deformation as the force per unit area over which the force acts, and the term *stress* is used for this purpose. Thus, *stress is the restoring force per unit area* and its interpretation depends upon the particular manner in which the load is applied to the body. Engineers commonly refer to this quantity as the *unit stress*.

FIG. 108. The dependence of stretch upon applied load

The deformation of an elastic body is expressed by the change produced by the applied force in terms of some original dimension of the body, and the term *strain* is used as the measure of deformation. Thus, if a sheet of rubber 10 in. square is stretched to 11 in. in both directions, the strain would appropriately be reckoned as the ratio of change in area to original area, or $\dfrac{121 - 100}{100} = 0.21$.

Hooke's observations can be expressed more definitely when the terms stress and strain are used respectively as the measures of restoring force and deformation, as follows: Hooke's Law states that *the stress set up within an elastic body is proportional to the strain to which the body is subjected* by the applied load. Expressed tersely

$$\text{stress} \propto \text{strain}$$

or

$$\text{stress} = k \times \text{strain}$$

and

$$k = \frac{\text{stress}}{\text{strain}} \tag{70}$$

where k is a constant for the material of the elastic body. This constant is known as the *modulus of elasticity* of the material, and its numerical value depends upon the units selected for the stress and the strain.

For each material there is a limiting stress beyond which the proportionality expressed by Hooke's Law does not hold, and this is called the *elastic limit* of the material. If the stress is larger than this value for a specimen under test, a permanent distortion will result, and at a still higher value called the *breaking stress* rupture will occur. This chapter deals with perfectly elastic bodies that are subjected to forces which do not cause the elastic limits to be exceeded.

102. Elasticity of Length (Young's Modulus).—The deformation of a body may occur in three different ways, depending upon the manner in which the external forces are applied. In one of these, the load tends to change the length of the body, in another to change its shape, and in the third to change its volume. Naturally, different procedures are necessary to evaluate the stress and the strain for these cases, but Hooke's Law applies equally to all three.

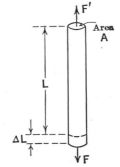

Consider a wire, of length L and cross-sectional area A, as shown in Fig. 109, to be subjected to tension by the application of two equal and opposite forces F, F' to its ends, as a result of which the wire elongates an amount ΔL. The strain in this case is the elongation ΔL divided by the original

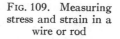

Fig. 109. Measuring stress and strain in a wire or rod

length L, while the stress is equal to the force F divided by the cross-sectional area A. Therefore, strain = $\Delta L/L$ and stress = F/A;

consequently their ratio, which is a constant of the material of the wire, is

$$Y = \frac{\text{stress}}{\text{strain}} = \frac{F/A}{\Delta L/L} \tag{71}$$

This constant Y, the stretch modulus of elasticity, is called *Young's modulus*, after Thomas Young (1773–1829), English philosopher.

Young's modulus for a material does not usually depend upon the dimensions of the particular sample used in a test. Suppose, for example, that a wire of the same material but having twice the length $(2L)$ and twice the cross-sectional area $(2A)$ is subjected to the same force (F) as before. The stress is now $\dfrac{F}{2A}$, which is half of the previous value. The elongation would be doubled because of the increased length of the sample and at the same time would be halved because of its increased area, consequently the elongation (ΔL) remains unchanged and the strain becomes $\dfrac{\Delta L}{2L}$, which is half of the previous value. Thus, the stress and strain are changed in the same proportion, and therefore their ratio remains constant. From this analysis it appears that tests can be made on rods or wires of any convenient dimensions and will yield·the same value for the modulus of a given material. This result agrees in general with experiment, although the modulus is influenced somewhat by the shape, size, and treatment of the specimen. Young's modulus applies equally well to decrease of length in compression and to increase of length in tension.

In British units the stress is often measured in pounds per square inch and the strain measured in inches of extension per inch of original length, consequently the unit for Young's modulus would be

$$Y = \frac{\text{lb/in.}^2}{\text{in/in.}} = \text{lb. per sq. in.}$$

In metric units the stress may be measured in dynes per square centimeter, in kilograms per square millimeter, or in similar units; the strain is usually measured in centimeters of extension or contraction per centimeter of original length. In this case also the unit for Young's modulus will be the same as the unit for stress.

The numerical values of Young's modulus are very large in comparison with the values of the elastic limit and of the breaking stress.

For example, for mild steel the stretch modulus of elasticity is 30,000,000 lb. per sq. in., the elastic limit is 35,000 lb. per sq. in., and the breaking strength is 60,000 lb. per sq. in. In designing structures, engineers allow a "unit stress" for steel of perhaps 16,000 lb. per sq. in. to give an ample factor of safety.

As a numerical example, compute the elongation of a steel tie bar 24 ft. long, 4 in. wide, and $\frac{1}{2}$ in. thick, when subjected to a tensile force of 30,000 lb. The stress is 30,000 lb. $\div$ $(4 \times \frac{1}{2})$ sq. in. = 15,000 lb. per sq. in. By equation (71), the strain is found to be

$$\text{strain} = \frac{\text{stress}}{Y} = \frac{15,000 \, \dfrac{\text{lb.}}{\text{sq. in.}}}{30,000,000 \, \dfrac{\text{lb.}}{\text{sq. in.}}} = \frac{1}{2000}$$

Since the strain is the elongation ΔL divided by the original length L, it follows that the elongation is

$$\Delta L = L \times \text{strain} = 24 \text{ ft.} \div 2000 = 0.012 \text{ ft.} = 0.144 \text{ in.}$$

The small extensions which occur when a rod is placed under tensile loads may be measured by an *extensometer;* in one type two pairs of opposed pointed screws are pressed into the rod at a known distance apart, and a lever system with a short-focus microscope measures the elongation of that portion of the rod. In measuring the larger extensions of thin wires, sufficient accuracy is attained by placing at the end of the wire a small vernier, which moves along a suitably supported scale when the wire stretches.

103. Elasticity of Shape (Shear Modulus).—Often a body is subjected to a pair of equal forces which act in opposite directions but not along the same line, as in a couple, § 23. Such a pair of forces *SS* is shown acting upon the upper and lower faces of a rectangular block *abcd* in Fig. 110, and would *shear* it into the parallelopiped *ab'c'd*, turning the end faces *ab* and *cd* through the small angle ϕ. Upon removal of the shearing forces the body will resume its original shape, provided the elastic limit of the material

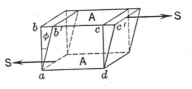

Fig. 110. Effect of shearing forces upon a block

was not exceeded. This type of elasticity is termed *elasticity of shape* or of *shear*, and is of great importance in structural design and shafting.

In order to study the behavior of materials under shear, it is usual to apply the general definitions for stress and strain to this particular kind of distortion. The block shown in Fig. 110 may be regarded as made up of a large number of horizontal sheets of area A, each of which is forced to slide along slightly with respect to its neighbors under the action of the shearing forces. The area A is obviously the surface which resists the shearing action caused by the force S, and hence the *shearing stress* is S/A, where A is the area of the upper or lower face of the block. The *strain* is measured by the angle ϕ through which the end of the block is sheared and is expressed in radians. The ratio of the stress to the strain is constant for a particular material, in accordance with Hooke's Law, and is expressed as

$$E = \frac{S/A}{\phi} \tag{72}$$

This constant E is called the *shear modulus of elasticity*, and is also known as the *coefficient of rigidity*. Since the angle of shear is a pure numeric, the unit in which the modulus is expressed is the same as that used for the stress.

Fig. 111 indicates how the angle of shear can be measured. A mirror is affixed to one end face of the block and a ray of light from

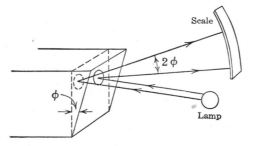

FIG. 111.   Measuring the angle of shear

a lamp is reflected by the mirror upon the scale shown. As the face of the block turns through an angle ϕ the reflected ray of light will be turned through 2ϕ (see § 394). If the scale is at a distance r from the mirror, and if the scale deflection due to shear is s, the angle $2\phi = s/r$. Consequently, measurements of r and s will determine the angle of shear ϕ.

As a numerical example, assume a cube of brass, having faces 5 × 5 cm., to be subjected to a shearing force of 12,000 kg. The angle of shear is observed by the lamp-mirror-scale arrangement just mentioned and the reflected beam is shifted a distance of 9.0 mm. along a scale which is located

3 meters from the mirror affixed to the cube. What is the shear modulus of brass? In this problem, the angle of shear is $\phi = \dfrac{s}{2r} = \dfrac{9.0}{2 \times 3000} =$ 0.0015 radian, and the shearing stress is $\dfrac{S}{A} = \dfrac{12{,}000 \text{ kg.}}{2500 \text{ mm.}^2} = 4.8 \text{ kg/mm.}^2$; therefore the shear modulus of brass is $E = 4.8 \div 0.0015 = 3200 \text{ kg/mm.}^2$

104. Elasticity of Volume (Bulk Modulus).—When a body is subjected to normal forces pressing all over its surface, it is said to be subjected to a *pressure*, the term pressure being defined as the force acting per unit area. Such pressure may be applied by submerging a body in a liquid, for the force due to the liquid will act perpendicularly to each portion of the surface, as described in the following chapter. Fig. 112 represents a cube of some material subjected to hydrostatic pressure, equal forces f acting normally on all its faces.

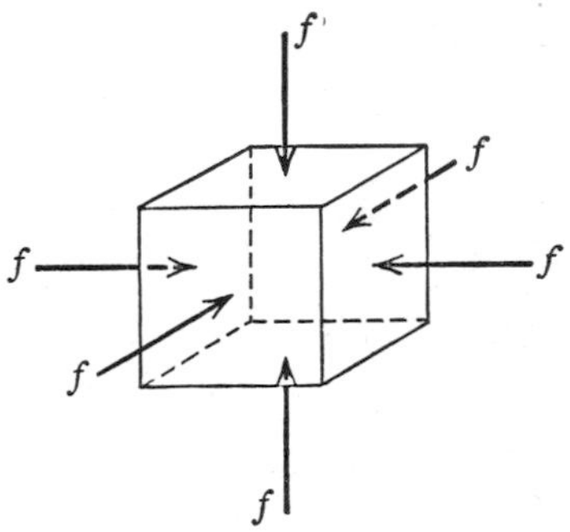

As the pressure on a body is increased, its shape remains unchanged but its volume decreases. A stress is set up within the material which is equal to the increase in pressure Δp. The corresponding strain is defined as the decrease of

FIG. 112. Equal forces acting on a cube in all directions

volume ΔV divided by the original volume V of the body; thus, strain is $\Delta V/V$. The ratio of the stress to the strain in this case is called the *bulk modulus of elasticity*, and is expressed as

$$B = \frac{\Delta p}{\Delta V/V} \tag{73}$$

The units in which the modulus B is expressed are the same as those used for the stress, since the strain is the ratio of two volumes or a numeric. This modulus is applied particularly to fluids; they offer resistance only to change of volume (§ 113) and so have only a bulk modulus of elasticity.

The reciprocal of the bulk modulus of a substance is known as the *compressibility* of that material. The bulk modulus of elasticity of steel is 18,000,000 lb. per sq. in.; therefore its compressibility is 0.000000055—meaning that an increase of hydrostatic pressure of 1 lb. per sq. in. would decrease a unit volume of steel by this amount.

105. Summary of Elastic Moduli.—In the foregoing, the three moduli of elasticity were all derived from Hooke's Law, the stress in all cases being measured in force units per unit area, and the strain in all cases being a ratio of two like dimensions and therefore a numeric; consequently the unit in which the modulus is expressed is the same as that used for the stress. The expressions used for elasticity of length, shape, and volume are summarized here for convenience of reference:

$$\text{Young's modulus} = \frac{\text{longitudinal stress}}{\text{change of length per unit length}} = \frac{F/A}{\Delta L/L}$$

$$\text{Shear modulus} = \frac{\text{shearing stress}}{\text{angle of shear}} = \frac{S/A}{\phi}$$

$$\text{Bulk modulus} = \frac{\text{increase of pressure}}{\text{decrease of volume per unit volume}} = \frac{\Delta p}{\Delta V/V}$$

Representative values of the stretch and shear moduli of several solids are given below in British and metric units:

Elasticity of Solids

Material	Young's Modulus		Shear Modulus	
	lb. per sq. in.	kg. per sq. mm.	lb. per sq. in.	kg. per sq. mm.
Aluminum.......	10,000,000	7,000	4,200,000	3,000
Brass...........	14,000,000	10,000	4,500,000	3,200
Copper (rolled)...	17,000,000	12,000	6,000,000	4,200
Glass (crown)....	10,000,000	7,000	3,600,000	2,500
Iron (cast).......	12,000,000	8,500	8,000,000	5,600
Steel (mild)......	30,000,000	21,000	12,000,000	8,500
Timber..........	1,400,000	1,000	140,000	100

Representative values of the bulk moduli of several liquids are tabulated on the next page.

Elasticity of Liquids

Material	Bulk Modulus	
	lb. per sq. in.	kg. per sq. mm.
Alcohol.........	163,000	114
Ether..........	87,000	61
Mercury........	4,000,000	2800
Water..........	310,000	220

106. Elasticity and Vibratory Motion.—In Chapter IX harmonic motion was defined as the motion of a body in which the acceleration and the restoring force are proportional to the displacement of the body from its equilibrium position. In this chapter it has been pointed out that an elastic body sets up a restoring force which is proportional to the displacement from its position of rest. Consequently when some part of an elastic body is displaced from its normal position, it will vibrate with harmonic motion about that position upon the removal of the displacing force. This vibratory motion will continue until the energy imparted to the body is completely dissipated in friction. The frequency of vibration of an elastic body, as well as the velocity at any point of its path, can be computed by applying the laws of harmonic motion, as given in §§ 93 and 94.

BEAMS AND RODS

*107. Bending of a Beam.—An important application of elasticity is the bending of a beam of uniform section. At first sight it might appear to involve the shear modulus, but usually the shearing effect is slight, and practically it is Young's modulus, rather than the shear modulus, that must be applied. The beam is regarded as composed of a number of longitudinal "fibers," some of which are in tension while others are in compression; the center line of the beam keeps its original length and is called the *neutral axis*. The outer lines concentric with the neutral axis are lengthened and the inner lines are shortened, consequently the outer fibers of the beam are in tension and the inner fibers are in compression. The greater the distance of a fiber from the neutral axis the greater will be the fiber stress. With excessive loading, the stress of the outer fibers may equal the breaking strength of the material; when this occurs the beam will fail by developing cracks along the outer edge and bulges along the inner edge.

In order to find the maximum fiber stress in a simple beam, assume the beam, supported at its ends A and B, to be uniformly loaded by vertical forces and bent into the form illustrated in Fig. 113. If this form is taken as circular it becomes a simple matter to determine the change of length of any fiber and then to calculate its strain; thereafter an application of Hooke's Law yields the stress in that fiber.

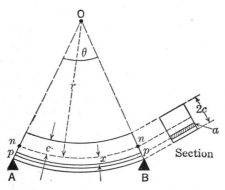

Consider a fiber pp at a distance x from the neutral axis nn, and let its cross-sectional area be represented by a. The original length of this fiber is the same as the original length of all fibers of this beam, and since the neutral axis remains

Fig. 113. Measuring the strain in a simple beam having a rectangular cross-section

unchanged, the original length of fiber pp is the length of the neutral axis in the diagram, namely $r\theta$, where r is the radius of the neutral axis and θ is the angle subtended at the center O by the beam. The length of fiber pp when bent is $(r + x)\theta$; therefore its change of length is $(r + x)\theta - r\theta = x\theta$. The ratio of this change of length $x\theta$ to the original length $r\theta$ of the fiber considered is the strain, namely x/r. The desired fiber stress F/a is now determined by using equation (71), which gives

$$\frac{F}{a} = Y\frac{x}{r} \tag{74}$$

The maximum fiber stress exists at the upper and lower edges of the uniform beam, and if the thickness of the beam is $2c$, the maximum stress is

$$S_m = \frac{Yc}{r} \tag{75}$$

Equation (74) shows that the stress at any cross-section of the beam at a distance x from the neutral axis is proportional to that distance; consequently the stresses may be plotted as in Fig. 114, the arrows showing the magnitudes and directions of the stresses at both sides of the section. It will be observed that the arrowheads lie on a straight line, and that these stresses collectively produce a torque about point N on the neutral axis, which torque is clockwise in the figure. Since the beam is at rest it is evident that this torque does not produce rotation of the beam about the section under consideration, consequently the torque must be balanced by the *bending moment of the external forces* acting at that section. The bending moment must equal the algebraic sum of the moments of the forces F acting on the section, and is obtained from equation (74) as

$$M = \Sigma Fx = \Sigma \frac{Yax}{r} \times x = \frac{Y}{r} \Sigma ax^2$$

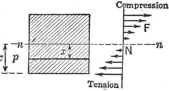

Compression

Tension

Fig. 114. Visualizing the bending stress at a cross-section of a beam under load

The summation Σax^2 is similar to the summation Σmr^2, which was defined in § 57 as the moment of inertia I of a mass about an axis. For this reason Σax^2 is spoken of as the *moment of inertia of cross-section*, and is also symbolized as I. Hence the bending moment at a section is given by

$$M = \frac{YI}{r}$$

From equation (75) the fraction $\dfrac{Y}{r} = \dfrac{S_m}{c}$, and consequently the maximum bending moment may also be expressed as

$$M = \frac{S_m I}{c} \tag{76}$$

where S_m is the maximum fiber stress at the upper and lower surfaces, c is the distance of the extreme fiber from the neutral axis, and I is the moment of inertia of cross-section about the neutral axis. The fraction I/c is called the *section modulus*.

The moment of inertia of cross-section of a rectangular-sectioned beam about its neutral axis is $\frac{1}{12}bd^3$, where b is the breadth and d is the depth of the beam ($d = 2c$), and it is usually stated in inches[4].

*108. Stress in a Simple Beam.—In determining the maximum stress in a simple beam it is necessary first to obtain the maximum bending moment of the external forces acting upon it. Consider a weightless beam of length l to rest on knife-edges at its ends and to support a single load W at the center, as shown in Fig. 115.   Each knife-edge would then exert a reaction of $W/2$ upon the end of the beam.   The conditions can be clarified by considering only half the beam (the shaded half) and regarding the left half embedded in a solid wall.   It is obvious that the bending

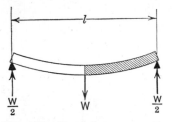

moment due to the load $W/2$ at the end will be a maximum at the wall, because the lever arm is the greatest possible; this moment equals

$$M = \frac{W}{2} \times \frac{l}{2} = \frac{Wl}{4}$$

FIG. 115.   Simple beam centrally loaded

It can be shown similarly that if the load on the beam is uniformly distributed, the maximum bending moment will be

$$M = \frac{W}{2} \times \frac{l}{4} = \frac{Wl}{8}$$

After this moment has been determined the maximum fiber stress can be computed by using equation (76).   The ultimate fiber stresses of various kinds of timber average from 4000 to 6000 lb. per sq. in., but the working stresses range from 800 to 1300 lb. per sq. in.   This allows a factor of safety of about 5.

As an illustration, determine the maximum stress in a timber joist 2 in. wide and 6 in. deep having a span of 9 ft., and bearing a uniform load, including the weight of the beam itself, of 120 lb. per linear foot.   In this problem, the maximum bending moment is $M = Wl/8$, the moment of inertia of the section is $I = \frac{1}{12}bd^3$, and the maximum stress is $S_m = Mc/I$. It follows that $M = 14,580$ lb-in., $c = 3$ in., $I = 36$ in.^{4}, and $S_m = 1215$ lb/in.^{2} This is the stress to which the upper and lower fibers of the rectangular-sectioned joist would be subjected.

*109. Twisting of a Rod.—In order to determine how much a rod of given material will twist when subjected to a certain torque, it is necessary to apply the shear modulus of elasticity of that material. Imagine a solid cylindrical rod fastened rigidly at its left end and twisted at its right end by a torque T in the direction shown in diagram I of Fig. 116.   An axial line AB drawn on the surface will then be shifted to a position such as AC, the angle of shift being indicated as ϕ; the radius OB of the right-hand cross-sectional area will be moved correspondingly to position OC, turning through an angle θ. The relation between the angle of shear ϕ and the angle of twist θ

can be obtained readily by considering the small arc BC (of length $R\theta$) also to be the arc of a circle having a center at A and a radius of $AB = l$. Then $R\theta = l\phi$, and the angle of shear becomes

$$\phi = R\theta/l$$

In considering the angle of shear previously (§ 103) as a measure of strain, it was applied to a block, and all parts of the block had the

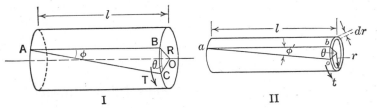

FIG. 116. Determining the stress and strain in a shaft under shearing forces

same stress and the same strain. This is not true for the cylindrical rod, and therefore it is necessary to consider the rod as made up of a series of telescoping tubes, and to ascertain their strains and stresses separately.

Imagine one such tube of mean radius r and of infinitesimal radial thickness dr, as shown in diagram II of Fig. 116, to be subjected to a torque t. An axial line ab on this tube will shift to position ac when the right-hand end of the tube twists through an angle θ. The line ab shifts through an angle ϕ', which is the angle of shear or the strain of the tube, and its value is $\phi' = r\theta/l$. This expression is similar to the foregoing one, but it involves the smaller radius r instead of the radius of the cylinder R which comprises the series of tubes.

Let f be the shearing force on the tube, acting over the entire end face, which has an area of $2\pi r\, dr$; then the shearing stress on this tube is $f \div 2\pi r\, dr$, and consequently the shear modulus, from equation (72), is

$$E = \frac{\dfrac{f}{2\pi r\, dr}}{\phi'} = \frac{\dfrac{f}{2\pi r\, dr}}{\dfrac{r}{l}\theta}$$

whence the torque twisting the tube is

$$t = fr = 2\pi r^3\, \frac{\theta\, dr}{l}\, E$$

The total torque T acting on the solid cylinder would then be the sum of a number of terms like the foregoing to include all tubes from the axis to the surface of the rod; such a summation is carried out by integration. Thus, the total torque becomes

$$T = \int_{r=0}^{r=R} 2\pi r^3 \frac{\theta}{l} E \, dr = \frac{\pi \theta E R^4}{2l}$$

This expression is used in computing the angular twist θ of a rod when its dimensions, its shear modulus E, and the applied torque T are known. When the dimensions are in inches and the modulus is in pounds per square inch, the torque will be in pound-inches.

MOMENTUM AND IMPACT

110. Momentum and Energy Relations During Impact.—The behavior of bodies during impact or collision was described in § 41, and the Law of Conservation of Momentum was introduced and illustrated. This law, to the effect that momentum cannot be destroyed, is universally true and applies to every collision. The energy transformations that take place during impact vary widely, however, depending upon the elasticity of the colliding bodies.

To illustrate the effect of elasticity, suppose a ball to be dropped upon a fixed level plate. If the ball were to rebound to its original height, the collision would be regarded as perfectly elastic; and if it did not rebound at all, the collision would be regarded as inelastic. Neither of these extremes would actually occur. Intermediate results can be expressed in terms of the speed of the ball after collision in comparison with that before collision. In general terms, the ratio of the relative speed of separation of two impacting bodies to their relative speed of approach is called the *coefficient of restitution* of the bodies. If this coefficient were 1, the colliding objects would be perfectly elastic, and if it were 0 they would be inelastic.

Impact between two bodies occurs in a very short interval of time, but in that brief period the bodies become deformed and a certain amount of energy is used to change their shape. The deformation of a golf ball when struck by a club is clearly evident in Fig. 47 of the earlier reference. With an elastic collision the energy used to produce a deformation is restored, but otherwise such is not the case. Hence, it may be said that for a collision between elastic bodies, the sum of their kinetic energies before impact equals the sum of their kinetic energies after impact. For collision between inelastic bodies, no such statement can be made.

It is interesting to note that, although the mass of a body is commonly regarded as fixed, advanced theory shows that when a body moves its mass changes, but the change is inappreciable except with very high speeds, approaching that of light, § 466. Hence, a more general statement of the expression for momentum would employ different symbols, m_f and m_o, to represent the final and initial values of the mass, and would become

$$Ft = m_f v_f - m_o v_o \qquad (77)$$

111. Illustrations of Momentum and Impact.—Elastic impact may be exemplified by collision between two blocks of steel which slide together on a smooth horizontal surface. It will be supposed that these bodies are perfectly elastic, which is a fairly close approximation, and that the impact is direct and central, § 41. The velocities of the blocks after impact can be found by the principles just outlined.

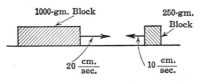

Fig. 117. Collision of elastic bodies

Suppose two blocks to be sliding together on a smooth level surface, as in Fig. 117. One block has a mass of 1000 gm. and a velocity toward the right of 20 cm. per sec.; the other has a mass of 250 gm. and moves toward the left at 10 cm. per sec. The velocities of the left and right blocks after impact will be designated respectively as v_1 and v_2. Since the total momentum of the two bodies is the same before and after impact, as stated in equation (32),

$$(1000 \text{ gm.})\left(20 \frac{\text{cm.}}{\text{sec.}}\right) + (250 \text{ gm.})\left(-10 \frac{\text{cm.}}{\text{sec.}}\right) = (1000 \text{ gm.})v_1 + (250 \text{ gm.})v_2$$

velocities to the right being considered positive. This expression when simplified becomes

$$4v_1 + v_2 = 70 \frac{\text{cm.}}{\text{sec.}}$$

Also, since the bodies are elastic, their total kinetic energy is the same before and after impact, whence,

$$\frac{1}{2}(1000 \text{ gm.})\left(20 \frac{\text{cm.}}{\text{sec.}}\right)^2 + \frac{1}{2}(250 \text{ gm.})\left(-10 \frac{\text{cm.}}{\text{sec.}}\right)^2$$
$$= \tfrac{1}{2}(1000 \text{ gm.})v_1^2 + \tfrac{1}{2}(250 \text{ gm.})v_2^2$$

which reduces to

$$4v_1^2 + v_2^2 = 1700 \left(\frac{\text{cm.}}{\text{sec.}}\right)^2$$

When the two simplified expressions are solved simultaneously, it is found that $v_1 = +8$ cm. per sec., and $v_2 = +38$ cm. per sec., showing that the small block reverses its direction, and moves to the right with a speed of 38 cm. per sec., while the large block follows behind it at 8 cm. per sec.

If the colliding bodies remain distorted after impact, or if there is other evidence of loss of energy, the collision is inelastic. This type of impact will be illustrated by a device known as the ballistic

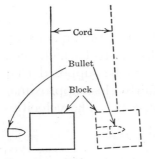

pendulum, which is sometimes used to determine the speed of a bullet. The bullet is fired horizontally into a stationary wood block suspended by a long cord, as shown in Fig. 118, and the resulting velocity is determined, usually by calculation based on the height to which the block swings. Although in this collision energy is wasted in tearing apart the fibers of the block, nevertheless the law of conservation of momentum holds; from this law the initial speed of the bullet can be obtained.

Fig. 118.   Measuring the
speed of a bullet

Suppose that a 10-gm. bullet, moving with a velocity v in the manner described, becomes embedded in a 20-kg. block of wood, the velocity of the block and bullet after impact being 25 cm. per sec. The combined momentum of the block and bullet is the same before and after impact; therefore, by equation (32),

$$(10 \text{ gm.})v + (20{,}000 \text{ gm.})(0) = (10 \text{ gm.} + 20{,}000 \text{ gm.})\left(25 \frac{\text{cm.}}{\text{sec.}}\right)$$

From this equation, v is found to be 50,025 cm. per sec., and this is accordingly the impinging velocity of the bullet.

*112. Angular Momentum.—The close analogy between linear and angular quantities has been repeatedly pointed out, and is further illustrated by the study of momentum. The *angular momentum* of a body is defined as the product of the moment of inertia of the body and its angular velocity, the similarity between this quantity and linear momentum being apparent. Just as an unbalanced force exerted upon a body for a certain time causes a change in its linear momentum, so an unbalanced torque T acting for a time t upon a body causes a corresponding change in its angular momentum, thus,

$$Tt = I_f\omega_f - I_o\omega_o \tag{78}$$

The product Tt is called an *angular impulse*. Equation (78) states that *an unbalanced angular impulse will cause a change in the angular momentum of a body,* and, moreover, that *these two quantities will be numerically equal.*

A rotating body which is not subjected to any angular impulse tending either to accelerate or to retard it, will consequently maintain a constant angular momentum. For example, a wheel or other rigid object turning without any friction would continue to rotate with undiminished speed. It is interesting to observe, however, that if it is possible to alter the moment of inertia of such a rotating body, its angular velocity will change in an inverse manner, so as to keep the product $I\omega$ constant. This effect can be illustrated by standing a man on a piano stool which has only a small amount of friction in its bearings and spinning him around a few times. If he extends his arms, thus increasing his moment of inertia, his speed will diminish; but if he draws the arms in to his sides, thereby reducing his moment of inertia, his speed of rotation will increase.

PROBLEMS

1. Fibers of spun glass are capable of sustaining unusually large stresses; a fiber 0.00035 in. in diameter was found to have a breaking strength of 0.385 oz. What is the breaking stress of this fiber?

2. A Monel-metal rod $\frac{3}{8}$ in. in diameter is subjected to a load of 2000 lb. by a testing machine. An 8-in. length of the rod is observed to increase in length by 0.0068 in. Compute Young's modulus of elasticity for Monel metal.

3. A hard-drawn copper wire having a diameter of 0.326 cm. is supported at one end and allowed to hang vertically; a load of 120 kg. is applied to the other end. The wire has an elastic limit of 2000 kg. per sq. cm. and a stretch modulus of 1,150,000 kg. per sq. cm. Will the wire return to its original length upon removal of the load? What elongation will take place per meter of length when the load is applied?

4. A steel wire 10 meters long and 1 mm. in diameter is subjected to a tension of 25 kg., and its elongation is observed to be 1.45 cm. Find the strain and the stress for the specimen, and also Young's Modulus for steel.

5. A load of 60 tons is carried by a vertical steel column having a length of 20 ft. and a sectional area of 10 sq. in. What decrease in length will this load produce if the elastic modulus is 30×10^6 lb. per sq. in.?

6. Rubber suitable for use in tension has a stretch modulus of 240 lb. per sq. in. for moderate elongations. A sheet of it 0.5 in. thick, 36 in. wide, and 60 in. long is stretched; what force will increase the length to 61 in.?

7. A copper cube measuring 2 in. along each edge is subjected to a pair of parallel shearing forces applied to its opposite faces. How large must each of these forces be in order to shear the block through an angle of 0.01°?

8. A square plate of metal 4 ft. on a side and $\frac{1}{2}$ in. thick is subjected to shearing forces which tend to twist the square surface into a rhombus. To apply these forces one edge is securely fixed, and a bar, fastened to the other edge, is pulled with a force of 150 tons. As a result the bar is observed to advance a distance of 0.057 in. in the direction of the pull. Find the shearing strain and the shearing stress of the plate, and also the coefficient of rigidity of the metal.

9. Calculate the bulk modulus of glycerine on the information that a liter of this liquid contracts 0.21 cu. cm. when subjected to a pressure of 10 kg. per sq. cm. What is the compressibility of glycerine expressed as the contraction per unit volume per unit of pressure?

10. The compressibility of turpentine is 79×10^{-6} per atmosphere of pressure (14.7 lb. per sq. in.). What is the bulk modulus of turpentine?

11. A cubical block of fused quartz, measuring 8 cm. on an edge, is subjected to a hydrostatic pressure of 50 kg. per sq. cm. What will be its reduction in volume if the bulk modulus of quartz is 1400 kg. per sq. mm.?

*12. A square steel rod 1 in. on a side is to be bent into the arc of a circle. What is the smallest radius to which it can be bent (cold)? Assume that the maximum stress is limited to 35,000 lb. per sq. in. and that the modulus of elasticity (stretch) is 30×10^6 lb. per sq. in.

*13. Find the dimensions of a horizontal timber beam that will carry the weight of three men (aggregating 500 lb.) at the center of a span of 14 ft. Allow a maximum fiber stress of 800 lb. per sq. in.

*14. A total load of 18,000 lb. (referred to as 18 "kips" by structural engineers) is distributed uniformly along a horizontal beam that has a span of 20 ft. What is the maximum bending moment of the beam?

*15. A steel shaft 18 in. in diameter and 30 ft. long is subject to a torque of 600,000 lb-ft. Compute the angular twist of the shaft.

*16. A steel rod 3 ft. long and $\frac{3}{4}$ in. in diameter is subjected to two torques, each of 20 lb-ft., applied at its ends in opposite directions. How much does one end twist with respect to the other?

*17. Calculate the torque per radian of twist for a hollow brass rod which is 10 ft. long and has diameters of 1.00 in. outside and 0.80 in. inside. What is the diameter of a solid brass rod for which the torque per radian of twist will have the same value?

18. An 8-gm. bullet is fired horizontally at 300 meters per sec. into a 10-kg. wood block resting on a smooth horizontal surface. Assume that the bullet stays embedded in the block and find the velocity of the two after impact.

19. A $\frac{1}{2}$-oz. bullet is fired with a speed of 1500 ft. per sec. and passes through a board 1 in. thick, emerging with a speed of 1000 ft. per sec. How much momentum did the bullet lose, and what average force did it exert upon the board?

20. A 40-lb. shell explodes while it is moving horizontally at 800 ft. per sec. Assume that it breaks into four equal fragments, that two of them fly away from each other horizontally at right angles to the direction of the shell with speeds of 1000 ft. per sec., and that the third is projected vertically

downward with a speed of 600 ft. per sec. What is the speed and direction of the fourth fragment?

21. Two elastic ivory balls, each of 200 gm. mass, are suspended by separate cords 30 cm. long, so that they rest in contact. One ball is then moved away as in a pendulum until its cord makes an angle of 60° with the vertical and is released. Find the velocity of this ball just before impact, and also the velocity of each ball after impact.

Liquids at Rest *Chapter XI*

113. The Liquid State.—Although most substances can be classified readily as to state; that is, as solid, liquid, or gaseous, the lines dividing these phases of a substance cannot always be sharply drawn. Thus, tar at ordinary temperatures can be fractured like a solid, and yet, to a slight extent, it flows like a liquid. Transitions frequently occur from one state to another, many solids becoming liquids when sufficiently heated, and liquids becoming solids when sufficiently cooled. Again, gases can be liquefied by sufficient cooling and compression, and liquids can be converted to gases by heating or, at ordinary temperatures, through the process of evaporation.

It is generally agreed that matter is composed of molecules which are in more or less violent agitation depending upon the temperature. In a solid the molecules are generally bound closer together than in a liquid, and their motion is more restricted, consisting of vibration over narrow ranges. In a gas the molecules are relatively far apart and move about with comparative freedom throughout the entire confining space. The liquid state is intermediate between the other two. Upon heating a solid, say a metal, the molecules become more violently agitated and less closely bound together; if the process is continued the metal will melt and become a liquid.

The outstanding characteristics of a liquid are that it conforms readily to the shape of any containing vessel and that it has a free surface. When the liquid is at rest this surface is horizontal except at its edges, § 125. Although liquids have elasticity of volume, they do not possess elasticity of length in the usual sense, and they have no elasticity of shape (Chapter X). A *perfect liquid* is defined as a substance which is incapable of exerting a shearing stress, and which, if not completely confined, presents a free horizontal surface when at rest. Most liquids do not conform exactly to this definition, but are able to exert small shearing stresses. This effect will be neglected for the present, and will be considered in the following chapter.

114. Liquid Pressure.—A liquid exerts a force against any surface with which it is in contact; the force per unit area is defined as pressure. Consequently pressure is measured in such units as pounds per square inch and dynes per square centimeter. In engineering practice, the term "pressure" or "total pressure" is frequently used with the meaning of "force," and the expression "unit pressure" or "intensity of pressure" is used to mean "pressure" as above defined. To avoid confusion, however, in the present consideration of this subject, the term "pressure" will be used to represent the force exerted per unit area. When a force F acts upon a plane area A, the corresponding pressure is $p = F/A$; and the force can therefore be expressed as

$$F = pA \tag{79}$$

The idea of *pressure at a point* is often found helpful in dealing with liquids. This term presupposes a small plane surface at the point in question, and is the ratio of the force ΔF exerted upon this surface to the area of the surface ΔA, as the surface is taken smaller and smaller, eventually becoming merely a point. To derive an expression for the pressure at a point, consider a surface of area ΔA placed horizontally at point P in Fig. 119. In this position it supports the column of liquid directly above it. This column of height h has a weight $\Delta F = hw\Delta A$, where w is the weight of the liquid per unit volume. Hence, the pressure at the point is $p = \Delta F/\Delta A$, or

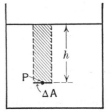

Fig. 119. Illustrating pressure at a point

$$p = hw \tag{80}$$

In British units, the pressure in pounds per square foot is the product of the depth in feet and the weight per unit volume of the liquid in pounds per cubic foot. Water weighs 62.4 lb. per cu. ft. and so the pressure at a point 100 ft. below the surface of water is 100 ft. $\times$ 62.4 lb/ft.^{3} or 6240 lb. per sq. ft.

In metric units, with which the absolute system is commonly used, the weight of the liquid per unit volume can be expressed more conveniently as $\dfrac{mg}{V}$ or dg, where $d = \dfrac{m}{V}$ is the density of the liquid (§ 12). Hence the pressure at the point P may be stated as

$$p = hdg \tag{81}$$

The pressure in dynes per square centimeter is the product of the depth in centimeters, the density of the liquid in grams per cubic centimeter, and the acceleration due to gravity, 980 cm/sec.^{2} The

density of water is 1 gm. per cu. cm. and so the pressure at a point
100 cm. below the surface of water is 100 cm. × 1 gm/cm.³ × 980
dynes/gm. or 98,000 dynes per sq. cm.

The density of a liquid does not change appreciably with pressure
because very large pressures yield only small percentage reductions in
volume; for this reason liquids are often regarded as incompressible.

The foregoing expressions give the pressure due to the liquid only;
if the total or *absolute pressure* is desired, the atmospheric or other
pressure on the surface of the liquid should be added to the value
found. Atmospheric pressure is discussed in Chapter XIII; it will
suffice here to record that its value is approximately 14.7 lb/sq. in.
or 1,013,000 dynes/sq. cm.

The pressure at a point due to a liquid is seen to be determined
completely by the depth of the point below the liquid surface and
the weight of the liquid per unit volume. This pressure is not
affected by the depth to which the liquid may extend below the point
in question, nor by the size or shape of the body of liquid in which the
point is located.

115. Direction of Force Due to Liquid.—*The force exerted by a
liquid at rest is normal to any surface with which the liquid is in contact.*
To show that this statement is correct, suppose the force to be in
some other direction, as in part I of Fig. 120, where *f*, the force

Fɪɢ. 120.   Force due to liquid is normal to surface

exerted by the liquid upon the wall at *P*, is (incorrectly) represented
as inclined to the normal. Under these circumstances *f* could be
resolved into two components *n* and *t*, these being respectively normal
and tangent to the wall. But the component *t* cannot exist, for it
tends to move the wall in the direction shown; if such a force existed,
the wall would exert a tangential force on the adjacent layer of
liquid. The liquid being unable to exert a shearing stress to oppose
this action would move in response to it, which is contrary to the
assumption that the liquid is at rest; hence the force *f* must be normal
to the surface. An experimental proof is indicated in part II of the

figure, where the liquid is observed to emerge normally through small openings made in various surfaces with which it is in contact.

It can also be shown that *the liquid pres-sure at a point is independent of direction.* To verify this statement, imagine a tiny wedge, of some material having the same density as the liquid, to be in equilibrium within it in the position shown in Fig. 121, under the action of the forces A, B, and C, exerted normally upon its faces having areas respec-tively a, b, and c. The force C can be resolved into a horizontal component $C \sin \alpha$ and a vertical component $C \cos \alpha$, where α is the

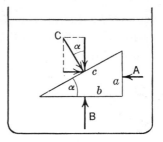

FIG. 121. Illustrating liquid pressure

angle indicated.   For equilibrium, $A = C \sin \alpha$ and $B = C \cos \alpha$. However, the areas are similarly related, for $a = c \sin \alpha$ and $b = c \cos \alpha$.   Hence $\dfrac{A}{a} = \dfrac{C \sin \alpha}{c \sin \alpha}$ and $\dfrac{B}{b} = \dfrac{C \cos \alpha}{c \cos \alpha}$; if the pressures be designated $\dfrac{A}{a} = p_a,$ $\dfrac{B}{b} = p_b,$ and $\dfrac{C}{c} = p_c,$ it follows that $p_a = p_b = p_c.$ Next, imagine the wedge to be taken smaller and smaller, eventually becoming a point; then the three forces will pass through a common point.   It is apparent that the same results would be obtained whatever the value of the angle α; consequently the pressure at the point is independent of direction.

116. Calculation of Force Due to Liquid.—The force due to liquid pressure on any plane submerged surface can be calculated from equation (79), $F = pA$.   For a horizontal surface, since the pressure is uniform throughout, p represents its value at any point.   For any other plane surface, *the same equation can be used, provided p represents the pressure at the center of the area subjected to liquid pressure.* This statement can be proved by imagining the surface to be divided into a number of elementary areas, upon each of which the pressure is substantially uniform; the fore-going expression may then be used to find the force on each individual area; and by adding the forces thus found, the total force can be obtained.

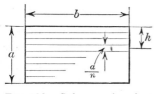

FIG. 122. Submerged surface divided into horizontal strips

Consider a vertical submerged rectangle of area ab, as shown in Fig. 122, with its upper edge in the surface of a liquid of which the weight per unit volume is w, and suppose it to be divided into n slender horizontal strips each of width $\dfrac{a}{n}$, located at depths h_1, h_2, h_3, $\cdots h_n$, below the surface of the liquid. The total force acting upon the surface will be the sum of the forces on the individual strips, thus:

$$F = h_1 w \frac{a}{n} b + h_2 w \frac{a}{n} b + \cdots + h_n w \frac{a}{n} b = \frac{wab}{n} \left[h_1 + h_2 + \cdots h_n \right]$$

The bracketed quantity consists of n terms, each greater than the preceding by an amount $\dfrac{a}{n}$, and thus forms an arithmetical progression, the sum of the series being

$$\left[h_1 + h_2 + \cdots h_n \right] = n \left(\frac{h_1 + h_n}{2} \right)$$

If the number of strips is very large, it can be assumed that $h_1 = 0$ and $h_n = a$. The sum of the series then becomes $n \left(\dfrac{0 + a}{2} \right) = \dfrac{na}{2}$ and accordingly the force is

$$F = \frac{wab}{n} \times \frac{na}{2} = \frac{wa^2 b}{2}$$

This value can be expressed as $F = \left(\dfrac{wa}{2} \right) A$, where $A = ab$ is the area of the rectangle. But the term in parenthesis represents the pressure at the center of this area, and thus the force exerted by the liquid on the surface is

$$F = pA$$

where p represents the pressure at the center of the area in contact with the liquid. Students familiar with calculus will be able to simplify the foregoing treatment by using the method of integration. Although this proof was based on a vertical rectangle with its upper edge located in the surface of the liquid, the same method of treatment may be applied to surfaces having any shape, located anywhere, and inclined at any angle, provided only that the surface considered is plane, so that the pressure upon it varies in direct proportion to the depth.

117. Some Illustrations.—In designing and building tanks, dams, retaining walls, and other structures used to confine liquids, it is necessary to know how much force the liquid will exert, in order that each surface may have the proper strength, weight, and bracing to withstand the applied load. In calculating such a force, the pressure is first determined, usually by equation (80), $p = hw$, and the force can then be found from equation (79), $F = pA$.

An interesting example appears in Fig. 123, which shows a cross-section of three tanks having bases of equal area, the tanks being

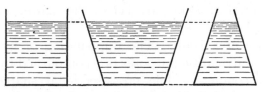

FIG. 123. Force on bottom of tanks is the same

filled with water to the same depth. The liquid will be found to exert the same force on the base of each tank, thus showing that the force does not depend on the shape of the tank.

Consider next the force exerted by a liquid on a rectangular sub-merged surface, either vertical as represented in Fig. 122 or inclined as shown in cross-section in part I of Fig. 124. The center of area, C, is midway between the top and bottom edges, at a depth h below the liquid surface; the pressure at this point multiplied by the area gives the force desired. This calculation gives the magnitude of the force, and since its direction is known to be normal to the submerged

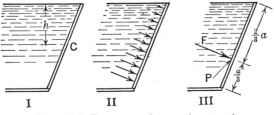

FIG. 124. Force on submerged rectangle

surface, there remains only to be found the point where the force is applied to the surface. This point is called the *center of pressure*. Such a point is easily located for a submerged *rectangle* which has its *upper edge in the surface of the liquid*. Although calculation gives a single value for the force acting upon the rectangle, it is known that the liquid actually exerts a series of parallel forces upon the surface, these forces increasing in proportion to the depth, as indicated in part II of the figure. Hence the calculated force F, which replaces this series of parallel forces, must be their resultant, and its line of action can be found by the method described in § 83. By working out a numerical example with ten or twelve forces, the student can locate the line of action approximately. With an infinite number of forces, calculus shows that the resultant acts two-thirds of the way down from the upper to the lower edge, when the upper edge of the rectangle lies in the liquid surface. The center of pressure of this rectangle is located at P in part III of the figure, wherein a is the slant height of the surface.

*118. Stability of a Dam.—The impounding of water for power, water supply and irrigation purposes is accomplished by dams, usually constructed of concrete. The cross-sectional shape of a dam is basically a right triangle with the vertical side in contact with water. Naturally, a dam is designed to resist sliding along its foundation as well as to resist overturning. These conditions of stability involve the principles of fluid pressure and equilibrium, and an example will emphasize their importance.

Consider a dam section having the dimensions shown in Fig. 125 and regard the width of the dam (perpendicular to the page) as 100 ft. for

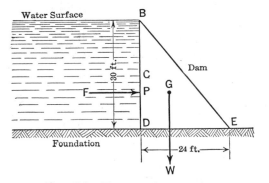

FIG. 125.   Forces acting on a dam

simplicity. With the water level at the top of the dam, the center of area C of the water face is halfway along BD, being 15 ft. below B. The water pressure at this point is $p = hw = 15$ ft. $\times$ 62.4 lb/cu. ft. $= 936$ lb/sq. ft. The resultant force of the water on the dam is $F = pA = (936 \text{ lb/sq. ft.}) \times 30$ ft. $\times 100$ ft. $= 2,808,000$ lb.; it acts perpendicularly to BD at point P, two-thirds of the way from B to D.

The density of concrete may be taken as 150 lb/cu. ft., hence the weight of the dam of this material is $W = \frac{1}{2}(30 \text{ ft.} \times 24 \text{ ft.}) \times 100$ ft. $\times 150$ lb/cu. ft. $= 5,400,000$ lb., and it acts at the center of gravity of the section at G. Then, if the coefficient of friction of the dam along its foundation is $\mu = 0.60$, the limiting force of friction (§ 49) will be 0.60 × 5,400,000 lb. = 3,240,000 lb. Since this force is greater than the force of 2,808,000 lb. exerted by the water, the dam will be safe against sliding.

To investigate the possibility of overturning the dam about the edge E, the moments of forces W and F are determined about this edge as axis. Since the center of area G is $\frac{2}{3}$ the distance from the vertex B to the midpoint of the base DE, the vector W will be 16 ft. from E. Consequently, the torque due to W is 5,400,000 lb. × 16 ft. = 86.4 × 10^6 lb-ft. counterclockwise. Similarly, the torque due to F is 2,808,000 lb. × 10 ft. = 28.08 × 10^6 lb-ft. clockwise. The factor of safety against overturning the dam is the ratio of these torques and amounts to over 3. It can be shown that the resultant of the forces F and W upon the dam will pass through the base DE, at a point 10.8 ft. from E.

Engineers do not regard concrete as satisfactory for use in tension unless reinforced by steel embedded in it. To eliminate the occurrence of tensile forces at the base of a dam without such reinforcement, the design should be such that the resultant force upon it will be directed through the middle third of the base.

119. Transmission of Pressure Change; Pascal's Principle.—A number of principles in the mechanics of fluids are associated with the name of the French philosopher, Blaise Pascal (1623–1662). One of these states that *an increase in pressure at any point in a liquid results in a like increase at every other point in the liquid.*

This principle is employed in the hydraulic press, as used for compressing goods into bales, for forming the lead sheathing upon electric cables, and the like. An elementary diagram of this device is shown in Fig. 126, which represents a confined body of liquid connecting two cylinders of areas a and A respectively, each fitted with a piston. Upon applying a force f to the small piston, a greater force F will be exerted by the large one, such that the pressures at the two pistons are equal, or $F/A = f/a$.

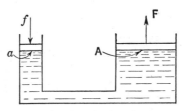

FIG. 126. The hydraulic press

By this means a large force, exerted through a small distance, may be obtained by exerting a small force through a large distance. The mechanical advantage of this machine may be computed as described in § 77.

Hydraulic brakes on automobiles operate on the principle of liquid pressure. A pressure or master cylinder is mounted near the fulcrum of the foot-brake pedal and is connected by copper tubing and flexible hose connections to cylinders at each of the four wheel brakes, the entire system being filled with non-freezing liquid. When foot pressure is applied, the piston of the master cylinder is forced inward, increasing the pressure on the liquid at that point; this increase of pressure is transmitted to the four wheel cylinders and their pistons are forced outward, causing the brake bands to tighten against the wheels.

120. Buoyancy; Archimedes' Principle.—It is well known that a stone can be lifted more easily in water than in air; that many objects float upon water; that a swimmer cannot sink in the Great Salt Lake; and that most metals will float upon mercury. These illustrations show that a liquid exerts an upward force upon a body placed in it. Archimedes (c. 287–212 B.C.), Greek mathematician and inventor, determined how much this buoyant force is. The principle known by his name states that *a body submerged wholly or partially in a liquid is buoyed up by a force equal to the weight of the liquid displaced.*

To show how this principle can be verified *experimentally*, suppose that a metal body, having for example a volume of 27 cu. cm. and a weight in air of 189 gm., is lowered into a vessel filled to the top with water. The body naturally displaces its own volume of water, and the overflow may be collected. The displaced water will be found to weigh 27 gm., and the apparent weight of the body when immersed in water will be found to be 162 gm. Thus, the apparent loss in weight, namely 27 gm., is the same as the weight of the liquid displaced.

Archimedes' Principle can be proved *theoretically* by calculating the buoyant force acting upon a submerged body and also calculating the weight of the displaced liquid, and noting that

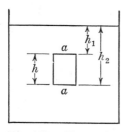

FIG. 127. Illustrating Archimedes' Principle

these quantities are equal. Consider a block of rectangular cross-section, having a height h and having top and bottom faces of area a, immersed in a liquid of which the weight per unit volume is w, as represented in Fig. 127. On the vertical faces, the liquid exerts horizontal forces which are balanced on all sides; on the top face it exerts a downward force h_1wa, and on the bottom face an upward force h_2wa. Since h_2 is greater than h_1, the liquid exerts a net upward force on the block amounting to $h_2wa - h_1wa = hwa$. However, the volume of the block, and hence that of the liquid displaced, is ha, and therefore the weight of the liquid displaced is hwa, which is identical with the buoyant force due to the liquid. Bodies of irregular shape may be considered as made up of a number of blocks as described; and so it may be said that any body submerged in a liquid is buoyed up by a force equal to the weight of the liquid displaced.

This principle is employed in the control of submarines. In submerging the boat, sea water is admitted into tanks and the effect of the buoyant force is reduced. The boat is brought to the surface by expelling the water from these tanks with compressed air or with pumps.

121. Density and Specific Gravity.—The *density* of a substance has already been defined in § 12 as the amount of matter per unit volume of the substance; that is, *density is mass per unit volume*, or

$$d = \frac{m}{V} \tag{82}$$

Density is usually expressed in pounds per cubic foot in British units, and in grams per cubic centimeter in metric units.

The specific gravity of a substance is the ratio of the density of the substance to that of water. This quantity is thus a pure numeric, and tells how many times a substance is as "heavy" (dense) as water. If a substance has a specific gravity of 5, one cubic foot of the substance has a mass of 5 × 62.4 or 312 lb. One cubic centimeter of

Specific Gravities

Liquids			Metals	
Benzene.......	0.89	(0° C.)	Aluminum, hard drawn	2.70
Glycerine......	1.26	(0° C.)	Brass...............	8.25– 8.70
Mercury.......	13.596	(0° C.)	Copper.............	8.80– 8.95
Oils, lubricating.	0.90–0.93	(20° C.)	Iron, gray cast.......	7.03– 7.13
Turpentine.....	0.873	(16° C.)	Lead................	11.34–11.36
Water, pure....	1.000	(4° C.)	Platinum............	21.50
Water, sea......	1.025	(15° C.)	Silver..............	10.4 –10.5
			Steel...............	7.82– 7.85
Woods			Uranium.............	18.7
Balsa wood...........	0.11–0.13			
Cedar................	0.49–0.57		*Miscellaneous*	
Cork.................	0.22–0.26		Diamond.............	3.5 –3.6
Lignum-vitae.........	1.17–1.33		Glass, common........	2.4 –2.8
Maple................	0.62–0.75		Ice..................	0.88–0.91
Oak.................	0.60–0.90		Kapok (in pillows)......	0.05–0.10
Pine.................	0.35–0.85		Masonry.............	1.85–2.3

this substance would have a mass of 5 × 1 or 5 gm. It will be noted that in the metric system of units, the specific gravity of a substance has the same numerical value as its density, since the density of water is 1 gm. per cu. cm. Density and specific gravity are independent of the size of the sample under test, and depend only upon the substance of which it is made. Some typical values of specific gravity are given in the table on the preceding page.

122. Measurement of Density.—The density of a solid can usually be determined by measuring its mass and its volume separately. The mass is obtained with an equal-arm balance, and the volume is found either from the dimensions of the body or by measuring the displacement it produces when submerged in water. With the mass and the volume known, the density follows from equation (82).

An indirect method which offers some advantages consists of weighing the body first in air and again when submerged in water, and using Archimedes' Principle to calculate the density from the data thus obtained.

Suppose, for example, that a body has a weight of 420 gm. in air and an apparent weight of 350 gm. when submerged in water. The buoyant force is 420 − 350 or 70 gm., and by Archimedes' Principle, this equals the weight of the water displaced by the body. Since 1 cu. cm. of water weighs 1 gm., neglecting slight variations due to temperature, it follows that the volume of the displaced water, and hence the volume of the body, is 70 cu. cm. As the mass of the body is 420 gm., and its volume is 70 cu. cm., its density is 420 gm. ÷ 70 cu. cm. or 6.0 gm. per cu. cm.

The density of a liquid can be determined by several methods. In one of these, a pyknometer or specific-gravity bottle of known weight is filled with the liquid and the mass is determined with an equal-arm balance. The volume of the container is usually known, or may be determined by another measurement using water, and the density of the liquid can then be calculated by a direct proportion. A second method for measuring the density of a liquid consists of weighing some solid body (1) in air, (2) when submerged in water, and (3) when submerged in the liquid under test; and calculating the density of the liquid by use of Archimedes' Principle.

In measuring the density of alcohol by the method just described, suppose that a body which weighs 420 gm. in air appears to weigh 350 gm. when submerged in water and 365 gm. when submerged in alcohol. The displaced alcohol has a weight of 420 − 365 or 55 gm. and a volume of 420 − 350 or 70 cu. cm.; and therefore the alcohol has a density of 55 gm. ÷ 70 cu. cm. or 0.79 gm. per cu. cm.

The density of a liquid can also be determined by means of a hydrometer, Fig. 128. It consists of a hollow glass chamber weighted at the bottom and having a graduated stem at the top. The hydrometer has a constant mass and when floated on a liquid sinks until it displaces its own weight of liquid (see following section); the "lighter" the liquid, the deeper it settles before coming to rest. By suitably calibrating the scale of this instrument, the specific gravity of the liquid can be read directly at the point where the stem projects through the liquid surface.

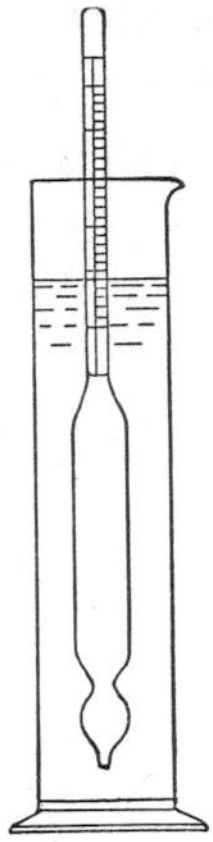

Still another method for determining the density of a liquid is that of balanced columns. In this method, illustrated in Fig. 129, the arms of an inverted U-tube are dipped respectively into water and into the liquid under test. When part of the air is removed from the tube through a valve at A, the two columns rise to heights h_w and h_x, which can be measured. Since there is the same

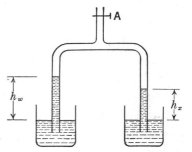

Fig. 128. Hydrometer

Fig. 129. Measuring density of liquid by balanced columns

difference in pressure between the top and bottom of each column, it follows that $h_w d_w g = h_x d_x g$, where d_w represents the density of water and d_x that of the liquid under test. From this equation, the value of d_x can readily be found.

123. Stability of Floating Bodies.—A floating body, as well as a submerged body, experiences an upward buoyant force equal to the weight of the liquid displaced, in accordance with Archimedes' Principle. A body floating at rest, moreover, is in equilibrium, and hence this buoyant force must be equal and opposite to the weight of the body. *A body which floats when placed in a liquid settles until it displaces its own weight of liquid.* A ship which displaces 20,000 tons of water also weighs this same amount. The forces acting upon such a ship are indicated in Fig. 130, where W represents the weight of the ship, acting downward through its center of gravity G, while B represents the equal buoyant force, which acts upward through C, the center of mass of the displaced water.

In order for a ship to be stable, it must tend to right itself when tipped to one side. Thus, the ship previously described is shown in

Fig. 131 in a tipped position. The weight W acts downward at G, as before, but the center of gravity of the displaced water is now shifted to C', at which point the upward force B acts. The forces B and W constitute a couple which tends to restore the ship to an upright position, and the ship is said to be stable. The stability of a ship is determined by the position of the *metacenter M*, this point being the intersection of two lines, one drawn vertically through the center of gravity of the displaced water, and the other being a line which was drawn vertically through the center of gravity of the ship when in an upright position. For stability, the design must be such that the

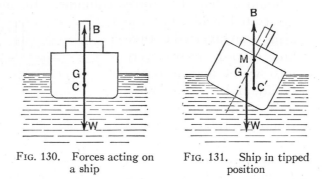

FIG. 130. Forces acting on   FIG. 131. Ship in tipped
a ship   position

metacenter is above the center of gravity of the ship, as in the figure, although in practice the *metacentric height MG* is kept reasonably small to provide riding comfort.

124. Molecular Motion and Molecular Forces.—There is experimental evidence to show that the molecules of a body are in a state of eternal motion, this motion being entirely erratic and irregular, and depending only upon the temperature of the substance. The molecules themselves are, of course, too small to be visible, and indirect methods must be used to study their motion. The first observations were made in 1827 by the English botanist, Robert Brown (1773–1858), who noted that very fine particles placed in suspension in a liquid move about in an irregular and life-like manner. This action he attributed to uneven bombardment of the particles by the moving molecules of the liquid, and this hypothesis has been amply borne out by further research and mathematical study. These erratic motions, termed Brownian movements, can be observed with a high-power microscope by viewing fine particles of insoluble carmine or some similar substance suspended in water and properly illuminated.

There is also evidence to show that as two molecules approach each other, a separation is reached where their combined potential energy is a minimum. In this condition, work is needed to move them either nearer together or farther apart, because of forces which are probably electrical. When molecules are very close together, these forces produce a tremendous repulsive effect, keeping the centers of the molecules at slight distances from each other. When the molecules are farther apart, the force becomes one of attraction; such forces are known to be very great. It is this molecular attraction, for example, that holds a solid body together, enabling it not only to retain its shape but also to support large external loads. The attraction between molecules of the same substance is called *cohesion*, while the attraction between molecules of unlike substances is called *adhesion*.

The attraction between two molecules falls off rapidly as their separation increases. It is therefore convenient for discussion to imagine a tiny sphere around each molecule, called its *sphere of action*, and to say that the molecule exerts an attractive force upon other molecules which lie within this boundary, but not upon those which lie outside of it. This conception of molecular attraction being limited by a sphere is entirely artificial, but is of value in indicating that the forces of cohesion and adhesion are very small except for molecules which lie close together. The sphere of action is usually considered as having a radius smaller than one-millionth of a centimeter.

125. Surface Phenomena.—The theory of molecular attraction explains the interesting behavior of a liquid surface. In Fig. 132, the line MN represents a free liquid surface, and A, B, and C represent molecules of the liquid, each surrounded by its sphere of action. The molecule A, which is well within the body of the liquid, will, on the average, be attracted equally in all directions by other molecules within its sphere of action, and its motion will be unaffected. The

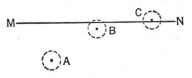
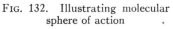

Fig. 132. Illustrating molecular sphere of action

molecule B, which is near the surface, will experience a downward force since there are more molecules in the lower half of its sphere of action than in the upper half. Similarly, the molecule C, which is represented just above the free surface, will be acted upon by a considerable downward force. Hence a molecule which in its motion tends to rise above the surface is pulled downward. The surface acts like a stretched membrane, tending to shorten itself as much as possible, and assumes at each point a direction at right angles to the resultant forces acting on the surface molecules. A small quantity of mercury poured upon a level surface does not spread out into a thin film, but assumes the shape of a sphere, except for a slight flattening due to gravity, because a sphere has the smallest surface for a given volume.

Again, the edges of a free liquid surface are usually curved, as in Fig. 133, in which the adhesive and cohesive forces acting upon a surface molecule of the liquid are shown. The force of adhesion *A*

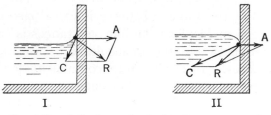

FIG. 133.   Adhesive and cohesive forces compared

exerted by the wall is perpendicular to its surface; the force of cohesion *C*, which is due to the surrounding molecules of liquid, has the general direction shown; and their resultant *R* is at right angles to the surface of the liquid. The shape shown in part I of the figure is characteristic of those cases where the liquid wets the wall, the adhesion between the liquid and the solid being greater than the cohesion of the liquid. Here any liquid molecules near the wall which happen to rise above the free liquid surface are pulled toward the wall by the force of adhesion, causing the liquid to pile up along the edge. When the liquid does not wet the wall, as in the case of mercury against glass, the adhesion is less than the cohesion, and the liquid surface curves downward as in part II of the figure. The *angle of contact* at the edge of a liquid surface is defined as the angle formed by the liquid surface and a vertical wall at the point of contact, measured within the liquid. The angle of contact varies with the substances used, being 0° between water and glass, 90° between water and silver, and 132° between mercury and glass, when pure liquids and clean surfaces are used.

126. Surface Tension and Capillarity.—It has been pointed out that the surface of a liquid tends to assume the smallest possible size, acting in this respect like a membrane under tension. This is illustrated in Fig. 134, which shows an enlarged view of the splash produced by a drop of milk falling upon a surface of that liquid, and reveals the rebounding droplets just before becoming detached spheres.

Any portion of the liquid surface exerts a tension upon adjacent portions or upon other objects with which it is in contact. This force

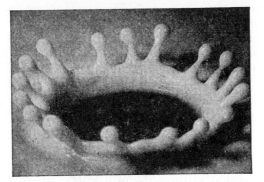

FIG. 134. Splash of a drop photographed in 1/100,000 second
(*Taken by Professors Edgerton, Germeshausen and Grier at Massachusetts Institute of Technology*)

is in the plane of the surface and its amount per unit of length is known as *surface tension*. Its value for water is about 75 dynes per cm. at ordinary temperatures. Thus, if a line 1 cm. long is imagined in the surface of water, the surface on either side of this line exerts a force of 75 dynes upon the surface on the other side.

Surface tension occurs not only at the free surface of a liquid, but also at the boundaries or interfaces separating two liquids. By way of illustration, the forces acting upon a drop of oil floating on hot water are shown in Fig. 135. The surface tension *A* of the water in contact with air tends to spread out the drop; while the surface tension *B* of the oil in contact with air, and the surface tension *C* of the oil in contact with water, tend to make the drop contract. Under the combined action of these forces, the drop assumes such a shape as to remain in equilibrium.

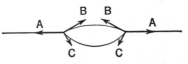

FIG. 135. Cross-section of oil drop showing forces on it

At lower temperatures, surface tension in general increases, although not equally for all substances. The drop shown in Fig. 135 spreads out into a thin film at ordinary room temperature because of the relatively great increase in the surface tension *A*. Some approximate values of surface tension, based on measurements at ordinary room temperature, appear in the accompanying table.

Surface Tensions of Some Liquids

	In contact with	Dynes/cm.
Benzene..........	air	29
Glycerine........	air	63
Mercury..........	air	470
Mercury..........	water	392
Olive oil..........	air	35
Olive oil..........	water	19
Water...........	air	75

The surface tension of a liquid may be measured by observing the force needed to pull an inverted U-shaped wire upward through the surface. Suppose that in order to pull a wire of length l through the surface a force F in excess of its weight is required, as indicated in part I of Fig. 136. As the wire leaves the surface a film of liquid

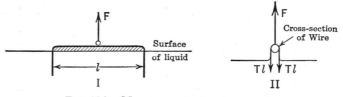

Fig. 136. Measurement of surface tension

becomes attached to it, which, having two surfaces, exerts a downward force on the wire amounting to $2Tl$, where T represents the surface tension of the liquid. These forces are shown in the sectional diagram forming part II of the figure. To move the wire uniformly, the applied force must balance the downward pull, hence,

$$F = 2Tl \qquad (83)$$

from which the surface tension can be found.

The rise of liquids in fine-bore tubes is a result of surface tension and is called *capillarity*. When a tube of small radius r is dipped into a liquid which wets it, a concave meniscus is formed, and the adhesion of the glass, being equal and opposite to the surface tension T of the liquid, has a vertical component $T \cos \theta$ which pulls directly upward on the liquid. As a result, the liquid rises in the tube as shown in

Fig. 137. Its elevation h will be such that the total upward force, which is $T \times \cos\theta \times 2\pi r$, just balances the weight of the column of liquid, which is $\pi r^2 h d g$, d being the density of the liquid and g being the acceleration due to gravity. From this fact the capillary rise of the liquid can be determined.

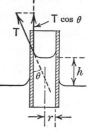

FIG. 137. Rise of liquid in small tube

*127. Diffusion and Osmosis.—When two miscible liquids which do not react chemically are placed in the same vessel, the molecular motion of each makes it penetrate the other, and by a slow process called *diffusion*, the liquid eventually becomes uniform throughout. The rate of diffusion increases with increased concentration and with higher temperatures. Diffusion may be observed, for example, between a solution of copper sulfate in the lower part of a glass jar and a solution of zinc sulfate carefully poured upon it. At first the liquids remain separated, with the denser copper sulfate solution at the bottom, as would be expected from the usual laws of liquids at rest; but gradually the sharp boundary between them disappears, and the liquids mix by diffusion.

Sometimes a liquid is able to pass through a membrane, presumably as a result of the bombardment of the membrane by the moving molecules of the liquid. Moreover, some membranes are selective in their action, allowing certain molecules to pass through them, but preventing others from doing so. Thus, a piece of animal membrane, such as parchment, when placed in contact with a sugar solution, permits the passage of the water molecules, but not of the larger and more complex sugar molecules. Such a process is called *osmosis*, and the membrane is termed a *semi-permeable* membrane.

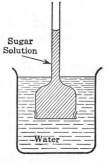

FIG. 138. Illustrating osmotic pressure

This action may be illustrated by the apparatus shown in Fig. 138, which represents an inverted thistle tube closed with a parchment membrane, the tube containing a small quantity of sugar solution, and the whole being dipped into a beaker of water. By molecular bombardment, the water molecules pass through the membrane in both directions, but more of them move upward than downward in a given time, since part of the upper surface of the membrane is obstructed by the sugar molecules inside the tube. As a result, the liquid rises in the tube, and the concentration of the sugar solution is reduced. An increased pressure being established within the tube, the rate at which the water molecules pass downward through the membrane is increased. Moreover, the reduced concentration of the sugar solution exposes more of the upper surface of the membrane, which also increases the rate at which the water molecules pass downward. When the upward and downward rates become equal, a state of equilibrium results, at which the pressure of the solute particles against the membrane has some maximum value determined by the conditions of the experiment. This pressure value is termed the *osmotic pressure.*

Osmotic pressure depends upon the solution used and upon its concentration; it increases with temperature and is independent of the material of the semi-permeable membrane. Osmosis is known to be an important factor in animal and vegetable life, owing to its influence on the transfer of liquids through membranes.

PROBLEMS

1. (*a*) Calculate the liquid pressure in pounds per square inch at a point 1 ft. below the surface of water. (*b*) Calculate the pressure in kilograms per square centimeter at a point 1 meter below the surface.

2. The depth in water to which a man can safely go in a diving suit is estimated to be 40 fathoms (1 fathom = 6 ft.). Compute the liquid pressure at this depth in sea water.

3. In 1934 Professor William Beebe reached a depth of 3028 ft. below the surface of the sea in his "bathysphere," and now Professor Auguste Picard plans to dive to a depth of 12,000 ft. in his "bathyscaphe." Calculate the liquid pressures at these depths.

4. A cubical tank measuring 4 ft. along each edge rests on one face and is filled with water. Calculate the liquid pressure on the base and also the force which the water exerts on the base.

5. The pressure in a water main is 80 lb. per sq. in. higher than that outside. To what static head of water is this pressure equivalent?

6. The pressure of a gas within a closed tank is 1 kg. per sq. cm. above that of the atmosphere. What head of water would yield the same pressure?

7. Calculate the force exerted by the water on one of the side walls of the tank described in Problem 4.

8. A tank suitable for use in testing tires for leakage has an open top, sides which are parallel and vertical, and ends which slope outward making an angle of 120° with the horizontal bottom. The tank is 12 in. wide and is filled with water to a depth of 9 in. Compute the force which the water exerts on one end of the tank.

9. A meter stick of negligible weight carries ten loads, 10 gm. being applied at the 5-cm. mark, 20 gm. at the 15-cm. mark, 30 gm. at the 25-cm.

mark, and so on up to 100 gm. at the 95-cm. mark, this loading being some-what like that on the underwater surface shown in part II of Fig. 124. At what point will the meter stick balance in equilibrium? and what reaction will it experience there?

10. A closed metal drum 3 ft. in diameter and 4 ft. high stands with its axis vertical, and from its top a pipe 1 in. in diameter extends to a height 6 ft. above the top of the tank. When the drum and the pipe are full of water, what force does the water exert upon the bottom of the tank?

11. A rectangular water gate 4 ft. wide and 10 ft. high is hinged along its top edge. The water on one side of the gate extends to a level 3 ft. below the hinge and on the other side to a level 8 ft. below the hinge. Compute the net torque due to the water tending to turn the gate on its hinge.

*12. A dam has a length of 30 ft. and a vertical height of 15 ft. Its cross-section is a right triangle of 9-ft. base. Assume that water extends to the top of the dam, in contact with its sloping surface, and calculate the force tending to slide the dam off its foundation; find also the torque tending to overturn the dam.

*13. A concrete dam has a vertical height of 40 ft. Its cross-section is a right triangle of 30-ft. base. Water stands behind the dam in contact with its vertical surface to an elevation 7 ft. below the top. Calculate per foot of length (a) the moment due to the water tending to overturn the dam, and (b) the moment due to the weight of the dam tending to prevent over-turning. Take the density of concrete as 150 lb. per cu. ft.

14. A hydraulic press has one piston 2 in. and the other 12 in. in radius. What force must be applied to the smaller piston to make the larger piston exert a force of 10,000 lb.? If the smaller piston is operated by a lever, what mechanical advantage must the lever possess in order that the operator need exert only 50 lb.?

15. Calculate the volume of a block of metal which weighs 461 gm. in air and has an apparent weight of 404 gm. when immersed in water. Find also the specific gravity of the metal.

16. A certain glass ball which weighs 240 gm. in air appears to weigh 150 gm. when immersed in water and 160 gm. when immersed in turpentine. Calculate the density of the glass and the density of the turpentine.

17. In order to buoy up his free-floating bathyscaphe for deep-sea exploration, Professor Auguste Picard plans to use a "float" consisting of 1000 cu. ft. of gasoline. If the specific gravity of this liquid is 0.74, how much load will it support in addition to its own weight when immersed in sea water?

18. A glass tube, closed at one end, is 40 cm. long, weighs 60 gm. and has an overall cross-section of 10 sq. cm. The tube is made to float upright in water by placing 300 gm. of lead shot in it. How much of the tube will project above the surface of the water?

19. The method of balanced columns illustrated in Fig. 129 is used to determine the specific gravity of benzene, a water column 4.8 cm. high balancing a column of benzene 5.4 cm. high. Find the specific gravity of

benzene, and find also the pressure in the communicating tube above the columns.

20. A hydrometer has a volume of 18.0 cu. cm. up to the reference mark at which it floats in water, and its stem has an external diameter of 6 mm. How much higher will the instrument float in sulfuric acid of specific gravity 1.200?

21. A block of wood floating on water is pushed down more and more, but is released before it becomes completely submerged. Show that the restoring force then acting upon it is proportional to its displacement, and that consequently the block will vibrate up and down with harmonic motion.

22. A plank 3 in. thick, 1 ft. wide, and 5 ft. long, floats on water with two-thirds of its volume below the surface. Find the weight of the plank.

23. A ship has a horizontal cross-section at her water line of 12,500 sq. ft. How much deeper will she ride in sea water when carrying an additional load of 400 tons? Assume that the sides of the ship are vertical at the water line.

24. Compute the volume of a submarine which displaces 1300 tons of sea water when completely submerged. If 45 tons of water are blown out of its tanks, how much of its volume will project above the surface?

25. The working surfaces of Johansson's gage blocks are plane within a fraction of a millionth of an inch. Two such blocks, each having surfaces measuring 0.70 x 0.70 in., when twisted tightly together, resisted a pull of 100 lb. without coming apart. With what force were the blocks held together (*a*) because of atmospheric pressure? (*b*) because of molecular attraction?

26. A fine wire formed into a loop of 1-cm. radius is placed horizontally in a liquid and then pulled slowly upward through the liquid surface. If this action requires a force of 465 dynes in addition to the weight of the wire, what is the surface tension of the liquid?

27. A glass tube open at the ends and having a bore 0.6 mm. in diameter is placed vertically in a dish of mercury. Compute the depression of the mercury within the tube.

28. A sample of glycerine is found to rise 2.05 cm. in a glass tube of 1-mm. bore by capillary action. Take the specific gravity of glycerine as 1.26 and its angle of contact against glass as 0°. Compute the surface tension of glycerine.

Liquids in Motion   *Chapter XII*

128. Types of Liquid Pumps.—Liquids may be raised from one level to another by means of pumps. In this process the liquid gains potential energy with respect to its initial level, and this energy is supplied by the pump. An expression for this energy can be found by supposing that an open-top tank containing liquid is equipped at the bottom with a cylinder having a tight-fitting piston of area A, as shown in Fig. 139, and that work is done in pushing the piston inward a distance s by the application of a force F. The force required is $F = pA$, where p is the liquid pressure at the pump, and hence the work done is $E = Fs = pAs$. During this stroke of the piston the quantity of liquid pushed from the cylinder into the tank has a volume

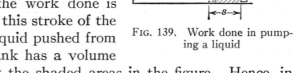

FIG. 139. Work done in pumping a liquid

$V = As$, represented by the shaded areas in the figure. Hence, in forcing this volume of liquid into a region where the pressure exceeds that of the atmosphere by p, the work done is

$$E = pV \tag{84}$$

In order that the pump indicated in Fig. 139 may force more and more liquid into the tank during successive strokes, valves must be fitted into the piston or cylinder so that a new supply of liquid will be furnished for each stroke. The so-called lift pump and force pump accomplish this in the manner shown in Fig. 140. In the *lift pump*, while the piston is being drawn upward, valve 1 is closed and valve 2 open, and the pressure is lowered in the cylinder and pipe below it. Liquid rises into this space because of atmospheric pressure on the water surface below. When the piston is pushed downward, valve 2 closes and the imprisoned liquid passes through valve 1 to the upper portion of the cylinder. Upon the next upstroke the cylinder fills with liquid again through valve 2, and the liquid above the piston flows out of the spout into the elevated tank *U*. The operation of the *force pump* can be described similarly, the liquid first being drawn into the cylinder by suction, after which it is forced to any desired height. In raising water, valve 2 of either pump must

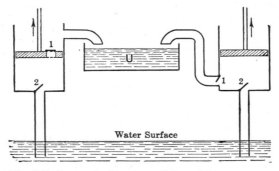

Fig. 140. Lift (or suction) pump at left and force pump at right

be less than 34 ft. above the water surface, because atmospheric pressure cannot support a column of water higher than this.

Another form of pump depends for its operation upon centrifugal force. In the *centrifugal pump*, water enters at the center of a rotating wheel, or impeller, provided with radial blades. As the blades revolve, the water is thrown outward into the watertight housing of the pump, and thence into the discharge pipe.

129. Velocity of Efflux.—Liquid flowing through an orifice gives up potential energy and gains an equal amount of kinetic energy, if no waste is assumed to occur in the process. From this fact, the velocity of efflux can be calculated. Consider a thin layer of liquid having a mass *m* and located in the liquid surface, at an average distance *h* above the orifice, as shown in Fig. 141. When an equal

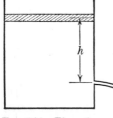

Fig. 141. Flow through an orifice

quantity *m* of liquid has flowed from the tank, this top layer has disappeared, and the potential energy is consequently reduced by an amount *mgh*. If the velocity of efflux is *v*, the gain in kinetic energy is $\frac{1}{2}mv^2$, whence

$$mgh = \tfrac{1}{2}mv^2$$

from which the velocity of the issuing stream is found to be

$$v = \sqrt{2gh} \qquad (85)$$

This result shows that, since the acceleration due to gravity may be regarded as constant, the velocity is dependent only upon the height of liquid above the orifice, and is proportional to the square root of this height.

To illustrate this relationship, consider a tank with an orifice 4 ft. below the liquid surface. The liquid will flow through the opening with a velocity of

$$v = \sqrt{2 \times 32 \frac{\text{ft.}}{\text{sec.}^2} \times 4 \text{ ft.}} = 16 \text{ ft. per sec.}$$

The volume of liquid discharged per unit time through an orifice can be calculated by geometry. Imagine an incompressible liquid flowing normally through an orifice of area A sq. cm. at a speed of

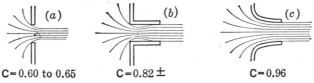

C=0.60 to 0.65   C=0.82±   C=0.96

Fig. 142. Types of orifices and their coefficients of discharge

v cm/sec.; the amount discharged in one second would fill a cylinder v cm. long and A sq. cm. in cross-section. Therefore, the volume discharged per second is

$$Q = Av \tag{86}$$

This expression may also be used to calculate the rate of flow past a point in a pipe line.

The actual efflux velocities will be somewhat smaller than given by equation (85) because of friction. Also, the actual discharge will be smaller than given by equation (86), because of the contraction of the jet due to stream-line flow. To find the actual discharge, the theoretical value obtained from equation (86) is multiplied by a coefficient of discharge, C. Values of the discharge coefficient, based on experimental test, are given in Fig. 142 for some orifices.

*130. Power from a Stream.—The water power which can be obtained from a stream depends upon the distance through which the water can fall, and upon the quantity of water available. The difference in elevation between the input and output water levels is termed the *head* of water. When 1 cu. ft. of water falls 1 ft., 62.4 ft-lb. of potential energy are transformed to kinetic energy, and consequently if Q cu. ft. of water drop per second through a head of h ft., energy is converted at the rate of 62.4 Qh ft-lb. per sec. By § 73 this rate of doing work may be stated in horsepower as

$$P = \frac{62.4Qh}{550}$$

The value of Q can be estimated for a proposed water-power development from equation (86), by measuring the velocity of the stream from observations of a body floating downstream and by measuring the cross-section of the stream from observations of width and depth at various places.

The power of the stream, as expressed by the foregoing equation, is made available by turbines, but in the transformation some energy is wasted by hydraulic and mechanical friction. For impulse wheels the best efficiency is about 82 per cent for all sizes, while for reaction turbines the efficiency ranges from 80 to 90 per cent with large sizes and from 60 to 80 per cent for small units.

131. Energy of a Moving Liquid; Bernoulli's Theorem.—When a liquid flows from one place to another it may undergo a change in

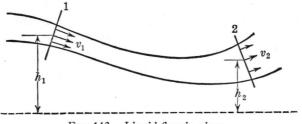

Fig. 143. Liquid flow in pipes

potential energy or in kinetic energy, but if it moves without waste of energy due to friction, then its total energy remains unchanged, in accordance with the law of conservation of energy. Consider a liquid to flow steadily through a tube of any section as illustrated in Fig. 143, and imagine that the liquid is incompressible and frictionless. Suppose further, that the motion is sufficiently slow to permit of stream-line flow, that is, flow without wasteful turbulence or eddies, and for simplicity regard the velocity at any cross-section to be uniform throughout that section. During a short interval of time, particles of liquid at section 1 and at section 2 will move as indicated by the arrows. Let the cross-sectional areas at these sections be respectively A_1 and A_2, the corresponding velocities of the liquid be v_1 and v_2, the elevations of the sections above a convenient datum plane be respectively h_1 and h_2, and the pressures of the liquid, as measured by manometers (§ 138) or pressure gages, be respectively p_1 and p_2.

Then since the liquid is incompressible, the same mass m will pass any section of the tube in a given time t; the volume of this mass will be $V = m/d$, where d is the density of the liquid. As this mass passes section 1 an amount of work $p_1 V$ or $p_1 m/d$ is done upon it by the oncoming liquid at the left, in accordance with equation (84); likewise at section 2 it will do work amounting to $p_2 m/d$ on the outgoing liquid at the right. The net work done by the mass m of liquid is $p_2 m/d - p_1 m/d$, and this must equal the reduction in its potential and kinetic energy as it moves from section 1 to section 2. In mathematical form:

$$\left(mgh_1 + \frac{1}{2} mv_1{}^2 \right) - \left(mgh_2 + \frac{1}{2} mv_2{}^2 \right) = p_2 \frac{m}{d} - p_1 \frac{m}{d}$$

When the terms are rearranged and each is divided by mg, the corresponding expression *per unit weight* of liquid becomes

$$h_1 + \frac{v_1{}^2}{2g} + \frac{p_1}{dg} = h_2 + \frac{v_2{}^2}{2g} + \frac{p_2}{dg} \tag{87}$$

These quantities are spoken of by engineers as follows: $h = $ *elevation head*, $\dfrac{v^2}{2g} = $ *velocity head*, and $\dfrac{p}{dg} = $ *pressure head*, and the sum of the three is called *total head*. If the pressure is determined by some height of liquid, say h', in a manometer tube, then $p = h'dg$, and the pressure head becomes h'. It may therefore be merged with the first term, reducing the equation to

$$H_1 + \frac{v_1{}^2}{2g} = H_2 + \frac{v_2{}^2}{2g} \tag{88}$$

where $H = h + h'$ is now the head due to elevation and pressure.

The law dealing with liquid flow expressed by equations (87) and (88) was proposed by Daniel Bernoulli (1700–1782). Bernoulli's Theorem states that *as an incompressible fluid flows, the total head remains unchanged*. It is supposed that waste of energy by friction is negligible and that no pressures are generated, as by pumps or turbines, in the region considered.

This relation shows that when a liquid speeds up in going from any position (1) to another position (2), then its head due to elevation or pressure decreases; in the notation used in the foregoing treatment, if $v_2 > v_1$, then $H_2 < H_1$, and vice versa. It should not be thought, however, that if the velocity is doubled the head due to elevation or pressure will be halved. This may be illustrated by a typical problem.

Water flowing at 100 cm. per sec. in a region (1), where the pressure is 2,000,000 dynes per sq. cm., passes through another region (2) at the same level where its speed is increased to 300 cm. per sec. Find the pressure in region (2). Rearrange equation (88) to read $H_1 - H_2 = \dfrac{v_2{}^2 - v_1{}^2}{2g} =$

$$\frac{\left(300 \dfrac{\text{cm.}}{\text{sec.}}\right)^2 - \left(100 \dfrac{\text{cm.}}{\text{sec.}}\right)^2}{2 \times 980 \dfrac{\text{cm.}}{\text{sec.}^2}} = 40.8 \text{ cm.} \quad \text{But } H_1 - H_2 = \frac{p_1 - p_2}{dg} \text{ and there-}$$

fore $p_1 - p_2 = 40.8 \text{ cm.} \times \dfrac{1 \text{ gm.}}{\text{cm.}^3} \times 980 \dfrac{\text{dynes}}{\text{gm.}} = 40,000 \dfrac{\text{dynes}}{\text{cm.}^2}$. Conse-

quently, the pressure in region (2) is only slightly less than that in region (1), namely 2,000,000 − 40,000 = 1,960,000 dynes per sq. cm.

Bernoulli's Theorem also explains in a qualitative manner a number of phenomena about the behavior of liquids which at first seem strange. Suppose two ships are steaming side by side in still water; the relative motion of the ships with respect to the water would be the same as if the ships were stationary and the water flowing with the same speed in the opposite direction. Fig. 144 shows that the water entrapped between the ships will speed up because of the narrower space. In conse-

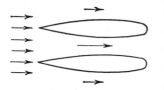

Fig. 144. Attraction of ships moving in the same direction

quence the pressure in the water between the ships will be reduced and will become less than the water pressure on the far sides of the ships. The excess pressure will cause the ships to come closer and closer together. The application of Bernoulli's Theorem to gases is discussed in § 143.

*132. Measurement of Liquid Flow.—The theorem of Bernoulli provides a means for measuring the flow of a liquid through a pipe. A horizontal section containing a constriction or throat is inserted in the pipe line and the pressures are measured both at the throat and in the pipe by pressure gages or their equivalent. Fig. 145 shows the arrangement employing small tubes called manometers, in which the rise of liquid indicates the pressure. The pipe beyond the throat flares out slowly so that the velocity of the liquid can be reduced without disturbing stream-line flow.

Since the velocity of the liquid is greater at the throat than in the pipe, the pressure at the throat will be less than that in the pipe, as demanded by equation (88), and consequently the liquid in the throat manometer will not rise as high as in the pipe manometer. The difference in manometer elevations together with a knowledge of the cross-sections of pipe and throat permit the liquid flow to be measured. This device is known as a *Venturi meter.*

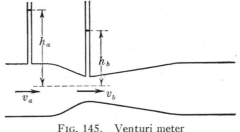

FIG. 145. Venturi meter

Let the cross-sectional area of the pipe be A and that of the throat be B. Further, let the velocities at these places be v_a and v_b respectively, and the heads be h_a and h_b respectively. Then from equation (88) for a frictionless liquid

$$h_a + \frac{v_a{}^2}{2g} = h_b + \frac{v_b{}^2}{2g}$$

Since the liquid may be regarded as incompressible,

$$Av_a = Bv_b$$

Next, eliminate v_b between these equations:

$$h_a + \frac{v_a{}^2}{2g} = h_b + \frac{A^2}{B^2} \times \frac{v_a{}^2}{2g}$$

Transpose and multiply by $2g$:

$$\left(\frac{A^2}{B^2} - 1 \right) v_a{}^2 = 2g(h_a - h_b)$$

Therefore the velocity of discharge is

$$v_a = \sqrt{\frac{2g(h_a - h_b)}{(A^2/B^2) - 1}}$$

But the rate of discharge is $Q = Av_a$, and if the difference in head $h_a - h_b$ be designated by the single symbol h, the volume of liquid discharged per unit time is

$$Q = A \sqrt{\frac{2gh}{(A^2/B^2) - 1}} \tag{89}$$

The actual discharge of a Venturi meter is less than that obtained by using equation (89); with large tubes carrying water, the actual discharge may be 98 or more per cent of the theoretical value just given.

As a numerical example, compute the discharge of water through a Venturi meter having a pipe diameter of 12 in. and a throat diameter of 6 in., the water pressure in the pipe and in the throat being 20 and 17 lb. per sq. in. respectively. Here the pressure difference can be expressed as an equivalent head from equation (80), $p = hw$, whence

$$h = \frac{p}{w} = \frac{(20 - 17)\dfrac{\text{lb.}}{\text{in.}^2} \times 144 \dfrac{\text{in.}^2}{\text{ft.}^2}}{62.4 \dfrac{\text{lb.}}{\text{ft.}^3}} = 6.93 \text{ ft.}$$

$$A = \frac{\pi}{4}\text{ft.}^2 \qquad \frac{A}{B} = \frac{\pi/4}{\pi/16} = 4 \qquad \frac{A^2}{B^2} = 16$$

Hence the discharge is

$$Q = \frac{\pi}{4}\text{ft.}^2 \sqrt{\frac{2 \times 32 \dfrac{\text{ft.}}{\text{sec.}^2} \times 6.93 \text{ ft.}}{16 - 1}} = 4.27 \text{ cu. ft. per sec.}$$

The flow of liquids is also measured in practice by the use of standard orifices, current meters, Pitot tubes, and weirs; these devices are described in books on Hydraulics.

*133. Viscosity of Liquids.—The property of a liquid that presents a resistance to flow is called *viscosity*. If two beakers, one containing some oil and the other some alcohol, are tilted from side to side, much less mobility is observed in the oil than in the alcohol, and the oil is said to be the more viscous of the two liquids.

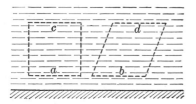

Fig. 146.   Shearing action in a liquid

When a liquid flows over a flat surface, the layer of liquid particles in contact with the surface remains stationary because of adhesion, the next layer of particles moves slowly over the first, the third layer moves with respect to the second, and so on, the speed of each layer increasing with its distance from the solid surface. This distribution of speed causes a portion of the liquid that is cubical in shape at one instant to become rhomboidal at a later instant, as illustrated in Fig. 146. The layer of liquid forming the lower face of the cube travels from a to b while the upper face travels from *c* to *d*. If the speed of the upper face exceeds that of the lower face by the amount *v*, and if the vertical distance between these faces is *h*, the liquid may be looked upon as shearing at the rate v/h, and this rate will be constant as long as the shearing stress to which the liquid is yielding remains unchanged.

The shearing stress acting on the cubical portion of the liquid in Fig. 146 is measured by the force per unit area of the upper (or lower) face, and can be represented by F/A. Experiment shows that the rate of shear v/h is proportional in any liquid under like conditions to the shearing stress F/A which causes the liquid to flow; that is,

$$\frac{F}{A} \propto \frac{v}{h} \quad \text{or} \quad \frac{F}{A} = \eta \frac{v}{h}$$

where η (eta) is the proportionality constant. This constant is called the *coefficient of viscosity* of the liquid; its value is given by

$$\eta = \frac{F/A}{v/h} \tag{90}$$

an expression which is similar to that for the shear modulus of elasticity (§ 103). The viscosity of a liquid decreases with a rise in temperature.

Equation (90) affords a physical idea of what is meant by unit viscosity. Imagine a layer of liquid 1 cm. thick to be at rest, and suppose a plane surface of large area to be drawn across the upper surface of the liquid with a speed of 1 cm. per sec. Then the force in dynes per sq. cm. of surface necessary to move this plane surface in the manner indicated is numerically equal to the coefficient of viscosity of the liquid under consideration. Its unit in the metric system is the dyne-sec. per cm.^{2}, and is called the *poise*. Coefficients of viscosity for some liquids are given in the following table:

Coefficients of Viscosity of Liquids

		Poises
Alcohol, ethyl........... at	20° C.	0.012
Benzene...............	20° C.	0.0065
Glycerine.............	20° C.	8.3
Mercury..............	20° C.	0.016
Oil, machine..........	19° C.	1.02
Water...............	20° C.	0.010
Water...............	100° C.	0.0028

The method of measuring viscosity described in the preceding paragraph is not easy to carry out directly. A more convenient method is to cause the liquid under test to flow through a vertical tube of small bore and to measure the rate of flow. Equation (90) must then be applied to each annular layer and the results integrated by the methods of calculus; the analysis yields the following equation for the rate of flow in cubic centimeters per second through a tube of length l cm. and radius r cm.:

$$Q = \frac{\pi P r^4}{8\eta l} \tag{91}$$

where P is the liquid pressure in dynes per square centimeter at the lower end of the tube. This relation is known as Poiseuille's Law, and is named after Jean L. M. Poiseuille (1799–1869). It applies to small velocities of flow that will not set up eddies in the liquid.

The Saybolt viscosimeter is widely used in this country for practical measurements of viscosity. It operates on the principle that the time for a definite quantity of liquid to flow through a short small tube is proportional to the coefficient of viscosity. In the usual instrument the number of seconds for 60 cu. cm. of liquid to flow out is used as the measure of viscosity. Water at room temperature gives a reading of about 30 sec.

PROBLEMS

1. A cylindrical container is filled with liquid, and an orifice in the bottom is opened. What are the theoretical velocities with which the liquid flows out of the container when the liquid surface is successively 2 meters, 1 meter, and 0.5 meter above the orifice?

2. A flume of V section, with its sides inclined 90° to each other, supplies water to a long trough of rectangular section 6 ft. wide. The resulting flow in the trough is 3 ft. per sec. and is 8 in. deep. If the width of the water surface in the flume is 3 ft., what is the velocity of the water just before it leaves the flume?

3. A tank 6 ft. deep has in the bottom an orifice 2 in. in diameter of the type shown in Fig. 142a, for which the discharge coefficient may be taken as 0.62. When the tank is full of water, with what discharge rate will it begin to empty?

4. What is the diameter of the orifice required to discharge at the rate of 24 gal. per min. from a water main into the atmosphere, if the pressure in the main is 75 lb. per sq. in. higher than the pressure outside?

5. At what pressure above that of the atmosphere is water emitted from "Old Faithful" geyser at Yellowstone, if it rises to a height of 125 ft.?

6. Calculate the horsepower developed by a liquid-circulating pump in lifting 250 gal. of water per min. against a 15-ft. head.

*7. A stream is 25 ft. wide and has an average flow of 1.5 ft. per sec. The depths of the stream, measured at 5-ft. intervals across from bank to bank, are 0, 3, 4, 6, 2, 0 ft. What is the maximum power which could be obtained from this stream if it were to yield an average head of 25 ft.?

8. Derive equation (85) from equation (88) by imagining an orifice at the bottom of a tank, and considering the kinetic energy of a frictionless liquid at the top of the tank to be zero, and the potential energy of the jet just outside the orifice to be zero.

9. Water at an elevation head of 6 meters is moving at the rate of 4 meters per sec. along an open inclined channel. What is the velocity of the water at a place where the elevation head has half its former value, if frictional losses are neglected?

10. An engineering formula for the loss of head due to friction in a pipe is

$$H = 0.00031 \frac{LV^2}{D}$$

where L = length of pipe in feet, D = diameter of pipe in feet, and V = velocity of flow in feet per second. If H is to be feet, what units should be assigned to the numerical constant?

11. A horizontal tube 6 cm. in diameter has a constriction 4 cm. in diameter. When a liquid of specific gravity 0.9 flows through it, the pressure of the liquid in the tube exceeds that in the constriction by 20 gm. per sq. cm. Determine the velocity of the liquid in the tube.

*12. A Venturi meter having a 9-in. throat is put into a 1-ft. pipe. The pressures are observed to be 16 lb. per sq. in. in the pipe and 12 lb. per sq. in. at the throat when water flows through the meter at a certain rate. What is the discharge in cubic feet per second?

*13. To measure the viscosity of a lubricating oil, it is allowed to flow through a vertical capillary tube 60 cm. long and 1.5 mm. in diameter. When the liquid pressure at the lower end of the tube is maintained at 40 cm. of mercury, the flow through the tube was found to be 1.10 cu. cm. per min. What is the viscosity of the oil?

*14. A capillary tube 20 cm. long and with a bore of 2-mm. diameter is sealed to a funnel. The tube is placed upright and a machine oil having a specific gravity of 0.87 is poured into the funnel and maintained at an elevation 26 cm. above the bottom of the capillary. Upon test 7.2 cu. cm. of the oil flows out in 30 min. What is the coefficient of viscosity of the oil?

Mechanics of Gases   *Chapter XIII*

134. Gaseous State of Matter.—The structure of a gas was described briefly at the beginning of Chapter XI, the accepted theory being that gas molecules are comparatively far apart and move about unceasingly throughout the entire space to which they are admitted. Gases differ from liquids in two respects: first, gases are very compressible; and second, they completely fill any closed vessel in which they are placed. In most other respects, however, gases resemble liquids, and since both are capable of flowing, they are designated by the common term *fluid*. Gases as well as liquids exert pressure upon surfaces with which they are in contact, and both exert upward buoyant forces in accordance with Archimedes' Principle; flowing gases conform to Bernoulli's Theorem when their compressibility is taken into account, and the velocity of effusion through an orifice can be found as for a liquid; again, gases, like liquids, adapt themselves to the shape of the containing vessel and, having no elasticity of shape, are unable to exert shearing stresses, except those due to viscosity.

The term *vapor* is applied to a gas which can be liquefied by pressure alone. At ordinary temperatures, steam and carbon dioxide are called vapors; but air, hydrogen and nitrogen are called gases.

135. Kinetic Theory of Gases.—Gases, because of their simple structure, are well adapted to mathematical study, and this fact has led to the development of a detailed theory of gas behavior called the *kinetic theory of gases*. Many results of this theory can be verified by test, and all are of theoretical interest.

Under the kinetic theory, a body of gas is composed of molecules which are all alike, and which behave like tiny elastic spheres. It is assumed that these molecules are comparatively far apart, on the average, and that they are in a state of motion, determined by the temperature, in which they continually strike against each other and against the walls of the container. At a given instant, some molecules are moving one way and some another, some are traveling fast and some slow, and some are even at rest; and the combined effect of these varying velocities corresponds to the temperature of the gas. Any appreciable volume contains so many molecules, however, that, in accordance with the laws of probability, some intermediate velocity can be found which, if possessed by all the molecules, would correspond to the same temperature. It is known that energy is needed to raise the temperature of a substance, and so *the temperature of a gas is assumed to be directly proportional to the mean kinetic energy of the gas molecules.* Consequently, the intermediate velocity v must be such as to impart the same kinetic energy to N molecules, each of mass m, as that due to their individual velocities, $v_1, v_2, \cdots v_N$. Hence,

$$N(\tfrac{1}{2}mv^2) = \tfrac{1}{2}mv_1{}^2 + \tfrac{1}{2}mv_2{}^2 + \cdots \tfrac{1}{2}mv_N{}^2$$

from which

$$v = \sqrt{\frac{v_1{}^2 + v_2{}^2 + \cdots v_N{}^2}{N}}$$

The varying individual velocities may therefore be replaced by a single velocity which is found by squaring the individual velocities, taking the mean of these squares, and then extracting the square root. The result is known as the *root-mean-square* or rms. velocity.

The rms. velocity of the molecules of a gas can be found in terms of the pressure and density of the gas, by summing up the impulses of the molecules against one of the confining walls; this sum calculated for unit time and unit area is equal to the pressure, and a rearrangement of terms yields the desired expression. Consider a cubical box of volume $V = l^3$, as shown in Fig. 147, containing N molecules of gas each of mass m, and let the rms. velocity of the gas molecules be v. The actual motions of the molecules within the box can be resolved into three components, as though one-

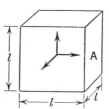

Fig. 147. Illustrating molecular velocities

third of the molecules were moving perpendicularly between each pair of opposite faces. Such a group of molecules moving between face A and the one opposite would encounter many collisions on the way. Suppose the collisions to occur after traveling a small uniform distance x from A. The number of molecules in a zone of this thickness would be $\dfrac{x}{l} N$, one third of which would strike A with a velocity v and rebound with a velocity $-v$. Each of these molecules thus undergoes a change of momentum of *2mv*, which is accordingly equal to the impulse imparted to the wall by collision, § 41. When all the molecules striking face *A* are included, the impulse per impact is

$$Ft = \frac{1}{3} \times \frac{x}{l} N \times 2mv$$

The molecules travel a distance *x* before collision and travel back to face *A*, a total distance of *2x* in a time *2x/v*, and thus strike the face $\frac{v}{2x}$ times each second. The total impulse exerted per second is equal to the force, or

$$F = \frac{xN}{3l} \times 2mv \times \frac{v}{2x} = \frac{Nmv^2}{3l}$$

and the pressure exerted on the face is

$$p = \frac{F}{l^2} = \frac{Nmv^2}{3l^3} = \frac{Nmv^2}{3V} = \frac{dv^2}{3}$$

where the density of the gas is $d = Nm/V$. By a rearrangement of terms, the rms. velocity of the molecules, for a gas of density *d* under an absolute pressure *p*, is found to be

$$v = \sqrt{\frac{3p}{d}} \tag{92}$$

As an illustration, the rms. velocity of hydrogen molecules (see § 141) under standard atmospheric pressure of 1,013,000 dynes/cm.[2] is

$$v = \sqrt{\frac{3 \times 1,013,000 \text{ dynes/sq. cm.}}{0.000090 \text{ gm/cu. cm.}}} = 184,000 \text{ cm/sec.}$$

which is considerably more than the velocity of a rifle bullet.

One may well inquire, in view of such high molecular velocities, why it takes so long for illuminating gas, for instance, to penetrate the distant corners of a room after a gas jet is accidentally opened. The reason is that each molecule is continually impeded by collision with other molecules, thus altering its speed and direction. As a result the molecules zigzag about and their advance in a given direction is fairly slow. It can be shown that each of the hydrogen molecules referred to undergoes billions of such collisions each second, and that, on the average, it travels only about 0.00002 cm. between collisions. The average distance traversed between collisions is known as the *mean free path* of the molecules.

136. Atmospheric Pressure.—The earth is surrounded by a layer of air extending to great heights and held to the earth by gravitational attraction. This body of air, like all fluids, exerts a pressure determined by its height and density, in accordance with equation (81), $p = hdg$. The existence of atmospheric pressure can be shown and its value measured by a mercury barometer, as in Fig. 148. In setting up this apparatus, a long glass tube sealed at one end is completely filled with mercury, and then placed in a vessel of mercury as shown. The mercury will settle down, leaving a vacuum above it. The height h of the mercury column is a measure of atmospheric pressure, the value 76.00 cm. at sea level at 0° C. being taken as standard. The corresponding value of the pressure is found from equation (81) to be 76.0 cm. × 13.596 gm/cm.³ × 980 dynes/gm. = 1,013,000 dynes/sq. cm. or about 14.7 lb/sq. in.

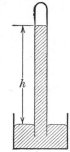

Fig. 148. Mercury barometer

The aneroid barometer is another device for measuring atmospheric pressure. This instrument consists essentially of a small sealed metal box from which most of the air has been removed, the box having a corrugated face which moves in and out as the atmospheric pressure varies. This slight movement is magnified by a system of levers and is communicated to a pointer which sweeps across a graduated dial or faceplate.

On account of its compressibility, the air near the earth is weighed down and compressed by that above, and conversely, the strata become rarer as the elevation is increased, although this effect is somewhat offset by the contraction due to cooling. Consequently the pressure does not vary uniformly with altitude, as it would in a medium of uniform density, but changes less and less rapidly at greater heights, as shown in Fig. 149, which is based on actual test. The diagram shows also that the altitude of a point can be estimated from a knowledge of the corresponding

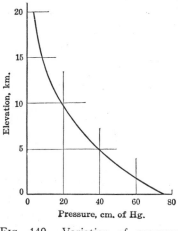

Fig. 149. Variation of pressure with altitude

atmospheric pressure. This fact is utilized on aircraft in the *altimeter*, a device which is essentially an aneroid barometer, calibrated to indicate altitude instead of pressure.

The force due to atmospheric pressure can be calculated by equation (79), $F = pA$, and is found to be very large, even upon a surface of moderate size. In most cases, however, both sides of an object are subjected to almost the same pressure, and consequently the surface does not have to sustain a great load.

137. Pressure of a Confined Gas; Boyle's Law.—One of the outstanding properties of a gas is its compressibility. Suppose that

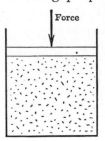

some gas is confined within a closed cylinder having a tight-fitting piston, as represented in Fig. 150, then upon applying a force as shown, the piston will move inward and come to rest at some new position where the pressure within the gas sets up a force equal to that exerted upon it by the piston. During this process the gas is compressed and its volume is reduced. Robert Boyle (1627–1691), an English philosopher, found a very simple relation between the pressure of a gas and its volume, which is known as Boyle's Law; namely, that *the volume of*

FIG. 150. Illustrating pressure on a confined gas

a confined body of gas varies inversely as the absolute pressure, provided the temperature remains unchanged. If p_1 and V_1 represent the pressure and volume of the gas under one condition, and p_2 and V_2 its pressure and volume under some different condition, then

$$V_1 : V_2 = p_2 : p_1$$

whence

$$p_1 V_1 = p_2 V_2 \tag{93}$$

An *ideal gas* will be defined for the present as one which conforms to Boyle's Law.

The kinetic theory, which pictures the pressure exerted by a gas as a continual bombardment of the enclosing walls by the moving molecules, may be used to derive Boyle's Law theoretically. Since the temperature of the confined gas remains unchanged, the mean kinetic energy of its molecules is assumed to be also unchanged. In the notation of § 135, this equality of kinetic energies under the two conditions may be expressed by

$$\frac{mv_1^2}{2} = \frac{mv_2^2}{2}$$

From equation (92) for the mean molecular velocity, $v = \sqrt{3p/d}$, it follows that $\dfrac{3p_1}{d_1} = \dfrac{3p_2}{d_2}$. But the density of the gas is $d_1 = \dfrac{M}{V_1}$, and similarly $d_2 = \dfrac{M}{V_2}$, where the mass M of the gas is the same under the two conditions. Therefore,

$$p_1 V_1 = p_2 V_2$$

as originally stated.

138. Manometers and Pressure Gages.—The pressure of confined gases can be measured by U-shaped manometer tubes containing mercury or other liquids. Fig. 151 shows two common types of

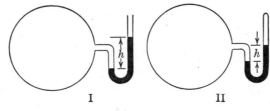

FIG. 151. Open and closed manometers

manometers connected to tanks of compressed gas. The pressure forces the liquid in the tube down at the near side and up at the far side. In the *open manometer*, the difference in height h between the two columns, multiplied by the weight per unit volume of the liquid, shows how much the gas pressure exceeds that of the atmosphere. This value is known as the *gage pressure* to distinguish it from *absolute pressure*, which includes the pressure of the atmosphere. In the *closed manometer*, the closed end of the tube contains air which is at atmospheric pressure when the columns are level. As the liquid in the tube is forced to the position shown, this air becomes compressed, and the absolute pressure in the tank is found by adding the pressure of the air entrapped in the tube to that due to a liquid column of height h. The closed manometer is adapted to the measurement of higher pressures than the open type, but is not so sensitive, especially at high pressures.

The *Bourdon gage* is an instrument used extensively for industrial purposes, as in the measurement of steam pressures. The operating element of this device consists of a bronze tube of elliptical cross-section, the tube being curved into a circular arc. One end of the tube is fixed and the other is connected by a mechanical linkage to a toothed sector which engages the instrument pointer. When subjected to internal pressure, the tube tends to assume a circular cross-section, and in so doing uncoils slightly, moving the pointer over a scale.

139. Mixtures of Gases; Dalton's Law.—It has been indicated that a gas upon expanding undergoes a reduction in pressure, a fact that will be of value in studying the mixture of several gases. Suppose that two or more closed vessels, originally containing different gases which do not react chemically, are joined so that each gas has access to all the containers. The molecular motion causes each gas to penetrate the entire volume of all the containers, and by diffusion the mixture eventually becomes homogeneous throughout. In this process, each of the constituent gases expands into the total available volume as though the other gases were not present, and the absolute pressure of each constituent is reduced, in accordance with Boyle's Law, to a lower value called its *partial pressure*. If the pressure of the gas mixture is measured, it will be found equal to the sum of the partial pressures of the various constituents. This relation, which was first established by John Dalton (1766–1844), English chemist and physicist, may be stated as follows: *A mixture of several gases which do not react chemically exerts a pressure equal to the sum of the pressures which the several gases would exert separately if each were allowed to occupy the entire space alone at the given temperature.*

As an illustration, suppose 1 liter of oxygen at a pressure of 2 atmospheres is allowed to mix with 3 liters of nitrogen at a pressure of 5 atmospheres. The oxygen in expanding from 1 liter to 4 liters will undergo a corresponding reduction of pressure, and in the final mixture its partial pressure will be $\frac{1}{4} \times 2$ or $\frac{1}{2}$ atmosphere. Similarly, the partial pressure of the nitrogen will be $\frac{3}{4} \times 5$ or $3\frac{3}{4}$ atmospheres. The pressure of the mixture will be the sum of the partial pressures, or $4\frac{1}{4}$ atmospheres.

140. Avogadro's Number; the Mol.—The Italian physicist Amadeo Avogadro (1776–1856) suggested that, at the same temperature and pressure, *equal volumes of different gases contain equal numbers of molecules.* This hypothesis has been verified experimentally and is called Avogadro's Law. Its agreement with the kinetic theory can be shown by considering two gases to have the same temperature and assuming that their molecules have the same mean kinetic energy. In the notation of § 135,

$$\frac{m_1 v_1{}^2}{2} = \frac{m_2 v_2{}^2}{2}$$

the subscripts being used to distinguish the two gases. From equation (92) it follows that $\dfrac{m_1}{2} \times \dfrac{3p_1}{d_1} = \dfrac{m_2}{2} \times \dfrac{3p_2}{d_2}$. When the density d is replaced by $\dfrac{Nm}{V}$, the equation becomes $\dfrac{m_1}{2} \times \dfrac{3p_1 V_1}{N_1 m_1} = \dfrac{m_2}{2} \times \dfrac{3p_2 V_2}{N_2 m_2}$. Under like pressure-volume conditions, $p_1 = p_2$ and $V_1 = V_2$, consequently $N_1 = N_2$, as stated in Avogadro's Law.

This law is frequently applied in Physical Chemistry to a particular quantity of a gas known as a *mol*, or gram-molecule. The mol of a substance is a mass in grams equal numerically to the sum of the atomic weights of the atoms in the molecule of that substance. The number of molecules in a mol of gas is known as *Avogadro's Number*; a mol of any gas contains 6.02×10^{23} molecules. At standard temperature and pressure (0° C. and 76 cm. of mercury) a mol of any gas occupies a volume of 22.4 liters.

141. Density of Gaseous Mediums.—For a gas, as for any substance, density is defined as mass per unit volume. Since the volume of any given mass of gas varies inversely as the pressure, it follows that the density of a gas will vary directly as the pressure. The density of a gas is also influenced by the temperature, it being known that gases expand when heated, and contract when cooled.

The density of air is of special importance, and has been determined with great care. One liter of air at standard temperature and pressure weighs 1.293 gm., and thus the density of air is 0.001293 gm/cu. cm., which is equivalent to about 0.081 lb/cu. ft. The specific gravity of a gas is usually expressed with reference to air as a standard, instead of with reference to water, as in the case of solids and liquids. Thus, coal gas, which is about four-tenths as dense as air, is said to have a specific gravity of 0.4 with respect to air.

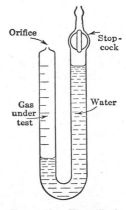

FIG. 152. The effusiometer

The density of a gas can be measured by weighing a hollow globe of known volume when filled with the gas and again when evacuated, but such a measurement requires very careful weighing, because a small volume of gas weighs so little. For industrial purposes, the *effusiometer*, Fig. 152, is used to compare the density of a gas with that of air. In this device the gas is admitted into a glass tube and is then forced out by water pressure through a tiny orifice, the time being measured during which the water pressure falls off a certain amount. A second measurement is then made under identical conditions, except that air is used instead of the gas. From the data thus obtained, the densities of the two gases can be compared, being directly proportional to the squares of the times of effusion.

To prove this relation, it should first be considered that in forcing a volume V of gas into the tube under a gage pressure p, the work required is $E = pV$, as given for liquids in equation (84). An amount of potential energy pV is therefore given to the gas, the amount of potential energy per unit volume consequently being p. Upon effusion, this potential energy is transformed into kinetic energy, the kinetic energy per unit volume being $\frac{1}{2}mv^2 \div V = \frac{1}{2}dv^2$. When these energy values are equated, the density of the gas is

$$d = \frac{2p}{v^2} \tag{94}$$

This equation shows that if two gases are tested under the same conditions of pressure, their densities will be inversely as the squares of their respective velocities of effusion. Thus, $d_1:d_2 = v_2^2:v_1^2$, where d_1 and d_2 are the densities of the gases, and v_1 and v_2 are the corresponding velocities. But the times of effusion for a given change in pressure are inversely proportional to the velocities, and therefore

$$d_1:d_2 = t_1^2:t_2^2$$

Density and Specific Gravity of Gases

Gas	Density		Specific gravity
	gm/liter	lb/cu. ft.	
Air.................	1.293	0.081	1.000
Air at 20° C..........	1.205	0.0755	0.932
Carbon dioxide.......	1.977	0.123	1.529
Hydrogen...........	0.090	0.0056	0.069
Helium.............	0.179	0.011	0.138
Nitrogen............	1.251	0.078	0.967
Oxygen.............	1.429	0.089	1.105
Steam at 100° C.......	0.598	0.037	0.462

where t_1 is the time of effusion for the gas of density d_1, and t_2 is the corresponding time for the gas of density d_2.

The densities and specific gravities of a few common gases are given in the accompanying table. These values are for standard temperature and pressure unless otherwise noted. The values for specific gravity are stated with respect to air as unity.

142. Buoyancy of the Atmosphere.—Archimedes' Principle, which was taken up in § 120 in connection with liquids, applies equally well to gases, and it may be said that *a body located in any fluid, whether liquid or gaseous, is buoyed up by a force equal to the weight of the fluid displaced.* As applied to gases, interest in this principle centers in the buoyancy of the atmosphere.

A balloon filled with gas that is lighter than the surrounding air is raised by the buoyant force, but as it rises through strata of less and less density, the buoyant force becomes smaller and smaller. Finally a height is reached where this upward force is equal to the total downward force, which includes both the weight of the balloon and its load, and also the weight of the gas with which it is filled. The balloon is then in equilibrium and does not rise higher. During the ascent, some of the gas is allowed to escape through a valve, so as to keep its pressure about equal to that of the surrounding air, and thus prevent bursting of the envelope. To reach greater heights, sand ballast is scattered overboard; and to descend, the light gas may be released.

Consider, for instance, a balloon of 35,000-cu. ft. capacity, designed to reach an altitude of 6000 ft. when filled with hydrogen, and calculate the allowable weight of the balloon and its load. At a height of 6000 ft. (1.8 km.) the atmospheric pressure, from Fig. 149, is reduced from 76 to 60 cm. of mercury. If temperature differences are neglected, the density of the air at this level is correspondingly lowered to 60/76 of its standard value, 0.081 lb. per cu. ft. (§ 141). The buoyant force on the balloon is therefore

$$35{,}000 \text{ cu. ft.} \times \frac{60}{76} \times 0.081 \frac{\text{lb.}}{\text{cu. ft.}} = 2240 \text{ lb.}$$

The hydrogen in the envelope is taken to have the same pressure as the surrounding atmosphere; its weight is 0.069×2240 lb. = 155 lb., and consequently the allowable weight of the balloon and load is 2240 lb. − 155 lb. = 2085 lb.

In precise weighing measurements it is sometimes necessary to apply corrections on account of the buoyancy of the atmosphere, if

the object being weighed is of different density than the weights
with which it is being compared.   In an equal-arm balance, the net
downward force at the end of each arm is the true weight of the
object there minus the buoyant force due to the atmosphere and,
when the instrument is balanced, the net downward forces are equal;
these facts make it possible to determine the true weight of an object.

Find the true weight w gm. of a sample of balsa wood (density = 0.12
gm/cu. cm.) which balances 100 gm. of brass weights (density = 8.5 gm/cu.
cm.) at 20°C.   The volume of the wood is $w/0.12$ cu. cm., and the buoyant
force upon it is $0.001205 \, w/0.12$ gm.   The volume of brass is $100/8.5$ cu. cm.,
and the buoyant force upon it is $0.001205 \times 100/8.5$ gm.   Consequently,

$$ w - \frac{0.001205w}{0.12} = 100 - 0.001205 \times \frac{100}{8.5} $$

whence the true weight of the wood is $w = 101.0$ gm.

143. Bernoulli's Theorem Applied to Gases.—It was implied in
§ 131 that Bernoulli's Theorem is applicable to gases as well as to
liquids.   The mathematical treatment, however, is complicated by
the fact that gases are highly compressible, so that in equation (87)
the density of the gas will be different for different values of the
pressure.   Nevertheless, the general effect is the same as previously
described; namely, that when a flowing stream of gas speeds up, its
pressure decreases, and vice versa.

A tennis ball that is set spinning when served undergoes a curved
flight as a result of the effect just described.   Suppose a ball to be
spinning in a clockwise direction while
it is moving toward the left in still
air, as indicated in part I of Fig. 153.
The effect is the same as if the ball
were spinning on a stationary axis in
a wind directed toward the right, as in
part II of the figure. As the ball spins,

FIG. 153.   Curved flight of ball

a layer of air clings to it and is carried around with it, and the velocity
of the air at any point near the ball can be regarded as made up of
two components, one due to the wind and the other due to the spinning of the ball.   Above the ball, these components have the same
direction, while below they have opposite directions.   It follows that
the velocity is greater at the top surface than at the bottom, and
according to Bernoulli's Theorem, the pressure is increased at the
bottom and reduced at the top.   Hence an unbalanced force is developed which causes the ball to rise as it moves forward.

An engineering application of Bernoulli's Theorem that is of very great importance is the lifting effect produced upon a moving airfoil. Consider an airfoil section which is assumed to be moving to the left in still air. The effects produced are the same as if the airfoil were stationary and the air were streaming past it toward the right, as indicated in Fig. 154. Observe that the top surface of the airfoil has the greater curvature; the air that flows close to it is deflected as shown, while that at a higher level is relatively undisturbed. Therefore the stream of air entering the region just above the airfoil is forced to flow through a constricted area and its speed is increased. In accordance with Bernoulli's Theorem the pressure in this region is correspondingly lowered, and the normal atmospheric pressure upon the lower surface forces the airfoil upward.

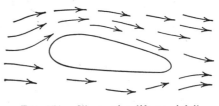

Fig. 154. Illustrating lift on airfoil

*144. Viscosity of Gases.—Molecular friction, or viscosity, is present in gases as in liquids, although to a smaller extent, as would be expected from the increased spacing of the molecules. This friction not only retards the motion of gases themselves in flowing through tubes, ducts, and the like; but also retards other bodies in moving through a stationary gas. Air friction increases with the velocity, and is an important factor in airplane construction, as evidenced by the stream-lining of surfaces to minimize its effects.

A study of scientific interest is the motion of a sphere falling through a viscous gas, such as a rain drop falling through the atmosphere. Suppose that such a drop starts falling with constant acceleration under the action of gravity; at first friction exerts only a small drag upon it, and it gains speed quickly, but as it does so the upward force of friction becomes greater and greater, until finally it equals the downward force of gravity. Thereafter the acceleration is zero and the drop descends with uniform motion. Sir George Stokes (1819–1903), British mathematician and physicist, found that for very small drops of radius r and density d the steady, or terminal, velocity acquired in falling through a medium having a coefficient of viscosity η is given by the expression

$$v = \frac{2dgr^2}{9\eta} \tag{95}$$

g being the acceleration due to gravity. When cgs. units are used, the values of η will be in poises. The coefficients of viscosity for some gases are given in the following table:

Coefficient of Viscosity of Gases

			Poises
Air....................	at	0° C.	173 × 10⁻⁶
Air....................		99° C.	220 "
Ammonia...............		0° C.	96 "
Hydrogen..............		0° C.	87 "
Mercury vapor..........		300° C.	532 "
Oxygen................		0° C.	189 "
Water vapor...........		0° C.	90 "
Water vapor...........		100° C.	132 "

It is interesting to note that a rise in temperature causes the viscosity of gases to increase; the reverse is true for liquids (§ 133).

145. Reduced Pressures.—When it is desired to exhaust the air from a vessel, an *aspirator* can be used. In this device, shown diagrammatically in Fig. 155, a stream of water, usually from the city mains, is admitted at W and flows through a small nozzle into the chamber C, which connects through a passage E to the vessel to be exhausted. The small size of the nozzle causes the stream to issue from it with high velocity, and the pressure in the chamber C is lowered in accordance with Bernoulli's Theorem. Thus, air is withdrawn from the vessel attached to E, and, mingling with the water, passes out at the outlet O. By using an aspirator, a reduction of pressure to about 3 or 4 cm. of mercury can be obtained; this corresponds to about one-twentieth of an atmosphere.

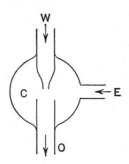

FIG. 155.   The aspirator

A higher vacuum can be secured with a *piston pump*, operating on the principle of an ordinary force pump, but arranged to withdraw air from the vessel instead of forcing it in. With the ordinary pump, however, there is a certain amount of dead space still left in the cylinder when the piston has advanced to the end of its stroke. Such dead spaces would make it impossible to secure a high vacuum, and are eliminated in the vacuum pump by covering the piston and valves with oil. Such an *oil pump* is capable of reducing the pressure inside a vessel of, say, 500-cu. cm. capacity to a small fraction of a millimeter of mercury in a few minutes.

Low pressures can be measured by a *vacuum gage*, a common type being represented in Fig. 156. This gage is actually a mercury barometer of small height mounted within an air-tight casing of glass which is attached to the system being exhausted. When the pressure is reduced to 10 or 12 cm. of mercury, the column falls away from the top of the closed tube, and lower pressures can be read directly from the graduated scale.

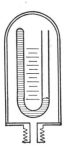

FIG. 156. A vacuum gage

*146. High-vacuum Technique.—The quantity production of incandescent and fluorescent lamps, radio tubes, vacuum bottles, and the like, all of which require a high degree of exhaustion, has led to the development of a more or less standard practice in the production of high vacua. As a preliminary step, it is customary to heat all glass parts to a high temperature, in order to drive off gases which cling to the surface of the glass or which are absorbed within its pores. Metal parts are baked in an atmosphere of hydrogen, which largely displaces the gases in the metal and which is itself given off readily during exhaustion. Heating is continued during the exhausting process, which is usually carried out by a diffusion pump. During the later stages of exhaustion, metal parts are heated by induced high-frequency currents to free them from gases. Finally, residual gases are removed by a minute amount of substance known as a "getter," that combines vigorously with them.

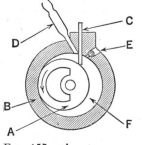

FIG. 157. A rotary vacuum pump

A type of *rotary pump* commonly used in high-vacuum work is represented in Fig. 157. This pump consists of an eccentric rotor *A* which revolves within a close-fitting cylinder *B*, a vane *C* being held tightly against the rotor by a spring, to separate the inlet tube *D* from the outlet port *E*. During each cycle the crescent-shaped space *F* fills with air by expansion from the vessel connected to *D*, and as the rotor turns, this air is compressed and forced through the valve and out at the outlet *E*. The entire pump is immersed in oil to prevent leakage. These pumps are quick acting and lower the pressure to perhaps 0.001 mm. of mercury.

The modern *diffusion pump*, Fig. 158, operates by means of the vapor which is formed when mercury is heated. Gas molecules passing by diffusion from the vessel A being exhausted, enter the blast of mercury vapor at B and are driven down to C, where they are transferred to the atmosphere by means of an auxiliary pump attached to the outlet D. The mercury vapor is condensed by a water jacket E and returns to the heater where it is evaporated again. A pump of this type is very rapid in action and can develop pressures as low as 10^{-8} mm. of mercury.

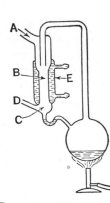

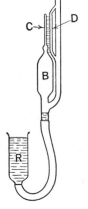

FIG. 158.   A diffusion pump   FIG. 159.   The McLeod gage

A standard instrument for the measurement of high vacua is the *McLeod gage*, shown in Fig. 159. The gage is attached at A to the vessel being exhausted, which is thereby placed in communication with a chamber B of which the volume is accurately known. By raising the mercury reservoir R, a known volume of the gas at low pressure is isolated in B, and as the mercury surface is raised higher, this gas is forced into a fine calibrated tube C. The pressure which this gas exerts when compressed in this manner is observed, and since the volume of B and tube C are known, the original pressure can easily be calculated by Boyle's Law. To avoid error due to capillarity a side-tube D is provided having the same diameter as the tube C.

It must not be thought, even with the highly developed technique now available, that it is possible to remove all of the gas molecules from a given space. Since under standard conditions there are 6.02×10^{23} molecules in a volume of 22.4 liters (§ 140), it can be appreciated that even at the low pressures reported for the diffusion pump, there are still hundreds of millions of molecules present in each cubic centimeter of space.

PROBLEMS

1. The extremes of barometric pressure recorded in New York City are 31.01 in. (Jan. 27, 1927) and 28.38 in. (Mar. 1, 1914), both corrected to sea level. What percentage of the standard atmosphere does this range of values represent?

2. What force is exerted by the atmosphere under standard conditions upon a surface 1 meter square?

3. Express standard atmospheric pressure in grams per square centimeter.

4. A closed tank having a volume of 50 cu. ft. contains air at atmospheric pressure. If 30 cu. ft. of fuel oil are pumped into the tank without allowing air to escape, what will be the absolute pressure of the entrapped air?

5. A "sounding tube," closed at the top and weighted at the bottom, is 80 cm. long. The tube is lowered into sea water, entrapping air originally under standard atmospheric pressure, until it strikes bottom. Upon raising the tube water was found to have risen 64 cm. within it. What is the depth of the sea at the place of observation?

6. A piston 10 in. in diameter and weighing 200 lb. is placed in the top of a vertical cylinder 1 ft. high, containing air. Assume that no leakage takes place and compute how far the piston will move downward in compressing the air before coming to rest.

7. Express Boyle's Law for a gas in terms of pressure and density rather than pressure and volume.

8. A cylinder having an internal diameter of 10 in. is supported vertically, and has its lower end closed by a 50-lb. piston to which a 200-lb. weight is attached. To what absolute value should the pressure within the cylinder be reduced in order that the piston and attached weight may be supported by atmospheric pressure? Assume no leakage.

9. A hand pump has a cylinder 15 in. long, containing air at atmospheric pressure. How far must the piston be pushed down to raise the gage pressure of the enclosed air to 20 lb. per sq. in.?

10. Compute the gage pressure and the absolute pressure in the tank of Fig. 151, part I; suppose that the manometer contains water and that the right-hand column stands 16 in. higher than the other.

11. Compute the gage pressure and the absolute pressure in the tank of Fig. 151, part II; suppose that the manometer contains mercury, the right-hand column being 8 cm. higher than the other, and extending to a point 8 cm. below the top of the closed tube.

12. Tank *A* contains 2 cu. ft. of oxygen under a gage pressure of 300 lb. per sq. in. and tank *B* contains 24 cu. ft. of air at standard atmospheric

pressure. What will be the resulting absolute pressure if tanks A and B are connected?

13. If the density of the atmosphere were uniform throughout at the value it has at standard temperature and pressure, to what height would it extend in order to produce the pressure that is commonly observed?

14. With what velocity theoretically will air effuse through a puncture in a tire which is pumped up to a gage pressure of 32 lb. per sq. in.?

15. A tank has a volume of 5 cu. ft. and contains compressed air at 20° C. and at 100 lb. per sq. in. gage pressure. (*a*) How many pounds of air does the tank contain? (*b*) What volume would the air in the tank occupy at standard atmospheric pressure?

16. The density of chlorine gas (Cl_2) under standard conditions is 3.21 gm. per liter. Calculate the mass of a chlorine molecule, also the average value of its kinetic energy due to molecular motion when the gas is under these conditions.

17. The air required to inflate the tires of a passenger air-liner weighs approximately 180 lb. How much would the weight of the plane be reduced if the tires were inflated with helium instead of air?

18. Calculate the buoyancy correction in weighing a cube of cork that measures 4 cm. along each edge and has a specific gravity of 0.24. An equal-arm balance is used, with brass weights of specific gravity 8.5.

19. A free balloon of 80,000-cu. ft. capacity weighs 1600 lb., not including the hydrogen with which it is filled, and its load and passengers weigh 3200 lb. The balloon is released from the ground at an air temperature of 20° C. Find the net buoyant force on the balloon and the acceleration with which it will begin to rise.

*20. With what constant velocity does a rain drop 0.2 mm. in diameter descend at 20° C., if the coefficient of viscosity of air at this temperature is 181×10^{-6}?

Heat

Effects of Heat   *Chapter XIV*

147. Nature of Heat.—In the early days of science, heat was thought to be a weightless fluid called caloric. All substances were supposed to contain more or less of this fluid, and the passage of heat from one body to another was explained as a flow of caloric from the hotter to the colder body. Count Rumford (Benjamin Thompson, 1753–1814), a British-American scientist, was impressed by the large amount of heat produced in attempting to bore some cannon with blunt tools. Since the supply of heat appeared to be inexhaustible, he concluded that heat could not be a substance but must be related in some way to motion. His investigations resulted in the present theory, confirmed by other investigators and now accepted without question, that *heat is a form of energy.*

When heat is applied to a body, it increases the energy of that body, and since in general, no change can be detected in either the kinetic or the potential energy of the body as a whole, it appears that the energy must have been given to the molecules of which the body is made. Molecules are known to possess kinetic energy, for there is ample evidence of their incessant motion. This property has been discussed earlier in connection with the kinetic theory, § 135. Some molecules also possess potential energy; this is true for the molecules of a solid or of a liquid which has been expanded by heating, for work must have been done upon the molecules to separate them in opposition to the forces of cohesion. Gas molecules have but little potential energy, since they are relatively far apart and as a result have only a slight attraction for one another. The heating of a body, therefore, has a direct effect upon its internal energy, whether kinetic or potential.

It is generally known that heat flows from a hot body to a cold one, and this means that one loses and the other gains internal energy. The tendency at present is to apply the term heat to this energy only while it is in transit, and not to the internal energy of the bodies themselves. According to this terminology, a body in a steady state does not contain heat but does possess internal energy·

when it emits or gives off heat its internal energy is reduced, and when it absorbs or takes on heat its internal energy is increased.

Also, the transfer of heat from one part of a body to another is explained by an increase of molecular motion. If one end of a metal rod is placed in a fire, the entire rod becomes warmer as heat is gradually conducted along it. It is supposed that the molecules of the metal in the fire are set into more rapid vibration and that these in striking neighboring molecules impart kinetic energy to them, and so on throughout the rod. When a gas is confined in a vessel and the vessel is heated, the gas molecules striking the heated sides of the vessel in their incessant motion rebound with greater speeds; these molecules then strike others, and so on; in this way the entire gas is heated.

148. Temperature Scales.—The application of heat to an object usually causes an increase in its *temperature*. The term temperature is used to express how cold or how hot an object is; cold implies a low temperature and hot a high temperature. A more definite idea of temperature can be realized by considering the result of bringing a hot object in contact with a cold one; for example, plunging a hot steel forging into cold oil. The forging becomes cooler and the oil warmer, the hot body giving up some of its energy to the cold one. This process continues until a state of thermal equilibrium is reached, in which the same temperature prevails throughout. A statement of the temperature of an object signifies that its molecules possess a particular amount of energy due to thermal agitation, and an increase of temperature implies a corresponding increase in internal energy.

Terms such as cold, cool, warm, and hot, although used in everyday speech to suggest the temperature of a substance, do not allow a given temperature to be stated with definiteness, and this fact has led to the adoption of certain thermometric scales. Such a scale is constructed by choosing two standard temperatures, called fixed points, that can be reproduced easily; next, assigning arbitrary numbers to these temperatures; and finally, dividing the interval between them into an appropriate number of equal parts. The divisions are extended above and below the fixed points, and a unit division is called a *degree* (°). Four such temperature scales are in common use. For each, the fixed points are taken as the melting point of ice and the boiling point of water, both at the standard pressure of 76 cm. of mercury. The *fahrenheit scale*, which is used largely for engineering and household purposes, was named after the German physicist, Gabriel D. Fahrenheit (1686–1736), who made the first mercury-in-glass thermometer. The *centigrade scale* is due to Anders Celcius (1701–1744), Swedish astronomer, and is universally used for scientific measurements. The other two scales reckon temperatures from a value which is considered theoretically to be the lowest possible (§ 185); they are used principally in thermodynamics. The one based upon centigrade divisions is called the *kelvin scale* in honor of the English scientist, Lord Kelvin (William Thomson, 1824–1907), and the other based upon fahrenheit divisions is called the *rankine scale* after the Scottish engineer, William J. M. Rankine (1820–1872). These scales are determined by the following data:

Temperature Scales

	Fahren-heit	Centi-grade	Kelvin	Rankine
Boiling point of water.......	212	100	373	671
Melting point of ice.........	32	0	273	491
Divisions between fixed points	180	100	100	180

These scales are shown aligned in Fig. 160 for comparison.

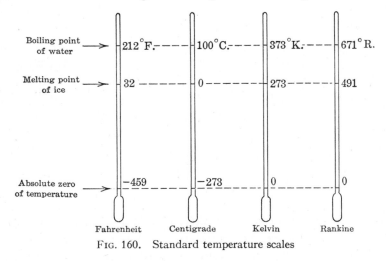

Fɪɢ. 160.   Standard temperature scales

It is frequently necessary to convert temperatures from one scale to another. In doing so, observe that a difference of 180 fahrenheit degrees is equivalent to a difference of 100 centigrade degrees, and that the melting point of ice which serves as the usual reference temperature is marked differently on the four scales.

For example, in converting a temperature of 60° F. to the centigrade scale, the degrees in excess of 32° F. are multiplied by 100/180, thus

$$(60 - 32) \times 100/180 = 15.6° \text{ C.}$$

The relation between fahrenheit and centigrade readings can be expressed by the proportion

$$\frac{F - 32}{180} = \frac{C}{100} \tag{96}$$

wherein the letters represent the corresponding temperatures.

To compare the absolute zeros on the centigrade and fahrenheit scales, the 273-degree range below 0 on the centigrade scale is multiplied by 180/100, yielding a range of 491 fahrenheit degrees, and this amount is subtracted from 32° F. to arrive at the result, namely −459° F. Again, by the proportion (96)

$$\frac{F - 32}{180} = \frac{-273}{100}$$

it is found that $F = -459$.

A *rise* or *fall* in temperature can be converted from one scale to another without reference to any fixed point. Thus, a motor which in operation shows a rise of 50 centigrade degrees would show a rise of (180/100) × 50 or 90 fahrenheit degrees.

149. Linear Expansion of Solids.—The application of heat to solids causes practically all of them to expand. A metal rod, heated uniformly over its entire length, expands, and every unit length of the rod becomes longer. The increase in length per unit length per degree rise in temperature is called the *coefficient of linear expansion*. This coefficient, denoted by α, has different values for different substances, and for a given substance varies somewhat over different temperature ranges. For iron at ordinary temperatures it may be taken as 0.000012 $\frac{\text{cm.}}{\text{cm.}}$ per centigrade degree or 0.0000067 $\frac{\text{in.}}{\text{in.}}$ per fahrenheit degree; this means that a 1-cm. length of iron becomes 1.000012 cm. long when subjected to a temperature rise of 1 centigrade degree, and similarly a 1-in. length becomes 1.000012 in. long under the same temperature change. Some representative values of α are given on the next page.

The values tabulated apply to a range around 20° C. except where particular temperatures are listed. If the coefficient of linear expansion and the length of an object are known at a given temperature, it is possible to compute the length at another temperature. Let L_c be the length at the lower temperature (cold); the increase of length due to a temperature rise of t degrees will be $L_c t \alpha$, and consequently the length at the higher temperature (hot) will be $L_h = L_c + L_c t \alpha$, or

$$L_h = L_c(1 + \alpha t) \tag{97}$$

As an illustration, suppose that a steel structure 1000 ft. long is to be designed to accommodate expansion over a range from −20° C. to +40° C. Assume 1000 ft. to be its correct length at −20° C.; it follows that its length at +40° C. will be

$$L_{40} = 1000 \text{ ft.} \left(1 + \frac{0.000011}{°\text{C.}} \times 60° \text{C.} \right) = 1000 \text{ ft.} \times 1.00066 = 1000.66 \text{ ft.}$$

An expansion sleeve of 0.66 ft. will take care of this change of length over the stipulated temperature range.

Coefficients of Linear Expansion of Solids

	Per C. degree	Per F. degree
Aluminum.	24×10^{-6}	13×10^{-6}
Brass or bronze.	18 "	10 "
Copper.	17 "	9.5 "
Glass (soft to hard)	8 to 9.5 "	4.5 to 5.3 "
Ice (range − 10° to 0° C.) . .	51 "	28 "
Invar steel (36% nickel).	−0.3 to +2.5 "	−0.2 to +1.4 "
Iron (wrought)	12 "	6.7 "
Lead.	29 "	16 "
Platinum.	9 "	5 "
Pyrex glass.	3 "	1.7 "
Silica, fused (0° to 30° C.) . .	0.42 "	0.23 "
Silver.	19 "	11 "
Steel.	11 "	6.1 "
Zinc.	26 "	14 "

The linear expansion of a body could be neutralized by the application of a suitable compressive force. In effect, such neutralization amounts to permitting the body to elongate a certain amount and then compressing it mechanically a like amount by a force according to equation (71) for Young's modulus of elasticity.

Several examples of linear expansion are illustrated in Fig. 161. In part I a strip of brass B and another of steel S are joined in one line; the total expansion due to heating will be the sum of the individual expansions of the two strips. The arrangement in part II of the figure shows these strips joined in another way to produce differential expansion. By properly choosing the lengths of the strips,

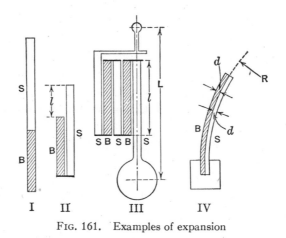

FIG. 161. Examples of expansion

the distance l between their free ends may be kept the same regardless of temperature changes. Such will be the case when the elongation $L_b t \alpha_b$ for the brass strip is equal to the elongation $L_s t \alpha_s$ for the steel strip over the same temperature range t. Under these conditions,

$$\frac{L_b}{L_s} = \frac{\alpha_s}{\alpha_b} = \frac{0.000011}{0.000018} = \frac{11}{18}$$

This principle is made use of in designing clock pendulums to keep their periods of oscillation constant. In part III of the figure is shown the left half of a clock pendulum made of steel and brass rods. In order to keep the length L of the pendulum constant at all temperatures, it is necessary for the lengths of brass and steel to be proportioned so that $2l\alpha_b t = (L + 2l)\alpha_s t$.

In part IV of Fig. 161 are depicted two strips of dissimilar metals, brass and steel, riveted or welded together side by side, their dimensions being the same at some initial temperature. The shape indicated is reached upon **heating** because brass expands more than steel. It can be shown that this shape is a circular arc having a radius of curvature expressed by $R = d \div (\alpha_b - \alpha_s)t$, where d is the thickness of either brass or steel strip, and t is the temperature elevation. In thermostats and similar appliances, the bending of a bimetallic strip is caused to make or break an electric contact and thereby control the operation of heaters or other apparatus.

A simple way of measuring the linear expansion coefficient of a metal is to use a rod of the material two or three feet long and place it within a pipe fitted with cork stoppers at each end to center the rod and to form an enclosure through which cold water or steam can be passed. The ends of the rod project slightly so that the length of the rod can be measured, and the measuring device is equipped with a micrometer for direct observation or with a lever system to magnify the changes of length. The lengths observed with the rod in cold water and then in steam, together with the corresponding temperature readings, permit the computation for the linear expansion coefficient to be made.

150. Surface and Volume Expansion.—The expansion due to heating affects all of the dimensions of a body. For an isotropic body, that is, one having the same physical properties in all directions, an expansion of 1 per cent in length is accompanied by an expansion of 1 per cent in width and 1 per cent in thickness.

To compute the expansion of a surface, consider a rectangular plate of dimensions a_c and b_c to have its temperature raised by an amount t. The dimensions then become $a_h = a_c(1 + \alpha t)$ and $b_h = b_c(1 + \alpha t)$, consequently the area of the surface at the higher temperature will be $S_h = a_h b_h = a_c b_c(1 + \alpha t)^2 = S_c(1 + 2\alpha t + \alpha^2 t^2)$, where $S_c = a_c b_c$ is the area of the plate at the lower temperature. The square of the small product αt is negligible, and the final expression for the area of the plate becomes

$$S_h = S_c(1 + 2\alpha t) = S_c(1 + \alpha' t)$$

where $\alpha' = 2\alpha$ is the *coefficient of surface expansion* of the material forming the plate.

Consider the expansion of a square plate of metal on which another square is marked out to form a frame of uniform width. Upon heating, the plate expands and the inscribed square expands proportionally. Had the inner square of metal been removed before heating, the expansion of the frame for the same temperature elevation would have been the same as though the plate were complete.

The expansion of a volume can be expressed in a manner similar to that of a length or a surface. When a body of volume V_c is heated through a temperature range t, its volume will be

$$V_h = V_c(1 + \beta t) \qquad (98)$$

where β is the *coefficient of volume expansion* (sometimes called the cubical expansion coefficient) of the substance. By following the procedure ahead, the student can show that, as a close approximation,

$$\beta = 3\alpha \qquad (99)$$

It is important to remember this relation in seeking cubical expansion coefficients of solids in tables of physical constants, since usually only linear coefficients of such bodies are listed.

The cavity in a hollow object expands as though it were a solid block of the same material. Thus, a liter flask of glass ($\alpha = 0.000008$ per C. degree) that is correct at $0°$ C. will have a volume of 1.0024 liter at $100°$ C., an increase of 2.4 cu. cm.

151. Expansion of Fluids.—Liquids, in general, follow the same law of expansion as that applicable to solids. The volume of a liquid at temperature t_h in terms of its volume at a lower temperature t_c is

$$V_h = V_c(1 + \beta t)$$

where β represents the coefficient of volume expansion of the liquid, and t is the temperature difference $t_h - t_c$. However, in measuring the expansion of a liquid it is usually necessary to consider the expansion of the containing vessel, and distinction must be made between the expansion observed and the true expansion of the liquid.

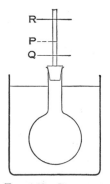

In the arrangement shown in Fig. 162, a glass flask contains the liquid under test originally at datum temperature t_c, at which temperature the liquid extends into the capillary tube to level P. The flask is next totally immersed in a hot liquid of temperature t_h contained in a large tank, as shown. If it were possible for the flask to attain the temperature t_h before transmitting any heat to the liquid under test, the glass would expand and cause the liquid level to fall to some position Q. Subsequent

FIG. 162. True and apparent expansion compared

heating of the liquid to temperature t_h causes its level to rise to position R. The difference QR is an indication of the *true* or *absolute expansion* of the liquid under test, while the difference PR measures its *apparent expansion.* Of course, position Q cannot be reached experimentally, because heat passes into the liquid before the flask has expanded its full amount. Consequently, it is necessary to deduce the true expansion from the observed apparent expansion of the liquid.

For definiteness, assume the flask to have a volume up to mark P of V cu. cm. at temperature $0°$ C., and the capillary to have a sectional area of A sq. cm. and to be calibrated in centimeters. (The *expansion* of the capillary will be neglected.) Let β_t and β_a be respectively the true and apparent coefficients of volume expansion of the liquid, and β_f the volume expansion coefficient of the containing flask. Then, in expanding to temperature $t°$ C., the changes of volume in cubic centimeters are

$$PQ \times A = V\beta_f t$$

$$QR \times A = V\beta_t t$$

$$PR \times A = V\beta_a t$$

The first of these expressions is subtracted from the second,

$$PR \times A = V(\beta_t - \beta_f)t$$

and the result is equated to the third expression,

$$V\beta_a t = V(\beta_t - \beta_f)t$$

from which

$$\beta_t = \beta_a + \beta_f \tag{100}$$

Therefore, *to find the true coefficient of expansion of a liquid, add to its apparent coefficient as measured in a particular flask, the cubical expansion coefficient of that flask.* The accompanying table gives the true coefficients of volume expansion for a few liquids, these being average values over ranges of temperature around $20°$ C.

True Expansion Coefficients of Liquids

	Per C. degree	Per F. degree
Alcohol (ethyl).........	110×10^{-5}	61×10^{-5}
Alcohol (methyl).......	122 "	68 "
Ether (ethyl)..........	163 "	91 "
Glycerine..............	53 "	29 "
Kerosene..............	83 "	46 "
Mercury...............	18.17 "	10.09 "
Sulfuric acid..........	57 "	32 "
Turpentine............	94 "	52 "

The density of a body is affected by temperature changes, since the volume increases with temperature and the mass does not. This is particularly important in dealing with liquids and gases for their expansion coefficients are much larger than those of solids. The volumes of a fluid of mass m are $V_h = \dfrac{m}{d_h}$ and $V_c = \dfrac{m}{d_c}$ respectively at temperatures t_h and t_c, where the corresponding densities are d_h and d_c. From equation (98),

$$d_h = \frac{d_c}{1 + \beta t} \qquad\qquad (101)$$

which shows that when the temperature of a body is raised, its density is reduced.

Gases as well as liquids follow the laws expressed by equations (98) and (101), provided they are tested at constant pressure, as was tacitly assumed in the case of liquids. The thermal behavior of gases is considered in Chapter XVI.

*152. Expansion of Water and Mercury.—Water and mercury are so often used for reference purposes that it is necessary to know exactly how they behave under changes of temperature. A table of densities at different temperatures (or a table of their reciprocals, called specific volumes) will be of great assistance in making volume calibrations. The following table gives the densities of these substances at a number of points over the temperature range from 0° to 25° C.

Density of Water and of Mercury

Temperature, °C.	Water, gm/cu. cm.	Mercury, gm/cu. cm.
0	0.99987	13.5955
2	0.99997	13.5905
4	1.00000	13.5856
6	0.99997	13.5806
8	0.99988	13.5757
10	0.99973	13.5708
15	0.99912	13.5585
20	0.99823	13.5462
25	0.99705	13.5340

In calibrating a glass flask so as to have a volume of 250 cu. cm. at 20° C., there is poured in $250 \times 0.99823 = 249.558$ gm. of water at that temperature, and a mark is placed at the liquid surface. For accuracy, the shape of the flask should be such that the mark will come at a position where the area is small.

When water is cooled it contracts steadily until its temperature reaches 4° C. At this temperature water has its greatest density.

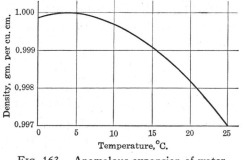

FIG. 163. Anomalous expansion of water

Upon further cooling to 0° C. it *expands* and its density becomes slightly less. The irregular expansion of water can be observed in the foregoing table; it is also represented in Fig. 163. This behavior of water is of particular importance in that it causes the freezing of lakes and ponds to begin at the surface rather than at the bottom. It is interesting to conjecture what would happen if the opposite were true.

The two French physicists Pierre L. Dulong (1785–1838) and Alexis T. Petit (1791–1820) devised a method for measuring the expansion coefficient of a liquid without considering the expansion of the container. The method was improved by their country-man, Henri V. Regnault (1810–1878), and his apparatus for studying the expansion of mercury is represented in elementary form in Fig. 164. The mercury under test is contained in two upright pipes, which are maintained at different temperatures, say 0° C. and $t°$ C., by means of enclosing jackets. These pipes are joined at the bottom by a connecting tube which is made small

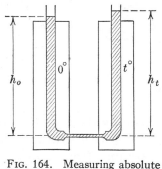

FIG. 164. Measuring absolute expansion

so that but little heat will be conducted from one pipe to the other.

It will be found in making a determination that the warm column of mercury, which has a lower density than the cold column ($d_t < d_0$), will extend to a height greater than the other ($h_t > h_0$) when a state of equilibrium is reached. This is explained by the fact that the two columns exert the same pressure at the bottom; consequently, by equation (81),

$$h_0 d_0 g = h_t d_t g$$

From equation (101), the density of mercury at the lower temperatures is $d_0 = d_t(1 + \beta t)$; therefore the expansion coefficient becomes

$$\beta = \frac{h_t - h_0}{h_0 t}$$

The absolute voluminal expansion coefficient β of the mercury can thus be obtained from readings of the heights and temperatures of the columns, the result being independent of the expansion of the container.

153. Change of State.—It was stated earlier that when a substance is heated, its temperature usually rises. This statement implies that in some instances the temperature does not rise, and such a result is often experienced. For example, when heat is applied to a block of ice at $0°$ C., the ice melts, and the resulting water, remaining in contact with the ice, will stay at a temperature of $0°$ until all the ice is melted. This situation is represented by the horizontal line AB on the temperature chart, Fig. 165. If the heating is continued, the water will rise in temperature uniformly until the value $100°$ C. is reached. This change is shown on the same chart by the straight line BC. At the temperature mentioned, the water boils and its temperature remains constant again (line CD) until continued heating converts it completely to steam. From this example it is seen that the absorption of heat does not always cause a temperature rise, but may serve to change the state of a substance from a solid to a liquid or from a liquid to a vapor. In connection with the foregoing example, it might be mentioned that ice melts at $0°$ C. and water boils at $100°$ C. only when the pressure upon the substance has the standard value of 76 cm. of mercury, the boiling point especially being influenced by the pressure. This subject is discussed more fully in § 163.

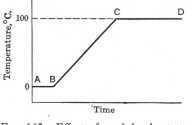

FIG. 165. Effect of applying heat to ice

154. Mercury Thermometry.—The effects of heat mentioned so far are: 1, change of temperature; 2, change of size; 3, change of state. Further, the application of heat to a body may produce: 4, incandescence, thereby causing the substance to emit light; 5, chemical changes, such as oxidation and reduction; 6, changes of electrical resistance; 7, generation of electromotive force at a junction of two dissimilar metals forming a thermoelectric couple. There are many other effects of heat, such as change of surface tension and viscosity, of magnetic properties, and of sound velocity; some of these will be considered elsewhere. Many of the effects enumerated are used for measuring temperature and several are considered later in this text.

For the great majority of temperature measurements, change of size is the operating principle, as exemplified by the familiar mercury thermometer, which covers a very important range of temperatures, from −20° C. to 500° C. In this thermometer the temperature measurement is based upon the expansion of mercury, or more strictly, upon the relative expansion of mercury and glass. The thermometer, in its simplest form, is made by fusing a glass bulb to the lower end of a length of capillary glass tubing; mercury is next introduced through a funnel attached to the top of the tube, the thermometer is boiled and annealed, and the capillary is sealed at the top. The next process is to calibrate the thermometer at two or more points. Finally, the graduations and figures are etched on the stem. Since glass softens at about 400° C. and mercury boils at 356.9° C., it is usual for the higher temperatures to make thermometers of boro-silicate glass and to fill them above the mercury column with an inert gas under pressure. For low temperatures, the use of mercury is limited by its freezing point, −38.87° C. In thermometers of similar construction the range may be extended downward by using toluol or pentane instead of mercury; these liquids freeze at −97° C. and −200° C. respectively.

The *clinical thermometer*, used by physicians, has a fine constriction in the stem near the bulb. Upon heating, the mercury expands through this opening and rises properly on the scale; but upon cooling, surface tension prevents the mercury beyond the constriction from returning to the bulb. This arrangement permits the indication to be read at any time after the thermometer is used; vigorous shaking is required to restore the mercury to the bulb.

The *Beckmann thermometer* devised by Ernst Beckmann is another interesting type; it is used for precise measurements of small temperature changes, particularly in physical chemistry. The device carries a small reservoir of mercury in a pocket at the top of the stem, from which more or less mercury as desired may be admitted into the bulb to suit the particular temperature range of a test. A typical instrument of this type covers any 5-degree range from $-25°$ to $+200°$ C. and its scale divisions indicate hundredths of a degree.

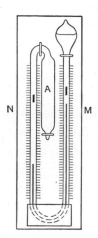

FIG. 166. Maximum and minimum thermometer

The *maximum and minimum thermometer*, shown in Fig. 166, employs glycerine as the thermometric substance, and mercury as an indicator. When subjected to a temperature rise, the glycerine in chamber A expands, causing the mercury column at M to rise. A fall of temperature causes the glycerine in A to contract, and the mercury at N to rise. Small steel indicators in the glycerine above the ends of the mercury column are raised by the motion of the columns as described, and are held at their highest positions by small springs. If this thermometer is exposed to varying temperatures, readings taken after the test showing the positions of the lower ends of the indicators in M and N will give the maximum and minimum temperatures which occurred during the test. The indicators may be reset by a small magnet.

Most mercury thermometers are calibrated for complete immersion of the mercury, but in actual use a portion of the stem containing mercury often projects into a region which is cooler than the bulb. Under these conditions a "stem-exposure" correction must be added to the reading, since the exposed mercury did not expand as much as allowed for in the calibration. This correction may be calculated from the observed thermometer reading t by noting the length of the exposed mercury column n, in degrees, and measuring its temperature t_s with an auxiliary "stem thermometer" held near its mid-point. The correction will be the amount that the exposed mercury would expand if heated from t_s to t; namely,

$$\text{correction} = n\beta(t - t_s)$$

where β is the apparent coefficient of volume expansion of mercury in glass.

For precision measurements with mercury thermometers, it is sometimes necessary to correct for a temporary depression of the zero point which occurs after a thermometer has been exposed to a high temperature, and also for slight errors due to pressure on the thin wall of the thermometer bulb.

PROBLEMS

1. The normal temperature of the human body is usually taken as 98.6° F. Convert this temperature to the centigrade scale.

2. Some common expressions used in describing high temperatures and their approximate equivalents on the centigrade scale are given as follows: Dark red heat—650 to 750°, Bright red heat—850 to 950°, Yellowish red heat—1050 to 1150°, and White heat—1450 to 1550°. Express their average values in fahrenheit degrees.

3. Bromine solidifies at −7.2° C. and vaporizes at 58.8° C. Express these temperatures on the fahrenheit scale.

4. During a thunder shower the outdoor temperature dropped 20° as measured with a fahrenheit thermometer. Compute the drop in temperature on the centigrade scale.

5. At what temperature are the readings of a fahrenheit and a centigrade thermometer the same numerically?

6. The base line for a triangulation system was measured with a 100-ft. steel tape when the temperature was 20° F. and the length of the line was recorded as 623.57 ft. The tape was standardized at 60° F. Compute the true length of the base line.

7. A steel tape correct at 0° C. is used to measure a distance when the temperature is 20° C. What is the percentage error in the measurement due to the expansion of the tape?

8. If steel rails are laid when the temperature is 30° F., the length of each rail being 40 ft. at this temperature, what should be the separation between successive rails to allow for expansion up to a temperature of 115° F.?

9. A gold ring has an average diameter of 0.8 in. By how much does the diameter change when the ring is transferred from ice water to boiling water, if the temperature coefficient of linear expansion is 14.3×10^{-6} per C. degree?

10. In order to fasten a steel shaft and a pulley together, the shaft is made oversize and then shrunk by cooling until it just fits the hole in the pulley. To what size should the shaft be turned down at 20° C. in order that when the shaft is packed in "dry ice" at −78° C. its diameter will be exactly 2 in. for insertion in the pulley?

11. With what force must a steel measuring tape $\frac{1}{2}$ in. wide and 0.014 in. thick be pulled in order to compensate for a temperature drop of 25 fahrenheit degrees? Take 30×10^6 lb. per sq. in. as Young's modulus for steel.

12. A copper rod 2.54 cm. in diameter expands in length by 1 part in 400 when its temperature is raised from 0° to 150° C. What compressive force must be applied to the rod to prevent this expansion?

13. Iron is poured into a spherical mold 5 in. in diameter at its melting point of 1530° C. In solidifying it shrinks 3 per cent in volume, and as it cools to 20° C. it contracts further. If α for cast iron has the average value of 0.000016 per centigrade degree over this temperature range, what is the volume of the casting at 20° C.?

14. A Pyrex glass flask is fitted with an open tube having a sectional area of 0.2 sq. cm. At 15° C., 250 cu. cm. of glycerine are placed in the flask, the free surface of the liquid being in the tube. If the flask and its contents are heated to 50° C., how far will the glycerine advance in the tube? Neglect the expansion of the tube.

15. A steel tank is filled with kerosene when the temperature is 30° F., at which temperature its volume is 55 gallons. How much of the liquid will overflow when the temperature becomes 60° F.?

*16. In carrying out Regnault's method for determining the absolute expansion of mercury, the two tubes of this liquid were maintained at temperatures of 0° C. and 100° C. and the top of the cold column stood 152.3 cm. above the horizontal connecting tube. What should be the reading at the top of the column of hot mercury?

17. A mercury thermometer which is used to measure the temperature of a steam bath reads 98.5° C., and the thermometer stem above the 30° mark projects into a region where the temperature is 20° C. The thermometer is made from Jena glass having a cubical expansion coefficient of 0.253×10^{-4} per centigrade degree. Compute the temperature of the bath.

Chapter XV

Calorimetry and Change of State

---

155. Heat Units.—Among the various effects produced by heat, two of the most important are change of temperature and change of state. Either of these effects might be used to establish units for quantity of heat. As a matter of convenience, heat units are based upon the change of temperature of definite quantities of water.

It is common experience that more heat is needed to bring a kettleful of water to the boiling point than a cupful, starting in both cases with cold water at the same temperature. Further investigation shows that the quantity of heat required to produce a given rise of temperature is directly proportional to the amount of water heated. Again, to increase the temperature of any given amount of water through, say 60 degrees, takes more heat than to raise the same amount through 30 degrees; in fact, it takes twice as much. Thus, the heat required is proportional to the *amount of water* and to the *rise of temperature*. In consequence, the unit of heat is chosen as the quantity of heat needed to raise the temperature of a unit mass of water through one degree.

Two units of heat are in common use: the calorie (cal.) and the British thermal unit (Btu.). The *calorie* is the quantity of heat required to raise the temperature of 1 gm. of water through 1 centigrade degree. The *British thermal unit* is the quantity of heat required to raise the temperature of 1 lb. of water through 1 fahrenheit degree. It can be shown readily that there are 252 cal. in 1 Btu. Once the units of heat are established, it is a simple matter to compute the amount of heat needed to produce a given temperature elevation in any mass of water. Thus, to raise 5 kg. of water from 10° C. to 70° C. requires $5 \times 1000 \times 60 = 300,000$ cal., and to raise 50 lb. of water from 40° F. to 200° F. requires $50 \times 160 = 8000$ Btu.

While the foregoing statements are sufficiently exact for most practical purposes, actually, the quantity of heat required to raise unit mass of water through one degree varies slightly from point to point along the thermometer scale. The *mean calorie* is defined as one one-hundredth part of the heat required to raise 1 gm. of water from 0° to 100° C.; the heat required to raise 1 gm. of water from 15° to 16° C. is very close to the mean value.

·**156. Specific Heat.**—While the calorie of heat will raise one gram of water through one centigrade degree, it must not be thought that the calorie will raise one gram of other substances through the same temperature interval. Roughly, only $\frac{1}{11}$ cal. is needed to raise 1 gm. of copper through 1 centigrade degree, $\frac{1}{30}$ cal. will suffice for platinum, and so on. The numerical value is a characteristic of the material and is known as its *specific heat*.

The specific heat of a substance is the number of calories needed to raise 1 gm. of it through 1 centigrade degree, or, what amounts to the same thing, *the number of British thermal units needed to raise 1 lb. of the substance through 1 fahrenheit degree.* The value of the specific heat varies slightly with temperature; thus, for copper it is 0.093 cal/(gm. °C.) or 0.093 Btu/(lb. °F.) at 20° C., but is 0.096 at 200° C.

The specific heats of some solids and liquids are given in the following table. These are average values for the temperatures listed and the units are those just mentioned.

Specific Heats

	Temperature, °C	Specific heat
Alcohol (ethyl).......	0– 40	0.59
Aluminum...........	0– 100	0.21
Copper.............	0– 100	0.093
Glass, ordinary.......	10– 50	0.14
Ice.................	−20– 0	0.50
Iron................	0–1000	0.15
Iron................	0– 100	0.11
Lead...............	0– 300	0.032
Mercury............	0– 100	0.033
Platinum...........	20– 100	0.032

The definition of specific heat shows that in order to raise a mass m of a body having a specific heat c through a temperature range t, the quantity of heat required is

$$Q = mct \qquad\qquad (102)$$

This expression also shows the quantity of heat which must be emitted by the body to lower its temperature by *t* degrees. In this equation *t* stands for *change* of temperature, say from t_1 to t_2 degrees, an interval small enough to permit the specific heat value to be regarded as constant.

Thus, 50 gm. of lead in being raised from 10° to 200° C. will absorb 50 × 0.032 × 190 = 304 cal. Again, if 10 lb. of iron are cooled from 800° F. to 30° F., the heat given off will be 10 × 0.15 × 770 = 1155 Btu.

157. Calorimetry.—The measurement of heat quantities is called *calorimetry* and is carried out by mixing the substances, originally at different temperatures, and allowing the temperatures to become equalized. This *method of mixtures* makes use of the following principles: 1. When two bodies, initially at different temperatures, are placed in good thermal contact with each other, *there is a transfer of heat from the hot body to the cold body*, the system finally reaching a condition of equilibrium at some temperature which is uniform throughout. 2. *The heat given off by the hot body is equal to that taken on by the cold body*, provided no heat is transferred to or from the surroundings. The application of these facts makes it possible to determine some unknown factor of an experiment in which several substances at different temperatures are brought together.

Suppose it is desired to find the temperature that results when 500 gm. of water at 80° C. are mixed with 200 gm. of water at 10° C. The resulting temperature *x* will be such that the heat given off by the 500 gm. of water in falling from 80° to *x*° equals that absorbed by the 200 gm. of water in rising from 10° to *x*°. Thus,

$$500 \times (80 - x) = 200 \times (x - 10)$$

from which the temperature of the mixture is found to be *x* = 60° C.

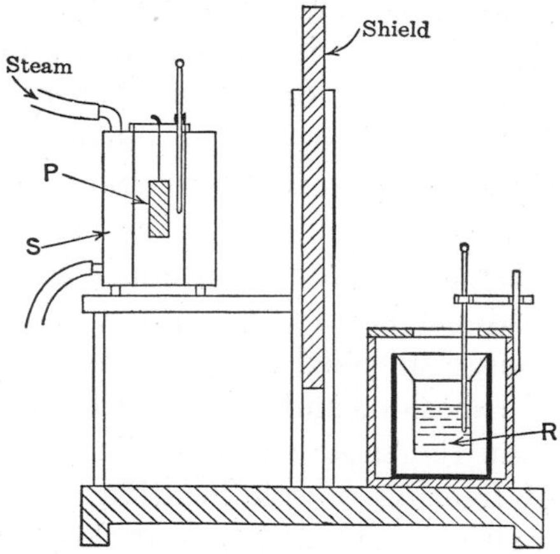

Specific heat may be measured by the method of mixtures; one form of apparatus for this purpose is shown in Fig. 167. A test sample *P* of known mass is heated in a steam-jacketed compartment

Fig. 167. Apparatus for measuring specific heat

S to a measured high temperature; the calorimeter *R*, a heat-insulated metal vessel containing a known amount of water at a known temperature, is pushed directly under the heated compartment and the sample is allowed to drop into it, whereupon the calorimeter is quickly moved away to prevent its absorbing heat from the jacket, and the resulting temperature of the mixture is noted. To find the specific heat of the test sample from the data thus obtained, equate the heat given off by the sample to that taken on by the water and calorimeter, using equation (102) to express each of these heat quantities.

In a particular test, a 300-gm. sample of unknown specific heat c was heated to 98.5° C. and dropped into 600 gm. of water at 19.0° C. contained in a 140-gm. copper calorimeter, and the resulting temperature was found to be 22.4° C. The heat equation follows:

$300 \times c \times (98.5 - 22.4)$

$$= 600 \times 1 \times (22.4 - 19.0) + 140 \times 0.093 \times (22.4 - 19.0)$$
$$= (600 + 13.0) \times 3.4$$

from which the specific heat of the sample is $c = 0.091$ cal/(gm.°C.).

The product of the mass of a calorimeter and its specific heat, called its *water equivalent*, is a quantity that is useful in calorimetric computations. In the foregoing illustration, the 140-gm. calorimeter is equivalent to $140 \times 0.093 = 13.0$ gm. of water, which means that 13.0 gm. of water would experience the same temperature rise as the 140-gm. copper calorimeter for an equal absorption of heat.

158. Melting and Freezing.—The change of state which occurs when matter is transformed from the solid to the liquid phase is called *melting* or *fusion*. When ice melts, the change of state occurs at a fixed temperature, as described in §153, it being assumed that the pressure remains constant. The property of having a fixed melting point is generally characteristic of crystalline substances; in contrast, amorphous substances, such as tar and glass, pass imperceptibly from one state to the other. During the process of melting, the heat energy supplied is used in separating the molecules against the forces of cohesion, and the melted substance has a greater internal energy than the same substance in the solid phase. Fusion is the opposite of freezing or solidification. A solid which has been heated to its melting point will melt at this temperature upon the further application of heat; the corresponding liquid when cooled to this same temperature will freeze as more heat is given off.

If a substance is melting and no heat is supplied to it intentionally, it must be absorbing heat from its surroundings; for this reason melting is sometimes referred to as a cooling process. Conversely, a liquid in freezing must give up heat to its surroundings, and so freezing is sometimes called a heating process. A gram of ice in melting absorbs a definite quantity of heat from its surroundings, and a gram of water in freezing gives up the same quantity of heat to its surroundings. It is reported that this latter fact is utilized in fruit cellars by placing large vats of water near the fruit; should the temperature fall dangerously low, the water would freeze, and the consequent emission of heat would prevent freezing of the fruit.

Most liquids contract in the process of freezing, but there are some important exceptions. Water undergoes a remarkable expansion when freezing, ice at 0° C. having a density only 0.91 that of water at the same temperature. This expansion accounts for the bursting of water pipes when the water in them freezes. Type metal, an alloy containing antimony as the principal constituent, also expands upon freezing (solidifying); this action fills the mold and produces a good casting.

The quantity of heat needed to melt a unit mass of a solid without change of temperature is called the *heat of fusion*. If the heat of fusion of a solid is represented by L, then the quantity of heat Q needed to melt a mass m at constant temperature will be

$$Q = mL \qquad (103)$$

This expression shows the number of calories which must be transferred to m gm. of the solid to melt it or transferred from m gm. of the corresponding liquid to solidify it, where the heat of fusion L is expressed in calories per gram. If m is expressed in pounds, then obviously L must be in British thermal units per pound in order that Q may be in British thermal units.

Under standard atmospheric pressure, the melting point of ice is 0° C. or 32° F. Experiment shows that 1 gm. of ice in melting under these conditions absorbs 80 cal. from its surroundings; conversely, 1 gm. of water in freezing dissipates 80 cal. to its surroundings. This means that under standard pressure the heat of fusion of ice is 80 cal. per gm.; this is equivalent to 144 Btu. per lb. The ratio of these quantities is 5 to 9.

The heat of fusion of ice can be measured by observing the temperature change when a measured amount of ice is dropped into a measured amount of hot water, and equating the heat given off by the water to that absorbed by the ice.

In such a test, some surface-dried ice at 0° C. was dropped into a calorimeter containing water at 25° C.; the mass of water (including the water equivalent of the calorimeter) was 190 gm. After the ice was melted, the temperature was found to be 15° C. and the calorimeter was observed to have 20 gm. of water more than previously. In this test the hot water gave off 190×10 cal., the heat required to melt the ice was $20 \times L$ cal., and the water thus formed absorbed 20×15 cal. in coming to the final temperature. Consequently, if any effects due to the surroundings may be neglected, $190 \times 10 = 20 \times L + 20 \times 15$; whence $L = 80$ cal. per gm.

The accompanying table gives the values of the heat of fusion for several substances, all at a standard pressure of 1 atmosphere.

Heats of Fusion

	Cal/gm.	Btu/lb.
Aluminum.........	71	128
Copper...........	43.3	77.9
Ice..............	80	144
Lead............	5.4	9.7
Mercury.........	2.8	5.0

159. Effect of Pressure on Freezing.—The freezing point of a liquid is affected by the pressure to which it is subjected, but only to a small extent. For liquids which contract upon freezing, an increase of pressure raises the freezing point; for liquids which expand upon freezing, such as water, an increase of pressure lowers the freezing point. This statement follows from the fact that pressure on a body tends to prevent its expansion, and consequently an increase of pressure upon a liquid that expands upon freezing would tend to prevent its solidification by lowering the freezing point.

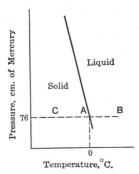

Fig. 168. Influence of pressure on the freezing point of water

The behavior of water is represented graphically in Fig. 168, in which pressure is plotted against temperature. The curve slopes upward to the left and a pressure increase of 100 atmospheres lowers the freezing point by less than 1 centigrade degree.

A curve such as that shown represents a state of equilibrium between the solid and liquid states of the substance in question. Consider a mixture of ice and water, for example, at 0° C. and 76 cm. pressure, to be represented by point *A* on the curve. To raise the temperature of the mixture at this pressure, say to temperature *B*, it would be necessary to supply enough heat first to melt all of the ice present, and then to cause the desired temperature rise. Similarly, to lower the temperature of the mixture, say to temperature *C*, enough heat must be transferred from it first to freeze all of the water present and then to lower the temperature. In the diagram, therefore, the region to the right of the curve represents the liquid state and that to the left of the curve represents the solid state. The line itself shows the relative conditions of temperature and pressure under which ice and water can coexist in equilibrium.

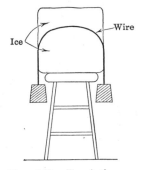

FIG. 169. Regelation experiment

The effect of increased pressure in lowering the melting point of ice is well illustrated by a classical experiment in which a small wire, weighted at the ends, is placed across a cake of ice as in Fig. 169. The wire gradually melts its way through the ice, and as it does so, the groove formed above becomes solid ice again, leaving the cake intact. This process, known as *regelation*, is explained as follows: The pressure beneath the wire is greater than atmospheric, causing the melting point of the ice there to be slightly below 0° C. But since that ice

Melting Points

	°C.	°F.
Aluminum.........	660	1220
Copper............	1083	1981
Hydrogen.........	−259	−434
Iron.............	1535	2795
Lead.............	327	621
Mercury..........	−38.87	−37.97
Platinum.........	1755	3191
Tin..............	232	450
Tungsten.........	3370	6098

is at 0°, it is momentarily above its melting point and a little of it
melts, causing a slight reduction of temperature; the wire settles
down and the water formed is squeezed into the region above it.
Here the pressure is standard and the water, which is now slightly
below 0°, freezes again. During the process the heat given off by
the water in freezing flows downward through the wire and serves
to melt the ice below.

The melting (or freezing) points of a number of substances at
standard atmospheric pressure are given in the table ahead.

*160. Fusion of Mixtures.—The presence of impurities usually has
the effect of lowering the melting point of a substance. In calibrating
a thermometer at 0° C. by immersion in a mixture of ice and water,
it is necessary to use distilled water to prevent errors from this
cause. The addition of table salt to ice (1 part of salt to 2 parts of
ice by weight) lowers the melting point from 32° F. to about 0° F.,
and forms a useful freezing mixture.

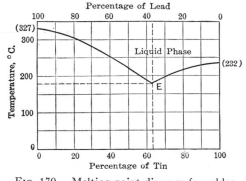

FIG. 170.   Melting-point diagram for solder

In a mixture of two metals to form an alloy, the presence of each
constituent lowers the melting point of the other. Fig. 170 is a
melting-point diagram for solder composed of lead and tin in various
proportions by weight. The different alloys thus formed start to
melt at various temperatures as shown, the minimum being 181° C.
for an alloy composed of 63 per cent of tin and 37 per cent of lead.
The alloy having the lowest melting point *E* is known as an *eutectic
mixture* and its melting point is called the *eutectic temperature*.

When an eutectic mixture is allowed to solidify slowly, its components crystallize out in the proportions in which they are present
in the liquid, and thus the liquid remains unchanged in composition
as solidification progresses. Other mixtures do not have this property.

If a mixture of 80 per cent of tin and 20 per cent of lead, for example, is completely melted and slowly cooled, some tin will crystallize out starting at 215° C. (see curve), and the remaining liquid if examined at 200° will be found to consist of 72 per cent of tin and 28 per cent of lead. The same conclusion is reached for alloys in which the lead predominates. A mixture of 20 per cent of tin and 80 per cent of lead when melted and slowly cooled will start to solidify at 305° C., and the liquid remaining at 200° will consist of 57 per cent of tin and 43 per cent of lead. In this case, the material which solidifies contains a little tin with the lead and forms a homogeneous substance; for this reason it is called a *solid solution* of tin in lead. As solidification progresses the concentration of tin in the solid solution increases until point E on the curve is reached. Only the eutectic alloy solidifies completely at a constant temperature and without change of·composition in either the liquid or solid phases as freezing progresses.

161. Process of Evaporation.—Changing a substance to the vapor state is a process called vaporization. The term vaporization is a general one and includes: (1) *evaporation*, which is a conversion from the liquid to the vapor state that occurs only at the surface; (2) *boiling*, which is similar to evaporation but which takes place throughout the interior of the liquid; and (3) *sublimation*, which is a conversion from the solid to the vapor state directly without passage through the liquid state. Boiling and sublimation are considered later in this chapter.

Evaporation goes on at all temperatures, and continues until the liquid disappears or until the space above the liquid has become saturated with the vapor. In the process of evaporation a liquid is gradually transformed to a vapor by loss of molecules at its surface. Since the molecules of the liquid are moving about in all directions and with various speeds, there will be many instances where they approach the liquid surface with sufficient velocity to carry them beyond the range of attraction of the surface layer; these will leave the liquid and become molecules of vapor.

It will be inferred from such a conception of evaporation that the molecules which succeed in escaping through the surface are those having the higher velocities, and that consequently the average molecular velocity in the liquid is lessened by evaporation. Such is the case, for evaporation lowers the temperature of the liquid; thus, water placed in a porous jar is cooled by evaporation through the walls, and the skin is cooled by evaporation of perspiration. A person uncomfortably warm through fever may be sponged with alcohol to afford relief.

162. Saturated Vapor.—A saturated vapor can be produced by allowing a liquid to evaporate into a confined space, as illustrated in Fig. 171. As the process of evaporation continues, more and more molecules leave the liquid and assume the vapor state. These molecules of vapor are also in motion, and some of them strike the liquid surface and return to the liquid. The number

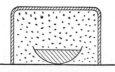

FIG. 171. Production of saturated vapor

which reenter will increase as evaporation continues, until finally a state of equilibrium is reached wherein the same number of molecules pass from the liquid into the vapor as from the vapor back into the liquid in a given time. The space above the liquid is then said to be *saturated* with the vapor. Sometimes an unconfined space may become virtually saturated with vapor, as occurs with the atmosphere on a humid day, but ordinarily the conditions necessary for the production of saturated vapor are: (1) *the presence of the generating liquid*, and (2) *a confined space.*

In the evaporation process, the vapor above the liquid becomes more dense and the pressure due to this vapor becomes greater, reaching a maximum value at the point of saturation. The maximum vapor pressure of a liquid is called the *saturated vapor pressure*. Thus, for water at 20° C. the vapor pressure would build up to a maximum value of 1.75 cm. of mercury; this value is the saturated vapor pressure of water at this temperature.

The value of the saturated vapor pressure is practically unaffected by the presence of other gases provided no chemical reactions occur. Thus, for water at 20° C., if the evaporation occurs in a vacuum, the pressure builds up to the value 1.75 cm. of mercury; but if the enclosure contains dry air at the standard pressure of 76.0 cm. of mercury, the pressure builds up to an absolute value of 76.0 + 1.75 or 77.75 cm. of mercury, of which 76.0 cm. is the partial pressure due to dry air and 1.75 cm. is the partial pressure due to water vapor, § 139. Evaporation continues, regardless of other gases, until a partial pressure due to the vapor is established which is equal to the saturated vapor pressure of the liquid at the existing temperature.

In describing the production of a saturated vapor, no reference was made to the size of the enclosure in which the evaporation occurred. The various effects mentioned take place whatever the size of the enclosure, the only difference being that the larger the enclosure, the longer the time required for saturation. The pressure of a saturated vapor is, then, independent of the volume occupied by the vapor. If the evaporation were to take place in an otherwise empty cylinder of variable volume, as in Fig. 172, the piston might be moved up or down without affecting the pressure in the cylinder. These considerations show that it is impossible to change the pressure of a saturated vapor by varying the volume. If the volume of the vapor is reduced, some of the vapor will condense to a liquid, and if the volume is increased, some of the liquid will vaporize, but the pressure remains constant and its value depends only upon the material and the temperature. In this respect a saturated vapor behaves quite differently from an ideal gas (§ 137), the pressure of which, in accordance with Boyle's Law, increases to double value when its volume is halved. The curves of Fig. 173 contrast the behavior of a saturated vapor and of an ideal gas on a pressure-volume diagram. The temperature is assumed constant in both cases.

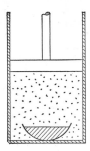

FIG. 172. Saturated vapor in cylinder

It is found by test that the saturated vapor pressure of a liquid has materially different values when measured at different tempera-

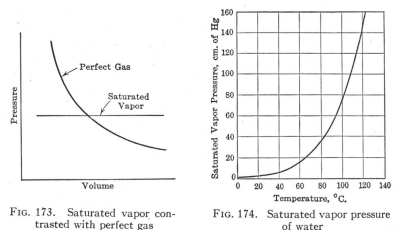

FIG. 173. Saturated vapor contrasted with perfect gas

FIG. 174. Saturated vapor pressure of water

tures. For example, the saturated vapor pressure of water when measured at 20° C. is 1.75 cm. of mercury, at 30° C. it has the value 3.17 cm., at 50° C. it is 9.25 cm., and at 100° C. the saturated vapor pressure is 76.00 cm. of mercury or exactly 1 atmosphere. These pressure-temperature values are plotted to scale in Fig. 174.

The saturated vapor pressures of a few liquids at various temperatures appear in the following table:

Saturated Vapor Pressure of Liquids

	Temperature, °C.	Pressure, cm. Hg.
Alcohol (ethyl).........	20	4.4
Alcohol (ethyl).........	50	22.2
Alcohol (ethyl).........	78.5	76.00
Mercury.............	20	0.00012
Mercury.............	100	0.0273
Mercury.............	356.7	76.00
Mercury.............	400	157.4
Water.................	0	0.458
Water.................	20	1.75
Water.................	50	9.25
Water.................	100	76.00
Water.................	150	357.0

163. Boiling.—Evaporation has been described as the escape of molecules from the liquid to the vapor state at the surface of a liquid. Boiling consists of evaporation throughout the body of the liquid, bubbles of saturated vapor being formed within the liquid which gather additional molecules and so increase in size as they rise to the surface.

The bubbles which are produced in the process of boiling would be unable to form if the pressure exerted upon them from the outside were greater than their own internal pressure. The external pressure consists of the atmospheric or gas pressure on the liquid surface plus whatever pressure is due to the liquid above the bubble. The internal pressure is the saturated vapor pressure of the liquid at its existing temperature. Hence, *a liquid cannot boil unless the saturated vapor pressure of the liquid is equal to* (or infinitesimally greater than) *the pressure exerted on the liquid.*

Boiling can be brought about either by *increasing the temperature* until the corresponding vapor pressure is equal to the pressure on the liquid (see Fig. 174), or by *reducing the pressure* on the liquid to the value of the saturated vapor pressure. Water, initially at 50° C., will serve as an illustration. When it is heated in the open air it will boil at 100° C., at which temperature the saturated vapor pressure will be 76.0 cm. of mercury or 1 atmosphere. Or, it may be made to boil at 50° C. by lowering the pressure upon it to 9.25 cm. of mercury, which is the value of the saturated vapor pressure of water at 50° C. From these considerations it is seen that the curve, Fig. 174, may also be called a boiling-point curve, since it shows the relation between boiling point and applied pressure. The difficulty of cooking by boiling at high altitudes, where low pressures prevail, may be inferred from this curve.

As in the case of the freezing-point curve, Fig. 168, the boiling-point curve, Fig. 174, represents a condition of equilibrium between two phases of a substance, in this case between the liquid and vapor states of water. The region to the left of the curve represents the liquid state and that to the right of the curve represents the vapor state.

The boiling point of a liquid is also influenced by the presence of impurities in it, impurities tending to raise the boiling point. Thus, a pinch of salt added to a kettleful of water will raise the temperature of boiling to a higher value, an effect desired sometimes in cooking. A thermometer which is being calibrated at 100° C. should be placed in the saturated steam close to the water surface rather than in the boiling water, for the temperature of the latter, if impure, may be uncertain.

The following table shows the boiling points of a number of pure substances at standard atmospheric pressure:

Boiling Points

	°C.	°F.
Alcohol (ethyl)	78.5	171.3
Copper	2300	4170
Helium	− 268.9	− 452
Hydrogen	− 252.7	− 422.9
Iron	3000	5400
Lead	1620	2950
Mercury	356.9	674.4
Oxygen	− 183.0	− 297.4
Sulfur	444.6	832.3

164. Heat of Vaporization.—The process of vaporization requires work to be done in overcoming molecular attraction and makes it necessary to supply heat in order to vaporize a substance. The quantity of heat which must be supplied per unit mass of liquid to convert it to vapor without change of temperature is called the *heat of vaporization*. The equation used in § 158 for calculating heat quantities during fusion, namely

$$Q = mL$$

may also be used to determine heat quantities during vaporization if L is taken to represent the heat of vaporization. This equation shows how much heat must be imparted to a mass m of liquid to vaporize it at constant temperature, or how much heat that mass of vapor must give off in order to condense under the same conditions.

The heat of vaporization depends on the temperature at which change of state occurs, and the temperature in turn is determined by the pressure. The values of the heat of vaporization L for a few liquids at standard atmospheric pressure are given in the following table:

Heats of Vaporization at Standard Boiling Points

	Cal/gm.	Btu/lb.
Alcohol (ethyl).........	204	367
Mercury..............	68	122
Oxygen..............	51	92
Water................	539	970

If heat is applied to some water in an open beaker, the pressure remaining at 76 cm. of mercury, the water will boil at 100° C. and the heat of vaporization will be 539 cal. per gm. If instead, water in a beaker at 0° C. is placed in the receiver of an air pump, and the air pressure therein is reduced to 0.46 cm., the water will boil at that temperature and the heat of vaporization will be 599 cal. per gm. For water boiling at high pressures and temperatures, the heat of vaporization is less than the values mentioned, and at the critical temperature (§ 177) the heat of vaporization is zero.

The heat of vaporization of water can be determined by passing saturated steam into cool water within a calorimeter, and measuring the change of temperature. The amount of steam condensed is found by weighing the contents of the calorimeter before and after the test, and the temperature rise of the calorimeter and its contents is measured by a thermometer. If m gm. of water are raised from t_c to $t_h°$ C. as a result of admitting M gm. of steam at $T°$ C., the heat absorbed by the water will be $m(t_h - t_c)$ and must equal that given off by the steam, namely, $M[L + (T - t_h)]$. From this relation, the heat of vaporization L at temperature T can be found readily.

Engineers frequently use "steam tables" in determining the performance of boilers. These tables include the temperature at which

Properties of Saturated Steam

Absolute pressure, lb. per sq. in.	Temperature, °F.	Btu. per lb. above 32° F.		
		Internal energy of water	Heat of vaporization	Total
1	101.8	70	1035	1105
2	126.1	94	1022	1116
5	162.3	130	1000	1130
10	193.2	161	982	1143
14.7	212.0	180	970	1150
20	228.0	196	960	1156
50	281.0	250	923	1173
75	307.6	277	904	1181
100	327.8	298	888	1186
150	358.4	330	863	1193
200	381.8	355	843	1198
250	401.0	376	824	1200
300	417.3	394	808	1202
400	444.6	424	780	1204
500	467.0	450	754	1204

change of state occurs, the internal energy of the water, the heat of vaporization, and the sum of the two preceding quantities. A few scattered entries from such a table will show the variation of the heat of vaporization with the temperature at which change of state occurs.

165. Sublimation.—Under the proper conditions of temperature and pressure, a substance can pass directly from the solid to the vapor state, without liquefying as an intermediate step. Iodine crystals vaporize in this manner under ordinary room conditions, and the same is true of naphthalene moth balls, and "dry ice" (solid carbon dioxide). It has been found recently that carbon behaves similarly at 3800° K. These are illustrations of sublimation.

The relation between sublimation, freezing, and boiling is illustrated for water in Fig. 175. The line *FX* is a redrawing of the freezing-point curve; *BX* is likewise a redrawing of the boiling-point curve; and *SX* is a corresponding curve representing equilibrium between the solid and vapor states, that is, the sublimation curve. The areas separated by these curves represent the solid, liquid, and vapor states, as indicated.

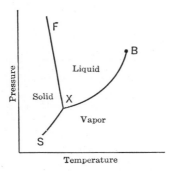

FIG. 175. Triple-point diagram for water

The point of intersection *X* of the three curves is of special interest. Every point on the curve *FX* represents a state of equilibrium between the liquid and solid states; similarly every point on *BX* represents a state of equilibrium between the liquid and vapor states; consequently, the intersection point *X* denotes a state of equilibrium among all three states. This point is called the *triple point*, and represents a condition of pressure and temperature at which the water can freeze and boil simultaneously. To reach this point the temperature is lowered sufficiently to cause freezing, and at the same time the pressure is lowered sufficiently to cause boiling. The triple point for water occurs at a temperature of +0.0098° C. and a pressure of 0.46 cm. of mercury.

The effect of high pressures upon the value of the freezing point has been investigated by Professor Percy W. Bridgman. The upper portion of the freezing-point curve *FX* is found to undergo some marked changes of shape, and several varieties of ice are formed having properties different from those of ice at atmospheric pressure. For one variety the freezing-point line shifts to the right at extremely high pressures to such an extent that at about 20,000 kg. per sq. cm. water may be frozen at 70° C.

The boiling-point curve, *BX*, comes to a definite end at a point *B*, for which the temperature is 374° C. This is the critical temperature of water (§ 177); at higher temperatures steam cannot be condensed into water, however great the applied pressure.

It might be mentioned that although freezing normally occurs at some point on the curve *FX*, water which is quiescent and free from impurities may be cooled several degrees below its freezing point without solidification. This phenomenon, called *supercooling* or *undercooling*, represents a condition of unstable equilibrium. Upon dropping particles of ice into the supercooled liquid, solidification takes place immediately, and the temperature rises rapidly to the normal freezing point. Similarly, under certain conditions water may be *superheated* several degrees above its boiling point, but when boiling starts the temperature falls to the normal value. This use of the term "superheated" should not be confused with the common use of the word in connection with steam. Steam is superheated by removing it from the water and heating it; the steam then becomes a vapor that is above its liquefaction temperature and acquires the behavior of an ideal gas. Supercooling and superheating are also observed with other substances.

166. Calorimetry Involving Change of State.—When substances at different temperatures, and possibly in various states, are mixed and allowed to settle to equilibrium, some of them may vaporize, condense, melt, or freeze. In these processes heat is either taken on or given off and must be considered in applying the method of mixtures. A hypothetical problem will illustrate the procedure.

Suppose 5 lb. of steam at atmospheric pressure, superheated to a temperature of 250° F., together with 10 lb. of ice at 20° F., to be introduced simultaneously into a copper calorimeter weighing 4 lb. and containing 60 lb. of water at 70° F. The specific heats in British thermal units per pound per fahrenheit degree are as follows for the temperature ranges involved: steam, 0.48; ice, 0.50; and copper, 0.093. The heats of fusion and vaporization for water are respectively 144 and 970 Btu. per lb. Calculate the resulting temperature of the mixture, neglecting heat dissipated to other bodies.

The problem will first be solved by equating the heat given off by the steam to that taken on by the ice, water, and calorimeter, assuming the resulting temperature x to be between 70° and 212° F. The heat given off by the steam consists of three parts: $5 \times 0.48 \times (250 - 212) = 91$ Btu. in cooling to 212° F.; $5 \times 970 = 4850$ Btu. in condensing into water at 212° F.; and $5 \times (212 - x)$ Btu. in cooling to the final temperature x. Similarly, the heat taken on by the ice consists of three parts: $10 \times 0.50 \times (32 - 20) = 60$ Btu. in rising to 32° F.; $10 \times 144 = 1440$ Btu. in melting; and $10 \times (x - 32)$ Btu. in rising to the final temperature. For the water and calorimeter, the heat taken on is $(60 \times 1 + 4 \times 0.093) \times (x - 70) = 60.37 \times (x - 70)$ Btu. Then

$$91 + 4850 + 5 \times (212 - x) = 60 + 1440 + 10 \times (x - 32) +$$
$$60.37 \times (x - 70)$$

from which $x = 120°$ F.

This problem will now be solved in another way by calculating the internal energy of the several components before mixture with regard to some convenient reference state, and then determining the effect that this energy will produce on the mixture.

With reference to water at 32° F., the internal energy values are:

Steam:
$$5 \times 0.48 \times (250 - 212) = + \quad 91$$
$$5 \times 970 = +4850$$
$$5 \times (212 - 32) = + \quad 900 \Big\} +8135 \text{ Btu.}$$

Water: $\qquad 60 \times 1 \times (70 - 32) = +2280$

Calorimeter: $\qquad 4 \times 0.093 \times (70 - 32) = + \quad 14$

Ice:
$$-10 \times 0.50 \times (32 - 20) = - \quad 60 \Big\} -1500$$
$$-10 \times 144 = -1440$$

$$+6635 \text{ Btu.}$$

This total energy value of 6635 Btu. is to be distributed among $5 + 10 + 60$ or 75 lb. of water and 4 lb. of copper. Since the 4-lb. copper calorimeter is the equivalent of $4 \times 0.093 = 0.37$ lb. of water, the 6635 Btu. will be imparted to 75.37 lb. of water. This will cause a temperature rise of $6635 \div 75.37 = 88$ fahrenheit degrees. Thus, the final temperature will be $88 + 32 = 120°$ F.

The second method is of advantage in that it is not necessary to make any assumption as to the probable final temperature. This method would also be helpful in solving a problem where the resulting temperature is 32° F. with some ice unmelted (total internal energy of system above water at 32° F. would be negative), or where the resulting temperature is 212° F. with some steam uncondensed (total internal energy of system sufficient to raise entire system to 212° F., leaving a surplus to vaporize part of the water). In such cases the calculation will show the amount of ice unmelted or the amount of steam uncondensed.

167. Heat of Combustion.—When a substance is burned or oxidized it produces heat, and the amount of heat liberated per unit mass upon complete oxidation is called its *heat of combustion*. The heats of combustion of several fuels are tabulated in round numbers as follows:

Heats of Combustion

	Cal. per gm.	Btu. per lb.
Coal (anthracite).....	7,600 to 8,400	13,500 to 15,000
Coke...............	6,900	12,600
Gasoline............	11,000 to 11,400	20,000 to 20,500
Illuminating gas......	5,500 to 6,400	9,900 to 11,500
Wood (various).......	4,000 to 4,500	7,000 to 8,000

The heats of combustion of carbon and of a few organic compounds are expressed below in calories per mol, § 140, but can be converted to calories per gram without difficulty. Methane (marsh gas) will be considered as an illustration. The chemical formula CH_4 implies that the molecule of this compound is composed of 1 atom of carbon (C) and four atoms of hydrogen (H). Since the atomic weights of these elements are $C = 12$, $H = 1$, the compound has a molar weight of $12 + 4(1) = 16$ gm., and therefore its heat of combustion

Heats of Combustion

	Formula	Cal. per mol
Acetylene............	C_2H_2	312,000
Alcohol (ethyl).........	C_2H_5OH	328,000
Alcohol (methyl).......	C_2H_3OH	170,900
Carbon...............	C	97,300
Methane.............	CH_4	210,800

per gram will be $210,800 \div 16 = 13,170$ cal. In engineering, heats of combustion are usually considered positive. In thermochemistry, the opposite practice is generally followed, heat evolved in a reaction being regarded as negative, and heat absorbed positive. The use of signs is conventional, and need cause no confusion.

Measurements of heat of combustion are made in combustion calorimeters, one type of which is shown in section in Fig. 176. The substance to be tested is placed in a platinum crucible *C* mounted within a strong steel container S lined with platinum, gold or porcelain to prevent corrosion. Oxygen under a pressure of several atmospheres is admitted at O and next the bomb is tightly sealed. It is then placed in a calorimeter containing water, and an electric current is passed through a small heating coil H which dips into the

test substance. When the wire becomes incandescent, combustion takes place and the rise of temperature of the water is observed.

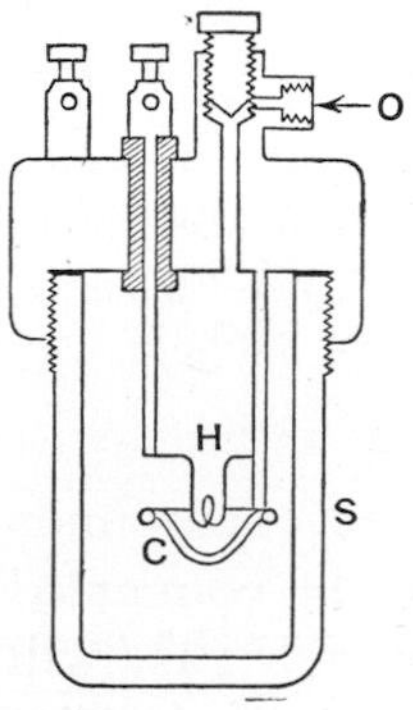

A different procedure is used for measuring the heat of combustion of gaseous fuels. The gas is burned at a constant rate within a chamber through which water is circulating uniformly. From a knowledge of the rate of water flow and of the temperatures of the water as it enters and leaves the chamber, the energy liberated per unit volume of fuel can be determined.

FIG. 176. Bomb of a combustion calorimeter

In some fields of study heat quantities are expressed in terms of the *kilogram-calorie*; this is equal to 1000 calories. Food values are stated in the larger unit for convenience; thus, the fuel value of the food consumed by the average American per day is 3250 kilogram-calories.

*168. Heat of Formation.—Every chemical reaction is attended by a definite exchange of heat. When elements unite to form a compound, the number of calories emitted or absorbed per mol of compound produced is called the *heat of formation* for the temperature prevailing. The following table gives the heats of formation for a few compounds at approximately 20° C., energy liberated being regarded as negative.

Heats of Formation

	Formula	Cal. per mol
Acetylene...............	C_2H_2	$+ 54,400$
Carbon dioxide.........	CO_2	$- 94,400$
Copper sulfate.........	$CuSO_4$	$-178,800$
Methane...............	CH_4	$- 20,400$
Sulfuric acid...........	H_2SO_4	$-189,800$
Water (liquid)..........	H_2O	$- 68,400$
Water (vapor)..........	H_2O	$- 57,800$
Zinc sulfate............	$ZnSO_4$	$-230,000$

The heat of combustion of a fuel can be calculated from a table of heats of formation, and the fact that compounds are not usually made directly from their elements does not detract from the usefulness of such a table. Let it be required to find the heat of combustion of methane, according to the equation

$$CH_4 + 2O_2 \rightarrow CO_2 + 2H_2O$$

If the heat of formation of 1 mol of CH_4 is subtracted from the heats of formation of 1 mol of CO_2 and 2 mols of H_2O, the remainder is the energy involved in combustion. Hence the heat of combustion of methane is $(-94,400) + 2(-68,400) - (-20,400) = -210,800$ cal. per mol. This result is the same as in the preceding section, with proper regard for signs.

Substances for which the heat of formation is positive have a peculiar interest. Acetylene (C_2H_2), for example, liberates the heats of combustion of the carbon and hydrogen in burning, and in addition surrenders 54,400 cal. for each mol in decomposing. It is because of this augmented liberation of energy that such compounds make superior fuels.

It will be observed that water has a larger heat of formation than water vapor. The difference between these values is the energy liberated by the condensation of the vapor, and is equal to the heat of vaporization per mol of water at 20° C.

PROBLEMS

1. How many British thermal units are needed to heat 5 gal. of water from 70° F. to 180° F.?

2. How many calories will heat 500 gm. of water from 20° to 90° C.?

3. Find the temperature of 1 cu. ft. of water initially at 40° F. after it has been supplied with 5000 Btu.

4. It is desired to raise the temperature of 5 liters of water at the rate of 1 centigrade degree per min. by means of an electric immersion heater. At what rate must this device supply heat, on the assumption that no energy is wasted?

5. How much heat is necessary to raise the temperature of the air in a room measuring 30 x 20 x 12 ft. from 40° F. to 75° F.? Take the specific heat of air to be 0.24 Btu/(lb. °F.) and the density to be 0.077 lb. per cu. ft.

6. A die-block made of steel is quenched at 850° C. by plunging it into water at 15° C. For careful control of the process it is desired that during the quenching operation the temperature of the water shall not change by more than 5 centigrade degrees. If the steel block weighs 2000 gm., what

is the smallest amount of water that may be used? Take 0.15 cal/(gm.°C.) as the specific heat of steel for the temperature range involved.

7. For heating small homes electrically, thermal storage systems have been devised in which a pile of cement blocks is heated at reduced cost during the off-peak period of the power system. If 2 tons of cement blocks are heated from 200° F. to 600° F. in 8 hr., at what average rate will they supply heat during the following 16 hr. in cooling back to 200° F.? Take the specific heat of cement to be 0.20 Btu/(lb.°F.).

8. How much heat is given off by a solid copper sphere 5 cm. in diameter in cooling from 38° to 30° C.?

9. Determine the resulting temperature when 1 lb. of mercury at 100° C. is poured into a 1-lb. iron dish at 20° C.

10. To determine the specific heat of a metal, a 150-gm. sample of it is heated to 98.0° C. and is dropped into 250 gm. of water at 18.00° C. contained in a copper calorimeter weighing 160 gm. The resulting temperature is 21.72° C.; find the specific heat of the sample.

11. A glass beaker weighing 120 gm. contained 300 gm. of water at 16.0° C. Into the water was placed a 100-gm. mass of aluminum, originally at a temperature of 99.2° C., and the final temperature was found to be 20.8° C. How much heat was dissipated by radiation?

12. A copper calorimeter weighing 150 gm. contains 300 gm. of water at 20° C. Into this are placed 100 gm. of lead at 65° C. and 200 gm. of iron at 80° C. Find the resulting temperature of the mixture.

13. Some water at 60° F. was frozen to form 12 ice cubes, measuring $1\frac{1}{2}$ in. along each edge. How much heat was given off by the water, if the temperature of the cubes is 32° F.?

14. What result is produced by supplying 150,000 cal. to 1 kg. of ice at 0° C.?

15. The windshield of an automobile was covered with a coating of ice at 32° F. An area of 300 sq. in. was melted in 2 min. by a heater that supplies 1 Btu. per sec. If one-third of the energy supplied by the heater is available for melting the ice, how thick was the ice coating?

16. Ice at 0° C. and water at 80° C. are mixed in equal parts by weight. Determine the resulting temperature.

17. How much cracked ice added to 300 cu. cm. of water initially at 18° C. will yield a final temperature of 10° C.?

18. A 150-gm. sample of an alloy is heated to 100° C. and then dropped into a cavity in a large block of ice. If 23 gm. of ice are melted, what is the specific heat of the alloy?

*19. A mixture composed of 40 per cent of tin and 60 per cent of lead is completely melted and cooled slowly. At what temperature will the mixture start to solidify? Describe the composition of the liquid remaining at 200° C.

20. How much heat is needed to convert 1 gm. of ice at 0° to steam at 100° C.?

21. Some steam at 100° C. under atmospheric pressure is passed into 400 gm. of water at 15° C. When the temperature of the water has reached

25° C. the test is stopped and weighing shows that 6.5 gm. of steam have been condensed. Compute the heat of vaporization of water at 100° C. as given by this test; neglect the heat supplied to the container.

22. How many calories will be required to change 1 gm. of ice at −30° C. to steam at 140° C. under atmospheric pressure? Take the specific heat of steam as 0.48 cal/(gm.°C.).

23. Steam at 212° F. and having a density of 0.037 lb/cu. ft. is supplied to a radiator at the rate of 100 cu. ft/hr., and leaves the radiator as water at 100° F. At what rate is heat given off by the radiator?

24. If 20 Btu. of heat are supplied to 1 lb. of water at 200° F., what will be the result?

25. If 100 gm. of steam at 100° C. give off 68,000 cal., what will be the result?

26. A copper calorimeter weighing 200 gm. contains 400 gm. of water at 18° C. Into this are introduced 20 gm. of steam at 135° C. and 40 gm. of ice at −20° C. Compute the resulting temperature. Take the specific heat of steam to be 0.48 cal/(gm.°C.).

27. How much fuel oil is needed to heat a 60-gal. tank full of water from 50° to 140° F.? Assume that the heat of combustion of the oil is 9000 Btu. per lb., of which 65 per cent is useful in heating the water.

28. The steam-heating plant in a small house uses 1 ton·of coal fortnightly in supplying steam at atmospheric pressure to the radiators. Assume that the heat of combustion of the coal is 15,000 Btu. per lb., of which 60 per cent is useful in heating water in the boiler, and that the steam leaves the radiators as water at a temperature of 140° F. Compute the average rate in pounds per hour at which the condensed steam will be returned to the boiler.

Thermal Behavior
of Gases
Chapter XVI

169. Temperature, Pressure, and Volume Relations.—The condition of a gas of known composition is completely determined by three variables; the *temperature* of the gas, the *pressure* which it exerts, and the *volume* that it occupies. For a given amount of the gas, if two of these variables are given, the value of the third becomes known; or if some one variable is kept constant, the relation between the other two can be found. These relationships for actual gases are complicated by the interaction of their molecules, particularly near the temperatures of liquefaction. The analysis is simplified by imagining a so-called "ideal" or "perfect" gas, § 173; such a gas will be assumed in the following analysis of the three gas variables. Air, hydrogen, and other fixed gases, behave very nearly like the ideal gas over wide temperature ranges.

Constant Temperature.—A mass of gas enclosed in a cylinder having a piston, part I of Fig. 177, will occupy a volume at some definite

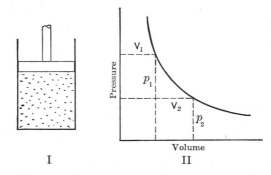

| I | II |

FIG. 177. Pressure-volume relation at constant temperature

temperature that depends upon the pressure exerted upon it. If provision is made to keep the temperature constant, the volume of the gas will vary inversely with the absolute pressure, in accordance with Boyle's Law. This relation is indicated for any two pressure-volume conditions by equation (93) as

$$p_1 V_1 = p_2 V_2$$

and is represented by the hyperbola in part II of the figure.

Constant Pressure.—A mass of gas may be kept at constant pressure by enclosing it in a chamber equipped with a freely moving piston, as indicated in part I of Fig. 178, for the slightest change of pressure

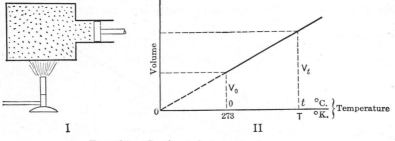

FIG. 178. Gas heated at constant pressure

will cause the piston to move in or out, keeping the pressure inside of the container constant at the value existing on the outside. Upon heating a gas under these conditions, the volume is found to increase with rising temperature in accordance with the relation attributed to the French mathematician and physicist, Jacques A. C. Charles (1746–1823), which is

$$V_t = V_o(1 + \beta t) \tag{104}$$

where V_o and V_t represent the volumes of the gas at $0°$ C. and $t°$ C. respectively, and β is the coefficient of volume expansion of the gas. This variation of volume with temperature is expressed in exactly the same way as for solids and liquids, but the coefficient β for gases is much larger than for those substances, and, moreover, has *almost exactly the same value for all gases.* This value is $\beta = 0.00367 (= \frac{1}{273})$ per centigrade degree, which means that a given amount of gas at $0°$ C. will expand $\frac{1}{273}$ of its volume when heated 1 degree, and will contract by the same amount when cooled 1 degree. Note carefully that this value for β applies only when V_o is the volume at $0°$ C.

Since $0°$ C. is the equivalent of $273°$ K., an increase of $\frac{1}{273}$ in the volume corresponds to an increase of $\frac{1}{273}$ in the absolute temperature. The volume of a fixed mass of gas thus varies directly with the absolute temperature, as shown in the curve forming part II of Fig. 178, which, if extended, would meet the axis of abscissas at $0°$ K.

Constant Volume.—To keep a mass of gas at constant volume, it may be confined in a tight container, as represented in part I of Fig. 179, the container being made of some material having negligible expansion. The application of heat causes the pressure to increase in a manner similar to that for the change of volume at constant pressure, namely,

$$p_t = p_o(1 + \beta' t)$$

p_o and p_t being the absolute pressures at $0°$ C. and $t°$ C. respectively. Herein β' is the so-called pressure coefficient of the gas, and repre-

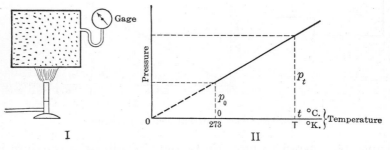

FIG. 179.   Gas heated at constant volume

sents the change in pressure per unit pressure per centigrade degree change of temperature.

It can be shown that the voluminal expansion coefficient β and the pressure coefficient β' have the same values for an ideal gas. Imagine a fixed quantity of gas to occupy a volume V_o and to exert a pressure p_o at $0°$ C., and suppose this gas to be heated to some temperature $t°$ C. at constant pressure. Its new volume will be $V_t = V_o \times (1 + \beta t)$ and its pressure will be the same as it was originally, or $p_t = p_o$; hence by multiplying terms,

$$p_t V_t = p_o V_o(1 + \beta t)$$

Suppose, next, that the gas is again heated from its original condition, that is, p_o and V_o, to the same temperature $t°$ C., this time at constant volume. Its new pressure will be $p_t' = p_o(1 + \beta' t)$, and its volume will remain unchanged, or $V_t' = V_o$. Multiplying these terms gives the expression:

$$p_t' V_t' = p_o V_o(1 + \beta' t)$$

Since in these two tests the same mass of gas has been brought to the same temperature, the products $p_t V_t$ and $p_t' V_t'$ must be equal in accordance with Boyle's Law; consequently,

$$p_o V_o (1 + \beta t) = p_o V_o (1 + \beta' t)$$

which proves that the coefficients β and β' are equal.

The numerical equality of the two coefficients for an ideal gas makes it unnecessary to distinguish between them, and hereafter β will be used to represent either. The equation for gas pressure at any temperature may therefore be written as

$$p_t = p_o (1 + \beta t) \qquad (105)$$

It follows that the pressure of a given mass of gas at constant volume varies directly as the absolute temperature, as indicated in part II of Fig. 179.

170. The Gas Thermometer.—The gas thermometer utilizes the change of pressure caused by heating or cooling a gas at constant volume as a means for measuring temperature.
The thermometer, Fig. 180, consists essentially of a thin-walled bulb B of glass or porcelain, in which the gas is confined, and to which is attached a flexible tube containing mercury. By keeping the top of the left-hand mercury column at a constant level A the volume of the gas is kept constant, and the pressure is obtained by reading the difference in height of the two columns A and C on the scale S. The gas thermometer is somewhat awkward to manipulate and is not direct-reading, but it is used as a basic standard for

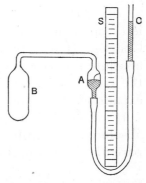

Fig. 180. Gas thermometer

the calibration of thermometers to serve as secondary standards. The gas used in the thermometer bulb is usually hydrogen; for measurements at very low temperatures helium is preferable.

To show how the gas thermometer is used for temperature measurement, suppose that the pressure of the gas in the bulb is p_o at $t_o°$ C., p_1 at $t_1°$ C., and p_2 at $t_2°$ C. Since the volume of the gas is constant, it follows from the foregoing that a change in temperature will produce a proportional change in pressure, whence

$$(t_1 - t_o) \propto (p_1 - p_o)$$

and

$$(t_2 - t_o) \propto (p_2 - p_o)$$

The proportionality is the same in both expressions, consequently

$$\frac{t_2 - t_o}{t_1 - t_o} = \frac{p_2 - p_o}{p_1 - p_o}$$

Specifically, let the pressure of the gas be p_o when the bulb is placed in melting ice ($t_o = 0°$ C.) and p_1 when the bulb is surrounded by steam at standard atmospheric pressure ($t_1 = 100°$ C.). If the pressure of the gas is p_2 at some unknown temperature t_2 °C., then that temperature is

$$t_2 = 100 \frac{p_2 - p_o}{p_1 - p_o}$$

in terms of the observed gas pressures.

171. General Gas Law.—The relation between the pressure, volume, and temperature of a fixed mass of gas developed in § 169, namely

$$p_t V_t = p_o V_o (1 + \beta t) \tag{106}$$

is of great importance and merges the relations due to Boyle and Charles. Herein, by way of summary, p_t and V_t are respectively the absolute pressure and the volume of the gas at $t°$ C.; p_o and V_o are the corresponding values at $0°$ C., and β is the mean coefficient of expansion of the gas over the range from $0°$ to $t°$ C.

It will be of value to express the foregoing equation in terms of the absolute temperature. To do so, first factor the quantity β from the parenthesis in equation (106), and then replace $1/\beta$ by 273, thus

$$p_t V_t = p_o V_o \beta \times (1/\beta + t) = p_o V_o \beta (273 + t)$$

The product $p_o V_o \beta$ for a known mass is constant and will be called MR, where M is the mass of the gas under consideration and R is a constant. Further, $(273 + t)$ may be replaced by the corresponding absolute temperature T. With these substitutions the subscripts are no longer needed, and the expression becomes the General Gas Law, namely:

$$pV = MRT \tag{107}$$

A still simpler form of this law may be obtained by making use of the fact that for a given mass of gas the quantity MR in equation (107) is constant, hence the values of p, V, and T must be so related that $\dfrac{pV}{T} = MR$ under all conditions. If subscript 1 denotes some particular condition of pressure, volume, and temperature, and subscript 2 denotes some different condition, it follows that

$$\frac{p_1 V_1}{T_1} = \frac{p_2 V_2}{T_2} \tag{108}$$

an expression which shows the relation between the absolute pressure and the volume of a fixed mass of gas at different absolute temperatures.

This law of gases confirms the theory that the temperature of a gas is directly proportional to the mean kinetic energy of the gas molecules (§ 135). It was there shown that the pressure exerted by a gas is $p = Nmv^2/3V$, where N/V is the number of gas molecules per unit volume, m is the mass of each molecule, and v is their rms. velocity. It follows that $pV = Nmv^2/3$, or $pV \propto mv^2$. But from equation (107), $pV \propto T$; therefore

$$T \propto mv^2 \propto \frac{mv^2}{2} \propto E_k$$

which shows the desired proportionality between the absolute temperature T of the gas and its kinetic energy E_k.

172. The Gas Constant.—The numerical value of the *gas constant* R referred to in the preceding section can be computed readily, since its equation is

$$R = \frac{p_o V_o \beta}{M}$$

The constant R has a particular value for each gas. For example, air at $0°$ C. and standard pressure has a density $M/V = 0.001293$ gm./cu. cm., whence the value of the gas constant for air is

$$R = 1{,}013{,}000 \frac{\text{dynes}}{\text{cm.}^2} \times \frac{0.00367}{°\text{K.}} \div 0.001293 \frac{\text{gm.}}{\text{cm.}^3} = 2.87 \times 10^6 \frac{\text{ergs}}{\text{gm. }°\text{K.}}$$

Although this value was computed for standard conditions, it is the same for air under all conditions of pressure, volume and temperature.

As a typical problem involving the gas constant, find the volume occupied by 1000 gm. of air at $100°$ C. when subjected to a pressure of 10 atmospheres. From equation (107)

$$V = \frac{MRT}{p} = \frac{1000 \text{ gm.} \times 2.87 \times 10^6 \dfrac{\text{ergs}}{\text{gm. }°\text{K.}} \times 373° \text{ K.}}{10 \times 1{,}013{,}000 \dfrac{\text{dynes}}{\text{cm.}^2}} = 106{,}000 \text{ cu. cm.}$$

By expressing the mass of a gas in mols (§ 140) instead of grams, the gas constant R is given a single value which is the same for all gases. Since 1 mol of any gas at 0° C. and 76.0 cm. of mercury occupies a volume of 22.4 liters, it follows that this universal value is

$$R = 1,013,000 \frac{\text{dynes}}{\text{cm.}^2} \times \frac{0.00367}{\text{°K.}} \times \frac{22,400 \text{ cm.}^3}{\text{mol}} = 83.1 \times 10^6 \frac{\text{ergs}}{\text{mol °K.}}$$

The value of the gas constant per molecule is obtained by dividing this result by Avogadro's number, thus, $83.1 \times 10^6 \div 6.02 \times 10^{23}$ $= 1.38 \times 10^{-16}$ ergs per °K.

173. Free Expansion.—A gas is said to undergo *free expansion* when it is allowed to expand without external opposition. For example,

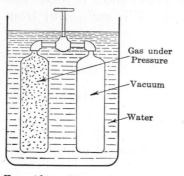

Gas under Pressure

Vacuum

Water

Fig. 181. Illustrating free expansion

suppose that a tank of gas under pressure is piped to a second tank from which the air has been evacuated, Fig. 181, and imagine the valve between the tanks to be opened suddenly; the gas then expands freely into the vacuum. An experiment of this kind was conducted by the French chemist and physicist, Joseph L. Gay-Lussac (1778–1850), to determine whether any temperature change would occur during free expansion. The tanks were immersed in a water bath, and the temperature of the water was observed before and after the valve was opened. In this test the temperature appeared to remain unchanged, which would indicate that the gas, taken as a whole, is neither cooled nor heated by free expansion. The experiment was not entirely convincing, however, because the bath contained so much water that a slight temperature change of the gas might readily escape notice. In a later and more delicate experiment conducted by Joule and Thomson, the gas was allowed to escape slowly through a porous plug from a region of high to one of low pressure, a thermoelectric couple being used to detect any temperature change during the process. The gases tested were found to undergo a slight cooling upon expansion. Hydrogen appeared at first to be an exception, but when tested at appropriate temperatures, was also found to become cooled.

As a consequence of the free-expansion experiment, an ideal gas can now be fully defined, and some distinctions made between ideal and actual gases. An *ideal gas* is one which *fulfils the General Gas Law, $pV = MRT$*, and which *does not exhibit cooling during free expansion*. These considerations show that in an ideal gas the molecules exert no force on one another. For, suppose the molecules of such a gas did exert a slight attraction for one another; then in freely expanding to a greater distance apart, work would have to be done upon them, and this work, being taken from the internal energy of the gas, would result in a lowering of the temperature. The same reasoning shows that in an actual gas there is a force action among the molecules, although small, and that it is a force of attraction.

Further, since an ideal gas shows no temperature change during free expansion, it is evident that no energy is abstracted from it, although both its pressure and its volume are changed. From this fact an important principle follows, namely: *the internal energy of an ideal gas remains constant regardless of changes in pressure and volume, provided the temperature is not changed*.

The kinetic theory offers a picture of what takes place when an actual gas expands through a small opening into a region of lower pressure. The gas molecules may be supposed to exert a force of attraction on one another, and a molecule passing through the orifice will be attracted by such other molecules as are within its sphere of action. Those ahead of it will attract it forward and those behind it will attract it backward. The predominating effect, however, will be due to the molecules behind it since the pressure, and consequently the molecular density, is greater in that region. The result is a slowing down of the molecule as it passes through the orifice, and this implies a reduction of its kinetic energy and a lowering of temperature. This theory shows that whenever an actual gas expands, its temperature will be lowered on account of the attraction among its molecules. At ordinary temperatures, this cooling is very small, but as the temperature is reduced the molecules come closer together (if the pressure stays unchanged) and the cooling effect is greatly increased.

174. Constrained Expansion.—When a gas under pressure is allowed to expand against a back pressure, the expansion may be termed *constrained* to distinguish it from free expansion into a vacuum. During constrained expansion the gas, either ideal or actual, does work in pushing back the atmosphere or other surrounding gases. Suppose that a cylinder, Fig. 182, contains gas under absolute pressure p, and that the gas pushes a piston of area A back a small distance Δs. During this process, the confined gas exerts a force $F = pA$ and does an amount of work $E = F\Delta s = pA\ \Delta s$. The product $A\ \Delta s$ is the increase in volume of the gas and may be denoted by ΔV, whence the work done by the gas during expansion becomes

$$E = p\ \Delta V \qquad\qquad (109)$$

This expression is true for any change in volume which is so small that during the change, the pressure p may be considered constant.

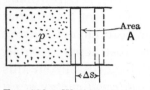

FIG. 182. Work done during expansion

If no energy is supplied to the gas during this expansion, the work $p\ \Delta V$ will necessarily be done at the expense of the internal energy of the gas, as a result of which its temperature will fall. When an actual gas expands against a back pressure, it is cooled by doing external work, and also by the internal work of separating its own molecules.

In the commercial manufacture of ice, the refrigeration is brought about by allowing anhydrous ammonia to pass through an expansion valve into a region of reduced pressure. The evaporation of the liquid and the consequent expansion of the vapor are both cooling processes; together they lower the temperature of the ammonia sufficiently to freeze water placed nearby.

In a similar manner it can be shown that the compression of a gas causes it to become hotter. The heating of air in a tire pump is a familiar example. In the Diesel engine (§ 189) air drawn into the cylinder is compressed and thereby heated to about 1000° F., which is sufficient to cause the fuel to ignite as it is sprayed into the cylinder.

The kinetic theory again offers a picture of these processes. The gas molecules in the cylinder, Fig. 182, are supposed to be continually striking against the cylinder walls and piston and rebounding from these surfaces. If the piston is moving outward, as during expansion, the molecules in rebounding from this receding surface will lose velocity. If, however, the piston is moving inward, as during compression, the molecules upon striking this advancing surface will gain velocity upon rebound. Thus, expansion lessens the velocity of the gas molecules, reduces their kinetic energy, and lowers the temperature of the gas; compression produces the opposite effect.

175. Specific Heat of Gases.—The specific heat of a gas, as of any substance, is the amount of heat necessary to raise the temperature of a unit mass of it one degree. In the case of a gas the specific heat is not single-valued but may have a range of values depending upon the constraints that are imposed upon the gas while it is being heated. The heat required to raise 1 gm. of gas 1 centigrade degree would be quite different if the gas were kept at *constant volume* than if it were kept at *constant pressure*, and still different values would be obtained if variations were allowed in both volume and pressure. The most important values of the specific heat of a gas are those at constant volume, c_v, and at constant pressure, c_p.

For solids and liquids the change in volume is so small that it need not be considered as affecting the specific heat, but such is not the case for gases, as the following consideration will show. When 1 gm. of gas is confined so that its volume cannot change, as illustrated in Fig. 179, the quantity of heat needed to raise its temperature 1 centigrade degree is its specific heat at *constant volume*. The heat supplied increases the internal energy of the gas and is completely accounted for in the increased velocity of the gas molecules. On the other hand if 1 gm. of gas is enclosed in a cylinder with a freely moving piston, as in Fig. 178, the quantity of heat needed to raise its temperature 1 centigrade degree is its specific heat at *constant pressure*. In this case the heat energy supplied must not only increase the velocity of the gas molecules, but a considerable amount must be expended in doing external work in pushing back the surrounding gases, and also a small (often negligible) amount must be expended in the internal work necessary to overcome the slight cohesion of the molecules as the gas itself expands. Consequently, *the specific heat of a gas at constant pressure exceeds its specific heat at constant volume.*

The following table gives the specific heats of several gases at constant pressure c_p (for atmospheric pressure) and at constant volume c_v, expressed either in calories per gram per centigrade degree or in British thermal units per pound per fahrenheit degree.

Specific Heats

	Temperature, °C.	c_p	c_v
Air.................	0–100	0.242	0.173
Carbon dioxide........	0–100	0.208	0.159
Hydrogen............	0–100	3.40	2.40
Oxygen.............	0–800	0.246	0.176
Water vapor.........	100	0.48	0.34

It is natural from the foregoing statements to expect that the difference between the two specific heats of a gas will be virtually the external work done by the confined gas in pushing back the surrounding gases. To verify this relationship, suppose 1 gm. of air to be heated from 0° to 1° C. at a constant pressure p of 1 atmosphere. The initial volume of the air is $1/0.001293 = 775$ cu. cm., and the increase in volume ΔV during a temperature rise from 0° to 1° C. is $\frac{1}{273} \times 775 = 2.83$ cu. cm. The external work done during expansion, by equation (109) is:

$$E = p\,\Delta V = 1,013,000\,\frac{\text{dynes}}{\text{cm.}^2} \times 2.83\ \text{cm.}^3 = 2,870,000\ \text{ergs} = 0.287\ \text{joule}$$

In § 182 it will be shown that this result is equivalent to 0.0686 cal. From the foregoing table, for air $c_p - c_v = 0.242 - 0.173 = 0.069$ cal., the two results being in approximate agreement. For an ideal gas, the agreement would be exact, and the difference between c_p and c_v would be due entirely to the external work done in its expansion.

It can also be shown that for an ideal gas, the quantity $c_p - c_v$ is equal to the constant R in the General Gas Law. Let 1 gm. of gas, initially under standard conditions, be heated through a small temperature range t in two different ways: first, at constant volume, and second, at constant pressure. Since the temperature limits are the same, the internal energy of the gas will be increased by the same amount in each test. In the first of these, the energy input is $c_v t$, all of which increases the internal energy of the gas. In the second test, the energy output is $c_p t$, but out of this an amount $p_o \Delta V$ is expended in external work; consequently the increase in internal energy is $c_p t - p_o \Delta V$. These values may be equated, thus: $c_v t = c_p t - p_o \Delta V$, and since the increase in volume is $\Delta V = V_o \beta t$ from equation (104), it follows that

$$c_p - c_v = \frac{p_o \Delta V}{t} = p_o V_o \beta$$

The resulting product $p_o V_o \beta$ is expressed in § 171 as R times the mass of gas under consideration; consequently, for unit mass

$$c_p - c_v = R \tag{110}$$

all terms being expressed in the same unit. Therefore, the difference between these two specific heats of a gas is equal to the gas constant R per unit of its mass.

176. Isothermal and Adiabatic Processes.—An expansion or contraction of a gas which occurs without change of temperature is said to be *isothermal*. This process has already been considered in connection with Boyle's Law; the relation between pressure and volume for an ideal gas when kept at constant temperature is shown in Fig. 177 and is given by the expression $p_1 V_1 = p_2 V_2$; or, more simply, the equation of an isothermal process is

$$pV = \text{a constant} \tag{111}$$

Since expansion is a cooling process, it follows that heat must be supplied to a gas during an isothermal expansion. This action will take place automatically if the gas is allowed to expand slowly while in good thermal contact with some source of heat which is maintained at the temperature of the gas. The cooling tendency during expansion will be offset by a flow of heat from the source to the gas, keeping its temperature constant. Also, since the internal energy of the gas remains constant at constant temperature, *the heat supplied during an isothermal expansion must be equivalent to the work done by the gas during expansion.* Similarly, during an isothermal compression, there must be a continual transfer of heat away from the gas in order to keep the temperature constant, and the heat transferred is equal to the work done in compressing the gas. Since the energy from the heat must penetrate the body of gas during these processes, isothermal changes usually take place somewhat slowly.

When a gas expands or contracts without the transfer of heat to it or from it, the process is called *adiabatic*. Such a process would result if the gas were contained in a cylinder completely surrounded by a perfect heat insulator, so that no heat could be taken on during expansion or given off during compression. During an adiabatic expansion some of the heat energy of the expanding gas is converted into mechanical work and the temperature of the gas is lowered; *the reduction in internal energy of the gas must be equivalent to the work done during an adiabatic expansion.* Again, during an adiabatic compression the work done upon the gas causes its temperature to rise. Actual expansions and compressions are neither isothermal nor adiabatic, but are intermediate between these processes.

To permit comparison between isothermal and adiabatic processes, an isothermal curve I and an adiabatic curve A are drawn on the same pressure-volume diagram in Fig. 183. The two curves start from point X, which represents a certain initial condition of pressure and volume of the gas under consideration. The gas, if expanded adiabatically to some lower pressure p', at point M, will be cooler and will therefore occupy less volume than if heat had been supplied to expand it isothermally to the same pressure at point N. Consequently, the curve representing the adiabatic process is steeper than than for an isothermal process.

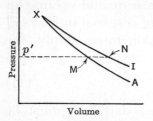

Fig. 183. Isothermal and adiabatic processes compared

A family of isothermal curves I_1, I_2, I_3, and a family of adiabatic curves A_1, A_2, A_3, are shown in Fig. 184. Since an increase of temperature tends to increase both the volume and the pressure of a gas, it is seen that isothermal curves for higher temperatures occupy positions farther from the origin than those for lower temperatures.

The equation of the adiabatic curve can be found by considering an adiabatic expansion to be made up of very small steps, then expressing the energy relations over one such step, and summing up the result for the entire curve. The result of carrying out such a procedure yields the following relationship between volume and pressure:

$$pV^\gamma = \text{a constant} \tag{112}$$

where the symbol γ is used to represent the specific heat ratio c_p/c_v.

The numerical value of γ depends upon the molecular structure of the gas. Most of the common gases, such as hydrogen, oxygen, and

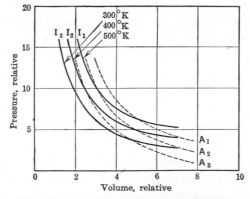

Fig. 184. Families of isothermal and adiabatic curves

nitrogen, are *diatomic*; that is, the molecule is composed of two atoms; while the inert gases, such as helium and argon, are chiefly *monatomic*, the molecule consisting of a single atom. It can be shown theoretically that for diatomic gases $\gamma = 1.40$ and for monatomic gases, $\gamma = 1.66$. For air, largely composed of diatomic gases, $\gamma = 1.40$.

177. Liquefaction of Gases.—Essentially a liquid differs from a gas in that its molecules are closer together; it is natural, then, that in attempting to liquefy a gas, the gas should be subjected to low temperature and high pressure, both of which cause it to contract. The behavior of a gas as it approaches liquefaction can be studied by investigating the relation between its pressure and its volume as the

temperature is held at lower and lower values. Such a series of tests was conducted on carbon dioxide by Thomas Andrews (1813–1885), Irish chemist and physicist, with results as plotted in Fig. 185.

In one test, the tube containing the carbon dioxide was maintained at a constant temperature of 48.1° C. while the volume of the gas was reduced from a large to a small value; during this process the pressure increased approximately in ac-

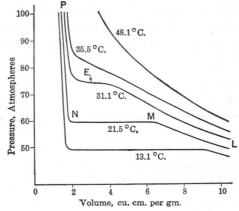

FIG. 185. Isothermals for carbon dioxide

cordance with Boyle's Law, as shown by the uppermost curve in the figure. A similar test at a lower temperature, 35.5° C., showed a noticeable departure from Boyle's Law. For tests at still lower temperatures, the departure became more marked, and the curve for the test at 31.1° C. shows a definite point of inflection at E. The curve for any temperature below this value exhibits a horizontal portion, signifying the presence of liquid as well as vapor, as described in § 162. In this temperature region, a curve such as $LMNP$ shows that as the volume of the gas is reduced the pressure at first increases (LM), much as for an ideal gas; next the point of saturation is reached and liquid begins to form (M); a further reduction in volume causes more and more of the vapor to liquefy, the pressure remaining constant (MN); eventually the liquefaction is complete (N); and from this point on a great increase of pressure (NP) is required to produce a small change in volume. The point E is called the critical point, and the corresponding properties of the substance under test are referred to as the critical values.

The *critical temperature* is that minimum temperature above which a gas cannot be liquefied, no matter how much pressure is applied; for carbon dioxide it has the value 31.1° C. The *critical pressure* is the absolute pressure (of gas and liquid) at the critical temperature. The *critical volume* is the volume of gas at the critical temperature and pressure which at 0° C. and 76.0 cm. of mercury would have unit volume.

An experiment on critical temperature may be conducted using some liquid carbon dioxide sealed in an evacuated tube, the tube having heavy glass walls which will withstand high pressures and still allow the interior to be seen. At room temperature the liquid will rest at the bottom of the tube and the space above it will be filled with saturated vapor. As the tube is heated, the liquid will expand and its density will decrease, while that of the vapor will increase. If the amount of liquid used is in the proper proportion to the volume of the tube, the critical point will be passed through when the temperature reaches 31.1° C. At this point the line of demarcation between the liquid and vapor will disappear and the tube will present a uniform appearance throughout. The liquid and vapor then have the same density, and the two states cannot be differentiated.

All gases show the same general behavior with reference to liquefaction as has just been described for carbon dioxide. The values of critical temperature, pressure, and volume, are, however, quite different for different substances, as tabulated below:

Critical Values

	Temperature, °C.	Pressure, atmospheres	Volume
Air....................	−140.7	37.2	0.0047
Alcohol (ethyl)...........	243.1	63.1	0.0071
Ammonia...............	132.4	111.5	0.0048
Carbon dioxide...........	31.1	73	0.0066
Helium.................	−267.9	2.3	0.0030
Hydrogen...............	−239.9	12.8	0.00264
Sulfur dioxide............	157.2	77.7	0.0075
Water..................	374	217.7	0.00386

*178. Behavior of Actual Gases; Van der Waals' Equation.—It has long been recognized that Boyle's Law, although used as a criterion for an ideal gas, is not followed exactly, even by the so-called fixed gases; and the curves in Fig. 185 show how widely a gas departs from this law as it approaches the liquid state. Numerous attempts have been made to formulate an expression which would agree more closely with the facts of experiment; one of these is due to the Dutch physicist, Johannes D. van der Waals (1837–1923). He considered that in an actual gas the attraction of the molecules for one another, which is ignored in the concept of an ideal gas, would be equivalent to a slight increase in the pressure applied to the gas. Any given molecule is affected by a number of others within its sphere of action, and this number will be proportional to the density of the gas. Further, for a given amount of gas, the number of molecules affected will also be proportional to the density. Hence the correction should be proportional to the square of the density or inversely proportional to the square of the volume V. For this reason van der Waals replaced the pressure p in Boyle's Law by a term $\left(p + \dfrac{a}{V^2} \right)$. He also considered that the volume, which is to be regarded as the volume into which the gas can expand, would be reduced in an actual gas because of the space occupied by the molecules themselves, and should be replaced by a smaller term $(V - b)$. When these corrections to Boyle's Law are made, the following relationship is established between the absolute pressure p and the volume V of a mass of actual gas at constant temperature:

$$\left(p + \frac{a}{V^2} \right) (V - b) = \text{a constant}$$

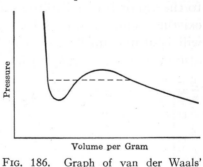

FIG. 186. Graph of van der Waals' equation

where a and b are constants which can be evaluated for various gases. For large values of p and V the corrections have but little effect, and the equation is represented by a curve which is nearly hyperbolic. For smaller values of p and V, the curve takes the form shown by the full line in Fig. 186. It conforms almost perfectly to the experimental curve $LMNP$ of Fig. 185 except that the horizontal portion is replaced by a sinuous line.

The relation between pressure and volume may therefore be found by van der Waals' equation for either the gaseous or the liquid state of a substance, and the transitional region in which the equation does not apply is known to be one of constant pressure.

It can be shown for a fluid which satisfies van der Waals' equation that the values of critical temperature, pressure, and volume are given respectively by

$$T_c = \frac{8a}{27bR} \qquad p_c = \frac{a}{27b^2} \qquad V_c = 3b$$

in terms of the constants a and b of the foregoing equation.

179. Atmospheric Humidity.—As a result of evaporation, the atmosphere always contains some moisture in the form of water vapor. This moisture does not consist of tiny particles of liquid held in suspension in the air, but is a vapor as truly invisible as the air with which it mixes. The weight of water vapor per unit of volume is known as the *absolute humidity*, and is usually expressed in grains per cubic foot (15.432 grains = 1 gm.) or in pounds per cubic foot.

Since the atmosphere is a mixture of dry air and water vapor, the total atmospheric pressure p has two components: the partial pressure due to dry air, p_a, and the partial pressure due to the water vapor, p_w; in accordance with Dalton's Law (§ 139),

$$p = p_a + p_w \tag{113}$$

Water evaporates into the atmosphere until the partial pressure due to the vapor is equal to the saturated vapor pressure of water at the existing temperature (§ 162); at 20° C., for instance, evaporation will continue until $p_w = 1.75$ cm. of mercury. At this point the atmosphere is *saturated*; that is, it contains all of the water vapor possible at that temperature, and evaporation ceases. Such a condition is uncomfortable in warm weather because perspiration cannot evaporate and the desired cooling effect is absent. The pressure of water vapor at saturation can be read for various temperatures from the curve in Fig. 174, but in the calculation of atmospheric humidity it is more convenient to use pressures in inches of mercury and temperatures in degrees fahrenheit. A similar curve in which these units are used is given for the lower temperature range in Fig. 187; the data from which it is plotted appear in the first two columns of the

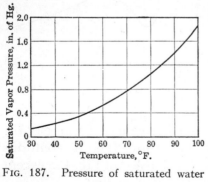

FIG. 187.   Pressure of saturated water vapor

following table. The absolute humidity at saturation and the heat of vaporization are also stated at the various temperatures.

Properties of Water Vapor

Temperature, °F.	Pressure of saturated vapor, in. Hg.	Weight of saturated vapor, grains per cu. ft.	Heat of vaporization, Btu. per lb.
0	0.0375	0.472	
10	0.0628	0.772	
20	0.1027	1.237	
30	0.1646	1.943	
35	0.2036	2.380	1076
40	0.2478	2.868	1073
45	0.3003	3.442	1070
50	0.3624	4.113	1067
55	0.4356	4.895	1064
60	0.521	5.80	1061
65	0.621	6.86	1058
70	0.739	8.07	1055
75	0.874	9.46	1052
80	1.031	11.06	1049
85	1.212	12.89	1046
90	1.421	14.96	1043
95	1.659	17.32	1040
100	1.931	19.98	1037

Usually, the atmosphere does not contain the full amount of water vapor which would produce saturation. The ratio between the amount of water vapor actually present and the amount necessary to produce saturation at the existing temperature is called the *relative humidity*; in equation form, this ratio becomes

$$\text{Relative humidity} = \frac{\text{amount of water vapor present}}{\text{amount of water vapor for saturation}}$$

The relative humidity can also be expressed in terms of pressures, since the pressure due to the vapor is approximately proportional to the amount of vapor present; thus, the relative humidity in per cent is

$$h = \frac{p_w}{p_s} \times 100 \qquad (114)$$

Herein p_w is the pressure of the water vapor actually present in the atmosphere, and p_s is the pressure which would be exerted by water vapor if the atmosphere were saturated at the existing temperature; that is, p_s is the saturated vapor pressure of water.

For example, if at 60° F. the atmosphere contained 3.442 grains of water vapor per cu. ft., then the relative humidity would be $h = (3.442/5.80) \times 100 = 59$ per cent. Or, in terms of pressures, $h = (0.3003/0.521) \times 100 = 58$ per cent, a result which agrees sufficiently with the foregoing.

With a given moisture content, if the temperature of the atmosphere rises, the relative humidity will be lowered, because the saturated vapor pressure has higher values; and the atmosphere will feel drier, although the amount of water vapor remains the same. On the other hand, a fall of temperature increases the relative humidity for the same moisture content. If the temperature falls to a sufficiently low value the atmosphere becomes saturated and the vapor begins to condense, forming dew; accordingly, this value of the temperature is called the *dew point*. Condensed vapor suspended in the air is familiar to the observer as fog when at the surface of the earth, and as a cloud when it is at greater altitudes. Upon further cooling, the water particles grow in size as more and more moisture condenses on the nuclei, and the drops so formed fall to the earth as rain. Condensation of water vapor at temperatures below the freezing point forms frost and snow.

The dew point of the air can be measured by cooling a very small portion of it so that it will become saturated, and observing the temperature at which condensation occurs. The device for making the measurement is called a condensing hygrometer; it consists primarily of a glass or metal plate so arranged that one face can be cooled either by circulating cold water or by evaporating ether until dew is observed to form on the other face that is exposed to the atmosphere. The corresponding temperature of the air, which is assumed to be the same as that of the plate in contact with it, is the dew point.

The relative humidity of the atmosphere can be calculated from a knowledge of the dew point and a reference to a vapor pressure curve like Fig. 187. The pressures read from this curve at the temperature of the dew point and of the air under test are called p_w and p_s respectively, and their ratio gives the relative humidity according to equation (114).

The relative humidity can be determined experimentally with a psychrometer which consists of two suitably mounted thermometers; one has its bulb exposed to the atmosphere (dry bulb) and the other is wrapped with muslin and kept moist with water (wet bulb). The dryer the atmosphere, the more rapid will be the evaporation of water from the muslin, and the lower will be the reading of the wet-bulb thermometer. Tables are available which give the percentage humidity in terms of the dry-bulb reading and the depression of the wet-bulb temperature.

The humidity of the atmosphere can also be measured conveniently, but only roughly, with the hair hygrometer. This instrument depends for its action upon the absorption of moisture by a hair (or by a strip of other hygroscopic substance) and upon the change of its length brought about by this absorption. A pointer moves across a dial as the length changes and indicates the condition of the atmosphere as moist, dry, and very dry.

*180. Air Conditioning.—The treatment of the atmosphere within rooms or buildings to control its temperature, moisture content, purity, and circulation, is called air conditioning. Its purpose is to provide air conditions that are conducive to human comfort and health, or that are best suited to the processing or manufacture of certain products. Air conditioning involves the use of apparatus for heating or cooling the atmosphere and for supplying or removing moisture. The process of supplying moisture is termed *humidification* and that of removing moisture is termed *dehumidification*. In addition, blowers or ventilating fans are needed for circulating the air. The various air-conditioning equipments differ in the type of apparatus used for the different functions and in the methods used to achieve automatic control of temperature and moisture.

To find the amount of water needed to bring the humidity of the air to any desired value, use is made of the General Gas Law to express the weight of water vapor in terms of the partial pressures of water vapor and air. Equation (107) that expresses this law is modified by introducing density $d = M/V$ and the terms are rearranged to give the gas constant as

$$R = \frac{p}{Td}$$

For convenience the pressure p is reckoned in inches of mercury, the temperature T in degrees rankine, and the density d in pounds per cubic foot. The density of dry air at 32° F. and atmospheric pressure (30 in. of mercury) is 0.081 lb/ft.³, whence the gas constant for dry air becomes

$$R_a = 30 \div [(459 + 32) \times 0.081] = 0.754$$

Similarly, the density of saturated water vapor at the standard boiling point (212° F.) and under atmospheric pressure is 0.037 lb/ft.³, and so the gas constant for water vapor becomes

$$R_w = 30 \div [(459 + 212) \times 0.037] = 1.21$$

From these values the masses of dry air and of saturated water vapor per cubic foot at any temperature $t°$ F. will be

$$M_a = \frac{p_a}{0.754(459 + t)}$$

$$M_w = \frac{p_w}{1.21(459 + t)}$$

Consequently, the weight of water vapor in pounds mixed with one pound of dry air is

$$M = \frac{\dfrac{p_w}{1.21(459 + t)}}{\dfrac{p_a}{0.754(459 + t)}} = 0.622\frac{p_w}{p_a}$$

where p_a and p_w are the partial pressures due respectively to dry air and water vapor expressed in inches of mercury, and t is the temperature in degrees fahrenheit.

As an illustration, consider that air is to be maintained at 65° F. with a relative humidity of 50 per cent at a time when the external atmosphere is at 20° F. with a relative humidity of 70 per cent, and a barometric pressure of 29.85 in. of mercury. From the table of saturated vapor pressures in the preceding section, the actual vapor pressures are found to be $p_w = 0.50 \times 0.621 = 0.311$ for the conditioned air, and $p_w = 0.70 \times 0.1027 = 0.072$ for the external air, both expressed in inches of mercury. Hence, the weight of water vapor per pound of dry air in the conditioned air should be $\frac{0.622 \times 0.311}{29.85 - 0.311} = 0.00655$ lb., and in the external air is $\frac{0.622 \times 0.072}{29.85 - 0.072} = 0.00150$ lb.; consequently the amount of water vapor to be supplied is 0.00505 lb. per lb. of dry air.

The amount of heat that must be taken on or given off by the atmosphere in conditioning it can be calculated by the methods used in Chapter XV.

To determine the heat required per pound of air for conditioning the atmosphere in the preceding problem, assuming the intake water to be at 50° F., take the specific heats at constant pressure to be 0.24 Btu/(lb. °F.) for dry air and 0.45 Btu/(lb. °F.) (average) for water vapor, and the heat of vaporization of water at 65° F. to be 1058 Btu. per lb. Then calculate the amounts of heat as follows:

Dry air	$0.24 \times 1 \times (65 - 20)$	$= 10.80$ Btu.
Water vapor	$0.45 \times 0.00150 \times (65 - 20) =$	$.03$ Btu.
Added water	$0.00505[(65 - 50) + 1058]$	$= 5.42$ Btu.

Total heat required per pound of dry air $= 16.25$ Btu.

Humidification may be accomplished by injecting steam or water mist into the air, by mixing with it air of higher absolute humidity, and by evaporation from water in pans, wicks or sprays. Dehumidification may be effected by absorption of moisture by anhydrous solids such as silica gel, by condensation on refrigerated surfaces or into water sprays, or by adding dry air. In many installations air to be conditioned is drawn by fans through a chamber in which a number of spray nozzles discharge water to form a sheet through which the air must flow. The desired humidity is obtained by supplying heat to or abstracting heat from the air, or water spray, or both. The sprays also serve to "wash" the air, that is, to free it from dust.

Much experimentation has been carried out to determine the dependence of human comfort and physiological efficiency upon the temperature, humidity, and air motion of the atmosphere. A composite index of these three elements is termed "effective temperature" and serves as an arbitrary measure of the warmth or cold experienced by the body. Its numerical value for a particular air condition expresses the temperature of saturated air which at a velocity of 15 to 25 ft. per min. induces a temperature sensation like that of the given condition. For example, an air condition is said to have an "effective temperature" of 70 when in practically still air it induces a sensation of warmth like that felt by the body in air at 70° F. saturated with water vapor and moving at the speed stated. Laboratory tests show that the average comfort zone has an "effective temperature" ranging from 63 to 75 depending upon the amount of clothing worn and upon the rate of working; mean values are 66 for winter and 71 for summer.

PROBLEMS

1. A tank has a volume of 10 cu. ft. and air is pumped into it until the pressure gage indicates 150 lb. per sq. in. What volume would the air in the tank occupy at atmospheric pressure, if the temperature remained unchanged?

2. A hand pump with a cylinder 15 in. long is being used to pump air into a tire in which the gage pressure is 24 lb. per sq. in. at the beginning of the stroke. How far must the piston be pushed down before air can enter the tire if the temperature is assumed to remain constant?

3. When the piston of a pump is completely pushed in, there remains between it and the cylinder head a certain so-called dead space (§ 145). Solve Problem 2 on the assumption that this dead space together with the tube which extends to the tire has a volume of 1.5 cu. in., and that the piston has a diameter of 1.25 in.

4. A cylinder filled with air has a volume of 1 cu. ft. and its gage indicates a pressure of 250 lb. per sq. in. If the valve on the tank is opened until the gage reading goes down to 150 lb. per sq. in., how many cubic feet of air, reckoned at atmospheric pressure, will escape from the tank? Assume that the temperature remains constant.

5. An automobile tire can just withstand a gage pressure of 60 lb. per sq. in.; its volume may be taken as constant at 1340 cu. in. Air is pumped into the tire to a gage pressure of 35 lb. per sq. in. at 15° C. If a test of the tire were made at increasing temperatures, at what temperature would it fail?

6. A volume of hydrogen which occupies 0.52 liter at 15° C. is heated at constant pressure to 30° C. What volume will it then occupy?

7. A steel tank contains air at a gage pressure of 10 kg. per sq. cm. when the temperature is 20° C. Find the pressure which would be developed if the tank were subjected to a temperature of 1000° C. in a fire. Neglect the expansion of the tank.

8. In the setting of an air thermometer, the elevation of the movable mercury column is 40 cm. when the bulb is surrounded by melting ice, 62.1 cm. when it is enveloped in steam at 100° C., and 44.2 cm. when it is exposed to the air in the room. What is the room temperature?

9. If a quantity of gas has a volume of 25 liters at a gage pressure of 100 cm. of mercury and at a temperature of 30° C., what volume will it occupy when the gage pressure is doubled and the temperature is raised to 60° C.?

10. If the volume of an automobile tire is constant at 0.9 cu. ft., and if the air within it is initially at 20° C., what volume of air (reckoned at 14.7 lb. per sq. in. and at 20° C.) must be pumped into the tire to increase the pressure gage reading from 25 lb. per sq. in. to 35 lb. per sq. in.? Assume all the air to be heated 5 centigrade degrees during the process.

11. A bell jar lowered partially into water entraps a mixture of air and saturated water vapor at 20° C., the absolute pressure being 80 cm. of mercury. The jar is then pushed down farther until the enclosed volume

is halved, the temperature remaining the same. Compute the absolute pressure within the jar.

12. A 3-liter container of hydrogen under an absolute pressure of 1400 gm. per sq. cm. and a 2-liter container of nitrogen under an absolute pressure of 1100 gm. per sq. cm., both at 0° C., are connected. What is the absolute pressure of the mixture when equilibrium is reached, (*a*) if the temperature remains constant? (*b*) if the temperature is raised to 40° C.?

13. Compute the weight of air in the tire described in Problem 5. See table in § 141.

14. If a tank of oxygen having a volume of 3 cu. ft. shows a gage pressure of 75 lb. per sq. in. at a temperature of 60° F., how many pounds of oxygen does the tank contain?

15. A metal cylinder has a volume of 5 cu. ft. It is first evacuated and then 4 lb. of oxygen are compressed into it at a temperature of 25° C. Find the gage pressure in the cylinder.

16. Heat is applied to some air as indicated in Fig. 178, the pressure remaining constant at 1 atmosphere. How much external work does the gas do while its temperature is being raised from 10° to 20° C., if it occupies a volume of 2 liters at the lower temperature?

17. A certain gas, having a density of 0.00125 gm. per cu. cm. under a pressure of 1 atmosphere and at a temperature of 0° C., occupies a volume of 8 liters under these conditions. If 40 cal. are required to raise the temperature of this gas to 20° C. at constant pressure, find the specific heat of the gas at constant pressure and also that at constant volume.

18. What volume does 1 gm. of air occupy at 0° C. and 76 cm. of mercury? Find the volume of this air when compressed isothermally to twice this pressure, and to three times this pressure. Repeat such computations for adiabatic compression by the use of logarithms. Plot the isothermal and adiabatic curves to scale for these compressions.

19. A liter of oxygen at normal atmospheric pressure is compressed to a volume of 500 cu. cm. Find the resulting absolute pressure of the gas (*a*) if the compression is isothermal, and (*b*) if the compression is adiabatic.

20. Find the relative humidity for a day when the temperature is 75° F. and the dew point is 55° F.

21. For a day when the temperature is 80° F., the relative humidity 70 per cent, and the barometer reading 77 cm. of mercury, find what portion of the atmospheric pressure is due to dry air.

★22. It is desired to cool air at 80° F. and 60 per cent humidity to 55° F. with the same relative humidity. Assume atmospheric pressure to be 30.10 in. of mercury, and find the weight of vapor which will condense on cooling one pound of the air, and the quantity of heat which must be transferred from the air if the condensate is ejected at 55° F.

Work and Heat   *Chapter XVII*

181. Laws of Thermodynamics.—The recognition of heat as a form of energy implies that transformations involving heat obey the principle of energy conservation. Thus, heat can be transformed into mechanical work or mechanical work into heat, and while some energy may be wasted in such transformations, none will be destroyed.

The science of thermodynamics is based upon two laws, the first of which deals with energy quantities involved in the transformations, and the second with the direction in which the transformations take place.

The *First Law* may be stated as follows: Whenever heat energy is transformed into any other kind of energy, or vice versa, the quantity of energy which disappears in one form is exactly equivalent to the quantity which is produced in the other form.

The *Second Law* has been expressed in many forms and its full significance involves the study of thermodynamics. For present purposes, the following statement will suffice: Heat does not pass from one place to another place that has a higher temperature unless work is done to accomplish this result. Heat naturally flows down a "temperature hill," so to speak, but work must be expended to take it up that hill. In a steam engine, heat flows from a high-temperature boiler to a low-temperature exhaust and does work in the process. In keeping a room cool by refrigeration, on the other hand, heat is transferred from that room to a place of higher temperature outside, but work must be done to effect the transfer.

182. Transformation of Work into Heat.—Every observer is familiar with the production of heat from other forms of energy; heat is produced from mechanical energy in an automobile brake, from electrical energy in an electric heater, and from chemical energy in many reactions. Heat is also produced as a by-product in most energy transformations, and in many of them much of the heat is wasted.

The numerical relation between heat and mechanical energy, which is implied in the first law of thermodynamics, was determined about 1845 by Joule, using several independent methods. In one of these a paddle wheel was placed in a vessel containing a known amount of water and was rotated by means of descending weights. The work done in turning the paddle wheel could be readily measured; this work was converted to heat by friction in stirring the liquid, and caused a rise in temperature. By measuring the energy E supplied to the paddle wheel and the heat Q produced in the water, it was found that these quantities varied in direct proportion to each other; their ratio

$$J = E/Q \qquad (115)$$

is known as the *mechanical equivalent of heat*. Joule's original results have been slightly modified in subsequent investigations; the accepted values follow:

Relation of Heat to Mechanical Work

Quantity of heat	Equivalent amount of mechanical work
1 cal.	$\begin{cases}4.186 \times 10^7 \text{ ergs, or} \\ 4.186 \text{ joules}\end{cases}$
1 Btu.	778 ft-lb.
0.239 cal.	1 joule

Whenever a specified amount of work is transformed into heat, the quantity of heat produced can be determined at once from the values given above. Thus, the number of heat units corresponding to 2,870,000 ergs, or 0.287 joule, of mechanical work mentioned in § 175 is

$$Q = \frac{E}{J} = \frac{0.287 \text{ joule}}{4.186 \dfrac{\text{joules}}{\text{cal.}}} = 0.0686 \text{ cal.}$$

As an example illustrating the conversion of mechanical energy into heat, consider a 15-ton trolley car moving at 30 mi. per hr. (that is, 44 ft. per sec.) which is brought to rest by the brakes. The kinetic energy of the car, by § 70, is

$$E_k = \frac{Wv^2}{2g} = \frac{30{,}000 \text{ lb.} \times \left(\dfrac{44 \text{ ft.}}{\text{sec.}}\right)^2}{2 \times 32 \dfrac{\text{ft.}}{\text{sec.}^2}} = 908{,}000 \text{ ft-lb.}$$

This mechanical energy is transformed into 908,000/778 or 1170 Btu. of heat. Suppose half of this heat (585 Btu.) to be expended in heating 8 iron brake shoes weighing 30 lb. each; their temperature rise (assumed uniform) would be found by equation (102) to be $t = Q \div mc = 585 \div (8 \times 30 \times 0.11) = 22.2$ fahrenheit degrees, wherein 0.11 is the specific heat of iron in Btu. per lb. per °F.

183. Transformation of Heat into Work.

The transformation of heat into mechanical work, which is the reverse of the process just described, is fundamental to the operation of every heat engine. This type of transformation is usually accomplished by heating a gas and causing it to do work as it expands.

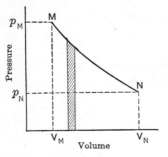

FIG. 188. Work done by expanding gas

The external work *done by* a gas in expanding by an amount ΔV is given by equation (109) as $E = p \Delta V$, provided the pressure p stays constant during the expansion. The same expression can also be used to show how much work must be *done upon* the gas in order to compress it a like amount under the same pressure.

Usually, as a gas expands, its pressure becomes lower. Fig. 188 indicates on a pressure-volume diagram the behavior of a gas which expands from M to N, its pressure falling from p_M to p_N as its volume increases from V_M to V_N. Obviously, the pressure of this gas cannot be considered constant, and the work done during expansion cannot be found directly from the expression $E = p \Delta V$. Such an expansion can be regarded, however, as composed of a number of smaller expansions, one of these being represented in the figure by the shaded strip over which interval the pressure may be assumed constant. The work done in the small expansion will then be the product of this pressure and the increase in volume. Since this pressure is represented by the height of the shaded strip and the increase in volume is represented by its width, the work done will be represented by the shaded area. Since the entire area beneath the curve may be divided into similar vertical strips, each of which represents the work done during a small expansion, it is apparent that the area under the complete curve, namely MNV_NV_M, represents the work done during the entire process from M to N.

In general, if the expansion or compression of a gas is represented as a pressure-volume curve, the area under this curve will represent either the work done by the gas during expansion or the work which must be done upon it during compression. Such an area may be measured with the planimeter, or may be computed by calculus if the equation of the curve is known. The work done, ascertained in these ways, will generally be expressed in mechanical units, such as joules or foot-pounds, but can be converted to heat units as shown in § 182.

When a gas is expanded and is compressed subsequently so as to return exactly to its initial condition, it is said to have completed a *cycle*. Consider a cycle in which the gas, initially in a condition represented by M, Fig. 188, is first heated so as to expand as represented by the curve MN, and is then compressed in exactly the reverse manner, so that the curve is retraced from N to M, completing the cycle. In such a process, the work done by the gas in expanding from M to N is exactly equal to the work done upon it in compressing it from N to M; consequently, over the entire cycle, the net amount of work done is zero. Naturally, there is no object in carrying a gas through a cycle in which the expansion and compression curves coincide. To accomplish a useful purpose, the gas must do more work in expanding than is done upon it during compression. In the ordinary heat engine the average pressure is higher during expansion than during compression, and the cycle is represented by a loop. The area of this loop is a measure of the mechanical work that the engine delivers in return for the heat supplied.

184. The Ideal Engine; Carnot Cycle.—The French physicist, Sadi Carnot (1796–1832), described an *ideal engine* that has an efficiency which cannot be exceeded by any heat engine working within the same temperature limits. This engine and its operating cycle will be explained with the aid of Fig. 189. The engine consists of a cylinder C containing a gas as the working substance, a source of heat at a high temperature T_1, a so-called refrigerator at a lower temperature T_2, and an insulating stand I. The cylinder walls and piston are supposed to be perfect insulators of heat (§ 196); and the bottom, or head, of the cylinder is a perfect conductor, through which heat will flow when the inside and outside temperatures differ by the slightest amount. The engine is also assumed to operate without friction.

Start with the cylinder standing upon the source of heat and with the piston held at rest near the bottom of the cylinder; the gas at temperature T_1 occupies a small volume at high pressure, as indicated by point A on the diagram. Then diminish slightly the pressure applied to the piston; the gas is allowed to expand, and a quantity of heat Q_1 flows into it from the source, maintaining the

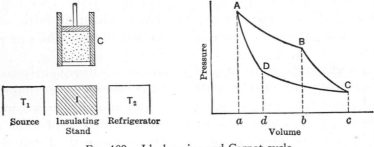

Fig. 189.   Ideal engine and Carnot cycle

temperature constant. The expansion is represented by the isothermal curve AB. Next, the cylinder is transferred to the insulating stand I and the gas is allowed to expand further. This expansion BC is adiabatic, and the temperature falls until at point C it reaches the value T_2. When the gas reaches this condition, the cylinder is placed on the refrigerator and by slightly increasing the pressure on the piston the gas is compressed. The heat generated, Q_2, flows into the refrigerator and the compression CD is isothermal at the lower temperature T_2. At a certain point D the cylinder is again moved to the insulating stand and further work is done on the gas, compressing it adiabatically along DA, thereby completing the Carnot cycle.

From the fact that the mechanical work in any process is measured by the area under the corresponding pressure-volume curve, it is seen that during expansion the gas does an amount of work equivalent to the area $ABba + BCcb = ABCca$, and that during compression the work done upon it is given by the smaller area $CDdc + DAad = CDAac$. The gas, therefore, does more work than is done upon it, and the net work done by the gas during the cycle amounts to $ABCca - CDAac = ABCD$, which is the area of the closed loop.

During a cycle, the ideal engine receives an amount of energy Q_1 from the source in the form of heat, of which an amount Q_2 is wasted in the refrigerator, and the balance is transformed into mechanical work; the latter is represented by $ABCD$ in mechanical units or $(ABCD)/J$ in heat units. Since friction is assumed absent, the latter amount represents the output of the engine, which is consequently $(ABCD)/J = Q_1 - Q_2$, using heat units for all terms. The efficiency of any device is the ratio of its output to its input; for the ideal cycle this becomes

$$\text{Efficiency} = \frac{Q_1 - Q_2}{Q_1} \tag{116}$$

and is independent of the working substance used in the engine.

In the ideal engine, work is done by the gas during expansion, and a smaller amount of work is done upon it during compression. It would be possible, theoretically, to store energy during the expansion portion of the cycle and to use part of this energy for compressing the gas during the compression portion. In the actual steam engine this result is accomplished by using a flywheel. The ideal engine is to be considered a theoretical ideal to which the actual engine should approach as closely as feasible.

Throughout the Carnot cycle the gas does not depart appreciably from a state of equilibrium. The slightest increase of external pressure during expansion would compress the gas and cause heat to be delivered to the source, and the slightest reduction of pressure during the compression CD would allow the gas to expand, removing heat from the refrigerator. It would be possible, therefore, by slight changes of pressure during the cycle, to operate the engine in the reverse manner, abstracting heat from the refrigerator and delivering heat to the source. Under such conditions there would be a net amount of mechanical work done on the gas rather than done by it during the cycle. A cycle which can be reversed in this manner is called a *reversible cycle*. If such a cycle is reversed at any point and returned to its initial state, everything connected with the process is restored exactly to its original condition. In practice, this ideal is never attained, one reason being that friction, which is always present, causes the dissipation of some energy. Actual cycles are thus *irreversible cycles*.

185. Thermodynamic Temperature Scale.—Lord Kelvin used the concept of an ideal engine to establish a theoretical temperature scale which would not depend upon the physical properties of any particular substance. Imagine a series of one hundred ideal engines to be so arranged that the first receives heat at the temperature of boiling water, the last one giving off heat at the temperature of melting ice, and each intermediate one having as its source the refrigerator of the one preceding. If it is assumed further that the output of each of these engines is the same, temperatures between the two fixed points may be assigned by considering the difference in temperature between the source and refrigerator of each engine to be the same. If the respective engine outputs are $Q_1 - Q_2 = Q_2 - Q_3 = \cdots$, and the corresponding temperature intervals are $T_1 - T_2 = T_2 - T_3 = \cdots$, then it follows from the definition of temperature on this scale that

$$\frac{T_1}{Q_1} = \frac{T_2}{Q_2} = \frac{T_3}{Q_3} = \cdots \tag{117}$$

The temperature scale constructed in this manner is based solely on thermodynamical principles, and is called the absolute or thermodynamic scale. Absolute zero on this scale is that refrigerator temperature at which the ideal engine would release no heat. The thermodynamic scale is followed very closely by the gas thermometer, and for engineering purposes may be considered identical with the Kelvin or absolute scale described in § 148. Absolute zero of temperature is $-273.16°$ C. or $-459.69°$ F.

186. Efficiency of the Ideal Engine.—The efficiency of the Carnot cycle, which was shown in § 184 to be $(Q_1 - Q_2)/Q_1$, can be expressed in terms of temperatures, by making use of the proportionality stated in equation (117), whence

$$\text{Carnot efficiency} = \frac{T_1 - T_2}{T_1} \tag{118}$$

where T_1 and T_2 are the respective *absolute temperatures* of the working substance as received and as released by the engine. Evidently, the efficiency can be increased by raising the temperature at which the working substance is received or lowering the temperature at which it is exhausted. Since the efficiency depends only upon these temperatures, all ideal engines operating between the same temperature limits would have the same efficiency.

Thus, for an engine supplied with saturated steam at an absolute pressure of 100 lb. per sq. in. and exhausting into the atmosphere, the steam table in § 164 gives the supply and exhaust temperatures as 327.8° and

212° F., whence by equation (118), it appears impossible to convert more than $\dfrac{(327.8 + 459) - (212 + 459)}{327.8 + 459} = 0.147$ or 14.7 per cent of the heat energy into mechanical form.

187. Carnot Vapor Cycle.—The Carnot cycle previously described, in which a gas was used as the working substance, does not apply directly to the ordinary engine using saturated steam, owing to the different behavior of these substances (§ 162). The engine parts are the same as before, Fig. 189, but the cylinder is assumed at the start to contain liquid at the boiling point T_1. This corresponds to point A in the Carnot cycle for vapor as represented in Fig. 190. The addition of a quantity of heat Q_1 from the source causes boiling at constant temperature and under constant pressure, as indicated by

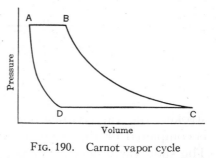

FIG. 190.   Carnot vapor cycle

line AB; when the vaporization is complete the cylinder is transferred to the insulating stand and adiabatic expansion follows (BC) with lowering of temperature to T_2; the cylinder is then moved to the refrigerator and the volume is reduced at constant pressure (CD), liquefaction taking place meanwhile without change of temperature, and the heat of vaporization Q_2 escaping to the refrigerator; at a certain point D the cylinder is again moved to the insulating stand and further pressure is applied, causing adiabatic compression (DA) and completing the cycle.

This vapor cycle, like the gas cycle previously described, is reversible, and is, moreover, a close approximation to that of the actual steam engine.

188. The Reciprocating Steam Engine.—The reciprocating steam engine, due to Watt, utilizes the expansion of steam for producing mechanical work. The simple engine, represented in Fig. 191, has a cylinder C with ports A and B, entrance to which is controlled by the slide valve V. These ports lead either to the steam chest S or to an exhaust pipe entering from the side at E. The piston P within the cylinder is joined to the cross head H, and thence, through the connecting rod R and crank D, to the main driving shaft of the engine. Upon this shaft is mounted the flywheel F and also an eccentric G which controls the slide valve.

Steam enters the steam chest under high pressure from a boiler, and, at the instant shown, is admitted through port *A* to one end of the cylinder; the other end is connected simultaneously through port *B* to the low-pressure exhaust. The piston is thus subjected to an unbalanced or "effective" pressure and is forced to the right (forward

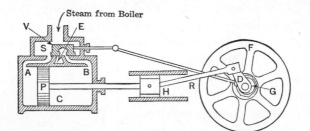

Fig. 191. A reciprocating steam engine

stroke); the valve closes port *A* at a suitable point and the stroke is completed by the expansion of the steam enclosed in the cylinder. The slide valve next interchanges the port connections, joining port *A* to the exhaust and port *B* to the steam chest. With this position of the valve, the steam drives the piston in the opposite direction (return stroke). This cycle is repeated over and over, the reciprocating motion of the piston being converted to rotary motion of the driving shaft and flywheel. The engine is commonly used to drive machinery and electrical generators either by direct connection or through belting.

A diagram showing the relation between the pressure and volume in an engine cylinder throughout a cycle can be obtained by an

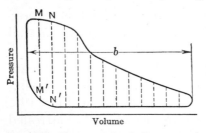

Fig. 192. Steam-engine indicator card

indicator. This device is piped to the cylinder like a pressure gage, and has a tracing point which moves up and down as the pressure changes. The point rests against a card which follows the forward and backward motion of the piston to a reduced scale. The vertical motion of the tracing point combined with the horizontal motion of the card results in a diagram of the form shown in Fig. 192. The student should correlate the different portions of the diagram with the various steps of the actual cycle as described at the beginning of the section, and should also note the similarity between this diagram and that of the Carnot vapor cycle. As before, the area of the indicator card represents that portion of the energy supplied during a cycle which is available for mechanical work.

It will be observed that in the ordinary steam engine the same ports are used alternately to admit the high-temperature steam and to exhaust this steam at a lower temperature after expansion. The repeated heating and cooling of the ports is a wasteful process, and is avoided in a later development known as the *uniflow* engine. In this engine steam is admitted at the ends of the cylinder and is exhausted at the center, the piston serving as an exhaust valve by covering and uncovering the exhaust ports at the proper times.

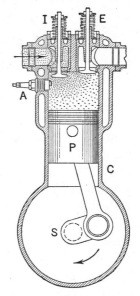

FIG. 193. Internal combustion engine

189. Internal Combustion Engines.—In the internal combustion engine, fuel is burned directly in the cylinder, and its chemical energy is in part converted into kinetic energy of the moving piston. This type of engine, as used for automobile propulsion, usually has six or eight cylinders of the form represented in Fig. 193. The water-cooled cylinder *C*, fitted with mechanically operated valves *I* and *E*, and with a spark plug *A*, encloses a piston *P* which is connected by a piston rod to the crank shaft *S*. The fuel used is gasoline, which is atomized and mixed with air in a *carburetor* so as to form an explosive mixture.

The complete cycle consists of four strokes. The figure shows the piston starting downward on the first stroke; the inlet valve *I* is open and a charge of fresh fuel is drawn in through it from the carburetor. When the piston has reached the bottom of its stroke and starts back, the inlet valve closes and the piston compresses the charge in the upper part of the cylinder. As the piston reaches the end of its upward stroke, the compressed charge is ignited by an electric spark at the points of the spark plug *A*. The resulting explosion drives the piston downward during the next, or working, stroke. On the return upward stroke of the piston, the exhaust valve *E* opens and the piston forces the burned gases out through the exhaust pipe, leaving the cylinder ready for the beginning of a new cycle. At each explosion, the heat of combustion (§ 167) of the gasoline consumed is liberated and this energy is partially converted into mechanical work.

The Diesel engine, invented by the German engineer, Rudolph Diesel (1858–1913), uses fuel oil and no spark plugs. Air is drawn into the cylinder and is highly compressed, thus raising it to a high temperature. A charge of fuel oil is then sprayed into the cylinder under high pressure, and ignites spontaneously as it mixes with the hot compressed air. Burning takes place without explosion, and the fuel supply is so regulated that the pressure remains almost constant during combustion.

190. Engine Horsepower and Efficiency.—The horsepower of an engine can be obtained quite easily from its indicator card. It will be recalled that of the heat energy supplied each cycle to the engine, the portion which becomes available for mechanical work is represented by the area of its indicator diagram. Since the area of any figure is the product of its average height and its base, for an indicator diagram as in Fig. 192 the area is the average of all the ordinates MM', NN', etc. multiplied by the base b. The average ordinate is known as the *mean effective pressure*, and represents the average difference in pressure in the cylinder on opposite sides of the piston; this value will be represented by P. The base b represents the volume swept out by the piston during one stroke; that is, $b \propto LA$, where L is the length of stroke and A the area of the piston. When P is expressed in pounds per square inch, L in feet, and A in square inches, the product PLA gives the work in foot-pounds for each working stroke. If there are N working strokes per minute, the horsepower of the engine as represented by the indicator card, known as the *indicated* horsepower (ihp.), will be

$$\text{ihp.} = \frac{PLAN}{33,000} \tag{119}$$

In practical testing, the mean effective pressure P is calculated from the indicator card, and the remaining quantities are obtained by direct measurement.

The actual engine may be regarded as a heat engine combined with a mechanical engine. As a heat engine, the input is the heat absorbed from the source, which per unit time may be expressed in horsepower, and the output is the indicated horsepower. The ratio of this output to the input is known as the *indicated thermal efficiency*, and will be less than the efficiency of an ideal engine operating over the same temperature range.

When the engine is considered as a mechanical device (§ 76), the input is the indicated horsepower, and the output is the horsepower as measured by a brake, called the brake horsepower (bhp.). Hence,

$$\text{Mechanical efficiency} = \frac{\text{brake horsepower}}{\text{indicated horsepower}}$$

For the purpose of assigning horsepower ratings to automobile engines, standard conditions have been adopted that are equivalent to the following: a mean effective pressure of 67.2 lb. per sq. in., and an average piston speed of 1000 ft. per min. In the automobile engine the piston travels $4L$ ft. for each working stroke, consequently, $4LN = 1000$. From these values, the rated horsepower per cylinder is found by equation (119) to be

$$\text{hp.} = \frac{PLAN}{33,000} = \frac{67.2 \times \dfrac{1000}{4} \times \dfrac{\pi d^2}{4}}{33,000} = \frac{d^2}{2.5}$$

where d is the piston diameter in inches. For an automobile engine having C cylinders, the rating is

$$\text{hp.} = \frac{d^2 C}{2.5}$$

191. The Steam Turbine.—The steam turbine utilizes the kinetic energy of a jet of steam, rather than the expansion of a vapor as in the cylinder of a reciprocating engine. High-velocity jets are formed by passing the steam through a set of fixed nozzles; these jets impinge against a series of curved vanes or blades evenly spaced around the rim of a rotary disk and set the disk into rapid motion. Typical turbine construction is shown in Fig. 194.

The energy of the steam jets cannot be absorbed by a single row of blades without involving excessive speeds. In the arrangement shown, the steam issues from the fixed nozzles NN, and after passing one row of rotating blades R, strikes a corresponding row of fixed blades F, and is redirected against a second

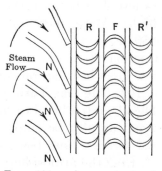

Fig. 194. Arrangement of blades in a turbine

row of rotating blades R' mounted on the same rotor. In a turbine having several *stages*, the rotor consists of a number of disks with blades, mounted on the same shaft, and the disks are separated by stationary diaphragms so that each disk is housed in a separate compartment within the casing.

The theoretical output developed by a turbine is equal to the reduction in kinetic energy of the steam in passing through the machine. Suppose that in t sec. W lb. of steam are supplied to the blades at a velocity v_1 ft. per sec. and are discharged at a velocity v_2 ft. per sec. The reduction in energy, by equation (50), is $\dfrac{Wv_1{}^2}{2g} - \dfrac{Wv_2{}^2}{2g}$ ft-lb., and this represents the theoretical energy output of the turbine. The corresponding *power output* in foot-pounds per second is consequently

$$P = \frac{W}{2gt}\,(v_1{}^2 - v_2{}^2)$$

and can be converted to horsepower by dividing by 550.

In some turbines, the blading is so designed that the steam expands, and thus gains speed, while passing through the moving blades. By this means, the blades, upon discharging the steam, experience a reactive force which assists their forward motion.

As suggested in § 186, an improvement in efficiency can be achieved by raising the temperature at which the working substance is received or lowering the temperature at which it is released. With saturated steam, intake temperatures much above 600° F. are not practicable because the corresponding vapor pressures become very high. With mercury, however, the absolute vapor pressure at 850° F. is only about 75 lb. per sq. in. This fact has led to the introduction of mercury as the working substance for turbines, and a few large installations of this type have already been made.

192. The Gas Turbine.—The processes that are carried out in the Diesel and other internal combustion engines of the reciprocating type can also be employed in rotary machines or turbines. In the *gas turbine*, now being widely built, a rotary compressor draws in air from the atmosphere and compresses it adiabatically to a pressure of three to six atmospheres. Fuel oil is then sprayed into the stream of compressed air and ignited, increasing its volume, at constant pressure, in proportion to the increase of absolute temperature. This greatly increased volume of air, mixed with products of combustion, then passes through the nozzles and blades of a turbine in which the gas expands down to atmospheric pressure; during this expansion it does 50 to 150 per cent more work than is required to drive the compressor.

The advantages of the gas turbine are compactness and light weight, freedom from vibration, the ability to use inexpensive fuel and to operate with very little cooling water. High speed of rotation is also an advantage in applications where it can be efficiently utilized, as in aviation.

The hot gases necessarily issue from the turbine exhaust at a high speed, and the corresponding kinetic energy is a loss in stationary turbines. In the gas turbine as applied to *jet propulsion* for airplanes, this jet of exhaust gas is intentionally made to have a very high velocity by raising the pressure, and is directed backward so as to drive the plane forward by the reaction. The air taken in at the front end of the engine is discharged from the rear with greatly increased velocity; the force required to produce this velocity change is equal to the force of reaction.

The efficiency of the gas turbine depends on the temperature which can be reached in the combustion chamber, and this is limited by the temperature at which metal parts of the turbine that are under high stress can safely operate for long periods; at present 1400° F. seems to be possible. The problem of raising this limit is a metallurgical one—to discover materials which will not deteriorate, which will retain a fair proportion of their strength, and which will not "creep" or slowly elongate under continued exposure to high temperatures.

193. Refrigeration.—The manufacture of ice, the cooling of rooms, and the preservation of food in cold-storage spaces, are processes which require apparatus for the production of low temperatures. The articles under refrigeration must give off heat to the surroundings which are at higher temperatures.

The evaporation of a liquid and the expansion of a gas or vapor are known to be processes in which heat is absorbed. These actions can be illustrated in the making of carbon-dioxide snow, by allowing some liquid carbon dioxide at the pressure of its saturated vapor to escape from the containing cylinder through a small opening into the atmosphere. The resulting evaporation and expansion take sufficient heat from the issuing stream to cause the CO_2 to solidify as snow; at atmospheric pressure its temperature is $-78°$ C.

In the commercial manufacture of ice, mentioned in § 174, anhydrous ammonia circulates continuously around a closed system, such as represented in Fig. 195. The vapor is compressed in a compressor cylinder *P* and passes through the coils of a condenser *C*. In these coils, which are cooled by water, the vapor liquefies and the liquid flows to an expansion valve *A* at the freezing tank *D*. Here the liquid vaporizes into an evaporator or brine coil *B* and is thereafter drawn into the compressor to repeat the cycle. The evaporation and expansion which occur at the expansion valve cause the absorption of heat from the brine within the freezing tank, and lower its

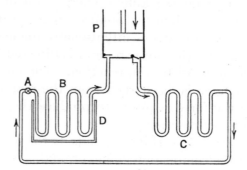

FIG. 195. Compression system of refrigeration

temperature. Cans filled with water are placed in the brine tank and their contents are frozen. This system may be regarded as a reversed heat engine, operating as described at the end of § 184. The working substance (ammonia vapor) absorbs heat from the refrigerator (freezing tank) and gives it off to the higher-temperature source (condenser), work being done (in driving the compressor) on the vapor during the process.

The electric refrigerator for household use operates as a compression system, essentially like the ice machine of Fig. 195, but with certain modifications to adapt it to domestic purposes. Sulfur dioxide and ethyl chloride are commonly used as the refrigerants; the evaporator coils are located in the food compartment, and the condenser coils, which are air cooled, are outside. The compressor is driven by an electric motor, arranged with a thermostatic switch to start and stop as needed.

194. Liquefaction of Gases.—The cooling produced through expansion is utilized in the liquefaction of gases. For the so-called fixed gases, however, the critical temperatures are too low to be attained by simple expansion, and this fact makes it necessary to resort to some cumulative cooling action. This procedure was perfected by Karl R. von Linde (1842–1934), German technologist. In liquefying air by this process, the air is compressed to about 200 atmospheres, next cooled by means of a freezing mixture, and then passed through a long tube from the end of which it is allowed to expand to a pressure of about 15 atmospheres. The air is appreciably cooled by this expansion, and is then allowed to expand again, this time to atmospheric pressure, which results in a further lowering of its temperature. Some of the air which has been cooled by each expansion circulates around the tube from which it issued, in order to cool the air stream before expansion cools it further. Thus, as the system operates, the cooling action is progressively intensified, and finally the temperature is lowered sufficiently to cause a small portion of the air to liquefy as it leaves the tube. The liquid air is collected in large containers resembling thermos bottles so that it can be transported to places where extremely low temperatures are desired.

By somewhat similar processes it has been possible to liquefy all known gases. Helium presented the greatest difficulty in liquefaction, but was eventually liquefied in 1908 at $-268.9°$ C. by the Dutch physicist, H. Kamerlingh Onnes (1853–1926). By the evaporation of liquid helium, lower and lower temperatures have been attained by many investigators; the lowest temperature reached is only a small fraction of one degree above absolute zero. These low temperatures can be measured by changes in the magnetic properties of certain salts (§ 282).

PROBLEMS

1. How much mechanical work converted into heat would be required to melt (*a*) 1 gm. of ice at 0° C.? (*b*) 1 lb. of ice at 32° F.?

2. At what rate in calories per second is heat produced by a 660-watt electric heater?

3. How much energy in watt-hours is needed to heat a pound of copper through 1 fahrenheit degree?

4. A paddle is used to stir 20 lb. of water, and 0.25 hp. is supplied to it continuously. Assume that the water receives the entire energy delivered by the paddle and calculate its temperature rise in 30 min.

5. A motor delivers 5 hp. continuously for 8 hr. at an efficiency of 81 per cent. Calculate the quantity of heat wasted in the machine during this time.

6. A blunt drill is used in attempting to bore a hole in a 1000-gm. block of iron initially at 20° C. The drill is rotated at 750 rev. per min. for 5 min.,

the average torque exerted upon it being 6,000,000 dyne-cm. If the iron block receives $\frac{3}{4}$ of the mechanical energy supplied, what is its resulting temperature?

7. How much heat is generated when a 2000-gm. block slides 1 meter along a surface inclined 30° with the horizontal, if the coefficient of friction between the sliding surfaces is 0.2?

8. Electricity is being considered for use in melting snow on a driveway 60 ft. long and 10 ft. wide. What would be the cost of melting 6 in. of snow on it at 2 cents per kw-hr.? Assume the snow to weigh 8 lb. per cu. ft., and take the temperature as 32° F. and the efficiency of operation as 50 per cent.

9. Air friction causes falling raindrops to attain a constant speed, and also causes their temperature to rise. What temperature rise will a drop experience in falling 300 meters at constant speed, if heat dissipated to the surroundings is negligible?

10. A cylinder with a freely moving piston contains 10 liters of air at 20° C. and at standard atmospheric pressure. Heat is applied, causing the air to expand at constant pressure, until the temperature is 45° C. Compute the work done by the air in expanding.

11. Steam is supplied to a large turbine at a temperature of 880° F. and is exhausted at a temperature of 540° F. for use with lower pressure prime movers. Determine the maximum theoretical efficiency of the turbine.

12. Find the efficiency of an ideal engine which receives saturated steam from a boiler at an absolute pressure of 400 lb. per sq. in. and exhausts it into the air at a pressure of 1 atmosphere.

13. A turbine operates with saturated mercury vapor from a boiler at 450° C., exhausting into a condenser at 175° C. Find the maximum efficiency possible with an ideal heat engine operating under these conditions.

14. An ideal engine operating at 120 cycles per min. delivers 5 hp. at a Carnot efficiency of 30 per cent and exhausts into a refrigerator at 20° C. Compute the temperature of the source and the amount of heat supplied by the source per cycle.

15. A reciprocating steam engine which runs at 120 rev. per min. has a piston diameter of 10 in. and a stroke of 14 in., and is subjected to a mean effective pressure of 24 lb. per sq. in. Compute the amount of work done per stroke, and also the indicated horsepower of the engine.

16. How much torque does a 600-hp. airplane engine develop at a speed of 2580 rev. per min.? Assume the mechanical efficiency of the engine at this speed to be 92 per cent and compute its indicated horsepower.

17. Calculate the indicated thermal efficiency of a four-cycle gas engine which consumes 24 cu. ft. of gas per indicated horsepower per hour, the gas having a heating value of 540 Btu. per cu. ft.

18. An automobile having 8 cylinders of $3\frac{1}{4}$-inch bore runs 15 mi. on 1 gal. of gasoline (specific gravity 0.74), at an average speed of 40 mi. per hr. If the indicated thermal efficiency is assumed to be 25 per cent, what is the indicated horsepower of the engine and how does it compare with the rated horsepower?

19. The "coefficient of performance" of a refrigeration cycle is the ratio of the heat given off at the low temperature to the work needed to operate the cycle, both energy values being expressed in the same units. What horsepower must be supplied to the compressor of a home freezer in which the freezing compartment is to give off 3130 Btu. per hr., if the coefficient of performance of the cycle is 2.5?

Transfer of Heat *Chapter XVIII*

195. Methods of Heat Transfer.—Heat energy may be transmitted from one place to another in several ways. The method called *conduction* is a point-by-point process in which one part of a body is heated by direct contact with a source of heat, and neighboring parts become heated successively. Thus, if one end of a metal rod is placed in a hot furnace, the heat travels along the rod by conduction. This is commonly explained by supposing that within the furnace the molecules of the rod are in violent vibration and that in jostling their neighbors, they set them into more rapid motion, and this process continues throughout the rod. A more complete explanation of the process of conduction would involve electronic motion. Good conductors of heat are also good conductors of electricity, and since the free electrons that are present in such conductors play an important part in the conduction of electricity they are probably instrumental in heat conduction as well.

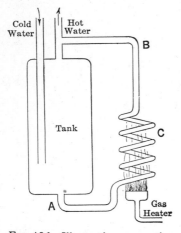

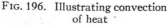

Fig. 196. Illustrating convection of heat

The method of heat transfer called *convection* involves a bodily movement of the material heated and applies to mobile substances, that is, to liquids and gases. The motion is brought about by changes of density that accompany the heating process. Water in a kettle on the kitchen stove is heated by convection, as is also the air in a room from a hot stove. The ordinary water heater, Fig. 196, comprising a tank, a heating coil C, and the connecting pipes A and B, forms a circulating system, all being filled with water. When the water in coil C is heated by the gas flame, it becomes less dense and rises, entering the tank through pipe B; meanwhile cold water from the bottom of the tank enters the coil through pipe A. This process continues and all the water in the tank becomes heated by circulation or convection.

The transfer of heat by radiant energy is called *radiation*. The process involves the conversion of internal energy into radiant form at the heater, and the reversion of radiant energy into internal energy wherever the radiation is absorbed. The electric radiator is an appliance operating on this principle; it has a heating element mounted at the focus of a parabolic reflector. When heated by an electric current, the element emits not only "light waves" that stimulate the eye, but also "heat waves" which do not. When a body absorbs waves of either kind its internal energy is increased, producing the various effects mentioned in Chapter XIV. The purpose of the reflector is to concentrate the heat waves into a beam, just as a searchlight reflector does with light waves.

The process of heating a house through the use of steam radiators involves boiling water over a flame in the cellar and condensing the resulting steam in the rooms above. When a pound of water is boiled at the normal boiling point it absorbs 970 Btu. from the flame (§ 164) and changes to steam at atmospheric pressure; and when that pound of steam is condensed within the radiators of the rooms, its heat of vaporization is given off to heat the air in the rooms by convection. This method of *evaporation and condensation* is also utilized in mechanical refrigeration, the heat from foods in the ice box being transferred to the surrounding air by evaporating particular liquids at relatively low pressures and condensing them at higher pressures.

196. Conduction.—Substances differ widely in their ability to conduct heat from one point to another; metals are relatively good conductors, while porous substances in which air is entrapped are poor conductors or good insulators. For a given material, the amount of heat that is conducted per unit of time along a specimen of uniform cross-section depends upon the linear temperature distribution or gradient and also upon the area of the section. The *temperature gradient* is the ratio of the temperature difference between two points along the line of heat flow to the separation of these points; for a temperature difference $t_1 - t_2$ over a distance s this ratio may be written as

$$G = \frac{t_1 - t_2}{s}$$

If the sectional area is A, the rate of heat transfer is

$$q = kGA \qquad (120)$$

where the proportionality constant k is called the *thermal conductivity* of the substance.

When the temperature gradient is expressed in centigrade degrees per centimeter, and the area is in square centimeters, then to have the rate of heat transfer q in calories per second, the conductivity k must be expressed in cal/sec. per °C. per cm. With these units, k is the number of calories of heat which would be transmitted per second through a sample of the material one square centimeter in cross-section and one centimeter long, when the opposite faces are maintained at a temperature difference of one centigrade degree.

In many commercial calculations of heat conduction, the temperature gradient is expressed in fahrenheit degrees per inch, the area is expressed in square feet, and the rate of heat transfer q is expressed in British thermal units per day; with these units the conductivity k will be the number of British thermal units transmitted in 24 hours through one square foot section of the material, one inch in thickness, when the opposite faces are kept at a temperature difference of one fahrenheit degree. Average values of thermal conductivities of a number of substances at ordinary temperatures in the metric and British units are listed below:

Thermal Conductivities (k)

	Calories per cm. per sec. per °C.	Btu-in. per sq. ft. per day per °F.
Air...............	0.000054	3.8
Aluminum.........	0.49	34,000
Brass............	0.26	18,000
Cement..........	0.0007	50
Copper..........	0.91	63,000
Cork............	0.0001	7
Cotton..........	0.0005	35
Glass............	0.002	140
Ice..............	0.005	350
Iron.............	0.15	10,400
Silver...........	0.99	69,000
Slate............	0.005	350
Water...........	0.0015	105

To measure the thermal conductivity of a substance, it is necessary to observe the rate at which heat passes through a given cross-section of it under a known temperature gradient. In testing metals, since their conductivity is relatively high, satisfactory precision can be attained by using specimens in the form of rods. In the usual method, the rod under test is fitted with a steam jacket at one end and with a coil of several turns of small metal tubing wound around the other end. Between these parts are placed two thermometers in good thermal contact with the rod and located a known distance apart. Thermometers are also used to measure the temperature of water entering and leaving the coil of tubing. The entire rod is surrounded by suitable insulation to reduce the emission of heat from the surface of the rod. Steam is passed through the jacket and when all four thermometers have attained steady readings the test may be conducted, for the heat given to the rod is conducted steadily along its length and transferred to the water.

In a typical experiment, a copper rod of 10 sq. cm. cross-section has thermal contacts 12 cm. apart. When one end is heated the thermometers indicate steady readings of 78 and 52° C. at these contacts. At the other end 3.9 gm. of water are heated each second through 5.0 centigrade degrees. The average temperature gradient over the rod length under test is $G = (78 - 52) \div 12 = 2.17°$ C/cm. and the heat transmitted along the rod is $q = 5.0 \times 3.9 = 19.5$ cal/sec. Therefore, the heat conductivity of copper is $k = q/GA = 19.5 \div (2.17 \times 10) = 0.90$ cal/(sec. cm. °C.).

In measuring the thermal conductivities of poor conductors of heat, accuracy requires that specimens in the form of sheets be used so that the heat path will be short and of large sectional area, but in other respects the method of test is the same as for good conductors. Liquids and gases are poor conductors of heat. Air in finely divided form serves as a good insulating substance since its thermal conductivity is very low and because circulating currents are largely eliminated. Textiles, such as wool and felt, are good heat insulators primarily because of the air entrapped in them. Saw dust, granulated cork, loose asbestos, and similar porous materials are used in the walls of refrigerators, frame buildings, and ice houses for insulation purposes.

*197. Heat Conduction Through Cylindrical Walls.—The escape of heat from bare steam pipes or through insulating coverings around them, and the heat transfer through boiler tubes or refrigerator piping, all illustrate the conduction of heat radially through the wall of a hollow cylinder. If the wall is imagined to consist of a series of telescoping tubes it will be clear that the heat flow takes place through layers of varying sectional area. However, the tubes, or annular elements, may be regarded as infinitesimally thin, and consequently the area of any one may be considered constant, and the rate of heat conduction through it evaluated as in the preceding section.

Consider a pipe, shown in section in Fig. 197, to carry steam at a temperature t_1, the surrounding temperature being t_2, and let dt represent the temperature difference over an annular element of infinitesimal thickness dr, so that the gradient at the element becomes $G = \dfrac{dt}{dr}$. The rate of heat conduction through the element is obtained from equation (120) as

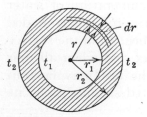

FIG. 197. Conduction of heat through pipe walls

$$q = -k \frac{dt}{dr} A$$

where k is the thermal conductivity of the wall material and A is the area normal to the flow of heat, which for a cylinder of length l is $2\pi r l$. The minus sign is introduced to show that an increase in the radius of the element corresponds to a decrease in temperature. The temperature difference over the element is consequently

$$dt = -\frac{q\,dr}{2\pi r l k}$$

By integration, the temperature differences over all the elements from the inner radius r_1 to the outer radius r_2 are summed up and give the temperature difference between the steam and the surroundings as

$$\int_{t=t_1}^{t=t_2} dt = -\frac{q}{2\pi l k} \int_{r=r_1}^{r=r_2} \frac{dr}{r}$$

whence

$$t_2 - t_1 = -\frac{q}{2\pi l k} \log_\epsilon \frac{r_2}{r_1}$$

It follows that the heat conducted through the walls per unit time is

$$q = \frac{2\pi l k (t_1 - t_2)}{\log_\epsilon (r_2/r_1)}$$

where ϵ (epsilon) is the base of natural logarithms.

In transferring heat through walls by conduction and transferring it further by convection through gases or liquids in contact with the walls, cognizance must be taken of thin films of these mediums which cling to the surfaces. Heat is transferred through these films principally by conduction, and since they have low conductivities, the temperature gradient over them is relatively large. The effects of such films can be allowed for through experimentally determined coefficients, but no corrections for them will be made in the problems on conduction.

198. Convection.—The transfer of heat by convection refers to the movement of warmed fluids, and is brought about by changes of density that accompany changes of temperature. This process is important in heating systems and ventilation. The heating of houses is accomplished by placing heating units at certain points, and by circulating the air which comes in contact with these units by convection. The so-called radiator (steam or hot-water) does transfer some heat by radiation but it transfers far more by convection. The draft in a stove or in a chimney is produced by convection; the heated gases in a chimney weigh less than a corresponding column of cold air, consequently the mass of gas in the chimney is buoyed up according to Archimedes' Principle (§ 120).

The trade winds are caused by the continued heating of the air near the equator and its movement away from the earth's surface. Cooler air from the tropical belts rushes to take its place, flowing from the north in northern latitudes and from the south in southern latitudes, and convection currents are set up which blow in the same direction for long periods. The rotation of the earth causes the deflection of these winds somewhat from the directions mentioned.

199. Radiation.—Energy reaches the earth from the sun by radiation, that is, by waves transmitted through the intervening space. In full sunlight, the energy received above the earth's atmosphere is about 2 cal. per min. on a surface 1 cm. square held perpendicular to the sun's rays; about one-third of this amount is absorbed in passing through the atmosphere. These waves are electromagnetic waves and pass through the vacuum which exists over most of the distance from sun to earth; they have the same character as light and electric waves; see Chapter XXX. Radiation impinging on a body may be reflected from it, transmitted through it, or absorbed by it. Substances which absorb radiation become heated, so the presumption is that the molecular and electronic motions within these substances are augmented by the waves.

An instrument often seen in opticians' shops and called a radiometer illustrates the effect of radiation. It consists of a delicately pivoted rotating element of four small vanes within a partially evacuated glass bulb. Each vane has one side polished and the other blackened. When radiation from the sun or other intense source falls upon a polished side it is reflected, and when the radiation falls upon a blackened side it is absorbed and that side becomes warm. The inequalities in temperature near the polished and blackened sides set up differences of pressure within the tube; the blackened sides are repelled more than the polished ones, and the vanes are set into rotation.

All bodies radiate energy, whether they are hot or cold; the hotter a body is the greater its radiation will be. Further, all bodies receive radiation from others. This exchange of radiant energy goes on continuously. Accordingly, a body that remains at constant temperature is not considered as having stopped radiating, but rather as receiving energy at the same rate that it gives off energy by radiation. A body that is a good radiator of energy is also a good absorber of energy. A black rough surface, such as that provided by a coating of lampblack, is an excellent radiator (as well as an excellent absorber) of radiant energy. A highly polished surface has opposite characteristics.

200. Laws of Radiation.—The quantitative relations that have been discovered concerning the transmission of energy by radiation are expressed in a number of laws. Some of these are discussed in this section; others are considered later in the chapter.

Stefan-Boltzmann Law.—The manner in which the temperature of a source affects the radiation proceeding from it was stated empirically by the Austrian physicist, Josef Stefan (1835–1893) and later deduced theoretically by his countryman Ludwig Boltzmann (1844–1906). The relationship which they developed applies to an idealized body, called a "black body," that is, a body which would absorb all of the radiant energy falling upon it and reflect none. Contrary to expectation, a black body is not one with a sooty surface, but rather an enclosure from which no energy can escape once it has been received. Such a body is closely approximated by a hollow object, blackened on the inside, and having a small opening. Radiation entering the opening undergoes repeated reflection inside of the enclosure and very little escapes. When such a body is heated and used as a source the radiation emitted from the interior is termed "black-body" radiation.

It is found that the rate at which energy is radiated from a black body is constant if the temperature of the source is steady; this rate of emission is called *radiant flux*. The energy density, called *radiant flux density*, is the amount of flux per unit area. Both terms apply to a source emitting radiation or to a surface receiving it.

For a radiating source, the value of the flux density depends principally upon the temperature of the body and also upon its surface characteristics. The Stefan-Boltzmann Law gives the relation between the radiant flux density E and the absolute temperature T of the body as

$$E = \sigma T^4 \tag{121}$$

where σ (sigma) is a constant depending upon the units used for expressing E and T. Experiment shows that when E is in calories per second per square centimeter, the value of σ is 1.355×10^{-12}. The equation shows how greatly the temperature of a body affects its radiation; if the absolute temperature of a body is doubled, for example, its radiation will increase sixteen fold.

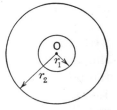

FIG. 198. Illustrating the Inverse Square Law

Inverse Square Law.—To study the radiation received by a surface, consider a spherical enclosure, as represented in Fig. 198, with a radiating body which emits an amount of flux Φ located at the central point O. If the radius of the sphere is r_1 the flux density at the surface of the enclosure will be

$$E_1 = \frac{\Phi}{4\pi r_1^2}$$

If the sphere were replaced by one of different radius, say r_2, the flux density at that surface would be expressed similarly, or

$$E_2 = \frac{\Phi}{4\pi r_2^2}$$

By division

$$\frac{E_1}{E_2} = \frac{r_2^2}{r_1^2} \tag{122}$$

which states that the radiant flux density at any surface varies in-

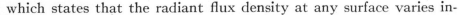

versely as the square of the distance of that surface from the source of radiation. This relation is commonly referred to as the Inverse Square Law.

Newton's Law of Cooling.—The rate at which a body cools by radiation after having been heated was investigated by Newton; he found that if the temperature of the body is not much above the surroundings, the rate at which its temperature falls is proportional to its temperature elevation above the surroundings. Expressed mathematically, the time rate of temperature change is

$$\frac{dT}{dt} = -K(T - T_s) \tag{123}$$

in which K is a constant of proportionality, and T and T_s represent the temperatures respectively of the radiating object and the surroundings, neither of which need be absolute values. This statement is called Newton's Law of Cooling; actually it may be regarded as an approximation to the Stefan-Boltzmann Law, discovered later.

An Application.—The temperature of the sun can be estimated with the aid of the Stefan-Boltzmann Law on the assumption that the sun is a black-body radiator. If T represents the absolute temperature of the sun, the radiant flux density at its surface will be $1.355 \times 10^{-12}T^4$ cal. per sec. per sq. cm. This radiation will spread radially, and at the average distance of the earth from the sun the density will be given by the Inverse Square Law as

$$E = \left(\frac{433,000}{92,900,000}\right)^2 \times 1.355 \times 10^{-12}T^4$$

where the sun's radius and the earth's solar distance are in miles.

The value of the solar constant E has been found by many investigators to average 0.033 cal. per sec. per sq. cm., which agrees with the value previously given, consequently the effective temperature of the sun is found to be 5790° K.

201. Pyrometers.—The measurement of temperatures of the order of 500° C. and over is commonly known as pyrometry. One type of instrument for observing such high temperatures is based upon the change in electrical resistance of a coil of wire and is considered in § 240. There are two other types of pyrometer and these are based upon the radiation emitted by the body itself acting as a source of radiant energy; they are the *optical pyrometer* and the *radiation pyrometer*, to be considered in this section.

The optical pyrometer utilizes the fact that the brightness of a radiating body increases as its temperature is raised, and allows the observer to compare the brightness of the body with that of a calibrated electric lamp. The instrument and its connections are shown

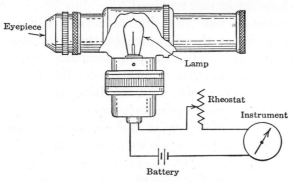

Eyepiece

Lamp

Rheostat

Instrument

Battery

Fig. 199. Optical pyrometer

in Fig. 199. An observation is made by focusing the telescope on the incandescent object under test, thereby bringing its image into the plane of the lamp filament, and then varying the current from a battery through the lamp until its filament appears to merge with the image of the hot body. The temperature is then determined by the current through the filament; usually the indicating instrument is calibrated in degrees. To eliminate the effect of color on the observation, a filter is used which permits only the red rays to reach the eye.

The radiation pyrometer makes use of the invisible heat rays as well as the visible light rays emitted by a radiating source. The

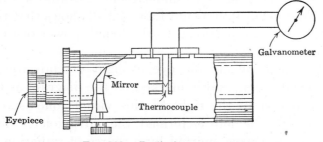

Galvanometer

Mirror

Thermocouple

Eyepiece

Fig. 200. Radiation pyrometer

radiation, coming from the right in Fig. 200, is focused by a concave mirror upon the tiny disk of a thermocouple (§ 316), and the electromotive force generated in this device is measured by a galvanometer which is graduated to read temperatures directly. If the radiation proceeds from the interior of a uniformly heated enclosure, approximating a black body, the radiant flux received upon the thermocouple disk is found to vary as the fourth power of the absolute temperature of the source. The galvanometer deflection is proportional to the amount of flux received.

It is interesting to note that the deflection of the galvanometer does not depend upon the distance of the heat source from the pyrometer if there is no absorbing medium between. This is true because the image of the source upon the receiving disk of the thermocouple is always greater in size than the disk. If, then, the telescope of the instrument is sighted upon the glowing source, the area visible through the eyepiece increases as the square of its distance away, while the radiant flux density varies inversely as the square of this distance. Hence the total flux received upon the thermocouple disk, and the deflection of the instrument, will be unaffected by the location of the pyrometer.

202. Granular Character of Radiation.—The radiation emitted by a heated body takes the form of waves in space; the lengths of these waves from crest to crest cover a wide range. The long ones are perceived by an observer as heat and the shorter ones as light. The energy of radiation is distributed over the range of wavelengths in a manner that depends upon the temperature of the radiating body and the nature of its surface. Fig. 201 shows the distribution of energy radiated by a black body as obtained by experiments conducted at two temperatures, namely 1250° and 1450° K. The curves represent the relative intensities at the various wavelengths up to 0.0006 cm. and the areas under them indicate the total energy radiated. The Stefan-Boltzmann Law (§ 200) shows that this energy for a black body is proportional to the fourth power of the absolute temperature.

Radiation which affects the eye as light extends roughly from 0.00004 to 0.00008 cm., and is marked on the diagram as the visible range. The region to the right of this visual zone is termed the infra-red, and to the left is termed the ultraviolet. The length λ (lambda) of the waves emitted by a source of radiation is related to the frequency f of the vibrating source and the velocity of wave propagation V by the expression derived in § 348 as

$$\lambda = \frac{V}{f}$$

The velocity of propagation is constant for any one medium, and therefore the frequency of vibration varies inversely with the length of the waves.

Increase of temperature causes not only an increase in total radiation but also shifts the peak of the radiation curve toward the shorter wavelengths. It is this effect which serves as the operating basis of the pyrometers described ahead. The shift in wavelength has been formulated by the German physicist, Wilhelm Wien (1864–1928), and is known as Wien's Displacement Law. It states that the product of the wavelength λ_m at which the energy density is a maximum and the absolute temperature T of the radiating body is a constant. This wavelength in centimeters is given by the equation

$$\lambda_m = \frac{0.2897}{T} \qquad (124)$$

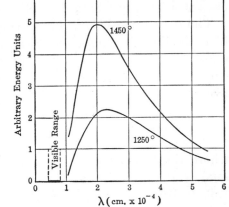

FIG. 201. Distribution of radiation energy among the various wavelengths

Much attention has been given to the study of radiation curves such as Fig. 201. The German physicist, Max Planck (1858–1947), introduced the idea in 1900 that a radiating body behaves as though it contained harmonic oscillators, each of which responds to one frequency of vibration and corresponds to the radiations which it is capable of absorbing or emitting, and he assumed these oscillators to absorb or emit energy in small steps rather than continuously. This has been interpreted to mean that energy is granular in nature, an idea that is radically different from that held back to the time of Newton, namely, that the energy of a body can change from one value to another through every conceivable intermediate value. According to the newer theory, each oscillator can absorb or emit one or more of these "grains" of energy, each of which is called a *quantum*. The magnitude of a quantum of energy for an oscillator which has a frequency f is given by the following equation:

$$E = hf \qquad (125)$$

where E is the energy in ergs, f is the frequency in vibrations per second, and h is a constant that has the value 6.62×10^{-27} erg-sec.

It will be evident that quanta are extremely tiny grains of energy, and that the quantum is smaller for low frequencies (long wavelengths) than for high frequencies (short wavelengths). The symbol h is called Planck's constant.

*203. The Quantum Theory.—The theory based upon the granular picture of energy, called the *quantum theory*, has been modified by many investigators, and now affords not only a satisfactory explanation of the radiation of energy, but also of the photoelectric effect, the structure of atoms, and all collision phenomena; these are considered in Chapters XXVII and XL.

The quantum explanation of the shape of the radiation curves for black bodies is an involved one and makes use of complicated mathematical steps. It will suffice here to give Planck's equation for the energy per cubic centimeter associated with the wavelength interval from λ to $\lambda + d\lambda$ cm., namely

$$E \, d\lambda = \frac{8\pi ch \, d\lambda}{\lambda^5 (\epsilon^{ch/k\lambda T} - 1)}$$

where the velocity c of the waves is very nearly 3×10^{10} cm. per sec. (§ 353), and k is the gas constant per molecule, which is 1.38×10^{-16} ergs/° K. (§ 172).

Planck's theory was applied by Professor Einstein to explain the variation of the specific heats of solids with temperature, and was later modified by Professor Debye to secure closer agreement with experimental results. These analyses indicate that the product of the specific heat and atomic weight of a substance falls to zero as the absolute zero of temperature is approached and that the product has a nearly constant value at relatively high temperatures. The ultimate value averages 6.3 cal. per gram-atom per degree for a large number of elements.

PROBLEMS

1. An enclosure measuring 6 x 9 x 4 meters is insulated on all its surfaces by a 10-cm. covering of glass wool having a thermal conductivity of 0.00008 metric units. It is desired to maintain the temperature inside the enclosure at 25° C. while that outside is 5° C. How much heat must be supplied to this enclosure per hour to replace that conducted through the walls? In figuring large areas, the inside dimensions may be used.

2. The space within an ice box measures 2 x 3.5 x 1.5 ft., and the walls are 2.5 in. thick. How much ice is melted per day when the contents are kept at an average temperature of 45° F. with a surrounding temperature

of 70° F.? Assume that the walls are made entirely of cork for which the conductivity is 7 British units, and that the melted ice drips out.

3. A home freezer has inside dimensions of 3 x 2 x 2 ft. and its walls are formed all around of Foamglas 6 in. thick. The heat conductivity of this material is 0.46 Btu-in. per sq. ft. per hr. per ° F. difference in temperature. Calculate the heat conducted through the freezer walls per hour when the interior temperature is 0° F. and the exterior is 90° F.

4. To measure the thermal conductivity of a liquid, it is placed between two concentric metal cylinders, heat is supplied electrically to the inner one, and the temperatures of both are read. With cylinders 8 in. long, having an annular space between them $\frac{1}{64}$ in. thick and $1\frac{1}{4}$ in. in circumference filled with benzene, a steady power input of 1.55 watts produces a temperature difference of 0.60° C. between the cylinders, when tested at about 30° C. Compute the thermal conductivity of benzene from these data.

5. A frame house measures 40 ft. by 20 ft. and is 20 ft. high. The walls consist of $\frac{3}{4}$-in. clapboard, 1-in. rough boarding, 4-in. studding, and a lath and plaster covering; for this type of wall construction the heat transmitted per square foot per day is 9.5 Btu. for 1 fahrenheit degree difference of temperature between the outer and inner faces. Consider the heat conduction through the roof the same as that through the walls, and neglect the correction for floor, window and door areas. (*a*) Compute the number of British thermal units per day necessary to maintain a difference of 30 fahrenheit degrees between house and outdoor temperatures. (*b*) If the house is to be heated by gas having a heating value of 540 Btu. per cu. ft. and costing 65 cents per thousand cubic feet, how much will it cost to maintain the stated temperature difference, assumed as an average throughout a heating season of 200 days?

6. Water is being converted into steam at an absolute pressure of 75 lb. per sq. in. in a steam boiler. How long will it take to vaporize 1 lb. of water for each square foot of boiler surface if the boiler walls are of iron $\frac{1}{2}$ in. thick, and if the outside surface has a temperature of 1800° F.?

★7. The coil of a hot-water heater consists of a 20-ft. length of copper pipe which has a $\frac{1}{2}$-in. average diameter and a $\frac{1}{16}$-in. wall. Water is supplied to the coil at 50° F. and is to emerge at 150° F., while the outer surface of the pipe is maintained at 210° F. What is the capacity of the coil in gallons of water per minute?

★8. A steam pipe having an outside diameter of 6.2 cm. is surrounded by a corrugated asbestos covering having a wall 2.2 cm. thick. If the temperatures of the outside surfaces of pipe and covering are respectively 90° and 40° C., how much heat is conducted through the covering per hour per meter length of pipe? The heat conductivity of the covering is 0.0002 metric units.

9. How many horsepower are received per square yard of the earth's surface from full sunlight perpendicularly incident? Neglect the absorption of radiant energy by the earth's atmosphere.

10. In a solar engine conceived by Dr. C. G. Abbot, the sun's radiation falling upon a mirror is focused upon a black liquid where it is absorbed,

the energy being used to generate steam and operate a small engine. With a mirror 30 sq. ft. in area, arranged for perpendicular incidence of the radiation, an overall efficiency of 15 per cent is predicted; what horsepower will the engine develop under these conditions?

11. A sphere 4 cm. in diameter is made of solid iron having a specific gravity of 7.7 and a specific heat of 0.15 cal/(gm.° C.). The sphere, having been heated to a high temperature, was allowed to cool, and its temperature was measured at 15-sec. intervals. During one of these the temperature drop was 10 centigrade degrees. At what average rate did the sphere give off heat energy during this interval?

12. At what rate will heat be emitted from a spherical body 8 cm. in diameter which has a temperature of 727° C., if the radiation constant in the Stefan-Boltzmann Law is assumed to be 1.1×10^{-12} cal. per sec. per sq. cm. for this body?

13. Recent discovery by infra-red photography of vegetation upon Mars raises the question as to the amount of solar energy which this planet receives. Estimate from the Inverse Square Law the radiant flux density upon Mars when it is 130×10^6 mi. from the sun.

14. A calorimeter is observed to cool from 30.2° C. to 29.7° C. in 1 min., the surrounding temperature being 20.0° C. As the cooling continues, how long will it take the calorimeter to cool from 26.0° C. to 25.5° C.?

15. A heated object cools from 80° F. to 78° F. in 2.5 min. within a room which has a temperature of 68° F. To what temperature will it fall in the next 2.5 min.?

16. At what wavelength would the radiated waves from a hot body have the greatest energy density when the temperature of the body is 1650° K.? What is the value of the quantum of energy corresponding to this wavelength?

Electricity and Magnetism

Electric Charge   *Chapter XIX*

204. Electrostatic Attraction and Repulsion.—The earliest electrical experiment ever recorded is probably that due to the Greek philosopher Thales (640–546 B.C.), who observed that a piece of amber when rubbed with cloth was able to attract light objects placed near it. Nowadays, the act of bringing about a very close contact between the amber and the cloth is said to give the amber a *charge of electricity*, and the attraction is called an electric or *electrostatic attraction*. The term electricity is derived from *elektra*, the Greek word for amber.

Many substances can be charged in the same way. An electric charge can be produced on a glass rod by rubbing it with silk. A hard-rubber rod rubbed with fur becomes highly charged; it can exert sufficient force upon a meter stick to turn it horizontally about a pivot at its midpoint.

The forces due to electric charges can be demonstrated best by using very light objects because the effects produced can be observed readily. Two pith balls, each suspended by a thread, and hung a few centimeters apart, will serve very well. When each of these is touched with a charged glass rod they fly apart and remain separated; they act the same way when both are touched with a charged hard-rubber rod. But if one pith ball which has been touched with the glass rod is brought near one which has been touched with the rubber rod, then they will pull together. From these tests it is evident that there is some difference between the electricity on the glass and that on the hard rubber; and quite arbitrarily, the glass rod is said to be charged *positively* and the rubber rod *negatively*. Furthermore, the tests show a fundamental fact of great importance, namely, that *like charges of electricity repel each other, and unlike charges attract each other*.

The presence of an electric charge on a body can be detected by an *electroscope*, the construction of which is indicated in Fig. 202.

341

Two leaves, ordinarily of aluminum or gold foil, hang side by side
from a metal rod which passes through an insulating bushing and
terminates in a metal knob outside of the case.   If the knob is touched
with the charged body, the leaves will acquire electricity of the same
sign and will repel each other, as represented in the
figure.   The larger the quantity of charge, the farther
the leaves will stand apart.

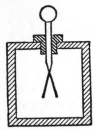

205. Electrical Structure of the Atom.—Any consideration of electrostatic phenomena involves the
structure of the atom, since the atoms themselves are
known to contain electric charges.   The planetary
picture of the atom, § 11, was proposed some years
ago by the British scientist, Lord (Ernest) Rutherford
(1871–1937), developed by the Danish physicist, Niels
Bohr, and subsequently modified through the discovery of the neutron by Rutherford's associate, James Chadwick.
This picture of atomic structure is a useful concept for clarifying
many facts of Physics and Chemistry.

F I G. 202. A
simple   electro-
scope

The simplest atom is that of hydrogen; it is pictured as having a
single proton for the nucleus and one electron whirling around the
nucleus, the positive nucleus and the negative electron being held
together by mutual attraction.   Next in order of simplicity is the
helium atom, composed of a nucleus and two planetary electrons,
the nucleus being regarded as a stable combination of two protons
and two neutrons.   The more complex atoms have more and more
protons and neutrons in the nucleus, together with a corresponding
increase of planetary electrons.   The electrons are supposed to occupy
shells around the nucleus, their arrangement under normal conditions
being as follows:

The hydrogen (H) atom has its one electron in the first shell, and
the helium (He) atom has both its electrons in that shell.   This
innermost shell accommodates only two electrons.   The lithium (Li)
atom, with a total of three planetary electrons, has one of them in the
second shell; beryllium (Be) has two in the second shell, boron (B)
three, carbon (C) four, nitrogen (N) five, oxygen (O) six, fluorine (F)
seven, and neon (Ne) eight, the last number filling the second shell.
The sodium (Na) atom has a total of eleven planetary electrons, of
which two fill the first shell, eight fill the second shell, the remaining
one being in a third shell.   By a continuation of this process to include the more complex atoms, in which the electrons are supposed

to be arranged in shells of various sizes, the entire Periodic Table of the elements may be constructed, § 470.

Certain elements are quite inert and it is concluded that their atomic structures are inherently stable. Perhaps because of compactness or symmetry, such stability is associated with electron shells that are completely filled. The helium atom with its first shell complete, the neon atom with the first and second shells complete, and other atoms similarly located in the table (argon, krypton, xenon and niton), are chemically inactive.

The ability of atoms to combine and form molecules is determined by the planetary electrons, and the tendency in combining is apparently to form arrangements in which the electron shells are completely filled. A lithium or sodium atom, with one electron in its outer shell, is in a condition which favors losing this electron, while a fluorine or chlorine atom, with one electron less than is needed to complete its outer shell, is in a condition which favors gaining one. When sodium and chlorine are allowed to mingle, each sodium (Na) atom joins a chlorine (Cl) atom to form sodium chloride (NaCl), in which process the loosely held electron of the sodium atom is transferred to the chlorine atom, thus filling the electron shells of both atoms. The measure of the ability of atoms to form molecules by combining in this manner is known as *valence*; for example, sodium, which has one electron more than is needed to fill its outer shell, is said to have a *valence number* of $+1$, and chlorine, which has one electron less than is needed to fill its outer shell, is said to have a valence number of -1.

Atomic quantities are much too small to be measured directly, but from indirect measurements results of great precision have been obtained. For example, the hydrogen atom, which is composed of a proton and an electron, has a mass of 1.674×10^{-24} gm. Of this amount, the electron forms only a small part; its mass when at rest is 9.11×10^{-28} gm. The dimensions of the hydrogen atom, with its components assumed to be spherical, are of the following order of magnitude: radius of nucleus and radius of electron, each about 2×10^{-13} cm.; least radius of electronic orbit, about 0.5×10^{-8} cm. A better appreciation of the relative proportions of these quantities can be obtained by imagining the atom to be magnified until the electronic orbit is as large as that of the earth about the sun. The electron would then be represented by a sphere about the size of the earth itself, and would rotate around a nucleus of equal size.

206. Production of Electric Charge.—The process of charging a body by rubbing it with another material may be viewed as a stripping of electrons from some of the atoms at the contacting surface. Atoms of some elements release electrons with comparative ease, and others acquire them readily. A neutral or uncharged body contains equal amounts of positive and negative electricity; when electrons are added, it becomes negatively charged, and when electrons are removed, it becomes positively charged. Thus, a hard-rubber rod, when brought into intimate contact with fur, gains electrons and becomes negative and the fur loses these electrons and becomes positive to an equal extent. A glass rod rubbed with silk loses electrons and becomes positive, while the silk gains these electrons and so becomes negative.

Examples illustrating the production of electric charge are familiar to everyone. The effect may be observed by passing a rubber comb through the hair or by shuffling the feet on a woolen carpet. A leather belt traveling on iron pulleys may acquire sufficient electricity to produce a spark to a person's finger held near it. The paper in a printing press usually manifests a charge when it is separated from the rollers, and means are provided to dissipate the charge.

207. Insulators and Conductors.—It is possible to charge a body from another that is already charged by simply bringing the two into contact. Thus, a metal sphere gains negative electricity if it is touched with a negatively charged rubber rod, Fig. 203. It appears that some electrons leave the rod at the point of contact by virtue of their mutual repulsion and attach themselves to the sphere, making it negative also. Or, if the sphere is touched with a positively charged glass rod it becomes positive, because electrons are attracted away from it to the rod at the point of contact.

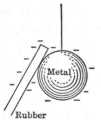

Fig. 203. Charging a metal sphere by contact

It is assumed that the sphere referred to is supported in such a way that the electricity acquired will not leak away. This can be done by suspending the sphere with a dry silk string or by supporting it on props of mica or glass. Evidently materials like these do not transfer or conduct electricity to any appreciable extent, and they are called *insulators* or *dielectrics*. If the sphere had been suspended by a metallic wire or mounted upon a metal support, practically the entire charge might escape to the earth. It can be concluded that metals aie good *conductors* of electricity. Many substances are neither good insulators nor good conductors but may be classed in an intermediate group as fair electrical conductors; for example, the human body, a piece of damp wood, and the earth.

208. Charging by Induction.—It is possible to charge a conductor from a charged body without touching them together; the process is called *induction*. The procedure for charging a conductor by induction is as follows: (1) bring the charged body close to, but not in contact with, the conductor to be charged; (2) connect the conductor to ground by touching it with the finger; (3) break the ground connection; and (4) remove the initially charged body. The conductor will then have acquired a charge which will be found opposite in sign to the original one.

This process will be explained by reference to Fig. 204, wherein the conductor is represented as a brass tube with rounded ends mounted on a glass stem for insulation, and the charged body is a negative rubber rod. The steps in the process are as follows: (1) When the charged rod is brought near the tube, it will repel some of

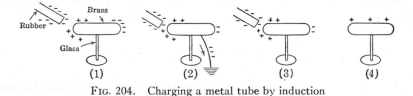

Fig. 204. Charging a metal tube by induction

the electrons of the tube, thus making the distant end of the tube negative, and leaving the adjacent end positive. A state of equilibrium will soon be reached in which any other electrons that are repelled by the rod, are prevented from moving to the distant end of the tube by the negative electricity already accumulated there. (2) When the tube is grounded, a path is provided for some of the electrons to escape, and there will be a flow of electrons through the ground connection to the earth. (3) When the ground connection is broken the body is again isolated and it will have a positive charge, since it has lost some electrons. Finally, (4) the removal of the inducing body allows the charges on the tube to distribute themselves in a normal manner, and the tube becomes positive over its entire surface.

209. Forces between Charged Bodies.—It has been shown that charges of like sign repel and those of unlike sign attract each other, but nothing has been said so far about the magnitude of the forces of repulsion or attraction. The first quantitative measurements of these forces were conducted by the French physicist, Charles A.

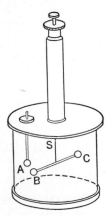

Coulomb (1736–1806), using a *torsion balance*. This instrument has a stationary sphere *A* and a suspended element consisting of two spheres *B* and *C* connected by a light rod, all within a glass enclosure, as shown in Fig. 205. When both *A* and *B* carry charges of the same sign, the repulsion between them twists the supporting wire *S* until the opposing torques are equal. These investigations, confirmed by the English chemist, Henry Cavendish (1731–1810), showed that the force between two charged bodies, whether of repulsion or attraction, varies directly as the product of the charges, varies inversely as the square of the distance between them, and is influenced by the surrounding medium.

FIG. 205. Torsion balance

For bodies concentrated at points, carrying charges Q_1 and Q_2 and separated a distance r, the value of the force which either one exerts upon the other is given by the expression

$$F = \frac{Q_1 Q_2}{\epsilon r^2} \qquad (126)$$

This expression is the foundation of a system of electrostatic units (esu.), and serves to define unit charge in that system. When the charges Q_1 and Q_2 are in electrostatic units of charge (often referred to merely as unit charges) and their separation r is in centimeters, the force F will be in dynes. The quantity ϵ is a physical constant of the medium surrounding the charges called *permittivity*; for a vacuum the permittivity is usually designated ϵ_v and its value is taken as unity.

Consequently, *the electrostatic unit of charge is a quantity of electricity which when placed 1 cm. in a vacuum from an equal one will be acted upon by a force of 1 dyne.* For practical purposes, the force may be considered the same in air as in a vacuum, the permittivity of air being practically unity (1.000586) at standard temperature and pressure.

When two charged objects are located in some physical medium, the net force that they exert upon each other is less than in empty space. The charged objects induce charges of opposite sign on the neighboring layers of the medium, so that each of the objects becomes surrounded by a surface charge of opposite sign. These induced charges depend in amount upon the nature of the medium but their effect is always to make the net force between the objects less than in a vacuum. Hence the permittivity of any physical medium is greater than unity.

210. The Electric Field.—The region about a charged body is referred to as an electric field of force, or briefly, an *electric field*, because any other charge located in this region will experience a force, either of attraction or repulsion. The amount of force acting upon a unit charge is taken as a measure of the strength or intensity of the field. *The intensity of an electric field at any point is defined as the force per unit positive charge placed at that point*, and the electro-static unit of field strength is the *dyne per unit charge*. Thus, if a unit of positive electricity experiences a force of 10 dynes toward the right at a particular point in an electric field, the field intensity at that point is 10 dynes per unit charge and is directed toward the right. In general, if Q units of electricity located in an electric field are acted upon by a force of F dynes, the intensity of the field $\mathscr{E}$ at that place is given in dynes per unit charge by

$$\mathscr{E} = \frac{F}{Q} \tag{127}$$

In this expression, Q represents a charge placed at some point in an already existing field, and $\mathscr{E}$ is the field strength at that point before Q was introduced.

Consider now the region around a charge of $+Q$ units, and suppose for simplicity that this electricity is concentrated at a point, as at O in Fig. 206. The direction and strength of the electric field which it produces at any point in the region is found by assuming a *unit positive* charge to be placed there and determining the force acting upon it. The directions of the field at four points A to D are shown in the figure by arrows all of which are radially outward from Q. The force on a unit charge at a point such as C is found from equation (126) to be

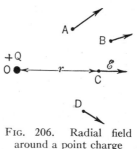

Fig. 206. Radial field around a point charge

$F = \dfrac{Q \times 1}{\epsilon r^2}$, where r is the distance from O to C. Hence, the field

intensity at any point distant r from a charge of Q units is

$$\mathscr{E} = \frac{Q}{\epsilon r^2} \tag{128}$$

where Q represents the charge which establishes the field, and $\mathcal{E}$ is the strength of the field in dynes per unit charge. To summarize, the field intensity due to a point charge varies directly with the amount of charge and inversely with the square of the distance away; furthermore, it is directed radially outward from a positive charge and radially inward toward a negative one.

The region around an electric charge is represented conventionally by *lines of dielectric flux* directed along the field at every point. The region near two spheres, one positive and the other negative, is represented in this manner in Fig. 207; the flux lines start at the positive charge and end at the negative one. It will be observed that the lines are closer together at some places than at others; the number of lines per square centimeter extending perpendicularly through a given region is called the *flux density* at that place. Maps of flux distribution such as that shown may be obtained experimentally by sprinkling tiny bits of straw or hair on an insulating plate held near the charges.

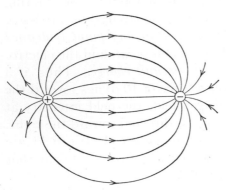

FIG. 207. Lines of dielectric flux

The medium in which the charges are located has no effect on the amount of flux or its distribution, although clearly, from equation (128), it does affect the field intensity everywhere in the field. In keeping with these facts, for a medium of permittivity ϵ, the flux density at a place where the field intensity is $\mathcal{E}$ is made equal to the product $\epsilon\mathcal{E}$. It follows that in air, which is the medium most often involved, the flux density at any place is numerically equal to the field intensity there.

To evaluate the amount of flux extending from a charge Q, imagine a sphere of radius r about it as center; the field is perpendicular to the spherical surface at all points and has the same intensity $\mathcal{E} = Q/\epsilon r^2$ all over. The flux through each square centimeter of the spherical surface is $\epsilon\mathcal{E} = Q/r^2$, and therefore the total flux extending from the central charge Q through the entire surface of area $4\pi r^2$ is $4\pi r^2 \times Q/r^2$ or $4\pi Q$, and is independent of the surrounding medium.

Since electric field intensity has direction as well as magnitude, it is a *vector* quantity (§ 20), and consequently field intensities can be resolved or combined in the same way as velocities or forces. When the field intensity at a point is due to several point charges, its value can be determined by computing the field intensity at the point due to each in turn, and then finding the resultant of these individual values. In part I of Fig. 208, the field intensity at point P has one

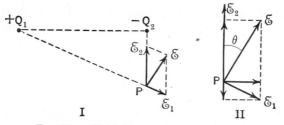

FIG. 208. Field due to two point charges

component $\mathscr{E}_1$ directed radially away from the positive charge Q_1 and another component $\mathscr{E}_2$ directed radially toward the negative one Q_2; the resultant field intensity at this point is shown at $\mathscr{E}$.

As an illustrative example, consider that the charges shown in part I of Fig. 208 are $Q_1 = +4000$ units and $Q_2 = -1000$ units, these being 12 cm. apart in air, and that the point P is located 5 cm. directly below Q_2. This point will then be 13 cm. away from Q_1. The components are $\mathscr{E}_1 = \dfrac{4000}{(13)^2} = 23.7$ and $\mathscr{E}_2 = \dfrac{1000}{(5)^2} = 40.0$, both in dynes per unit charge. To compute the resultant, first resolve $\mathscr{E}_1$ into a vertical component $\frac{5}{13} \times 23.7 = 9.1$ downward and a horizontal component $\frac{12}{13} \times 23.7 = 21.9$ to the right, as in part II; then subtract the first of these from $\mathscr{E}_2$, leaving $40 - 9.1 = 30.9$ vertically; and finally combine this result with 21.9 horizontally to give $\mathscr{E} = \sqrt{(30.9)^2 + (21.9)^2} = 45.6$ dynes per unit charge. The direction of this resultant field intensity is given by $\tan \theta = 21.9/30.9$, whence $\theta = 35.3°$ to the right of the vertical.

211. Electric Potential.—From the fact that an electric field exerts a force upon a charge located within it, it is evident that work must be done upon such a charge in moving it against this force. If the field is uniform in intensity, the work done will be the product of the constant force and the distance the charge moves, provided it moves along the line of force action. If the field is not uniform, the force will vary from point to point, and the determination of work done becomes more involved.

Such determinations are simplified by introducing the idea of "electrical level," a concept called *potential*. In Mechanics, if a body is to be moved from one level to a higher one, work must be done upon it; in Electricity, if a +charge is to be moved from one potential to a higher one, work must be done upon it. Thus, points in space near charged objects have definite potentials. *The potential at any point is the work per unit positive charge required to move it from an infinitely great distance up to the point in question.* Let W be the work done upon a test charge Q to bring it from infinity to a particular point in an electric field; then basically the potential at that point is

$$V = \frac{W}{Q} \tag{129}$$

To derive an expression for the potential due to a specific charge, consider the electric field about a charge $+Q$ located at point O in Fig. 209, and compute the amount of work that is done upon a unit positive charge in moving it from a remote point at the right up to a point R distant r cm. from O. When the unit charge is at a distance x cm. from O, it is repelled by Q with a force of $\frac{Q}{\epsilon x^2}$ dynes, and an equal

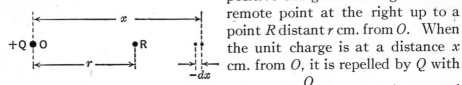

FIG. 209.   Illustrating electric potential

force directed toward Q is required to hold it at this position. Hence, the work done in moving it an infinitesimal distance $- dx$ nearer to Q is $- \frac{Q}{\epsilon x^2} dx$ ergs. The total work done in moving the unit charge from an infinitely great distance to point R is found by integrating this expression between the limits $x = \infty$ and $x = r$, giving

$$\int_{x=\infty}^{x=r} - \frac{Q}{\epsilon x^2} dx = \left[+ \frac{Q}{\epsilon x} \right]_{\infty}^{r} = \frac{Q}{\epsilon r}$$

Consequently, the potential at a point R distant r cm. from a point charge of Q units is

$$V = \frac{Q}{\epsilon r} \tag{130}$$

and is expressed in electrostatic units of potential, or ergs per unit charge.

Potential is completely expressed by a statement of magnitude; it is therefore a *scalar* quantity. The potential at a single point due to several charges would be found by adding algebraically the individual potentials due to the several charges.

The difference in potential between two points is found by subtracting the potential at one point from that at the other point. This difference represents the work done in moving a unit positive charge from one point to the other. In practice, difference in potential is used more often than absolute values.

The work done in transferring a quantity of electricity from one point to another in an electric field can now be determined readily. Since the work done in transferring unit charge between two points is equal to the potential difference V between the points, the work done in transferring any charge Q between these points is

$$W = QV \qquad (131)$$

It will be clear that if Q is expressed in electrostatic units of charge and V is in ergs per electrostatic unit of charge, the work done will be in ergs.

Two charges of $+600$ units and $+500$ units are spaced 12 cm. apart in air, and it is desired to compute the work needed to reduce their separation to 10 cm. Suppose the 600-unit charge to remain at rest; the potential which it establishes at a point 12 cm. away is $V_{12} = 600/12 = 50$ and that at a point 10 cm. away is $V_{10} = 600/10 = 60$, both expressed in ergs per unit charge. The work needed to move the 500-unit charge through the potential difference of 10 ergs per unit charge is $500 \times 10 = 5000$ ergs. The same result can be obtained by supposing the 500-unit charge to be fixed and to establish a potential difference through which the 600-unit charge is then moved.

Work must be done to move a positive charge from a point of low potential to one of high potential; under the same circumstances a negative charge would move of itself, if free to do so, and would do work in the process. Thus, the free electrons in a conductor will move, producing an electric current, if there is a potential difference between any two points on the conductor. Further, if a conductor bears a charge which is not moving to produce a current, its surface must have the same potential at all points. Such a surface is called an *equipotential* surface, and it follows from the definition of potential that no work would be required to transport electricity from one point on it to another.

212. Motion of Electric Charge in Solids.—The transfer of electric charge within a medium, spoken of as conduction of electricity, takes place differently in solids than it does in fluids. The closeness of the atoms to one another in solids makes it possible for the outer electron orbits of neighboring atoms to overlap. Moreover, most conducting solids are metals in which the atom has only a few electrons in the outer shell (see Periodic Table), a condition which favors the loss of these electrons. Under these circumstances, and possibly because some electrons serve in a double capacity in two adjoining atoms, it is believed that a large number of electrons are comparatively free to move.

When one end of a conducting wire is maintained negative by supplying it with electrons and the other end is maintained positive by withdrawing electrons from it, the *free electrons* within the wire are repelled from the negative end and attracted toward the positive end. These electrons acquire a definite drift from atom to atom toward the positive end of the wire. It is this flow of electrons which constitutes an *electric current*, § 226. Ordinarily the free charges in a body are pictured as being in a state of unceasing, unordered motion, depending upon the temperature. When there is current through the body, the directed drift is superposed upon this random motion.

It is interesting to note that in solids the positively charged atoms remain fixed in position except for thermal agitation, and that the *current is attributed entirely to a movement of electrons*. The free electrons are also believed to assist in the conduction of heat, as well as of electricity, through solids.

In insulating solids the electrons are not readily detachable from the atoms. If one surface of a glass plate, for example, is maintained negative and the other positive, the electrons in the dielectric do not drift through it, but undergo only a slight shift or *displacement*.

213. Distribution of Charge on Conductors.—The shape of a conducting body has a marked effect on the distribution of electricity over it, and in general the amount of charge per unit area will not be uniform over its surface. The amount of the charge at any spot can be determined by using a *proof plane*, consisting of a small metal disk fastened to one end of an insulating rod, together with an electroscope. The disk of the proof plane is applied to the spot under test and then to the electroscope; the resulting separation of the electroscope leaves becomes a measure of the *surface density of charge*.

A charged sphere, whether hollow or solid, when tested in this way will show the same separation of its leaves after the plane is touched to any point on the outer surface. It is supposed that the sphere is isolated so as to be uninfluenced by its surroundings and the test indicates that the surface density is uniform. On an elongated conductor, such as a rod or tube, this density will be found greater at the ends than at the middle, a result which shows the tendency of the individual charges to repel one another to the greatest possible distance.

The distribution of electric charge can be studied further by repeating an experiment originally conducted by the British chemist and physicist, Michael Faraday (1791–1867), using a metal ice pail, an electroscope, and a metal sphere, arranged as in Fig. 210. When the sphere is charged from an outside source and lowered into the pail the leaves of the electroscope diverge. The sphere may then be moved around inside the pail, touched to its inner surface, and removed, without causing any further change in the electroscope. After the sphere is touched to the pail and removed, both the sphere itself and the inner surface of the pail will be found entirely free from charge.

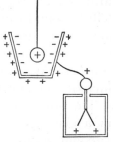

FIG. 210.   Faraday's ice-pail experiment

To explain this result, assume a positive sphere lowered to the position shown. It attracts some of the free electrons in the metal pail to the inner surface, and consequently the outer surface, together with the electroscope, are left positive. When the sphere is touched to the pail the induced charge on the inside of the pail and the inducing charge on the sphere neutralize each other. The charge on the outside of the pail, which before contact was as large as that on the inside, must therefore be equal to the initial amount on the sphere, and of the same sign. Consequently it may be concluded that *a charge induces an equal and opposite charge on the surrounding surface.* It is also seen that *a charge cannot exist inside of a conductor*, unless this region also contains an equal and opposite charge, instead, *it will reside on the outer surface.* In the experiment, it is desirable to have the opening in the receptacle as small as possible, for the action will not be complete unless the hollow conductor is completely closed.

214. Conduction in Gases; Ionization.—To demonstrate the flow of electricity through gases, suppose that an electroscope has been charged so that its leaves stand apart as in Fig. 202, and that the flame of a gas jet is brought near the electroscope knob. It will be found that the leaves fall together promptly, showing that the electroscope has lost its charge. The molecules of the heated gases collide with each other and with air molecules so forcibly as to knock some electrons out of the atoms. As a result, the neutral molecules become interspersed with molecules carrying negative and positive charges. These are called *ions* (go-ers), a term which is applied to atoms or atomic groups when electrically charged. If the electroscope is positive it will attract the negative ions, and if negative it will attract the positive ions. Its charge in either case will be neutralized, and the air around it will be *ionized*.

Again, if a charged electroscope is exposed to the radiation from uranium, radium, or other radioactive substance, the electroscope will be found to lose its charge, because the radiation has ionized the air. Ionization of the air is also produced by x-rays and ultraviolet light, as well as by cosmic radiation received by the earth from remote sources. Whatever the cause, practically every sample of air will include some ions.

The flow of electricity through air and other gases can be studied in a glass tube fitted with sealed-in electrodes and attached to a vacuum pump as shown in Fig. 211. One electrode A is maintained

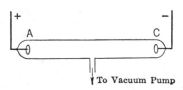

FIG. 211. Gaseous discharge tube

positive and the other one C negative; these are called the *anode* and *cathode* respectively. At atmospheric pressure no action is observed, but when the pressure is reduced a discharge takes place in the tube, which is attributed to the ions present in the enclosed air, moving in accordance with their attraction or repulsion by the electrodes. Depending on the pressure, the discharge may be a luminous thread of bluish color between the electrodes or a glow which fills the entire tube. At low pressure the discharge is in the nature of a radiation directed away from the cathode, to which the name *cathode rays* is given. These rays cause certain substances to glow, and have electromagnetic properties by which they are recognized as a stream of high-velocity electrons. Such conduction through the tube is explained by supposing that the bombardment of positive ions knocks electrons out of the cathode, and that these electrons have sufficient energy to ionize the air within the tube by collision. At moderate pressures the tube is so crowded with air molecules that the emitted electrons do not gain sufficient velocity to produce much ionization, and at very low pressures the air molecules are so widely spaced that the collisions are comparatively infrequent. The maximum conduction of the gas occurs at some intermediate pressure value.

If a conductor has a sharp point, a large part of its charge will pass to the point, and the few ions already present in the neighboring air will be accelerated so strongly that they create more ions by cumulative collision, thus permitting the electricity to escape from the conductor. A similar effect is produced by bringing a pointed object *near* a charged conductor, because of the charge that is induced on the point. If a sufficient charge is placed upon a pointed electrode, the discharge is accompanied by a glow which may be seen in the dark, and is called a *brush discharge* or *corona*. To minimize such leakage, rounded knobs are used instead of sharp points on electrostatic apparatus.

When two pointed electrodes, separated by air at ordinary pressure, are brought sufficiently close to each other, a *spark* will jump between them; this so-called *disruptive discharge* is accompanied by a sharp, quick snap or crackle. The few ions which are always present in the air are hurled along so violently that they produce others by collision; these in turn produce still more, and by this cumulative action the air becomes highly conducting almost instantly. Disruptive discharge may occur not only in gases but also in insulating liquids and solids.

Under certain atmospheric conditions the clouds gather electricity, either by contact of electrically dissimilar layers of air or by the falling of charged rain drops, and this induces a charge of opposite sign on the surface of the earth below. If the intervening electric field is sufficiently intense, a disruptive discharge will occur as a stroke of lightning. To protect buildings and other structures from damage which may result from lightning strokes, they are equipped with *lightning rods*. These are large conductors, well grounded at the bottom and terminating in sharp points at the top, arranged to form as complete an enclosure of the building as is practicable. Such an arrangement tends to prevent the interior of the building from becoming electrically charged, since it forms at least a partial conducting shell around it. It also allows the electricity induced on the neighboring portion of the earth to escape from the sharp points and in this way tends to prevent the accumulation of sufficient charge to result in a lightning stroke. In the event of a stroke, the large conductors provide an easy path for the current and tend to divert it from the building. Although there is no doubt that buildings equipped with lightning rods have been injured by lightning, nevertheless, a well designed and properly installed system of lightning rods is recognized as a valuable safeguard against such injury.

Gaseous ionization is utilized in the *Cottrell process* for smoke elimination. A long negatively charged wire of small diameter is suspended vertically within the column of rising smoke and sets up an intense field in the region directly around it. Here the gas becomes ionized by collision and the suspended carbon particles acquire negative charges by contact with the gaseous ions. They are then repelled by the negative wire and deposited on the surrounding walls.

215. Electrostatic Generators.—For the operation of discharge tubes, the production of x-rays of high penetration, and the acceleration of charged particles for research on the atomic nucleus, use is often made of electrostatic generators to develop the necessary high potentials. Such machines were built for many years with rotating glass plates equipped with metal disks for carrying the charges produced by induction, but nowadays the machines are of a type developed by Robert J. Van de Graaff in which the charges are transported on a traveling belt.

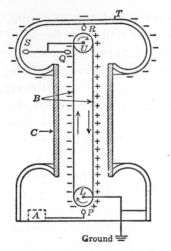

A typical design is represented diagrammatically in Fig. 212. It consists essentially of a hollow metal terminal T mounted on an insulating column C, within which a motor drives an endless belt B of insulating material for conveying electricity between the terminal and ground. The terminal may be made either positive or negative; the operation will be described for the latter case.

FIG. 212. Van de Graaff type of electrostatic generator (*Unit 4 ft. high develops up to 500,000 volts with a rubber-fabric belt 10 in. wide driven at 5000 ft. per min.*)

A row of metal points represented by P is directed toward the lower metal pulley L and receives continuously a small supply of negative electricity from an auxiliary source A. The air in the vicinity of the points becomes ionized and the negative charges are repelled toward the pulley and deposited on the intervening insulating belt. This neutralizes the positive charge that may be on the belt from its downward run and leaves a net negative charge to be carried to the upper terminal.

The collector Q transfers this charge partly to the upper insulated pulley U and partly (through suitable control devices not shown) to the point S and thence to the terminal. The charges are so distributed as to make the pulley more negative than the terminal itself, and so the pointed electrode R connected to the terminal may now be regarded as positive with respect to the pulley. In consequence, the air between the two becomes ionized and positive charges are attracted toward the pulley and deposited on the belt. This action neutralizes the negative charge remaining on the belt and leaves a residue of positive charge to be carried downward. It is evident that as the machine is driven there is a continuous transfer of negative electricity up one side of the belt and positive electricity down the other side. As a result, the terminal acquires a large negative charge, and this brings about a high negative potential, as explained in § 286.

216. Field between Parallel Charged Plates.—The electric field between two parallel plates is uniform at all points, except at the edges; the edge irregularities may be neglected if the plates are large compared with the distance between them. Under these conditions, the field intensity can be computed by considering the work done by a charge in moving from one plate to the other.

In Fig. 213, the work done by the charge $+Q$ in moving from the positive plate to the negative one in the direction of the field will be some force F multiplied by the distance s between the plates. This amount of work can also be expressed as QV from equation (131), where V is the potential difference between the plates. It follows that $Fs = QV$, or $F/Q = V/s$. But F/Q, being

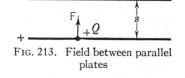

Fig. 213. Field between parallel plates

the force per unit charge, is the field intensity, by equation (127). Whence, the field between the plates has an intensity given by

$$\mathscr{E} = \frac{V}{s} \tag{132}$$

If V is in ergs per unit charge and s is in centimeters, $\mathscr{E}$ will be in dynes per unit charge, as previously.

217. Measurement of the Electronic Charge.—An achievement of great importance, which furnished an insight into the nature of electricity, was the determination of the charge of the electron by Robert A. Millikan in 1913. His method in its simplest form was to charge a tiny oil drop, place it in an electric field so directed as to urge the droplet upward against the pull of gravity, and to adjust the field strength so as to hold the droplet stationary.   Under this condition the upward force due to the field equals the downward force of gravity, a fact which permits the quantity of electricity on the droplet to be computed.

Millikan's apparatus, shown in Fig. 214, consists of a closed chamber C containing near the top an atomizer A, and near the bottom a pair of parallel plates PP which can be connected across

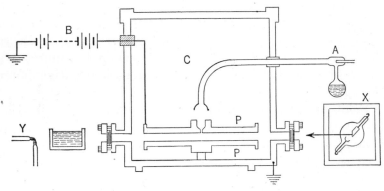

FIG. 214.   Millikan's oil-drop apparatus

the battery B.   The plates are separated by a few insulating blocks, not shown, and the air between them is ionized by x-rays from the tube X.   The central region between the plates is illuminated by the arc lamp Y, and observations can be made in that region by means of a telescope at the front.

Oil is sprayed from the atomizer into the chamber and falls as a mist, some of the droplets entering the space between the plates, the upper one of which is pierced with a pinhole for this purpose.   After a droplet is singled out, a preliminary measurement is made with the plates uncharged to determine its uniform velocity of fall; this is done by noting the time required to fall a small known distance.   A knowledge of this velocity makes it possible to determine the radius of the droplet from Stokes's Law, § 144, which gives the radius as

$$r = \sqrt{\frac{9\eta v}{2dg}}$$

where η is the coefficient of viscosity of the air, d is the density of the oil, g is the acceleration due to gravity, and v is the velocity of the droplet. The mass m of the droplet can then be found from its radius and density, namely,

$$m = \tfrac{4}{3}\pi r^3 d$$

The plates PP are next connected across the battery, and the potential difference between them is adjusted to a value V such that the same droplet will remain stationary at some convenient point between the plates. The electric field strength under this condition will be $\mathscr{E} = V/s$, where s represents the separation of the plates. If the droplet has acquired an amount of electricity Q from the ionized air, it will experience an upward force $F = QV/s$. But this is equal to the downward force on the droplet due to gravity, whence $QV/s = mg$, from which the quantity of electricity on the droplet becomes

$$Q = \frac{mgs}{V} \tag{133}$$

In the foregoing equations, Q is expressed in esu. of charge, V is in ergs per unit charge, and all mechanical quantities are expressed in the cgs. system of units.

Millikan found that the smallest charge ever acquired by a droplet has a definite value, 4.80×10^{-10} esu. according to the latest determinations, and that all others are exact multiples of this value. From these facts it is inferred that electricity consists of tiny discrete charges, and that the elementary quantity, the charge of the electron, is $e = 4.80 \times 10^{-10}$ esu. No electrical charge smaller than this has ever been discovered.

PROBLEMS

1. A charge of $+1000$ esu. is situated 50 cm. in air from a charge of -300 esu. Compute the force upon each.

2. Two small objects carrying positive charges of 100 esu. and 200 esu. are spaced 6 cm. apart in a horizontal plane, the surrounding medium being air. How much force does each exert upon the other?

3. The practical unit of electric quantity, the coulomb, is equal to 3×10^9 esu. of charge. If it were possible to bring a charge of 1 coulomb to a point in air 1 meter away from another just like it, what force in tons would these charges exert upon each other?

4. Two pith balls, each having a mass of 0.04 gm., are supported in air from a common point by silk threads each 10 cm. long. When equal charges are placed upon the pith balls, their supporting threads stand 30° apart. Compute the charge on each pith ball.

5. A charged body which weighs 0.01 gm. is held stationary in space by placing it in an upwardly directed electric field having an intensity of 7.5 dynes per unit charge. Find the charge on the body.

6. A charge of $+20$ esu. experiences a downward force of 600 dynes at a certain point in an electric field. Find the field intensity at that point.

7. Refer to the charges in Problem 2 and locate a point on the line connecting them at which the field intensity due to the charges is zero.

8. Points P, Q, and R are at the corners of a triangle measuring 10 cm. along each side; the triangle is in a vertical plane with line PQ horizontal and point R below it. A charge of $+1000$ esu. is located at P and another of unknown strength is located at Q. If the field intensity at R due to these charges is horizontal, what is the value of the charge at Q?

9. A "dipole" formed of charges Q and $-Q$ separated by a distance $2s$ is located in a medium of permittivity ϵ. Show that the electric field intensity due to the dipole at a distance r from its midpoint and in line with the charges is $\dfrac{4Qrs}{\epsilon(r^2 - s^2)^2}$.

10. Find the field intensity due to the charges described in Problem 2: (a) at a point midway between the charges, and (b) at a point 4 cm. below the center of the line connecting the charges.

11. Determine the location of a point on the line connecting the charges of Problem 1 at which the potential due to the two charges is zero.

12. Refer to the charges described in Problem 1 and find the field intensity and also the potential at a point 30 cm. away from the 1000-esu. charge and on the line connecting the two.

13. Compute the potential due to the charges described in Problem 2: (a) at a point midway between the charges, and (b) at a point 9 cm. vertically above the smaller charge.

14. Charges are placed at the corners of a rectangle with diagonals 10 cm. long so as to produce a potential of -40 ergs per esu. of charge at the center of the rectangle, the surrounding medium being air. If three of the charges are $+1000$ esu., $+800$ esu., and -600 esu., what is the charge at the fourth corner?

15. Charges of -800 and -100 esu. are located respectively at the corners A and B of a triangle ABC having a right angle at B; $AC = 10$ cm. and $BC = 5$ cm. Calculate the field intensity and also the potential at C due to the charges, the surrounding medium being air.

16. Find the potential at a point 30 cm. from a charge of $+600$ esu. in a vacuum, and also at a second point 20 cm. from this charge. How much work would be necessary in order to move a quantity of $+5$ esu. from one of these points to the other?

17. Two large conducting plates are supported so that their planes are vertical, parallel, and 5 cm. apart. The plates are charged and a pith ball weighing 0.05 gm. and charged with 300 esu. is suspended in the air space between them. What potential difference between the plates will cause the thread supporting the pith ball to stand at 30° with the vertical?

18. Two horizontal plates, each 15 cm. in diameter, are spaced 0.4 cm. apart in air. A drop of oil of radius 0.00006 cm. and of density 0.86 gm/cm.³ is introduced into the region between the plates. If the drop carries 2 electrons, what potential difference must be maintained between the plates in order to hold the drop at rest?

19. At what speed must the electron in the hydrogen atom revolve to prevent it from being pulled into the nucleus by electrostatic attraction, if the radius of its orbit is taken as 0.5×10^{-8} cm.?

20. A particle of radius r carrying a charge Q is located in an electric field of intensity $\mathcal{E}$, the surrounding medium having a coefficient of viscosity η. Show by means of Stokes's Law that the velocity of the particle due to the field can be expressed as

$$v = \frac{\mathcal{E}Q}{6\pi\eta r}$$

21. Suppose a charged dust particle of 0.001 mm. diameter to be located in a horizontal electric field having an intensity of 6 dynes per unit charge, the surrounding medium being air at 20° C., for which the coefficient of viscosity may be taken as 181×10^{-6} poise. From the expression developed in Problem 20, find the number of electrons on the dust particle if it travels a horizontal distance of 3 cm. in 1 sec.

22. An electron is shot horizontally at a speed of 1.5×10^{10} cm. per sec. into a vertical electric field having an intensity of 4 dynes per esu. of charge. How far will the electron be deflected vertically by the field while traveling a horizontal distance of 10 cm. through it? Take the mass of the electron at this speed to be 10.5×10^{-28} gm.

Magnetism   *Chapter XX*

218. Magnets.—A *magnet* is a body which has the property of attracting iron and steel, and which if suspended freely will turn so as to point in a definite direction. The magnet will also attract certain other materials, such as nickel and cobalt, although rather feebly. Any material which a magnet attracts is known as a *magnetic substance.*

The property of magnetism has been known for centuries. Ancients recognized that a black mineral ore called lodestone or magnetite exhibited this property, and it is believed that the word magnetism was derived from Magnesia, a district in Asia Minor, where the ore was plentiful. The approximate composition of this natural magnet is Fe_3O_4.

A bar of steel can be made into a magnet very simply; it is only necessary to rub it with a piece of lodestone or with another magnet. It can be magnetized much more strongly, however, by placing it within a coil of wire carrying an electric current. When the bar is of hard steel, it retains its magnetism for long periods of time and is styled a *permanent magnet.* Soft iron does not have such permanence. If a soft-iron bar is placed inside the coil just mentioned, forming what is known as an *electromagnet*, it will be magnetized strongly while there is a current in the winding, but will lose almost all of its magnetism as soon as the current is interrupted, retaining only a small amount known as *residual* magnetism. The magnetizing action of the electric current is explained in § 260.

219. Magnetic Poles.—Experiment shows that magnetism is not exhibited uniformly over the surface of a magnet; the regions where its effects are pronounced are called *poles.* A straight magnet, for example, if dipped into iron filings will hold them in large clusters near its ends and will show practically no attraction at its center; thus such a magnet as ordinarily made has two poles. Precise tests reveal the fact that *the two poles of a magnet have exactly the same strength.*

It is also found that when a bar magnet or a magnetized needle is suspended or pivoted it rotates to a general north-and-south direction, and the same end always points toward the north. This fact suggested appropriate names for the two magnetic poles. The magnet pole which points to the arctic region of the earth is termed the north-seeking pole, or briefly the *north* (N) pole of the magnet; the other is termed the *south* (S) pole.

If a bar magnet is brought near another, it will be observed that the north pole of one attracts the south pole of the other, that the two north poles repel each other, and that the two south poles repel each other. In short, *unlike magnetic poles attract each other; like poles repel.*

The magnitude of the force between two magnetic poles was measured by Coulomb in 1785, using a torsion balance as in the study of electrostatic forces, but substituting magnetic poles for the electric charges. His results, later confirmed with greater accuracy, showed that the force is proportional to the pole strengths and inversely proportional to the square of the distance between the poles.

Suppose that two magnet poles have strengths m_1 and m_2, that they are separated a distance r, and that they are concentrated at points located in empty space. The force action between them, whether of attraction or repulsion, is given by

$$F = \frac{m_1 m_2}{\mu_v r^2} \tag{134}$$

This equation not only shows the factors which determine the force of one pole upon another, but serves also to define the unit of pole strength. When the pole strengths m_1 and m_2 are expressed in these units and their separation r is in centimeters, the force F is in dynes. The quantity μ is a property of the medium surrounding the poles called *permeability*; for a vacuum it is usually designated μ_v and its value is taken as unity. For practical purposes the result is the same when the poles are located in air, for the permeability of air differs but slightly from unity. Consequently, the *unit magnet pole is one of such strength that it will exert a force of 1 dyne upon an equal pole in vacuum (or air) when placed 1 cm. away from it.* There is no characteristic name for this unit of pole strength, it is merely called *unit pole.*

As an application of the Inverse Square Law of magnetic action, equation (134), consider two bar magnets each 10 cm. long placed in one line with their N poles 5 cm. apart and their S poles 25 cm. apart. Assume that each pole has a strength of 200 units, that it is localized in a central point on the end face of the magnet, and that the medium is air. There will be four force actions:

Repulsion $\dfrac{200 \times 200}{(5)^2} = 1600$ dynes $\qquad \dfrac{200 \times 200}{(25)^2} = 64$ dynes

Attraction $\dfrac{200 \times 200}{(15)^2} = 178$ dynes $\qquad \dfrac{200 \times 200}{(15)^2} = 178$ dynes

Thus, the net force will be a repulsion of $1600 + 64 - 2(178) = 1308$ dynes.

220. The Magnetic Field.—The region about a magnet where its influence can be detected is called a *magnetic field*. Throughout this region forces will act upon magnetic substances or magnet poles. The force that is experienced by any given pole within the field will vary in direction and in amount as that pole is moved about, and this fact indicates that the magnetic field must have a certain direction and a particular intensity at every point. *The direction of a magnetic field is that of the force acting upon an isolated N pole*; the idea of an isolated pole is convenient and implies that the companion pole of the magnet is too far away to affect the resulting action appreciably. *The intensity of the magnetic field at any point is defined as the force that would be exerted upon a unit N pole placed there.*

The unit of field intensity is called the *oersted*, and is named after Hans Christian Oersted (1777–1851), the Danish physicist who discovered electromagnetism. *The oersted is the intensity of a magnetic field in which a unit magnet pole experiences a force of 1 dyne.* From this definition it follows that if at any point in a magnetic field a pole of strength m units experiences a force of F dynes, the field intensity at that point in oersteds will be

$$H = \frac{F}{m} \tag{135}$$

Thus, if an isolated N pole of 20 units strength placed at a point in a magnetic field is acted upon by a force of 240 dynes to the left, the field intensity there is $240 \div 20 = 12$ oersteds to the left.

The foregoing facts explain the motion of a suspended magnet in seeking a position of equilibrium within a magnetic field of uniform intensity. The magnet, of length l cm. between poles, is shown in the plan view of Fig. 215 to be displaced at an angle θ from the direction of the field, the field being represented by the light arrows. From equation (135) the N pole of the magnet is acted upon by a force $F = mH$, where m is the pole strength and H is the field intensity. The torque due to this force about the center of the magnet is $Fd = F \dfrac{l}{2} \sin \theta$. The force on the S pole produces a torque of the same value and direction, consequently the total torque is

$$T = 2mH \frac{l}{2} \sin \theta = MH \sin \theta$$

where $M = ml$ is a constant of the magnet called its *magnetic moment*. This torque tends to lessen the angle θ, and the magnet, because of its inertia, will oscillate until friction brings it to rest in the direction of the field.

If a light magnet is mounted on a piece of cork and floated on water in a uniform magnetic field, it will be observed to rotate in the manner described. Furthermore, it will have no motion of translation, showing that the uniform field acts equally but oppositely upon the two poles. This result confirms a previous statement that the two poles of a magnet are equal in strength.

221. Field Near a Magnet Pole.—When the region around a magnet pole is explored it is found that the magnetic field is not uniform, but diminishes rapidly in intensity as the distance from the pole is increased.

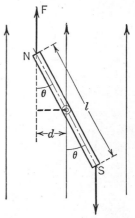

Fig. 215. Magnet oscillating in a magnetic field

Suppose that the intensity of a field due to a pole of strength m is to be determined at any point distant r from the pole, and assume as before that the pole is located within a vacuum. Imagine a test pole of N polarity and of strength m_1 to be placed at this point; it will experience a force Hm_1, where H is the field intensity, as yet unknown, at the point selected. It is apparent that pole m_1 is separated from pole m by a distance r and that the force action between them can also be expressed by equation (134) as

$F = \dfrac{mm_1}{\mu_v r^2}$, both poles being regarded as point poles. Since the two foregoing expressions must represent the same force, they may be equated, giving as the field intensity at the point in question:

$$H = \frac{m}{\mu_v r^2} \tag{136}$$

This expression shows that the field intensity produced by a magnet pole varies inversely with the square of the distance from the pole; specifically, it gives the field intensity in oersteds due to an isolated pole of strength m units at a point r cm. away from it.

The direction of the field at any point is the same as that of the force which would act on a N test pole placed there; naturally it is radially outward from a N pole and radially inward toward a S pole. The intensity and direction of the field due to a magnet can be obtained at any specified point by applying equation (136) to both of its poles, and combining the component intensities by vector addition.

As an illustrative problem, compute the magnetic field intensity at points A and B due to the bar magnet shown in Fig. 216. The magnet is 6 cm. long and has poles of 2000 units. Point A is 4 cm. from the N pole on the axis of the magnet and point B is 4 cm. from the magnet on its perpendicular bisector. The surrounding medium is air. At A the field intensity has two components, $2000 \div (4)^2 = 125$ dynes per unit pole radially away from N, and $2000 \div (6 + 4)^2 = 20$ dynes per unit pole radially toward S; these are drawn from A and extend in opposite directions and their resultant,

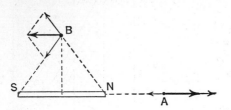

FIG. 216.   Field intensity near a bar magnet

shown by the heavy arrow, is $125 - 20 = 105$ dynes per unit pole away from N. At B the components each have the value $2000 \div (3^2 + 4^2) = 80$ dynes per unit pole; one is directed away from N, the other is toward S, and their resultant is found by similar triangles to be $\frac{6}{5} \times 80 = 96$ dynes per unit pole parallel to the magnet and directed toward the left in the figure.

222. The Earth's Magnetic Field.—The fact, mentioned in § 218, that a suspended magnet orients itself in a particular direction at every point on or near the earth, shows that the earth is surrounded by a magnetic field. The distribution of the field is such as might be produced roughly by a huge bar magnet within the earth, located about 17° away from its axis and having a length much less than the earth's diameter. The two places at the earth's surface where the field is vertical are called the magnetic poles. The region of the magnetic pole in the northern hemisphere was long believed to be on Boothia Peninsula in Northern Canada (latitude 70° N., longitude 96° W.). Explorations in 1947 indicate that this region possesses three poles, the major one on Prince of Wales Island and the others on Boothia Peninsula and Bathurst Island. The magnetic pole in the southern hemisphere is near Ross Sea, Antarctica (latitude 72° S., longitude 157° E.). The magnetic equator is a line on the earth's surface connecting points where the field is horizontal. The line is irregular and varies in latitude from 16° S. in South America to 11° N in Africa.

The fact that a pivoted magnet aligns itself with the earth's magnetic field makes possible its use as a *compass* for guidance in travel and navigation. Such use dates back a number of centuries, and there is evidence to show that pieces of lodestone were suspended for this purpose by the Chinese perhaps as far back as ten centuries B.C. A modern magnetic compass is shown in Fig. 217. At the center of the card carrying the scale is a spheroidal air vessel to buoy the card and magnets, which are immersed in a mixture of water and alcohol that entirely fills the bowl. The magnets are visible below the card and are formed of sealed cylindrical tubes filled with magnetized steel wires.

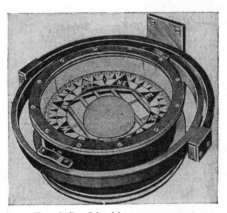

FIG. 217. Liquid-type compass
(*Courtesy of E. F. Ritchie & Sons*)

Naturally the N pole of a compass points in the general direction of the earth's magnetic pole in the northern hemisphere; this terrestrial pole must have south polarity but this fact need cause no confusion. The magnetic polar region is far away (1400 miles) from the north geographic pole, and besides, the compass is influenced by regional effects. In consequence, the compass does not point true north; the angle that it makes with the geographic meridian is called the *magnetic declination* or *variation* of the compass. A compass at New York City points 12° west, and at San Francisco points 18° east, of geographic (true) north.

Fig. 218 shows a chart on which points of equal magnetic variation are joined by lines, the amount and direction of the declination being indicated; these lines are called *isogonic lines*. The isogonic line for which the declination is zero is called an *agonic line* and is indicated by a heavy line on the chart. At a place through which an agonic line passes, a compass needle will point true north.

The variation at any place does not remain the same year after year, but changes somewhat over long periods of time. Besides these so-called *secular changes*, there are fluctuations within the year and also changes of small extent throughout the day. Large erratic irregularities occur during "magnetic storms"; these are often concurrent with the appearance of sun-spots. Much work has been done in attempting to explain terrestrial magnetism and to account

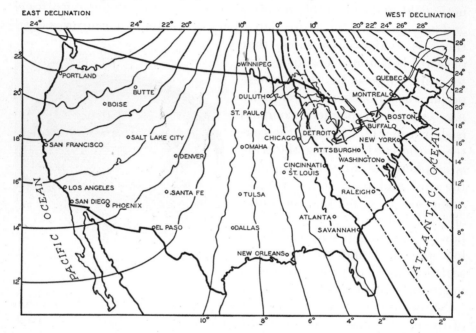

FIG. 218.   Isogonic lines for the United States (1945)
(*Courtesy of U. S. Department of Commerce*)

for its variations, but too little is known at present about the magnetic sources within the earth and about atmospheric currents to establish a satisfying theory of the earth's magnetism.

The direction of the earth's magnetic field is not horizontal (except at the magnetic equator), as can readily be observed by balancing a magnetized needle on a horizontal spindle, and placing it so that its vertical plane of movement includes the direction of the field. At New York such a *dip needle* would point downward at an angle of 72° with the horizontal.

The horizontal and vertical components of the earth's field can be expressed in terms of the angle of dip β as

$$H_h = H_e \cos \beta \quad \text{and} \quad H_v = H_e \sin \beta$$

respectively, where H_e is the total intensity of the field. It is the horizontal component which is most frequently utilized in magnetic measurements. Its value in the United States ranges from 0.13 oersted at Gull Island in Lake Superior to 0.28 oersted near Brownsville, Texas.

223. The Magnetometer.—Theoretically, the intensity of a magnetic field can be measured by observing the force acting upon an isolated magnet pole of known pole strength placed in it, and then applying equation (135); but since magnet poles do not exist singly, it is customary to make measurements of field intensity with an instrument called a *magnetometer*. This device consists merely of a magnetic needle and some means for observing its deflection; in a simple magnetometer the needle is pivoted and carries a pointer that swings over a scale. A determination is made by comparing the field to be measured with another that is taken as a standard; the latter may be the earth's field if its value is definitely known, or else may be produced by an electric current, § 261.

To measure the magnetic field X shown in the plan view, Fig. 219, this field is arranged horizontally at right angles to the earth's field of known horizontal intensity H_h. The needle of the magnetometer placed at M will point in direction H_h when the unknown field X is absent, and will point in the direction of the resultant R of the two fields when both act upon the instrument. The angle ϕ, through which the needle deflects in moving from one position to the other, is observed. It follows that the intensity of the

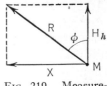

FIG. 219. Measurement of a magnetic field

field under test may be expressed in terms of the known intensity H_h as

$$X = H_h \tan \phi \qquad (137)$$

Another way to determine the intensity of a magnetic field in a definite plane is to allow a compass needle to swing freely in that plane and measure its rate of vibration. It can be shown in a manner similar to that for a physical pendulum (§ 97) that the time of one vibration of small amplitude is

$$T = 2\pi\sqrt{\frac{I}{MH}}$$

where I is the moment of inertia of the magnet about its center, M is its magnetic moment, and H is the field intensity sought.

224. Magnetic Lines of Force.—The configuration of a magnetic field can be observed by placing a sheet of glass or cardboard in the region being surveyed and sprinkling it with iron filings. When the sheet is tapped, the filings align themselves with the field and form strings or chains, as represented in Fig. 220 for a bar magnet. Such tests indicate that the space around a magnet is in a peculiar magnetic condition. Faraday regarded it to be in a state of stress, whereby it is able to exert a force on any pole brought into it. Lines drawn along the direction of the field will indicate the directions of the forces and are called appropriately *lines of force*. The iron filings in the test just described lie along such lines.

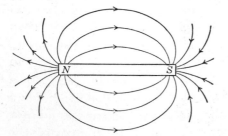

FIG. 220. Lines of force about a bar magnet

Lines of force are directed *away from the* N *pole* of a magnet and *toward the* S *pole*, and since the field can have only one direction at a given point, the *lines of force never cross one another*. The magnetic stresses produced by the field can be pictured by imagining that the lines tend to shorten themselves (like stretched elastic bands) and that lines extending side by side exert a sidewise thrust upon one another. The attraction or repulsion between two magnets can then be ascribed to the interactions of lines of force in the intervening field.

225. Theory of Magnetism.—An explanation of magnetism is suggested by a simple test which consists of breaking a magnet in two, then breaking one of these parts in two, and so on. As far as actual tests like this have been carried out the parts of the original magnet are always found *to be magnets themselves*, so it is presumed that if the breaking process were continued until parts of molecular magnitude were reached, each minute part would prove to be a magnet. The hypothesis that a magnetic substance is composed of molecular magnets, but not necessarily that each molecule be a magnet, is called the *molecular theory of magnetism*.

According to this theory, when a substance is unmagnetized its molecular magnets point in all conceivable directions and form small stable groups that exhibit no outside magnetism. When placed in a magnetic field, the molecular magnets align themselves more and more in a definite direction as the intensity of the field is increased, and magnetic poles of increasing strength are produced in the substance. Hard steel requires a more intense field than soft iron to produce a given magnetization, because its molecular magnets turn with greater difficulty; for the same reason, upon withdrawal of the field most of the molecular magnets of the steel retain their positions, while most of those of the iron again assume random positions. This explains the difference in behavior of permanent magnets and electromagnets, and accounts for residual magnetism in the latter.

If a bar of unmagnetized steel is held in the direction of the earth's field and jarred by striking it repeatedly, some of the molecular magnets will align themselves with the field, and the bar will become permanently magnetized. On the other hand, if a permanent magnet is heated to a dull red, the increased motion of the molecules will throw them out of their orderly arrangement, and the magnet will lose its magnetism.

Again, if a piece of unmagnetized iron or other magnetic substance is placed in a magnetic field, its molecular magnets will align themselves with the field to a certain extent, and poles are *induced* in the specimen so long as it remains in the field. It is because of these induced poles that a magnet attracts a piece of unmagnetized iron.

A more complete theory attributes magnetism to the motion of electrons within the atom, for it is known that a moving electron constitutes an electric current and that an electric current produces a magnetic effect. It is believed from spectrum analysis that the planetary electrons in the atom not only revolve about the nucleus but also that each electron spins about an axis through its center, and that in the crystals of highly magnetic substances each atom has more electrons spinning in one direction than in the other. Throughout a tiny region called a "domain" these uncompensated spins have the same directions in the atoms of all the crystals, and the entire magnetic specimen is composed of a large number of such domains, these being highly magnetized but turned at random with respect to one another. There are certain directions in which it is relatively easy to magnetize a crystal, and when a small external field is applied to the specimen, the direction of magnetization of the individual crystals is shifted to one of these "easy" directions that has a component along the field, and the specimen becomes slightly magnetized. As the strength of the applied field is increased, the magnetization of the crystals is gradually shifted in direction toward that of the field and the magnetization of the specimen is more complete.

PROBLEMS

In the following problems the medium in which the magnets are located is assumed to be air.

1. A U-shaped electromagnet having two poles 16 cm. apart is magnetized to have pole strengths of 800 units each. What force does one pole exert on the other?

2. A N pole of 500 units strength is brought near the electromagnet of Problem 1. When placed 10 cm. from both poles of the electromagnet, what force will act upon the test pole?

3. Two bar magnets, one 10 cm. long and having poles of 300 units strength and the other 15 cm. long and having poles of 200 units strength, are placed in a straight line with their N poles 5 cm. apart and their S poles 30 cm. apart. Compute the force between the magnets.

4. A magnet 12 cm. long has poles of 65 units strength at its ends. It is suspended horizontally over an identical magnet that is located directly below it on a table. What is the vertical force between the magnets when they are 5 cm. apart and in the same vertical plane?

5. A compass needle 5 cm. long and having poles of 10 units strength is held crosswise in a uniform horizontal magnetic field of 20 oersteds intensity. What torque acts upon the needle in this position?

6. An isolated N magnet pole of 10 units strength experiences a force to the right of 180 dynes at a certain point in a magnetic field. Compute the field intensity at that point.

7. Find the field intensity at a point midway between the poles of the electromagnet described in Problem 1.

8. Calculate the magnetic field intensity at a point along the axis of a bar magnet 10 cm. long, the point being 10 cm. beyond one end of the magnet. The magnet has poles of 400 units strength.

9. Assume that the poles of the magnets shown in the accompanying figure have strengths of 800 units each, and find the magnitude of the field intensity at a point P between the magnets and equally distant from all four poles.

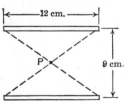

10. Compute the field intensity at a point 8 cm. vertically above the S pole of the magnet shown in Fig. 216.

11. Two points are chosen near a bar magnet, A on its axis and B on its perpendicular bisector. Let the distance from either point to the center of the magnet be l and the length of the magnet be $2\,d$. Prove that if d is small compared with l, the field intensity due to the magnet at A is twice that at B.

12. Near the Malay Peninsula, the horizontal component of the earth's magnetic field has its greatest value, namely 0.41 oersted, and the angle of dip there averages 10°. Compute the vertical component and the resultant field intensity at this location.

13. At the magnetic observatory in Cheltenham, Maryland, the components of the earth's magnetic field are 0.182 oersted horizontal, and 0.540 vertical. Compute the total intensity and the inclination of the field.

14. A pivoted magnet makes 1 vibration in 2 sec. in a field having an intensity of 0.2 oersted. What is the field intensity in a region where this magnet makes 2 vibrations per sec.?

15. Determine the intensity of the magnetic field produced by a given electric current if this field, when arranged horizontally at right angles to the earth's field of horizontal intensity 0.22 oersted, displaces a compass needle through an angle of 40°.

Current and Resistance

Chapter XXI

226. Electric Current.—When the potential at one end of a conducting wire is different from the potential at the other, the free electrons in it will undergo a drift or flow. Such a flow takes place in an electric lamp, for example, when a potential difference is applied across its terminals, and the lamp is said to have an *electric current* in its wire filament. In order for this flow to continue, the potential difference must be maintained by some electrical *source*, such as a battery or generator, connected across the ends of the filament. The source and lamp together with the connecting wires form a complete conducting path, or *circuit*; the part external to the source is called the *external circuit*.

The current is capable of producing a number of effects in electric circuits; the principal ones, familiar to most observers, are *heat*, *magnetism*, and *electrolysis*. A current in a lamp heats the filament to incandescence, and thereby produces illumination. A current in the electromagnet of a telegraph sounder magnetizes the iron core and causes a pivoted piece of iron to be attracted, thereby producing a click. A current in acidulated water (H_2O) causes the liberation of the component gases, hydrogen and oxygen, by electrolysis.

227. The Simple Circuit.—A circuit in which the effects of the current may be demonstrated is shown in Fig. 221. In part I a

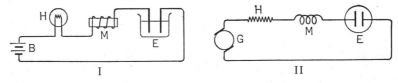

FIG. 221. Circuit to show the principal effects of an electric current

battery *B* supplies current to a lamp *H*, a coil or electromagnet *M*, and an electrolytic cell *E*, these circuit elements being shown pictorially. Part II shows a generator *G* in a circuit having the same elements represented conventionally.

A battery or direct-current generator urges the electrons continuously in one direction. If it is desired to have them flow in the opposite direction in the external circuit, the terminals of that circuit must be reversed with respect to the battery or generator. For this reason, these sources of electricity are said to have fixed polarity, and one terminal of the source is called positive and the other negative.

From the early days of electrical science, current has been considered to flow in the external circuit from the positive terminal of the source to its negative terminal. It is now known that a current is actually a movement of electrons, and since these are negative, they travel around the external circuit from the negative terminal to the positive terminal. The *electron flow* is, therefore, opposite to the conventional direction of the *current*, making it necessary, in order to avoid confusion, to distinguish one from the other by name.

228. The Coulomb and the Ampere.—The electrostatic unit of charge is so small a quantity of electricity that for practical purposes a larger unit called the *coulomb* is used. *A coulomb is a quantity of electricity equal to 3×10^9 electrostatic units of charge.* The reason for choosing this particular number will be apparent after the magnetic effect of the current has been considered, § 261. Since the charge of the electron is 4.80×10^{-10} esu. of charge, it follows that a coulomb is a charge of $3 \times 10^9 \div 4.80 \times 10^{-10}$ or 6.25×10^{18} electrons.

The current in a metallic circuit is essentially a drifting of electrons through it; quantitatively, *current* is defined as *the time rate of flow of electric charge.* The unit of flow is appropriately taken as the transfer of one coulomb of charge per second of time past some point in the circuit. Because the concept of current is so commonly used, a shorter name is applied to the unit; it is called the *ampere* (abbreviated amp.) in honor of the French scientist, André M. Ampère (1775–1836). *The ampere is a rate of flow of electric charge of one coulomb per second.* If electricity flows at a uniform rate such that Q coulombs pass a point in t sec., the current at that point, expressed in amperes, is

$$I = \frac{Q}{t} \tag{138}$$

Current is measured by an instrument called an *ammeter*. It comprises a coil, pivoted between the poles of a permanent magnet and provided with a pointer that moves over a scale. The coil is deflected by the magnetic effect of the current through it, and the size of the deflection is a measure of the current.

Electric current is sometimes confused with electric charge. The difference can be explained through analogy with hydraulics, by considering a pump which circulates water in a pipe line, just as a battery or generator circulates charges in an electrical circuit. The quantity of water would be reckoned in gallons while the charge would be in coulombs. The rate of flow of water past any point in the piping would be expressed in gallons per second while the flow of electricity would be in coulombs per second (or amperes).

229. Electromotive Force and Potential Drop.—In the study of electrostatics it was found that work is always done in moving an electric charge between two points which have different potentials. The work done is equal to the product of the charge and the potential difference, in accordance with equation (131). This statement applies also to the circulation of charge around an electric circuit. The *charge does work* in traversing the circuit, as evidenced by the evolution of heat and the operation of electromechanical devices; the *charge has an equal amount of work done upon it* as it moves through the battery or other source of electrical energy. The battery or other source is said to have an *electromotive force* (abbreviated emf.), which is measured by the work done upon each unit of charge as it passes through the source.

A source within which a charge Q has an amount of work W done upon it has an electromotive force given by

$$E = \frac{W}{Q} \tag{139}$$

Also, the work done by a unit charge in passing between two points of a circuit is equal to the *potential drop* between those points. If W is now taken to represent the work done by the charge Q in moving between two such points, the potential drop between the points is

$$V = \frac{W}{Q} \tag{140}$$

The term *potential difference* applies to both emf. and potential drop; the practical unit is the *volt*. *The potential difference between two points is one volt if a charge of one coulomb either requires or expends one joule of energy in moving from one point to the other.* This unit was named after the Italian physicist, Alessandro Volta (1745–1827). In equations (139) and (140), if W is expressed in joules and Q in coulombs, then E and V are in volts.

To give a practical idea of the volt, a few illustrations will be cited. The emf. of the familiar dry cell is 1.5 volts. Practically all electric lamps are illuminated by direct or alternating current supplied at 110 to 120 volts. Many direct-current railways are operated on 500 to 600 volts. For long-distance transmission of electrical energy, values over 100,000 volts are often employed.

Since the energy which the charge receives from the source must be the same as that which it expends throughout the circuit, it follows that the emf. of the source must equal the sum of the potential drops around the circuit.

The difference of potential between two points in an electric circuit is measured by an instrument called a *voltmeter*, by merely connecting the instrument across the points under consideration. It operates on the same principle as the ammeter but is designed to take very little current and is calibrated to read in volts.

230. Electrical Energy and Power.—It was shown in the foregoing section that the electrical energy supplied to a circuit by a source of emf. E is given by $W = EQ$, but this result can be expressed more usefully in terms of the current I rather than the charge Q. Since the quantity of charge transferred is equal to the average current multiplied by the time of transfer, or $Q = It$, the energy may be expressed as

$$W = EIt \tag{141}$$

Also, in any portion of a circuit across which the potential drop is V, the energy liberated is

$$W = VIt$$

In these expressions the energy W is expressed in joules, the emf. E or potential drop V is in volts, the current I is in amperes, and the time t is in seconds. The energy may appear in any form, such as heat, mechanical energy, or chemical energy.

The rate of expending energy in a circuit is the *power* supplied to it; this is found by differentiating the foregoing expressions with respect to time. Thus, the power supplied to the entire circuit is

$$P = \frac{dW}{dt} = EI \tag{142}$$

and to a portion of the circuit is

$$P = \frac{dW}{dt} = VI$$

In these equations the unit in which power is expressed is the joule per second, or watt. Therefore 1 watt = 1 volt × 1 amp.

231. Ohm's Law and Resistance.—Experience with metallic circuits shows that the current established in such a circuit is directly proportional to the emf. of the source, if no other emf.'s are acting in the circuit. Thus, the current I varies directly with the emf. E. By the use of a constant R, the relation between these quantities can be expressed as an equation, namely

$$I = \frac{E}{R} \tag{143}$$

This relation was first given by Georg S. Ohm (1787–1854), a German physicist, in 1827, and is known as Ohm's Law. The factor R is called the *resistance* of the circuit.

The law states that the current in a circuit equals the emf. in that circuit divided by the resistance of the circuit; if either the emf. or the resistance is altered, the current will automatically adjust itself by a corresponding amount. Each of the symbols in the equations should be interpreted as applying to the entire circuit, thus R stands for all the resistance of the circuit, including the internal resistance of the source.

Ohm's Law may also be stated for part of a circuit as follows: The current in any part of a circuit equals the potential drop across that part of the circuit divided by the resistance of that part. In symbols

$$I = \frac{V}{R} \tag{144}$$

This equation further serves to establish the unit in which resistance is expressed. Thus, if the potential drop across a resistance is 1 volt when the current in it is 1 ampere, then the resistance must have unit value; this unit is called the *ohm*. *The ohm is a resistance across which there is a potential drop of one volt when the current in it is one ampere.*

A few examples will serve to give an approximate idea of the unit of resistance. A copper wire 1000 ft. long and 0.1 in. in diameter (No. 10 American wire gage) has a resistance of 1 ohm. A copper wire 2.4 ft. long and 0.005 in. diameter (No. 36) has the same resistance.   An iron rod $\frac{3}{4}$ km. long and 1 cm. square also has a resistance of 1 ohm.

The resistance of a wire or device can be determined by connecting it in a circuit to a battery and using an ammeter to measure the current in it and a voltmeter to measure the potential drop across it, as shown in Fig. 222.   If the current is I and the potential drop is V, the value of the resistance is $R = V \div I$.   The instrument connections shown are also suitable for measuring the power expended in the resistance, this being the product of the ammeter and voltmeter readings, as indicated by the equation $P = VI$.

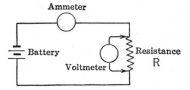

Fig. 222.   Measuring resistance with ammeter and voltmeter

The current in a resistance is 0.25 amp. when a potential difference of 120 volts is applied across its terminals.   Find the value of the resistance and also the power expended.   By Ohm's Law, the resistance is $\dfrac{120}{0.25} = 480$ ohms.   Also, the power expended is $120 \times 0.25 = 30$ watts.

232. Joule's Law of Heating.—The flow of electricity through a wire or other conductor of electricity always produces heat.   The quantity of heat produced in a given conductor naturally depends upon the duration of flow and upon the value of the current.   That twice as much heat will be produced by a given current in double the time would be expected; however, doubling the current does not double the heat developed under like conditions.   Experiment shows that the heat produced is proportional to the *square* of the current.   Still another factor is involved, namely, the resistance of the conductor.   If the same current prevails for equal periods of time through pieces of wire having the same dimensions, one of copper and the other of iron, the iron will become hotter than the copper; consequently, iron is said to offer more opposition to the current and to have a higher resistance than copper.   To summarize, the *heat produced in a conductor is proportional to the resistance of the conductor, to the square of the current, and to the time.*   This statement is known as Joule's Law of electric heating.

The amount of energy W converted into heat in a time t, by a current I, in a conductor of resistance R is given by this law as

$$W = RI^2t \tag{145}$$

If R is expressed in ohms, I in amperes, and t in seconds, then the energy will be given in joules. By means of the ratio 0.239 cal. = 1 joule (§ 182) the heat developed may be expressed in calories as

$$H = 0.239RI^2t$$

When a current of 1 amp. is maintained for 1 sec. through a conductor of 1 ohm resistance, the amount of heat produced is exactly 1 joule, or 0.239 calorie.

The correctness of these expressions can be verified by using a calorimeter containing oil or other insulating liquid and immersing the conductor in it as shown in Fig. 223. The current can be measured by an ammeter, and the duration of the test by a stop watch. The heat liberated by the conductor can be determined by measuring the water equivalent of the calorimeter and its contents, and observing the change of temperature that occurs during the test (§ 157).

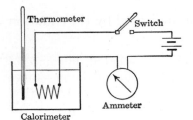
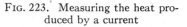

FIG. 223. Measuring the heat produced by a current

In the experiment just described the electrical energy supplied to the immersed coil is all converted into heat. If the source produces a potential difference of V volts at the heater with a current of I amp. through it the energy supplied to the heater in t sec. will be VIt, and this must equal the heat energy as expressed by equation (145). Consequently, $VIt = RI^2t$, and

$$V = RI$$

which, of course, is Ohm's Law.

Since the energy appearing as heat is given in joules by $W = RI^2t$, the *power* dissipated in heat is given in watts by

$$P = RI^2 \qquad (146)$$

The same expression applies equally well to an entire circuit or to any part of it if the symbols are properly interpreted.

Compute the rating of an electric heater which will heat 10 liters of water from 20° C. to 80° C. in 15 min., on the assumption that no heat is wasted. Also, what current must be supplied to this heater if its resistance is 5 ohms? The heat needed is $10,000 \times (80 - 20)$ or 600,000 cal. or $600,000 \div 0.239 =$ 2,511,000 joules. The power dissipated is $2,511,000 \div (15 \times 60) = 2790$ joules per sec. or watts; this is equivalent to a rating of 2.79 kw. From equation (146), $2790 = 5 \times I^2$; whence the current is 23.6 amp.

233. The Practical Electrical Units.—For convenience of reference the electrical quantities so far dealt with are summarized below, together with their practical units and the definition of each.

Quantity or charge: The coulomb is a quantity of electricity equal to 3×10^9 electrostatic units of charge. The esu. of charge is defined as one which exerts a force of 1 dyne upon an identical charge at a distance of one centimeter in a vacuum (§ 209).

Current: The ampere is a unit of current which is equal to a rate of flow of electric charge of one coulomb per second.

Energy: The joule is an amount of work or energy equivalent to 10^7 ergs. The erg (§ 64) is defined as the work done by a force of one dyne exerted through a distance of one centimeter.

Electromotive force and potential drop: The volt is the difference in potential between two points when a charge of one coulomb either requires or expends one joule of energy in moving from one point to the other.

Power: The watt is the unit of power and represents a rate of doing work of one joule per second; also the watt equals a volt-ampere.

Resistance: The ohm is a resistance across which there is a potential drop of one volt when the current in it is one ampere.

Certain prefixes are commonly used with these units when large or small values are referred to. These include: meg $= 10^6$, kilo $= 10^3$, milli $= 10^{-3}$, and micro $= 10^{-6}$. Thus, 1 megohm $= 1,000,000$ ohms, and 1 microvolt $= 0.000001$ volt.

The relations between the practical units and the electrostatic units can be found directly from the definitions in the two systems. Thus, for potential difference, to compare the volt (joule per coulomb) and the erg per esu. of charge (§ 211), note that 1 joule $= 10^7$ ergs and that 1 coulomb $= 3 \times 10^9$ esu. of charge, whence 1 erg per esu. of charge $= 300$ volts.

234. Factors Affecting Resistance.—The resistance of an electrical conductor opposes the flow of electricity in somewhat the same way that friction in a pipeline opposes the flow of water. As might be expected from this similarity, electrical resistance is directly proportional to the length of the conductor and inversely proportional to its cross-sectional area. Further, it is found that two conductors of the same dimensions will have different resistances if made of different substances. This is ascribed to their different resistivities, the *resistivity* being the resistance of a sample of the substance having specified unit dimensions. Consequently, a conductor of length l, cross-sectional area A, and resistivity ρ (rho), has a resistance R which is given by the equation

$$R = \rho \frac{l}{A} \tag{147}$$

When the length l is expressed in centimeters, the cross-section A in square centimeters, and the resistance R in ohms, the unit for resistivity will be

$$\rho = \frac{RA}{l} = \frac{\text{ohm} \times \text{cm.}^2}{\text{cm.}} = \text{ohm-cm.}$$

Copper has a resistivity of 1.72×10^{-6} ohm-cm., which means that a specimen of copper 1 cm. long and 1 sq. cm. in cross-section will offer 1.72×10^{-6} ohm resistance between opposite faces of the cube.

To illustrate the calculation of conductor resistance, consider a copper wire having a diameter $d = 0.1$ cm. and a sectional area $A = \pi d^2/4 = 0.00785$ sq. cm. A length of 100 cm. of this wire will have a resistance of

$$R = \rho \frac{l}{A} = 1.72 \times 10^{-6} \text{ ohm-cm.} \times \frac{100 \text{ cm.}}{0.00785 \text{ cm.}^2} = 0.0219 \text{ ohm.}$$

235. Resistances of Wires.—In calculating the resistances of wires for industrial purposes, it is common practice in this country to express the length of the wire in feet, and the cross-section in units of *area* called *circular mils* (abbreviated CM.). One circular mil is the area of a circle 0.001 in. (1 mil) in diameter. Since the area of a circle varies as the square of its diameter, a wire having a diameter of 2 mils will have an area of 4 CM., one having a diameter of 3 mils will have an area of 9 CM., and so on. Thus, *to find the cross-section of a wire in circular mils, express the diameter in mils and square this number.* The circular mil is a convenient unit of area for round wires because it avoids the use of the factor $\pi/4$ in the calculations.

When the length of a wire is expressed in feet and its cross-section in circular mils, the corresponding unit for resistivity in equation (147) is the ohm-circular mil per foot. Thus, copper has a resistivity of 10.4 ohm-CM. per ft., meaning that a specimen of copper 1 ft. long and 1 CM. in cross-section will have a resistance of 10.4 ohms. This specimen is shown in Fig. 224, together with that representing the ohm-centimeter.

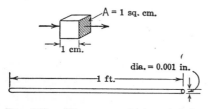

Fɪɢ. 224.   Shapes on which resistivity values are based

The following table lists the resistivities of a number of common materials. The resistivity of a substance is affected somewhat by temperature changes, and the values shown apply to temperatures around 20° C. By comparing this table with that in § 196, it will

Resistivities of Conductors

Substance	Microhm-cm.	Ohm-CM. per ft.
Aluminum....................................	3.21	19.3
Carbon......................................	4000 to 7000	24,000 to 42,000
Constantan (Cu 60%, Ni 40%).................	49	295
Copper......................................	1.72	10.4
Iron..	12 to 14	72 to 84
Lead..	20.8	125
Manganin (Cu 84%, Ni 4%, Mn 12%)...........	43	258
Mercury.....................................	95.76	575
Nichrome (Ni 60%, Cr 12%, Fe 26%, Mn 2%)....	110	660
Platinum....................................	11.0	66
Silver......................................	1.65	9.9
Tungsten....................................	5.5	33
Zinc..	6.1	36.7

be observed that those substances which are good conductors of heat usually have low resistivity and are, therefore, good conductors of electricity as well.

It will be of interest to compare these resistivities with those of insulators. Thus, the resistivity of gutta percha is 2×10^9 ohm-cm. and that of mica is 9×10^{15} ohm-cm.

Low resistivity is necessary in wires that are used for transmitting electricity efficiently from place to place. On the other hand, conductors of moderately high resistivity are used when the primary purpose of the current is the production of heat. Thus, electric heaters are wound with wire of Nichrome or of similar alloy. For electric fuses, a relatively high resistivity is desired, combined with a low melting point; lead alloy is frequently used for this purpose. The fuse consists essentially of a metal strip connected directly into a circuit, and is designed to melt upon excessive current, thus protecting the circuit against overheating. In commercial fuses the fusible element is mounted within a casing to confine the arc which is produced upon melting.

For the wiring of electric circuits and the windings of electrical apparatus, copper is used almost exclusively, on account of its low resistivity and moderate cost. In this country, wire sizes are standardized in terms of the American wire gage (Awg.), also called the Brown & Sharpe gage. A few entries from copper wire tables are listed below; the resistance values are carried only to three places since this precision is sufficient for most practical purposes. The resistances are based on the International Annealed Copper Standard, and the allowable current-carrying capacities are as published by the Fire Underwriters in the National Electrical Code. The complete gage extends to wires as small as No. 40 and as large as No. 0000. Larger sizes than this are designated by their cross-sections in circular mils.

236. Calculation of Wire Size.—The wires in an electric light or power circuit form a line connecting the generator with the lamps, motors, or other load. The line wires are kept small for the sake of economy, but if they are too small, their resistance will be unduly high. As a result, the potential drop along the line will be excessive, leaving too low a potential difference across the load to operate it

Table for Copper Wire

Awg. No.	Diameter, mils	Cross-section, CM.	Resistance, ohms per 1000 ft.	Allowable carrying capacity, amp.		
				Rubber insulation	Varnished-cambric insulation	Asbestos insulation
2	258	66,400	0.156	95	120	165
3	229	52,600	0.197	80	105	145
4	204	41,700	0.249	70	90	120
6	162	26,300	0.395	55	70	95
8	129	16,500	0.628	40	50	70
10	102	10,400	0.999	30	40	55
12	81	6,530	1.59	20	30	40
14	64	4,110	2.53	15	25	30

properly. It is common practice to restrict the potential drop along the line wires to about 3 per cent on lighting circuits and to 5 or 10 per cent on power circuits. A second objection to undersized line wires is the excessive heating which the current would produce in them. To prevent deterioration of the insulation surrounding the wires, the allowable carrying capacities, as listed in the foregoing table, should not be exceeded.

As an illustrative problem, consider an installation of lamps requiring 30 amp. and located in a room 200 ft. away from a generator which maintains 120 volts across its terminals. What is the smallest size of rubber-insulated copper wire to use for the line conductors connecting the generator to the lamp load, if a potential drop of $2\frac{1}{2}$ per cent is allowed along the line? Clearly, the resistance of the *line* is to be found; this may be done by evaluating the potential drop across it and the current in it. A $2\frac{1}{2}$-per cent potential drop amounts to 0.025×120 or 3 volts across the two line wires of total length 400 ft., leaving 117 volts available for illuminating the lamps. The resistance of the line should be such as to give this 3-volt drop with a current of 30 amperes; the resistance is given by Ohm's Law as $R = 3/30 = 0.10$ ohm. Hence the cross-section of the line conductors is $A = \rho \dfrac{l}{R} = \dfrac{10.4 \times 400}{0.10} = 41{,}600$ CM., from equation (147). From the table of copper wire sizes, the next larger standard size is found to be 41,700 CM. = No. 4 Awg.; this is the wire size as determined by potential-drop considerations. Before adopting it, the allowable current-carrying capacity should be found. Further reference to the table shows that a rubber-insulated wire of this size is rated at 70 amp. Since the line current is less than this value, a No. 4 wire will be adequate for use as line conductor in this installation.

237. Series and Parallel Connections.—In Fig. 225 are shown two simple forms of electric circuit. In part I, a battery B supplies

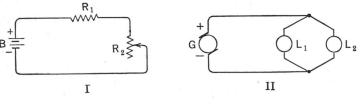

I   II

FIG. 225.   Series and parallel circuits

current to the two resistors R_1 and R_2 connected in *series*. In part II, a generator G supplies current to the two lamps L_1 and L_2 connected in *parallel* or *multiple*.

In the series arrangement the current has the same value throughout the circuit; that is, the current is the same in the battery, in the fixed resistance R_1, and in the adjustable resistance R_2. Also, the sum of the potential drops across the several resistors is equal to the emf. applied to the circuit, § 229.

In the parallel arrangement the current supplied by the generator divides between the two lamps L_1 and L_2, and the current in each is determined by its resistance. The potential difference between the terminals of lamp L_1 will be the same as that for lamp L_2. In any parallel circuit the potential drop is the same across all branches and the currents in the branches add up to the value of the main current.

The resistance within the source, whether battery or generator, is usually small but may not be negligible. It is in series with the external circuit and carries the same current. Its effect is to lower the potential difference at the terminals of the source whenever the source delivers current. Let the internal resistance of the source be r, and the current be I; the potential drop within the source is Ir, by equation (144). When a path is traced through the source from the — to the + terminal, there will be encountered a rise of potential equal to the emf. E, and also a drop of potential amounting to Ir. Hence, the potential difference across the terminals of the source will be

$$V_t = E - Ir \tag{148}$$

238. Equivalent Resistances.—Electric circuits are often composed of resistors which are connected in series or in parallel, and it may be desired to find the effect of such grouping upon the resistance of the circuit. Imagine several resistances, R_1, R_2, R_3, $\cdots$, to be combined in any manner, let I_1, I_2, I_3, $\cdots$, be the respective currents in them and let V_1, V_2, V_3, $\cdots$, be the respective potential drops across them. The entire group of resistors may be replaced by an equivalent single resistance R such that the current I supplied to it will be the same as the current supplied to the entire group if the potential drop V across R is the same as the potential drop across the entire group. Some simple groupings will be considered in the following paragraphs.

Series Connection.—When the resistors are connected in series, as in Fig. 226, it follows from the properties of the series circuit that

$$I = I_1 = I_2 = I_3 = \cdots$$

and

$$V = V_1 + V_2 + V_3 + \cdots$$

By Ohm's Law,

$$IR = I_1R_1 + I_2R_2 + I_3R_3 + \cdots$$

or

$$IR = IR_1 + IR_2 + IR_3 + \cdots$$

whence the total resistance of the group of resistors is

$$R = R_1 + R_2 + R_3 + \cdots \tag{149}$$

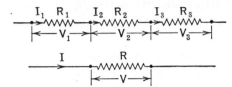

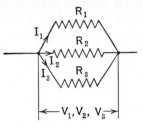

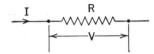

FIG. 226.   Resistors connected in series
and their equivalent resistance

This equation shows that the equivalent resistance of several devices connected in series is equal to the sum of their individual resistances.

FIG. 227.   Resistors connected in parallel and their equivalent resistance

Parallel Connection.—When the resistors are connected in parallel as in Fig. 227, the properties of the parallel circuit show that

$$V = V_1 = V_2 = V_3 = \cdots$$

and

$$I = I_1 + I_2 + I_3 + \cdots$$

By Ohm's Law,

$$\frac{V}{R} = \frac{V_1}{R_1} + \frac{V_2}{R_2} + \frac{V_3}{R_3} + \cdots$$

and therefore

$$\frac{V}{R} = \frac{V}{R_1} + \frac{V}{R_2} + \frac{V}{R_3} + \cdots$$

or

$$\frac{1}{R} = \frac{1}{R_1} + \frac{1}{R_2} + \frac{1}{R_3} + \cdots \tag{150}$$

which shows the relation between the individual resistances R_1, R_2, R_3, $\cdots$, and the equivalent resistance R when these are joined in parallel.   It is an interesting fact that the group resistance is less than the lowest of the individual resistances.

The connection of *only two* resistances in parallel is of frequent occurrence in electrical circuits.   For two resistances R_1 and R_2 in parallel the equivalent resistance is given by equation (150) as

$$R = \frac{R_1 R_2}{R_1 + R_2}$$

that is, their product divided by their sum.

239. The Wheatstone Bridge.—The Wheatstone Bridge is an instrument for measuring the value of an unknown resistance by comparing it with a known standard. This method, devised in 1833 by S. Hunter Christie, was brought to public attention by the English physicist, Sir Charles Wheatstone (1802–1875), and has remained associated with his name.

The bridge consists of four resistances, M, N, P, and X, connected

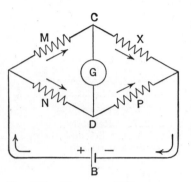

FIG. 228.   Diagram of Wheatstone Bridge

to a battery B and a sensitive current-measuring device called a galvanometer G, as shown in Fig. 228. One of the resistances, X, is unknown, and the other three are known and adjustable in value. In using the bridge, resistances M and N are given suitable values, and then resistance P is manipulated until the galvanometer G shows no deflection. The bridge is then said to be balanced, and the resistance of X can be found from a knowledge of the values of resistances M, N, and P.

To derive the equation of the balanced bridge, it should be observed that since there is no current in the galvanometer, the current in M must be the same as that in X; call this current in the upper branch of the bridge I_C. Similarly, the current in N is the same as that in P; call this current in the lower branch I_D. The fact that there is no current in the galvanometer also shows that the potential at the point C must be the same as that at the point D. Hence the potential drop across M must be the same as that across N; also the drop across X must be the same as that across P. In symbols, these statements become:

$$I_C M = I_D N$$

$$I_C X = I_D P$$

The first of these expressions is divided by the second, term by term, whereupon $\dfrac{M}{X} = \dfrac{N}{P}$, and the resistance of the unknown is

$$X = \frac{M}{N} P \qquad (151)$$

which is the equation of the balanced bridge. The resistances M

and N which appear as a ratio in the equation are called the *ratio arms* of the bridge, and resistance P is called the *rheostat arm*.

Commercial bridges are made in various designs. In the form illustrated in Fig. 229, the resistances M, N, and P are included within the case, and binding posts are provided for external connections to the battery and galvanometer and to the resistance being measured. Both ratio arms are controlled by a single dial, and the rheostat arm is arranged with four dials by which it can be adjusted in steps of 1

FIG. 229. Wheatstone Bridge and its internal arrangement
(*Courtesy of Leeds & Northrup Company*)

ohm from 0 to 9999 ohms. Switches known as keys are provided in the battery and galvanometer circuits, since in the use of the bridge these circuits are closed only while a balance is being obtained.

240. Influence of Temperature upon Resistance.—The resistance of a metallic conductor usually increases as the temperature is raised. The law governing this change has the same form as that which applies to the expansion of a rod (§ 149), but the variation of resistance with temperature is usually much greater than the corresponding change of size. If R_c represents the resistance at the lower temperature (cold), the resistance at the higher temperature (hot) is expressed by

$$R_h = R_c(1 + \alpha t) \qquad (152)$$

where α is a constant of the material called its *temperature coefficient of resistance*, and t is the temperature elevation. Numerically, α represents the increase of resistance of a 1-ohm resistance of the material when subjected to a temperature rise of 1 degree.

The temperature coefficient is positive for metallic conductors, and for all pure metals the values have the same order of magnitude. Certain alloys have been developed in which α is very small; these materials are useful for the resistance elements in Wheatstone Bridges, resistance boxes, and other measuring instruments in which constancy of resistance is desired. For practical purposes, where the temperature change involved is small, the temperature coefficient is usually considered as remaining constant at the value which it has at the lower temperature taken as a reference point; actually it varies somewhat with the temperature, and for accurate calculations the average value for the given temperature range should be used. The law expressed by equation (152) applies also to non-metallic substances, including carbon, liquids, and insulating materials; for these the temperature coefficient is usually negative.

The following table lists the values of the temperature coefficient for a number of materials commonly used. Unless otherwise specified, these values apply to reference temperatures around 20° C.

Temperature Coefficients of Resistance

Material	α per centigrade degree
Aluminum	0.0038
Carbon (0 to 1850° C.)	−0.00025
Constantan	−0.00004 to +0.00001
Copper (at 20° C.)	0.00393
Iron	0.0062
Lead	0.0043
Manganin	0.000002 to 0.00005
Mercury	0.00090
Nichrome	0.00017
Platinum	0.0038
Silver	0.0040
Tungsten	0.0045
Zinc	0.0037

The Resistance Thermometer.—The fact that the resistance of a conductor changes with temperature is utilized in the so-called *resistance thermometer*. This device consists of a calibrated coil of wire, which is placed in the location where the temperature is to be determined, together with suitable instruments for measuring its resistance.

This type of thermometer is useful over a wide temperature range, is very precise, and can be read from a remote point.

To illustrate the measurement of temperature by a resistance thermometer, consider a coil of platinum wire to have a resistance of 10.0 ohms at 20° C. and 15.0 ohms when placed in a certain oven. Assume α to be 0.0038 over the temperature range involved; then the temperature elevation t of the oven above 20° C. is given by equation (152) as

$$ t = \frac{R_h - R_c}{\alpha R_c} = \frac{15.0 - 10.0}{0.0038 \times 10.0} = 132 \text{ centigrade degrees,} $$

and the desired oven temperature is $132 + 20 = 152°$ C.

241. Super-conductivity.—Certain metals are found to exhibit a remarkable drop in resistance at very low temperatures; this effect was discovered by Professor Onnes and is known as *super-conductivity*. As the temperature is lowered, the resistance of the specimen is observed to decrease in the manner to be expected from equation (152), but at a certain temperature, which seems to have a characteristic value for each material, and which is only a few degrees above absolute zero ($-273°$ C. or $0°$ K.), the resistance drops abruptly to an extremely low value. The resistance of lead, for instance, becomes less than 10^{-12} of its value at $0°$ C.

As early as 1914, Onnes reported a test of 1-hr. duration, in which current was produced in a lead ring at a very low temperature and the source of electromotive force was removed, nevertheless the current in the closed ring persisted without appreciable reduction throughout the test. Super-conductivity has been observed in numerous metallic elements, including tin at $3.69°$ K., mercury at $4.12°$ K., and lead at $7.26°$ K., as well as in a large number of alloys.

242. Electric Networks.—The circuits that are employed in electrical work cover a variety of types; they may consist of simple series and parallel groupings like those described in § 238, or combinations of these groupings, or arrangements which take the forms of the letters Y and delta (Δ), or they may be repeated groupings in the form of a ladder. The term *electric network* is used for the more complicated circuits.

In analyzing electric networks the plan is usually to simplify them step by step, and then solve for the unknown factors. To illustrate the procedure, consider the circuit shown in part I of Fig. 230. It consists of the branches BF and CD in parallel, and this pair connected in series with path AG which includes the battery. First branch *BF* with a parallel group is simplified as shown in part II, and then the two parallel paths *BF* and *CD* are merged as shown in part III. By repeated application of Ohm's Law, it becomes possible to compute the current supplied by the battery, the current in each of the resistance elements, and the potential drop across each.

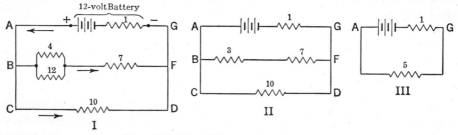

FIG. 230.   Simplifying an electric network

For the circuit shown in Fig. 230 with the resistances in ohms noted on the individual resistors, find the current in each resistor. The solution for the circuit in part I follows: The 4-ohm and 12-ohm parallel combination is equivalent to a single resistance of $\dfrac{4 \times 12}{4 + 12} = 3$ ohms; this is in series with the 7-ohm resistance, as shown at II. The resistances of branches *BF* and *CD* are each 10 ohms; when combined in parallel an equivalent load resistance of 5 ohms is obtained, as in part III.

The current supplied by the battery is $I = E \div R = 12 \div 6 = 2$ amp. The potential drop across the 1-ohm battery resistance is $V = I \times r = 2 \times 1 = 2$ volts, leaving $12 - 2 = 10$ volts across the battery terminals *A* and *G*. This same potential difference will be available to the two branches *BF* and *CD*, and since each of these has a resistance of 10 ohms, the current in each is 1 amp. In the branch *BF*, the potential difference across the 7-ohm resistance is $V = I \times R = 1 \times 7 = 7$ volts, and that across the 4-ohm, 12-ohm parallel combination is $V = 1 \times 3 = 3$ volts. The currents in the 4-ohm and 12-ohm resistances are $I_4 = 3 \div 4 = 0.75$ amp. and $I_{12} = 3 \div 12 = 0.25$ amp.

Other procedures for the solution of electric networks are given in the two following sections.

243. Kirchhoff's Network Laws.—The more intricate networks are not easily solved by the method used in the preceding section, and recourse is had to two generalizations pointed out by the German physicist, Gustav R. Kirchhoff (1824–1887), as follows:

1. *At any point in an electric circuit where two or more conductors are joined, the sum of the currents directed toward the junction equals the sum of the currents directed away from the junction.* This law can be

rephrased to state that the algebraic sum of the currents at a junction equals zero. Regard currents toward the junction as positive and those away from the junction as negative; then symbolically

$$\Sigma I = 0 \qquad (153)$$

2. *Around any closed path in an electric circuit, the algebraic sum of the potential differences equals zero.* Consider rise of potential positive and drop of potential negative, and introduce the fact that a current I in a resistance R corresponds to a potential difference IR; then this law may be stated as

$$\Sigma E - \Sigma IR = 0 \qquad (154)$$

In the application of these laws to the solution of a network, first assume some direction for the current in each branch and then express Kirchhoff's Laws in as many independent equations as there are unknown currents. Then solve these equations simultaneously to find the currents in the several branches of the circuit. If the result gives a negative value for any current, this indicates that the direction is opposite to that originally assumed.

To illustrate the foregoing procedure, consider the network of Fig. 231, in which the numbers on the resistors represent their resistances in ohms. Current is supplied to the network by two batteries. Find the values of the currents marked I_1, I_2, and I_3. The assumed directions of these currents are shown. From the First Law (at point C): $I_1 + I_2 - I_3 = 0$. From the Second Law (around path ACD): $+18 - 3I_1 - 6I_3 = 0$, also (around path BCD): $+4 - 8I_2 - 6I_3 = 0$. These equations are then solved simultaneously for the currents, but the details are omitted here. The results are found to be: $I_1 = 2.53$ amp., $I_2 = -0.8$ amp., and $I_3 = 1.73$ amp. The negative sign for I_2 shows that the direction of this current should be reversed, but no other changes are required.

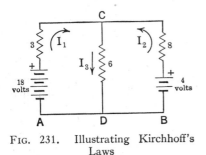

FIG. 231.   Illustrating Kirchhoff's Laws

*244. Thévenin's Method.**—Another important method for analyzing a network is due to M. L. Thévenin; this makes it possible in many instances to replace some complicated part of the network by a single equivalent emf. and a single equivalent resistance connected in series, and in this way to reduce the entire network to a simple circuit. The method can be applied whenever the part that is to be replaced is joined to the rest of the network at only two points.

To calculate the equivalent emf. and resistance of part of a network, imagine the rest of the network to be disconnected at the two points; the equivalent emf. is the potential difference that would then exist between the points, and the equivalent resistance is the resistance that would be found by measurement between the points. If any sources of emf. are included in the replaced part of the network, their emf.'s are disregarded in finding the equivalent resistance, but their internal resistances are included if stated in the problem.

The Thévenin method will be illustrated by solving the same problem that was solved in the preceding section by Kirchhoff's Laws.

To find the current in the 8-ohm resistor, disconnect it at points C and D as shown at I in Fig. 232, and find the equivalent emf. and equivalent resistance of the left part of the network between these points. Since the

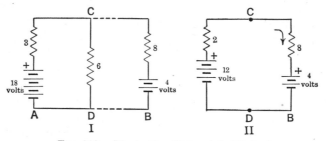

FIG. 232.   Illustrating Thévenin's Method

current in path ACD is $18 \div (3 + 6) = 2$ amp., the potential difference between C and D is $2 \times 6 = 12$ volts, with C positive. The resistance between these points, not considering the battery, is $\dfrac{6 \times 3}{6 + 3} = 2$ ohms. Therefore the portion ACD can be replaced by an equivalent emf. of 12 volts in series with an equivalent resistance of 2 ohms, as shown in part II. Hence the current in the 8-ohm resistor is $\dfrac{12 - 4}{2 + 8} = 0.8$ amp. and its direction is as shown by the arrow.

To find the current in the 3-ohm resistor, disconnect it at points C and D, and proceed similarly. The equivalent emf. and resistance of the right part of the network are found to be 1.72 volts and 3.43 ohms. Consequently the current sought is $\dfrac{18 - 1.72}{3 + 3.43} = 2.53$ amp. directed upward in the figure.

Naturally the current in the 6-ohm resistor is $2.53 - 0.8 = 1.73$ amp.

PROBLEMS

1. A 20-hp. motor operating at full load takes a current of 71 amp. from 240-volt supply mains. Compute the efficiency of the motor.

2. An electric heater takes 6.8 amp. at 220 volts. How much does it cost per hour to operate the heater, if electrical energy costs 5 cents per kw-hr.?

3. Sheet rubber, with sufficient carbon black to make it conducting, has been used in a test installation for house heating. The house has a space volume of 6400 cu. ft. and its ceiling panels have 590 sq. ft. of conductive rubber, each square foot taking 20 watts. What would it cost to supply 100 Btu. per cu. ft. of space per day from the heating panels if electrical energy costs 0.5 cent per kw-hr.?

4. The total electrical energy produced in the United States in 1946 was 223.1 billion kw-hr., of which about 65 per cent was generated from steam and 35 per cent from hydro developments. How many square miles of the earth's surface would need to be utilized to produce this amount of energy by radiation from the sun if the solar radiation is equivalent to 2 cal. per min. per sq. cm. over an average of 8 hr. per day? Assume one-third of the radiation to be absorbed by the atmosphere and the remainder transformed to electrical energy at an efficiency of 20 per cent.

5. A slidewire resistance has 280 turns wound on an insulating cylinder. A current of 1.75 amp. traverses the entire length of the wire, which has a resistance of 50 ohms. What is the potential difference between adjacent turns of the winding?

6. A 10-volt, 5-watt lamp is connected in series with a resistor across a 32-volt battery. Find (a) the value of the series resistance in order that the lamp may operate in the normal manner, and (b) the power wasted in heating this resistor.

7. To measure a high resistance, a 15,000-ohm voltmeter was connected in series with it across 120-volt supply mains. The voltmeter reading was 6.2 volts; find the value of the high resistance.

8. The current in a heater of 30 ohms resistance is 3.7 amp. At what rate in watts is electrical energy converted into heat?

9. Where electrical energy costs 4 cents per kw-hr., how much will it cost to heat 2.5 kg. of water from 20° C. to the boiling point, if no energy is wasted?

10. A 40-ohm immersion heater carrying a current of 3 amp. is placed in $\frac{1}{2}$ kg. of water. What temperature rise will occur in 5 min. if all the heat liberated is absorbed by the water?

11. A 120-volt electric heater consists of a coil of wire having a resistance of 24 ohms. Find the time required to produce 10,000 cal. with this heater.

12. A cubical cabinet, averaging 3 ft. along each edge, has insulating walls 2 in. thick made of rock wool having a thermal conductivity of 7.2 Btu-in. per sq. ft. per day per °F. An electric heater operated continuously within the cabinet keeps the interior at a temperature of 98° F. when the surroundings are at 60° F. Find the rating of the heater in watts.

13. Air breaks down at about 30,000 volts per cm. between flat plates or curved surfaces of large radius. Express the corresponding field intensity in dynes per esu. of charge.

14. A resistance coil is to be wound with manganin wire 1.45 mm. in diameter. What length of wire will be needed for a 10-ohm coil?

15. What is the resistance of 100 ft. of stranded copper wire, made of 17 strands each 0.032 in. in diameter?

16. A copper bus bar is $\frac{1}{2}$ in. thick. How wide must it be to provide a cross-section equivalent to 1,000,000 CM.?

17. An experimental resistor is to be constructed of manganin wire having a diameter of 0.01 in. What length of wire in feet will be required if the resistance is to dissipate 250 watts when connected across 115-volt supply mains?

18. In some transmission lines the conductors are hollow tubes. Compute the resistance of 1000 ft. of copper tube having an inside diameter of 1 in. and a wall thickness of $\frac{1}{8}$ in.

19. In tensile tests on metals, it is convenient to determine the elongation of specimens by a strain gage based upon change of electrical resistance. A constantan wire serving as a gage was initially 6 in. long and 0.00314 in. in diameter; when stretched in a certain test its length increased 1 per cent and its cross-sectional area decreased 1 per cent. Compute the resistance of the wire (*a*) initially, and (*b*) when stretched.

20. A farm-lighting plant includes a storage battery having 31.8 volts across its terminals. From the battery a pair of No. 12 Awg. copper line wires extend to a point 65 ft. away, where a load drawing a current of 10 amp. is connected. Compute the potential difference across the load.

21. A lamp load which takes a current of 35 amp. is located at a distance of 275 ft. from a generator which maintains 120 volts across its terminals. What gage rubber-insulated copper wires are needed for the line connecting the lamps to the generator, if the allowable potential drop is 3 per cent?

22. A dry cell has 1.492 volts across its terminals when on open circuit; this is lowered to 1.453 volts when the cell delivers current to an external circuit of 2.5 ohms resistance. Calculate the internal resistance of the cell.

23. A battery having an emf. of 6.0 volts and an internal resistance of 0.25 ohm supplies a current of 2.4 amp. to a lamp load. Find the potential difference across the terminals of the battery and also the resistance of the load.

24. A 60-watt lamp and a 40-watt lamp are operated in parallel at their rated potential difference, 120 volts. Find their combined resistance.

25. A resistor of 2 ohms and another of 3 ohms resistance are connected in parallel and this combination is joined in series with a 4-ohm resistor across a battery. The current in the 2-ohm resistor is 2 amp.; compute the potential drop across the 3-ohm resistor and the power expenditure in the 4-ohm resistor.

26. Suppose that two resistors of 2 ohms and 6 ohms are connected in parallel and this combination is joined in series with a 10-ohm resistor and a battery having an emf. of 3 volts and an internal resistance of 0.5 ohm. Find the current in the 6-ohm resistor.

27. An electric heater has two heating elements, one of 20 ohms resistance and the other of 30 ohms; they can be used singly, in series, and in parallel. What are the corresponding power ratings of the heater on 120-volt service mains?

28. A field winding on a motor consists of a copper coil having a resistance of 280 ohms at 20° C. What will be its resistance if the temperature of the machine rises 40 centigrade degrees?

29. A platinum wire is used as a resistance thermometer for measuring temperatures around 20° C., its resistance being 50 ohms at this temperature. How much will its resistance increase for a temperature rise of 1 centigrade degree?

30. Airplane instruments are subjected to tests over a temperature range from −60° C. to +65° C. Copper over this range has a temperature coefficient of resistance averaging 0.00418 per centigrade degree. A copper coil has a resistance of 20.0 ohms at the lower temperature stated; find its resistance at the higher one.

31. Five resistors, of 360 ohms each, are arranged in two groups, the first group comprising 3 resistors in parallel and the second group comprising 2 resistors in parallel. If the groups are connected in series across a 240-volt line, what is the potential drop across each group?

32. Two resistors of 6 and 12 ohms are connected in series to form a group. Two more resistors of 12 and 24 ohms are connected in series to form another group. These two groups are connected in parallel across a battery having an emf. of 24 volts and an internal resistance of 1 ohm. Calculate the current in the 6-ohm resistor and that in the 24-ohm resistor; also find the potential drop across each of these resistors.

33. The accompanying diagram shows a network supplied by two batteries, E_1 of 6 volts and E_2 of 1.5 volts, and the numbers on the resistors indicate their resistances in ohms. Use Kirchhoff's Laws to determine the current in each battery.

*34. Solve Problem 33 by the use of Thévenin's Method instead of Kirchhoff's Laws.

Electric Cells   *Chapter XXII*

245. Electrolytic and Voltaic Cells.—It is generally known that the electric current can be used to produce hydrogen and oxygen from dilute acid by electrolysis, or to deposit a metal coating on an electrode in a plating bath. The apparatus used in either process is called an *electrolytic cell*. In such a cell, electrical energy supplied from an outside source serves to produce the chemical changes involved, a small part being wasted as heat. Electrolytic cells are used not only for gas manufacture and electroplating, but also for the refining of metals and in many industrial chemical processes.

Other forms of cells, such as the dry cell and storage cell, can supply electrical energy; these are called *voltaic cells*. In this type, chemical energy is liberated within the cell and transformed into electrical energy, part being converted to heat. Voltaic cells are called *primary* cells if the elements need replacement after use, and *secondary* or *storage* cells if they can be restored to their initial condition by charging from an electric supply circuit.

246. Electrolytic Action.—The conduction of electricity in liquids is similar to that through gases, as explained in § 214; such conduction is attributed to the presence of positive and negative ions in solutions of acids, bases or salts, and to the motion of these charges between the electrodes when a potential difference is applied across them. Such solutions are termed *electrolytes*, and the process of conduction through them is called *electrolysis*. Except for chemical actions which may occur, the behavior of any electrolytic cell is based entirely upon the attraction of unlike charges and the repulsion of like charges.

A solution of hydrochloric acid, for example, presents evidence of containing H atoms, each having lost an electron and therefore being positively charged, and Cl atoms, each with a surplus electron and therefore being negatively charged. The charged particles or ions are represented with appropriate + or − signs. The foregoing is described by saying that the acid *dissociates* into positive hydrogen ions and negative chlorine ions, or symbolically,

$$HCl \rightleftarrows H^+ + Cl^-$$

The ions of a substance do not have the properties of the corresponding atoms. For example, a solution of H^+ ions affects indicators such as litmus; a solution of hydrogen gas does not. A change of properties would, indeed, be expected from the modifications in atomic structure.

Evidence indicates that bare H^+ ions are practically non-existent in aqueous solutions; instead they are believed to occur in a hydrated form as *hydronium* ions, H_3O^+, each being a combination of H^+ and H_2O. To avoid complexity, however, the hydrogen ion will be represented in this book by the simpler notation H^+.

The mechanism of electrical conduction through liquids will be illustrated by specific examples.

Electrolysis of Hydrochloric Acid.—Suppose two platinum plates A and C, connected to a battery as shown in Fig. 233, to be dipped into a dilute solution of hydrochloric acid. The H^+ ions will be attracted by the negative plate C and repelled by the positive plate A, also the Cl^- ions will be attracted by the positive plate and repelled by the negative one. The result will be a drifting or migration of ions in both directions through the liquid (this motion being in addition to the unordered motion of the particles corresponding to the temperature). Each H^+ ion upon reaching plate C combines with an electron there, forming a hydrogen atom:

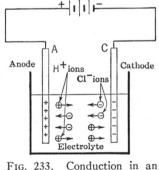

Fig. 233. Conduction in an electrolytic cell

$$H^+ + e \rightarrow H$$

From these atoms hydrogen molecules are produced and pass off as gas. The Cl^- ions upon reaching plate A give up their electrons and become chlorine atoms:

$$Cl^- - e \rightarrow Cl$$

the atoms combining to form molecules of chlorine which will be liberated at this plate.

Decomposition of Water.—As a typical illustration of the decomposition of water, consider the effect of passing electricity through a dilute sulfuric acid solution (H_2SO_4), using chemically inert electrodes of platinum or carbon. The H^+ ions of the acid will be attracted by the negative plate and repelled by the positive one, also the $SO_4^=$ ions will be attracted by the positive and repelled by the negative plate. The result will again be a drifting of ions in both directions through the liquid. Each H^+ ion upon reaching the cathode combines with an electron there, forming a hydrogen atom. These atoms combine into molecules and escape as gas, that is:

$$2H^+ + 2e \rightarrow H_2 \uparrow$$

When the $SO_4^=$ ions reach the anode, electrons are given to the electrode and oxygen is liberated as a gas, while more sulfuric acid is formed. That is,

$$2SO_4^= - 4e + 2H_2O \rightarrow \underbrace{4H^+ + 2SO_4^=}_{2H_2SO_4} + O_2 \uparrow$$

Electroplating.—Consider next an electrolytic cell in which the electrolyte is a dilute copper sulfate solution, and suppose at first that inert electrodes of platinum are used. The following equations represent the reactions which are believed to occur at the electrodes:

At cathode $\qquad Cu^{++} + 2e \rightarrow Cu \downarrow$

At anode $\qquad SO_4^= - 2e + H_2O \rightarrow \underbrace{2H^+ + SO_4^=}_{H_2SO_4} + O$

These show that copper is plated upon the cathode, but that the $CuSO_4$ electrolyte gradually changes its composition. To overcome this defect in practice, copper is substituted for platinum as the material of the anode, the anode reaction becoming:

$$SO_4^= - 2e + Cu \rightarrow CuSO_4$$

while the cathode reaction remains unchanged. In this process copper is dissolved from the anode and plated on the cathode, and the electrolyte remains unchanged.

Many metals may be electroplated under the general conditions just described, the anode being made of the metal to be electroplated and the electrolyte being a solution of one of its salts. For example, silver may be deposited from silver nitrate using a silver anode. In contrast, chromium is generally plated from a chromic acid bath, in which lead is used as anode material, and the chromium content of the electrolyte is replenished when necessary. Zinc and copper may be liberated simultaneously from a cyanide solution in which these elements are present, and produce a plating of brass.

Rubber is deposited electrolytically from rubber latex, the milky juice of rubber trees. The latex particles are in suspension as a colloid; they have negative charges and become affixed to the anode of the cell.

Electrolytic Corrosion.—Electrolysis sometimes produces unexpected and destructive effects. An example illustrating electrolytic corrosion of an underground pipe from the leakage currents of an

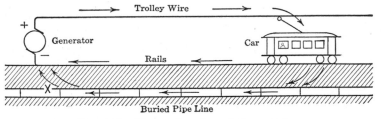

Fig. 234.   Illustrating electrolytic corrosion

electric railway line is indicated in Fig. 234. This diagram represents a generator at a power station supplying current through a trolley wire (or third rail) to the motor on an electric car. The current is returned to the generator partly by way of the rails and partly along the grounded pipe line. The pipe is likely to become corroded at the region marked *X*, for here the moist earth around the pipe serves as the electrolyte, and the pipe itself acts as the anode of an electrolytic cell. Continued current through this "cell" will wear away the anode, as previously described. To eliminate this corrosion, the point *X* and the negative terminal of the generator should be bonded together by a wire, thereby providing a metallic path for the current leaving the pipe.

247. Faraday's Laws of Electrolysis.—It will be observed that whenever *hydrogen or any metal is liberated in an electrolytic cell*, this action, with rare exceptions, occurs *at the cathode*, and that the liberation of other substances takes place at the anode. It will also be observed that, if electrolysis is to continue, the external circuit must continuously supply electrons to the cathode and remove them from the anode; in other words, a current is necessary in the circuit containing the cell. Moreover, in forming a hydrogen or other univalent atom at the cathode one electron is required, while for a bivalent atom two electrons are required, and so on. Similarly, at the anode one electron is released in forming a univalent atom, and two electrons in forming a bivalent atom. Since a flow of 6.25×10^{18} electrons per second constitutes a current of one ampere (§ 228), it follows that in an electrolytic cell a current of 1 amp. maintained for 1 sec. (that is, a quantity of electricity of 1 coulomb) is capable of liberating at the cathode 6.25×10^{18} hydrogen or other univalent atoms, or half this number of bivalent atoms, and so on. A corresponding liberation of atoms will also occur at the anode of the cell.

Quantitative measurements in electrolytic cells are based on two laws due to Faraday, as follows:

1. *The mass of a substance liberated in an electrolytic cell is proportional to the quantity of electricity passing through the cell.*

2. *When the same quantity of electricity is passed through different electrolytic cells, the masses of the substances liberated are proportional to their chemical equivalents.* The chemical equivalent of an element is the ratio of its atomic weight w in grams to its valence number z; in the case of radicals the chemical equivalent is the sum of the atomic weights of the component elements divided by the valence number of the radical.

The atomic weights and usual valence numbers of several elements are given in the accompanying table.

Atomic Weights and Valence Numbers

Element	Atomic weight	Valence number
Chlorine........	35.46	−1
Copper.........	63.57	+2
Hydrogen.......	1.008	+1
Oxygen.........	16.00	−2
Silver..........	107.88	+1
Zinc...........	65.38	+2

In the application of Faraday's Laws of electrolysis, it is first desirable to find what quantity of electricity will liberate 1 chemical equivalent of a substance. Consider silver, for example, which has a chemical equivalent of 107.88 gm. Since this element is univalent,

1 coulomb of electricity will deposit 6.25×10^{18} atoms. But Avogadro's constant, 6.02×10^{23}, is the number of atoms in a gram-atom of a substance; hence there are 6.02×10^{23} atoms in 107.88 gm. of silver. To deposit this amount of silver will therefore require $(6.02 \times 10^{23}) \div (6.25 \times 10^{18}) = 96,500$ coulombs. This quantity of electricity, which is also known as 1 *faraday*, will liberate 1 chemical equivalent of any substance.

As further examples, consider the three cells represented in Fig. 235, which are connected in series and, therefore, receive the same current from

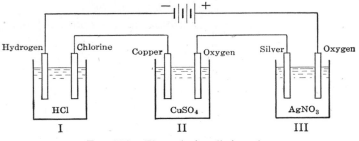

FIG. 235.   Electrolytic cells in series

the battery. A flow of 96,500 coulombs in the circuit will liberate in the various cells w/z gm. of the following substances:

Cell   I $\quad \dfrac{1.008}{1} = 1.008$ gm. of hydrogen and $\dfrac{35.46}{1} = 35.46$ gm. of chlorine

Cell II $\quad \dfrac{63.57}{2} = 31.8$ gm. of copper and $\dfrac{16}{2} = 8.0$ gm. of oxygen

Cell III $\quad \dfrac{107.88}{1} = 107.88$ gm. of silver and $\dfrac{16}{2} = 8.0$ gm. of oxygen

The mass of a substance liberated in electrolysis can be found by simple proportion, from the fact that 96,500 coulombs will liberate 1 chemical equivalent. Thus, to determine how much copper would be plated from a solution of a cupric salt by a current of 10 amp. maintained for 1 hr. (that is, by 36,000 coulombs), let m represent the desired mass, and write:

$$m : \frac{63.57}{2} = 36,000 : 96,500$$

from which $m = 11.86$ gm.

The preceding proportion can also be written as an equation

$$m = \frac{It}{96,500} \times \frac{w}{z} \tag{155}$$

wherein the quantity of electricity is expressed as the product of the current I in amperes and the time t in seconds.

248. Single-electrode Potentials.—When a metal plate is dipped into a solution of one of its salts, a contact is established between the metallic *atoms* of the plate and the positive metallic *ions* of the solution. Two tendencies exist, either of which may determine the action that results; first, *metallic ions tend to acquire electrons and deposit themselves on the plate as atoms*, and second, *the atoms of the plate tend to lose electrons and go into solution as ions*. The tendency for metal to deposit on the plate is proportional to the concentration of the ions, and theoretically, a sufficiently high concentration could cause deposition in all cases. On the other hand, if the ionic concentration is low, the tendency of the plate to dissolve will predominate. At some intermediate concentration value, neither deposition nor dissolution will occur; it is supposed under this condition that the tendency toward deposition is exactly neutralized by a so-called *solution pressure*. Although the real significance of this term is in doubt, it is usual to think of the solution pressure of a metal as an agency which tends to throw the metal into solution in the form of positive ions.

Solution pressure has a characteristic value for each metal. Copper has a low solution pressure, and if a copper plate is dipped into a copper sulfate solution of ordinary concentration, a few Cu^{++} ions will take electrons from the plate, forming atoms of copper which deposit upon the plate. The action will stop almost immediately, however, because the plate becomes positive and repels the advance of other positive ions. Again, consider a zinc plate dipped into a zinc sulfate solution. The solution pressure of the zinc is large, and a few atoms of the plate dissolve, leaving their electrons behind, and go into solution as Zn^{++} ions. This effect is also of very slight magnitude because the plate becomes negative, and the throwing off of further positive ions is prevented by electrostatic attraction between plate and ions. The mass of metal deposited or dissolved in these cases is very minute. The processes could be made continuous, however, by removing the charges from the plates as fast as they are formed.

The foregoing analysis shows that a copper plate placed in a solution of a copper salt assumes a higher potential than the solution, and that a zinc plate placed in a solution of a zinc salt assumes a lower potential than the solution; such potential differences are called *single-electrode potentials*. When the two solutions are put in contact, the combination forms a voltaic cell with the copper positive and the zinc negative. If any small potential difference at the junction of the solutions is neglected, the emf. of the cell would be the sum of the single-electrode potentials of the two metals. The materials referred to are used in the gravity cell, which is described in § 253.

The potential of a given metal with respect to a solution of one of its salts under specified conditions can be expressed precisely. Its value is called the *normal electrode potential* if the solution is "normal"; that is, if 1 liter at 25° C. contains an effective concentration of 1 chemical equivalent of the metallic ions. The normal electrode potential of copper is $+0.3448$ volt and that of zinc is -0.7581 volt. Potential values for a number of substances are tabulated in § 250.

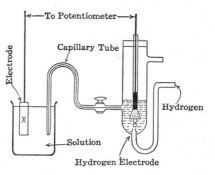

Fig. 236 illustrates the apparatus for making measurements of normal electrode potential. The metal X under test is placed in a normal solution of one of its salts to form a half cell, a *hydrogen electrode* is

FIG. 236. Hydrogen electrode used in measuring normal electrode potential

immersed in a solution of normal hydrogen-ion content to form another, and the two are joined by a capillary. The hydrogen electrode is commonly used as a reference electrode; its potential with respect to its own solution is constant and is arbitrarily taken as zero. Hydrogen, which is non-conducting as a gas, is passed over a plate of platinum covered with platinum black. Here the gas is *adsorbed*, that is, condensed and held upon the surface; in this condition, hydrogen is conducting like a metal electrode. The normal electrode potential of the metal is found by measuring the potential difference between the electrodes, a potentiometer (§ 258) being generally used for this purpose.

*249. Hydrogen Ion Measurements.—The degree of acidity or alkalinity of a solution is determined by placing a hydrogen electrode in it to serve as a half cell, combining this with another half cell having a different reference electrode, and measuring the potential difference of the combination.

All acids yield hydrogen ions when dissolved in water, and the degree of acidity of a solution depends upon the quantity of hydrogen ions per liter of solution. Pure water, which represents a state of true neutrality, dissociates into H^+ and OH^- ions, but so feebly that at ordinary temperatures it contains only 10^{-7} gm. of H^+ ion per liter. In acid solutions, the hydrogen-ion concentration is greater than this value, and in alkaline solutions it is less. Suppose that in a certain HCl solution, each liter contains 0.001 gm. of hydrogen ions, that is, the hydrogen-ion concentration in grams per liter is $0.001 = 10^{-3}$. The numerical value of the exponent is called the *pH value*; for the solution considered the *p*H value is 3. Any *p*H number between 0 and 7 indicates an acid solution, the acidity decreasing as the numbers increase. For *p*H numbers larger than 7 the solution is alkaline, the alkalinity increasing as the numbers increase.

The potential of the hydrogen electrode is directly proportional to the *p*H value of the surrounding solution; hence this *p*H value can be found from the measured potential difference by subtracting the potential of the other reference electrode and multiplying the result by a constant. This method of measurement is particularly useful with solutions in which the acidity or alkalinity is so feeble as to escape detection by other means.

250. Electromotive Series of the Metals.—The relative chemical activities of the metals can be indicated by arranging them in tabular form with the most active one at the top of the series. Each metal in the list displaces those below it from chemically equivalent solutions of their simple salts, and is itself displaced by those above it, under ordinary conditions. The result is attributed to differences in solution pressure.

The accompanying table indicates the more important metals and gives their normal electrode potentials. Each of these values represents the emf. of a cell having a hydrogen electrode and an electrode of the metal referred to. The emf. of a cell having any two metals for its electrodes in a uniform electrolyte can be predicted from the individual potential values. Consider, for example, a copper-zinc cell. On the potential scale, copper is +0.34 volt and zinc is −0.76

volt, each with respect to hydrogen, consequently the potential of copper is $0.34 + 0.76$ or 1.10 volts higher than that of zinc. The copper-zinc cell has an emf. of this value, and its positive terminal is the one attached to the copper electrode. The emf. of a voltaic cell depends upon the materials used and not upon size.

Electromotive Series of the Metals

Element	Symbol	Normal electrode potential (referred to hydrogen electrode) volts	
Potassium.........	K	-2.92	high solution pressure
Sodium...........	Na	-2.71	↑
Magnesium.......	Mg	-1.55	
Zinc.............	Zn	-0.76	
Iron.............	Fe	-0.44	
Tin.............	Sn	-0.13	
Lead............	Pb	-0.12	
Hydrogen.........	**H**	**0.00**	
Bismuth..........	Bi	$+0.20$	
Copper...........	Cu	$+0.34$	
Mercury..........	Hg	$+0.80$	↓
Silver...........	Ag	$+0.80$	low solution pressure

251. The Voltaic Cell; Polarization.—A primary cell of elementary type may be constructed by placing electrodes of copper and zinc in a dilute sulfuric acid solution, as indicated in Fig. 237. Such a cell will set up a current from copper to zinc in the external circuit R. The action of the cell is explained by supposing that the solution of sulfuric acid contains H^+ ions and $SO_4^=$ ions.

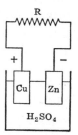

Fig. 237. Diagram of a voltaic cell

At the copper plate, because of the low solution pressure of copper, the H^+ ions in solution deposit themselves upon the copper plate, thereby giving it a positive charge.

At the zinc plate, since the solution pressure of zinc is high, zinc atoms dissolve, throwing Zn^{++} ions into solution and leaving electrons on the plate, a process which makes the zinc plate negative.

The electrons on the zinc plate repel one another along the wire, this action being assisted by the attraction of the positively charged copper plate; thus, a current is established through the external circuit *R*.

Impurities in the electrodes act like tiny short-circuited cells, and the electrodes are consumed wastefully. This so-called *local action* can be reduced by amalgamating the surface of the zinc; the amalgam spreads over the surface and keeps the impurities from coming in contact with the electrolyte.

The current supplied by the simple voltaic cell is quickly reduced in value during even a short period of use because of the accumulation of hydrogen on the positive plate. This action not only introduces a high resistance into the circuit, but alters the material of the electrode and sets up an opposing emf. which must be overcome before the cell can supply current to the external circuit. This effect, called *polarization*, is present in many types of cells. Polarization of a voltaic cell is due primarily to the formation of hydrogen on its positive plate and to changes in concentration of its electrolyte. In voltaic cells which are subject to polarization some substance is usually added to combine chemically with the hydrogen gas as it forms. This substance is called a *depolarizer*.

In the operation of an electrolytic cell having like electrodes, it frequently happens that the electrodes become coated with dissimilar materials. Such a cell then acts like a voltaic cell opposing the applied emf., and its own emf. must be overcome before current can be set up in it. Thus, a cell with platinum electrodes in a solution of hydrochloric acid may cease to conduct current because hydrogen and chlorine accumulate on the electrodes and set up an emf. of polarization opposing the outside source. So long as both electrodes of an electrolytic cell remain of the same substance and the electrolyte is uniform throughout, whatever electrode potential is developed at one of them will be neutralized by an equal and opposite potential at the other. The smallest potential difference applied to the cell will then set up a current in it.

252. Leclanché and Dry Cells.—In the primary cell devised by Georges Leclanché, Fig. 238, a positive electrode of carbon and a negative plate or rod of zinc are immersed in a solution of ammonium chloride (NH_4Cl). A porous cup around the carbon electrode contains manganese dioxide as a depolarizer. The familiar dry cell employs the same materials, but the construction is different; a section of this cell is shown in Fig. 239. It consists of a zinc container lined with blotting paper and provided with a carbon electrode at the center. The space between is filled with ground carbon and manganese dioxide, moistened with ammonium chloride and a little zinc chloride. Either cell may be represented diagrammatically as

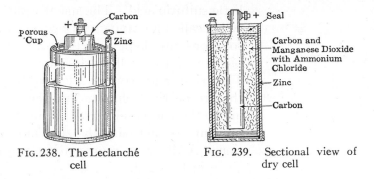

FIG. 238. The Leclanché cell

FIG. 239. Sectional view of dry cell

in Fig. 240. When the cell delivers current, the zinc dissolves, leaving electrons behind, which repel one another along the external circuit to the carbon plate. The Cl^- ions in the electrolyte migrate toward the Zn^{++} ions near the zinc electrode and the NH_4^+ ions migrate toward the carbon electrode. The formation of hydrogen gas is prevented to a considerable extent by the reduction of the manganese dioxide. The initial cell reaction is probably of the form:

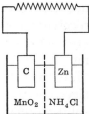

$$2NH_4^+ + 2e + MnO_2 + H_2O \rightarrow 2NH_4OH + MnO$$

The complete reactions within the cell are obscure, and apparently are influenced by the conditions under which the cell is used.

FIG. 240. Diagram of Leclanché and dry cells

This type of primary cell has an emf. of about 1.5 volts and is best adapted to "open-circuit" work, that is, service in which the cell is called upon to deliver current only for short periods, its circuit at other times being open. The operation of annunciators, door bells, and flash lamps are typical illustrations of such service. The depolarizing action in the ammonium chloride cell is imperfect and the emf. falls off with continued use; however, the cell recuperates during periods of open circuit because the layer of gas which may have been formed has an opportunity to disappear. In a typical test, a dry cell was caused to deliver current to a 3-ohm load continuously for 1 hr., and during this period its emf. was observed to fall from 1.53 to 1.43 volts, but upon standing on open circuit for 30 min., the emf. increased again to 1.49 volts.

*253. Daniell and Gravity Cells.

—A cell invented by J. F. Daniell comprises a copper electrode in a saturated copper sulfate solution and a zinc electrode in a dilute zinc sulfate solution, containing a little sulfuric acid. The usual form of this cell is called a gravity cell because the two solutions are kept apart by gravity. A picture of this cell is shown in Fig. 241. The zinc and copper electrodes are in their respective solutions and the wire leading to the copper electrode is insulated to prevent contact with the zinc sulfate solution. A diagram representing the cell is given in Fig. 242.

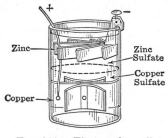

FIG. 241. The gravity cell

The copper electrode is positive and the zinc electrode is negative, and the copper sulfate solution surrounding the copper serves as a depolarizer. The zinc dissolves because of its high solution pressure, displacing hydrogen from the sulfuric acid and leaving the electrode negative; while the copper, on account of its low solution pressure, receives a copper deposit and becomes positive. When the electrodes are connected by an external circuit, a current is established, discharging the electrodes and allowing the process to continue.

As the cell operates, the zinc electrode wears away and the copper electrode gains weight, while the concentration of the zinc sulfate solution increases and that of the copper sulfate solution diminishes. The changes in concentration affect the emf. of the cell somewhat, but not enough to interfere with its practical use. The emf. is about 1.10 volts.

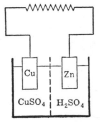

FIG. 242. Diagram of the gravity cell

This type of primary cell is best adapted to closed-circuit work, in which it continually delivers a small current, because this action helps to prevent the solutions from mixing by diffusion. It is used principally in the operation of railway signal circuits.

254. Standard Cells.

—Voltaic cells of special form are used as standards of emf. for measuring potential differences. These measurements are made with a potentiometer as described in § 258, under conditions such that the standard cell delivers only very small currents for brief periods of time.

In the Weston standard cell, Fig. 243, the electrodes are placed in the opposite sides of an H-shaped glass vessel which serves as a container for the electrolyte. The positive electrode is a paste of mercurous sulfate and the negative electrode is composed of cadmium amalgam. The electrolyte is a solution of cadmium sulfate, which may be kept saturated by having crystals of cadmium sulfate present.

The emf. of the saturated cell is 1.01830 volts at 20° C., and varies slightly but definitely with temperature changes. These cause slight variations in the amount of cadmium sulfate which dissolves in the solution, thereby altering the concentration, and consequently affecting the emf. of the cell to some extent. In the unsaturated cell, temperature changes do not affect the concentration of the electro-

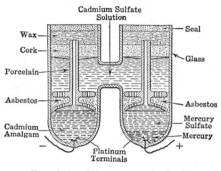

FIG. 243.   Weston standard cell

lyte, and their effect on the emf. is so small that it is usually neglected. Each unsaturated cell made must have its emf. determined by comparison with an emf. of known value.

255. The Lead Storage Cell.—For purposes requiring steady currents larger than can be supplied by primary cells, storage batteries are used. Typical applications include: stand-by service in power substations to supply the load for short periods in the event of temporary interruptions of the main circuits, propulsion of submarines and trucks, and automobile starting and lighting.

When a storage battery is delivering current, it is said to be on *discharge.* After a period of discharge the battery may be restored to its original condition by supplying current to it in the opposite direction from an outside source; this action is called *charging.* The energy supplied to a battery during the charging process is not all delivered on discharge, usually 30 to 40 per cent being wasted in heat. The efficiency depends upon the size and construction of the battery.

The lead storage cell when charged consists essentially of a positive plate of lead dioxide and a negative plate of spongy lead, immersed in sulfuric acid as an electrolyte. As the cell discharges, Fig. 244, both plates become coated with lead sulfate and the electrolyte

becomes less dense. The principal cell reactions are believed to be
as follows:

On Discharge

At negative plate $Pb \rightarrow Pb^{++} + 2e$

$$Pb^{++} + SO_4^{=} \rightarrow Pb^{++}SO_4^{=}(solid)$$

At positive plate

$$PbO_2 + 2H^+ + \underbrace{2H^+ + SO_4^{=}}_{H_2SO_4} + 2e \rightarrow Pb^{++}SO_4^{=}(solid) + 2H_2O$$

During discharge both plates become coated with lead sulfate and
the sulfuric acid is partly converted into water, thereby lowering the
specific gravity of the electrolyte.

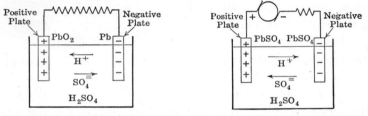

FIG. 244.   Discharge of lead storage cell   FIG. 245.   Charge of lead storage cell

When the cell is charged, Fig. 245, the lead sulfate on the positive
plate is reconverted to lead dioxide and that on the negative plate to
lead. The electrolyte returns to its original density and preserves an
overall equality of positive and negative charges. Thus:

On Charge

At negative plate

$$Pb^{++}SO_4^{=}(solid) + 2e \rightarrow Pb + SO_4^{=}$$

At positive plate

$$Pb^{++}SO_4^{=}(solid) + 2H_2O - 2e \rightarrow PbO_2 + 2H^+ + \underbrace{2H^+ + SO_4^{=}}_{H_2SO_4}$$

This action restores the cell to its original condition. If the cell is
overcharged, hydrogen and oxygen are liberated as in the decomposition of water in an electrolytic cell. This effect is known as
"gassing" and indicates the completion of charge.

During discharge of the lead storage cell, the emf. falls quickly
from an initial value of approximately 2.1 volts and remains nearly

constant at 2.0 volts throughout most of the discharge period. At the approach of complete discharge the emf. falls rapidly from this value. The state of charge of the cell is tested by measuring the specific gravity of the electrolyte with a hydrometer. For an automobile battery, the specific gravity of the electrolyte is 1.285 when the battery is fully charged, and when discharged it may be as low as 1.150.

A storage battery is charged for 8 hr. from 110-volt direct-current mains, the current being maintained at 10 amp. by a rheostat connected in series in the circuit. If the average emf. of the battery during the charging period is 24 volts, find the total energy supplied from the mains, the amount transformed into chemical energy, and the amount wasted in heat.

The total energy supplied from the mains is found by equation (141) to be 110 × 10 × 8 = 8800 watt-hr. and the amount transformed into chemical energy is found similarly to be 24 × 10 × 8 = 1920 watt-hr. The difference between 8800 and 1920, namely 6880 watt-hr., is wasted in heat.

256. The Edison Storage Cell.—The storage cell devised by Thomas A. Edison (1847–1931) employs nickel oxide for the positive electrode and finely divided iron for the negative electrode, these materials being packed into pockets carried by steel grids. The electrolyte is a solution of potassium hydroxide. As the cell discharges, the nickel oxide becomes reduced and the iron becomes oxidized, but the electrolyte remains unchanged. The chemical reactions are complex and not fully understood.

This cell, which was designed for vehicle operation, is lighter than the lead storage cell, is less subject to mechanical derangement, and is not injured by freezing. Moreover, cells of this type can be discharged and left in that condition without injury. The emf. is lower than that of the lead storage cell and drops somewhat during discharge, having an average value of about 1.2 volts.

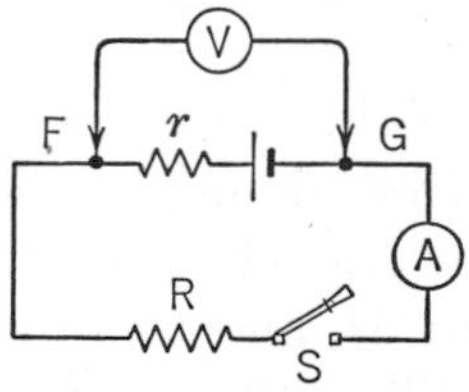

257. Measurement of Cell Resistance.—The ammeter-voltmeter method described in § 231 can be used to determine the internal resistance of a voltaic cell. The connections are shown in Fig. 246, in which F and G represent the terminals of a cell having an internal resistance r. Across these terminals there is connected a high-resistance voltmeter V, and also a low-resistance load R in series with a switch S and an ammeter A. With the switch open, the current in

Fig. 246. Measuring internal resistance of cell

the cell will be very small, and the voltmeter reading V_1 may be taken as practically equal to the emf. of the cell. With the switch closed, the ammeter will indicate the current I in the cell, and the voltmeter reading V_2 will be lower than the former value V_1 because of the potential drop Ir in the cell. Consequently

$$r = \frac{V_1 - V_2}{I} \tag{156}$$

is the internal resistance of the cell.

258. The Potentiometer.—The emf. of a cell is not given exactly by the reading of a voltmeter connected across the cell terminals, because even a high-resistance voltmeter takes some current. Such emf.'s can be compared accurately with the known emf. of a standard cell by means of a potentiometer. An advantage of the potentiometer method is that the measurement is made when the cell is not supplying any current, and since there is *no potential drop* in the cell and *no polarization*, the value measured is truly the emf.

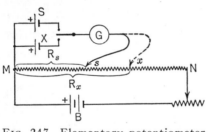

FIG. 247. Elementary potentiometer circuit

The apparatus used in a potentiometer measurement is indicated in Fig. 247. A storage battery B maintains a steady current in the slidewire MN, to one end of which connections are made to a standard cell S or to the cell X under test. By means of a double-throw switch, either of these cells may be connected through the galvanometer G to a slider which can be touched at different points along the wire MN. The battery B should have a constant emf., which should be larger than that of either S or X.

The current I from the battery B establishes a uniform potential drop along the slidewire MN, the potential being higher at M than at N. The cells S and X both have their positive terminals connected to M, and these terminals, therefore, have the same potential as M. When the double-throw switch is closed either way, the slider, if free from the slidewire, will have a potential which is lower than that of M by an amount equal to the emf. of the cell which the switch has placed into the circuit. There will be some point along MN which will have the same potential as the slider; this point can be found by touching the slider to different points until one is found for which the galvanometer shows no deflection. Under these conditions there will be no current in the circuit branch containing the cell and galvanometer, and the potential drop along the wire to the point of contact will then be equal to the emf. of the cell which is in circuit. Thus, with the double-throw switch connected to the standard cell of emf. E_s, a balance will be obtained at some point s such that $E_s = IR_s$, where R_s is the resistance of the slidewire from M to s. Then with the double-throw switch connected to X, another balance will be obtained at some other point x such that $E_x = IR_x$, where E_x is the emf. being measured and R_x is the resistance of the slidewire from M to x. From these relations,

$$\frac{E_x}{E_s} = \frac{IR_x}{IR_s}$$

whence

$$E_x = E_s \frac{R_x}{R_s} \tag{157}$$

giving the unknown emf. in terms of that of the standard cell and the known resistances.

This result may be verified by applying Kirchhoff's Second Law (§ 243) around a path from M along the slidewire to the contact point, returning through the cell S or X. For balance at s with the standard cell there is obtained: $-IR_s + E_s = 0$; and for balance at x with the other cell: $-IR_x + E_x = 0$. These equations yield the same result as found previously.

Since the resistance of the slidewire is proportional to its length, the unknown emf. may also be expressed as

$$E_x = E_s \frac{l_x}{l_s}$$

where l_x and l_s are the wire lengths from M to x and from M to s respectively.

In commercial potentiometers, the slidewire is usually replaced, at least in part, by resistance coils arranged with dial switches, and potential differences up to about 1.5 volts can be read directly from the setting of the instrument at balance. Higher values than this can be measured with the potentiometer when used with a potential divider; this is an arrangement of resistances for dividing the total potential difference into two definite parts, one of which is less than 1.5 volts.

259. Cells in Series and in Parallel.—Cells are frequently connected in series in order to obtain an increased emf. They are sometimes connected in parallel in order that jointly they may supply a large current to a low-resistance load without demanding an excessive current from any single cell.

When a number of cells are connected in series, their combined emf. is the sum of the emf.'s of the individual cells.

When a number of cells having equal emf.'s are connected in parallel, the emf. of the combination is the same as that of any individual cell. Cells having appreciably different emf.'s would not be connected in parallel in practice, because wasteful circulating currents would be set up in the cells themselves, even if the external circuit were open.

PROBLEMS

1. How much oxygen is liberated in an electrolytic cell by 1000 coulombs of electricity?

2. An ammeter was calibrated by connecting it in series with an electrolytic cell containing copper sulfate solution. During a 10-min. test the weight of the cathode increased by 1.940 gm., the instrument reading being constant at 10.00 amp. What correction should be applied to the ammeter at this scale reading?

3. How much silver will be deposited from a silver nitrate solution in an electrolytic cell by a current of 4 amp. maintained for 3 hr.?

4. A current of 500 amp. is supplied for a period of 12 hr. to 24 electrolytic cells containing acidulated water and connected in series. How many kilograms of oxygen will be liberated?

5. In copper refining, pure copper is deposited from a copper sulfate solution in an electrolytic cell using impure copper as the anode. If the potential difference across the cell is 0.3 volt, how much energy is used in depositing 1 lb. of copper?

6. A current of 35 amp. leaves an underground iron pipe. How long would it take to remove a pound of iron from the pipe through electrolytic corrosion? The atomic weight of iron is 55.84 and its valence number is 3.

7. An ionic constant known as the *electrochemical equivalent* is the mass of an element in grams liberated through electrolysis by 1 amp. in 1 sec. Compute the electrochemical equivalents of silver and gold. The atomic weight of gold is 197.2 and its valence number is 3.

8. A metal article having a surface of 150 sq. cm. is coated with silver in a plating bath containing silver nitrate solution, through which a current of 0.25 amp. is maintained for 20 min. Find the thickness of the plating. The specific gravity of silver is 10.45.

9. What quantity of electricity must be passed through an electrolytic cell in order to decompose 1 gm. of water?

10. How many atoms of hydrogen will be liberated by the passage of 100 coulombs of electricity through an electrolytic cell containing acidulated water?

*11. What is the *p*H value of a solution which contains 0.01 milligram of hydrogen ions per liter of solution? Also what would the *p*H value be if the solution contained half that many ions?

*12. For each ampere-hour delivered by a gravity cell, compute the amount of zinc dissolved and the amount of copper deposited within the cell.

13. What is the difference in weight of a cubic foot of electrolyte for a lead storage battery between the charged and discharged conditions for which the specific gravities are respectively 1.28 and 1.20?

14. (*a*) A 6-volt automobile storage battery, having an internal resistance of 0.02 ohm, is being charged at a constant rate by a current of 25 amp. during a run lasting 5 hr. How many coulombs of electricity and watts of power are supplied to the cell? (*b*) Find the potential difference across the terminals of this battery when it is delivering 10 amp. to the headlights, and when delivering 150 amp. momentarily to the starting motor.

15. A 32-volt storage battery is charged from 115-volt direct-current supply mains, a resistance being connected in series with the battery to limit the charging current to 15 amp. Compute the rate at which energy is wasted in heat.

16. A certain voltaic cell is found to establish a current of 0.078 amp. in an external circuit of 10 ohms resistance. When the resistance of the external circuit is reduced to 5 ohms, the current increases to 0.122 amp. Compute the emf. of the cell and also its internal resistance.

17. Two dry cells, each having an emf. of 1.5 volts and an internal resistance of 0.2 ohm, are to be connected in such a manner as to supply as large a current as possible to an external circuit. Should the cells be connected in series or in parallel (*a*) if the external circuit has a resistance of 0.1 ohm, (*b*) if the external circuit has a resistance of 1.0 ohm?

18. Six voltaic cells, each having an emf. of 1.5 volts and an internal resistance of 0.3 ohm are connected in two groups, each composed of three cells in series. The two groups are joined in parallel and supply current to an external circuit of 2 ohms resistance. Find the current in each cell.

19. Two batteries, one of 3 volts and the other of 6 volts, are connected in series with two resistors, one of 3 ohms and the other of 6 ohms. Then a

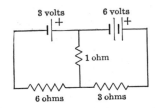

1-ohm resistor is connected as illustrated in the accompanying sketch. Neglect the resistance of the batteries and determine the current in the 1-ohm resistor by the use of Kirchhoff's Laws.

20. Two storage cells connected in parallel supply jointly a current of 15 amp. to an external circuit. The cells have emf.'s of 2.1 volts and 2.0 volts, and each has an internal resistance of 0.05 ohm. Find the current in each cell by the use of Kirchhoff's Laws.

21. To show why cells having unequal emf.'s are not connected in parallel, imagine the cells in the diagram to have emf.'s E_1 = 6 volts and E_2 = 5

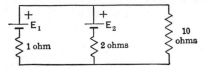

volts, and internal resistances of 1 ohm and 2 ohms respectively; the cells are placed in parallel across a 10-ohm load. By the use of Kirchhoff's Laws, determine the current in each cell and in the load.

Electromagnetism *Chapter XXIII*

260. Magnetic Effect of the Current.—The discovery of electro-magnetism was made by Oersted in 1820, through his observations that an electric current in a conductor is surrounded by a magnetic field. He also found that the direction of the field about a current-carrying wire is tangentially perpendicular to the wire and that the intensity of the field diminishes in receding from the wire. The lines of force about an isolated wire are concentric with it, as can be proved by arranging the wire vertically and moving a suspended magnet or compass around it.

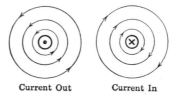

Current Out · · · · · Current In

Fɪɢ. 248. Diagrams of field around a current-carrying wire

Fig. 248 shows two diagrams of the magnetic field around a wire; the heavy circles indicate the wire in section and the light circles represent lines of force. When the current is directed toward the observer, as represented by a dot within the wire, the magnetic flux will be counter-clockwise, as shown at the left. When the current is reversed in direction, the flux will also be reversed, as shown at the right.

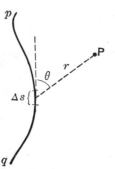

Fɪɢ. 249. Finding intensity of magnetic field around a wire

A simple rule for determining the relative directions of current and flux makes use of the *right hand*, the fingers being curved as though grasping the wire carrying the current, and the thumb being outstretched. *When the thumb points in the direction of the current the fingers will point along the lines of force.* Another popular rule applies the direction of advance of a right-handed screw.

The magnitude of the field due to an electric current can be computed by means of a fundamental expression due to Ampère. This relationship will be explained with the aid of Fig. 249, which depicts a curved wire *pq* in which there is an electric current. Each elementary

419

length of the wire contributes something to the magnetic field intensity at all points around the wire. As expressed by Ampère, the contribution of the element Δs to the field at any point P is

$$\Delta H = \frac{I \sin \theta \, \Delta s}{r^2}$$

where I is the current, r is the length of a line joining the wire element and the point in question, and θ is the angle between this line and the direction of the current. The total field intensity at the point P is, therefore

$$H = \sum \frac{I \sin \theta \, \Delta s}{r^2} = \int \frac{I \sin \theta \, ds}{r^2} \tag{158}$$

the latter form being in calculus notation.

That the field intensity should vary inversely as the square of the distance from a wire might be expected by comparison with the field intensity due to a magnet pole or an electric charge. Further, it is reasonable to suppose that doubling the current or doubling the length of the element would double the field intensity. The fact that the flux is concentric about the wire suggests that the field intensity due to the element has its greatest value in the direction normal to the element and its least value along the direction of the element, but experimentation was required to prove that the intensity varies as the sine of the angle θ.

261. Current in Circular Path; Electromagnetic Units.—The laws for determining the direction and magnitude of the field produced by an electric current apply to all forms of circuits and will now be adapted to a few simple shapes. Suppose, first, that a wire is bent into the arc of a circle and that it is desired to compute the field intensity at the center of the arc.

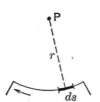

FIG. 250. Illustrating the definition of unit current

Fig. 250 shows a wire forming an arc of radius r centered at P and carrying current in a clockwise direction, with the wires connecting the arc to the rest of the circuit arranged radially so that they will not affect the field at the center. From the right-hand rule, it is found that the magnetic field is directed into the page in the region toward the center of the arc and out of the page in the region away from the center. For all positions of the element ds the radius r is constant and perpendicular to the element, so that the angle θ of equation (158) is 90°. Hence, the field intensity at the center of the arc becomes

$$H = \frac{I}{r^2} \int ds = \frac{I}{r^2} s$$

in which the integral $\int ds$ gives the full length s of the arc.

The foregoing equation is used to define unit current on the basis of its magnetic effect, the current having unit value when each of the other quantities is unity. Thus, the *electromagnetic unit of current*, called the *abampere*, is a current such that in an arc 1 cm. long and having 1-cm. radius, it will produce at the center of the arc a field intensity of 1 oersted. The ampere is one-tenth of an abampere.

If the arc in Fig. 250 is extended to form a complete circular loop having a radius of r cm., the integral becomes the circumference of the circle, $2\pi r$. When the current in the loop is in amperes, the field intensity at the center in oersteds becomes $H = I \times 2\pi r \div 10r^2$. A coil of N turns will have a field intensity N times as great, provided the turns are concentrated so that the entire coil has little axial length compared with its radius. The field intensity at the center of such a coil is consequently

$$H = \frac{2\pi NI}{10r} \tag{159}$$

From this expression the *ampere may be defined as the current which in a coil having 1 turn and a radius of 1 cm. will produce at the center a field of intensity* $2\pi/10$ *oersted.*

The study of Electricity and Magnetism involves several systems of units. The *electrostatic* system is based on electricity at rest, as described in Chapter XIX. The *electromagnetic* system is based on the magnetic effect of the current. The *practical* system, referred to in Chapter XXI, is closely associated with the electromagnetic system in that each practical unit bears a ratio to the corresponding electromagnetic unit which is some integral power of ten. There is also the *meter-kilogram-second* system, described in Chapter XXIX.

All of these systems are definitely related to one another, and any electrical entity can be expressed in the units of any system. Consider, for example, electric quantity or charge. In the electromagnetic system, the unit of charge, called the *abcoulomb*, is naturally the quantity of electricity transferred by a current of 1 abampere maintained for 1 sec. This quantity is entirely independent of the electrostatic unit of charge, which is defined (§ 209) on the basis of its force action upon a like charge. Careful tests have been made comparing the two systems, as a result of which it is found that 1 abcoulomb is equal to 3×10^{10} esu. of charge. The coulomb is one-tenth of an abcoulomb, and consequently equals 3×10^9 esu. of charge.

262. Magnetic Field about a Straight Conductor.—The general expression for field intensity given by equation (158) was verified experimentally by the French physicists Jean B. Biot (1774–1862) and Felix Savart (1791–1841), as applied to the magnetic field produced by current in a long straight conductor.

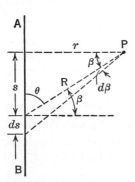

In Fig. 251 let AB represent a portion of such a wire extending indefinitely in both directions, and let it be required to determine the field intensity at a point P in space at a perpendicular distance r from it. The field at this point may be considered as made up of the contributions of successive elementary lengths, such as ds, comprising the whole wire. In terms of the symbols R, s, θ, and β as in the figure, the field intensity at P due to a current of I amp. in the elementary length ds is found to be

FIG. 251. Field intensity near a straight wire

$$dH = \frac{I \sin \theta \, ds}{10R^2} = \frac{I \cos \beta \, ds}{10R^2}$$

where $\beta = 90° - \theta$.

The total field intensity at the point under consideration due to the entire wire will be the summation of a series of terms like the foregoing. This is obtained by calculus, after first rewriting the equation in terms of the single variable β. Since $s = r \tan \beta$, $ds = r \, d\beta / \cos^2 \beta$, and $R = r \sec \beta$, it follows that

$$dH = \frac{I \cos \beta \, r \, d\beta}{10r^2 \sec^2 \beta \cos^2 \beta} = \frac{I}{10r} \cos \beta \, d\beta$$

The total field intensity at P is expressed as

$$H = \frac{I}{10r} \int_{\beta=-\frac{\pi}{2}}^{\beta=\frac{\pi}{2}} \cos \beta \, d\beta$$

Upon integration, this expression gives the field intensity in oersteds at a point r cm. from a long straight wire carrying a current of I amp. as

$$H = \frac{2I}{10r} \tag{160}$$

Compute the magnitude of the field intensity due to a current of 8 amp. in a long straight wire at a point 5 cm. from the wire. By equation (160) the magnetic field at this point has a magnitude of $(2 \times 8) \div (10 \times 5)$ = 0.32 oersted.

263. Motion of Pole in Magnetic Field.—It is of interest to calculate the amount of work that must be done in moving an isolated magnet pole once around any closed path in opposition to a magnetic field. Consider first a long straight conductor, as represented in part I of Fig. 252, in which there is a current of I amp., and suppose that a pole of unit strength is moved along the dotted path of radius r cm. once around the wire. The force in dynes acting upon this pole will be numerically equal to the field strength given by the foregoing

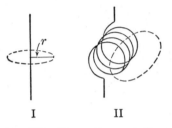

I   II

Fig. 252.   Illustrating work done on magnet pole

equation as $H = \dfrac{2I}{10r}$. To move the unit pole completely around the wire in a circular path of length $2\pi r$ cm. against this force would require

$$W = 2\pi r \times \frac{2I}{10r} = \frac{4\pi I}{10}$$

ergs of work. Since the radius disappears from the result, the work required is found to be independent of the path, and would be the same for any closed path around the conductor, whether circular or not. The work remains the same if the wire is not straight, or even if it is bent into a closed coil. Thus, to move a unit pole through a coil of N turns, as in part II of the figure, would require $4\pi NI/10$ ergs to link its path with all of the turns.

264. The Solenoid.—A coil of wire wound uniformly in a long helix is termed a *solenoid*. Solenoids have a wide application in magnetic apparatus, and it is important to be able to determine the field intensities within them. This can be done by considering the amount of work needed to move a unit magnet pole around a closed path in opposition to the field, as in the preceding section.

In a ring solenoid the helix is bent to form a toroid, as though the wire were wound around an automobile tire. For such a solenoid of N turns carrying a current of I amp., the work done in moving a unit pole once around the median line of the toroid would be

$4\pi NI/10$ ergs, since its path would be linked with all of the turns. The work can also be expressed as Hl, where H is the field intensity in oersteds along the solenoid axis and l is the length of this median line in centimeters. Therefore, $4\pi NI/10 = Hl$, and the field intensity along the axis is

$$H = \frac{4\pi NI}{10l} = \frac{4\pi nI}{10} \tag{161}$$

where $n = N/l$ is the number of turns per unit of length. The same expression may be used for a straight solenoid, but applies only to its central portion; the field intensity is less at the ends.

265. Lines of Induction; Magnetic Flux.—The student is familiar with the use of lines to represent magnetic field intensity and needs only to be reminded that field intensity means force per unit pole to appreciate why these lines are called lines of force. In the preceding sections the presence of a magnetic field around an electric current has been explained, and values for field intensity have been found for a number of circuit shapes. A generalization might be drawn, using the idea of magnetic lines, to the effect that an electric current always establishes lines of force around it. One might naturally inquire whether the situation can be reversed, that is, whether a current can be produced in a circuit by placing a magnetic field near it. Experiment shows that such a result cannot be obtained unless the number of magnetic lines passing through the circuit is *changing* (§ 271). The process is described by saying that while the number of magnetic lines is changing an emf. is set up, and this emf. develops a current in the circuit. An emf. set up in this manner is said to be *induced*, and the process is called *induction*.

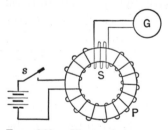

FIG. 253.   Illustrating magnetic induction

The generation of such an emf. can be demonstrated with two coils wound upon a wooden ring as illustrated in Fig. 253. The *primary coil P* is a ring solenoid which is connected to a battery through a switch *s*, and the *secondary coil S* is joined to a galvanometer *G* to indicate the emf. induced in that coil. While the switch in the primary circuit is being closed or opened the galvanometer will show a momentary deflection each time, but there will be no steady deflection when the switch is left closed.

Now suppose the foregoing experiment to be repeated with the coils wound upon a core of iron or other magnetic material. Under these circumstances the deflection produced upon closing or opening the primary circuit will be much larger than before. The presence of the magnetic core evidently causes a large increase in the number of magnetic lines within the solenoid. This is not due to any increase in the field intensity H, which, as shown by equation (161), depends only upon the number of turns per unit length and the current, and so is independent of the material within the solenoid. The result is due to additional lines produced by the magnetization of the iron; these lines together with the lines of force which represent H are all effective in inducing emf. and are called *lines of induction*.

Collectively, the lines of induction are spoken of as *magnetic flux*. The unit of magnetic flux is the *maxwell*; it is named after the English physicist, J. Clark Maxwell (1831–1879). *One maxwell is one line of magnetic flux.* The total flux extending through a region is represented by the symbol Φ.

The number of lines of induction passing perpendicularly through an area of 1 sq. cm. is known as the *flux density* and is symbolized by B. The unit of flux density is called the *gauss*, after Karl F. Gauss (1777–1855), German mathematician and physicist. *A gauss is a flux density of one maxwell per square centimeter.* It is represented by a single line of magnetic flux extending perpendicularly through an area of 1 sq. cm. If the flux is uniform over an area A sq. cm., with B lines perpendicularly through each square centimeter, the total flux extending through the area will be

$$\Phi = BA \qquad (162)$$

The experiment described earlier in this section shows that inside of a magnetic material there are more lines of induction than lines of force; the ratio

$$\mu = \frac{B}{H} \qquad (163)$$

is the permeability of the material, § 219. For a vacuum, and practically for air, the flux density and field strength are numerically equal, and the permeability μ_v is unity. For a magnetic material, the permeability is greater than unity, often many times as large; moreover, it does not have a fixed value even for a particular specimen, but varies with the flux density in it and with its previous magnetic history. These variations are discussed in the next chapter.

266. Force on Conductor in a Magnetic Field; Ampère's Law.—The analysis of the circular loop considered in § 261 can be extended to show that a current-carrying conductor experiences a force when

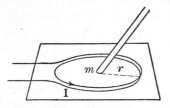

located in a magnetic field. To determine this force consider the action between a coil in air and a magnet pole placed at its center, as represented in Fig. 254. The coil, of radius r, is composed of N closely wound turns in which there is a current of I amp. directed as shown. Suppose that the field intensity is H oersteds at the center of the coil, and that the N magnet pole of strength

Fig. 254. Finding the force on a conductor

m units is placed at that point. The pole will be acted upon by an *upward* force having a value in dynes of

$$F = mH = m\,\frac{2\pi NI}{10r}$$

by equations (135) and (159). Since the current-carrying coil acts with this force on the magnet pole, the pole must react *downward* upon the coil with an equal force, by Newton's Third Law of Motion. The force on the coil is, therefore,

$$F = \left(\frac{m}{r^2}\right)\frac{I}{10}(2\pi rN)$$

which is exactly the same as the preceding equation except that both numerator and denominator have been multiplied by r.

This equation can be simplified by considering the significance of the term within each parenthesis. The first expresses the flux density of the radial magnetic field at a distance r cm. from a magnet pole of strength m in accordance with equations (136) and (163), so that $\frac{m}{r^2} = \mu_v H = B$. Since every part of the wire is at this common distance r from the pole, B represents the flux density in gausses at the wire due to the pole. The second parenthesis is the total length of the wire in the coil and will be represented in centimeters by l. Consequently, the force on the wire in dynes will be

$$F = \frac{BIl}{10} \tag{164}$$

and will be directed downward in Fig. 254.

Equation (164) is a mathematical statement of Ampère's Law for the force on a conductor; it asserts that any conductor carrying a current and located in a magnetic field at right angles to the flux will be pushed by a force that is proportional to the flux density, to the current, and to the length of the wire. Although the equation was derived for a particular shape of coil (that is, circular) by consideration of the field intensity at a particular point (that is, the center of the coil), it is perfectly general and can be applied to all forms of circuits.

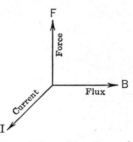

In applying Ampère's Law, it should be noted that for any straight piece of wire of length l the directions of F, B, and I are mutually

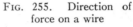

Fig. 255. Direction of force on a wire

perpendicular. Fig. 255 shows these directions along the three geometric axes. If the conductor is not at right angles to the flux, but makes an angle ϕ with it instead, then the effective length is the component $l \sin \phi$, and the force is expressed by

$$F = \frac{BIl}{10} \sin \phi \qquad (165)$$

The relative directions of the magnetic flux, conductor current, and force on the conductor shown in Fig. 255 can be visuallzed by the concept that magnetic lines tend to become as short as possible,

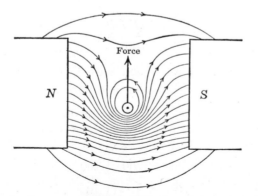

Fig. 256. Composite magnetic field of magnets and conductor

and when in the same direction exert a sidewise thrust upon one another (§ 224). Fig. 256 illustrates a wire located in a magnetic field produced by the poles N and S. The current is shown by the dot within the conductor to be directed toward the reader and, consequently, the magnetic flux which it produces will be counter-clockwise. In the region below the conductor the lines produced by the poles and those produced by the conductor have the same direction and the resultant field will be strong, but in the region above the conductor the fields are in opposition and therefore the resultant field will be weak. The fact that the wire will be pushed upward as a result of this flux distribution can be visualized by the tension along the lines of the field from N and S and by the repulsive action between them below the conductor where all the lines have the same direction.

267. Force between Conductors.—The force acting between two parallel wires can be determined by considering one wire to be in the magnetic field produced by the other, and applying Ampère's Law. Thus, the field produced at distance r cm. from a straight wire carrying a current of I_1 amp. is given by equation (160) in oersteds as

$$H = \frac{2I_1}{10r}$$

If another wire is placed parallel to the first at this distance r, and if the second wire carries a current I_2 amp., then by equations (163) and (164) the force action in dynes between them is

$$F = \frac{BI_2l}{10} = \frac{\mu H I_2 l}{10}$$

or

$$F = \frac{2\mu I_1 I_2 l}{100r} \tag{166}$$

where l is the length of the second wire in centimeters and μ is the permeability of the region between the wires.

For example, if two wires carrying currents of 200 amp. each were placed parallel and 5 cm. apart in air (for which $\mu = 1$), then the force between the wires per meter of length would be

$$F = \frac{2 \times 1 \times 200 \times 200 \times 100}{100 \times 5} = 16,000 \text{ dynes}$$

268. The Galvanometer.—The instruments ordinarily used for measuring electric currents depend for their operation on the force action on conductors in magnetic fields. In the usual form of such instruments, a coil of wire is supported in a magnetic field and a current is established in it; the forces thus produced on the coil deflect it from its rest position, and the amount of deflection serves as a measure of the current. This operating principle applies to most ammeters and voltmeters used in electrical testing and also to the *d'Arsonval galvanometer* (named after the French physicist, Arsène d'Arsonval 1851–1940), which is used for the measurement of small currents.

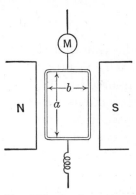

Fig. 257 shows the coil of a galvanometer between the poles of a strong permanent magnet. It carries a mirror M so that its deflections can be read with a telescope and scale. Assume that there are N turns on the coil, that it is located in a uniform field of flux density B gausses, and that a current of I amp. circulates around the coil in a clockwise direction. This current is conducted to the coil by a flat

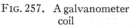

FIG. 257.   A galvanometer coil

metal ribbon which serves as the suspension and is led out by a helix of similar material below the coil. By Ampère's Law, the left side of the coil, of length a cm., will experience a force in dynes of

$$F = \frac{BINa}{10}$$

and the force on the other side will be of like amount. These forces act in opposite directions but combine to produce a torque in a common direction, the right side of the coil moving forward out of the page and the left side moving backward into the page. When the coil lies in the plane of the magnet as shown, the deflecting torque in dyne-centimeters will be

$$T_d = 2\frac{BINa}{10} \times \frac{b}{2} = \frac{BINS}{10}$$

where $S = ab$ is the surface area of the coil face. As the coil turns in response to this torque the lever arm becomes less than $b/2$, and ultimately the coil would come to rest in a position at right angles to that shown. However, the suspension exerts a restoring torque T_r on the coil as it moves from the position shown, the value of which is proportional to the twist ϕ of the suspension, or

$$T_r = \tau\phi$$

where τ is a constant determined by the stiffness of the suspension. The coil will come to rest where $T_d = T_r$, and therefore

$$\tau\phi = \frac{BINS}{10}$$

showing that the twist ϕ for a given instrument (that is B, N, S and τ fixed) is proportional to the current I. With a parallel field, as assumed in Fig. 257, this expression would be true only for small deflections. In the galvanometer as actually constructed a stationary cylindrical core is mounted within the moving coil and the pole pieces are usually curved. A radial magnetic field is thus established, and the coil always swings perpendicularly to the flux. By this means the twist is made proportional to the current throughout the entire range of the instrument.

Another form of this galvanometer, called a *ballistic galvanometer*, has a coil of considerable width in order to give it a high moment of inertia; this instrument measures electric charge rather than current. When a small quantity of electricity is discharged through such a galvanometer a deflecting torque is set up for a brief interval. The coil continues to rotate after the discharge has been completed and the maximum *throw* of the instrument is read. This throw is proportional to the charge and the instrument can be calibrated to measure quantity of electricity.

269. Ammeters and Voltmeters.—Instruments for measuring current and potential difference in commercial testing are galvanometers of more substantial type in which the coil is pivoted and fitted with a pointer that moves over a suitably calibrated scale. Current is supplied to the coil through flat spiral springs which also serve to return the pointer to the zero position when the current ceases. There is no structural difference between an ammeter and a voltmeter, and both deflect in proportion to the current in the movable coil. The difference between them is one of electrical resistance; in this respect the instruments are designed so that their introduction into a circuit for purposes of measurement will not change appreciably the quantities they are intended to measure.

In the ammeter, Fig. 258, the coil is provided with a by-pass, called a *shunt*, connected directly across the terminals A and B, so that the current in the coil will be only a small but definite part of the entire current in the circuit. The ammeter has a very low resistance so that the potential drop across it will be small; naturally care must be taken to have enough resistance in the circuit associated with this meter so that the current will be limited to a value within its range. An ammeter is connected in series with a circuit and never across the service mains.

In the voltmeter the movable coil is connected in series with a resistance, so that the instrument may be connected directly across a generator or service mains and yet take only a small current. A voltmeter has a high resistance so as to divert as little current as possible from the circuit to which it is connected. In a sense the voltmeter protects itself because of its high resistance, but care must be exercised not to apply potential differences exceeding the range of the instrument. The range of a voltmeter can be extended if desired by the use of an additional series resistance external to the instrument. Such an auxiliary resistance is called a *multiplier*.

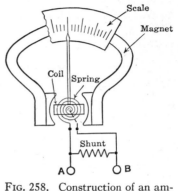

FIG. 258.   Construction of an ammeter

The resistance of the shunt or series resistance for a particular instrument can be found by applying Ohm's Law, as the following examples will show:

Suppose an ammeter to have a moving coil of 5 ohms resistance, which deflects across the entire scale when carrying a current of 0.01 amp. Find the shunt resistance necessary to make this instrument a 10-amp. ammeter, that is, one which deflects full scale when the main-line current is 10 amp. At full-scale deflection, the potential drop across its coil is $E = I \times R = 0.01 \times 5 = 0.05$ volt, and this must then also be the potential drop across the shunt. But the current in the shunt is $10 - 0.01 = 9.99$ amp., consequently, its resistance should be $R = E \div I = 0.05 \div 9.99 = 0.005005$ ohm.

Likewise, suppose a voltmeter to have a coil of 5 ohms resistance, which deflects full scale when carrying a current of 0.01 amp. Find what resistance must be connected in series with the coil if this instrument is to have a range of 150 volts, that is, the instrument is to deflect full scale when 150 volts are impressed across its terminals. Since the current is the same in the coil and series resistance, the resistance of the entire instrument is $R = E \div I = 150 \div 0.01 = 15,000$ ohms, and inasmuch as the coil has a resistance of 5 ohms, the series resistance must have the value of $15,000 - 5 = 14,995$ ohms.

270. The Wattmeter.—Since power is the product of potential difference and current (§ 230), an instrument to measure power must be arranged so that the deflection of the coil will be proportional to the potential difference as well as to the current. The permanent magnet common to voltmeter and ammeter is replaced in the *wattmeter* by a heavy winding that is connected in series with the load circuit like an ammeter; in this way the flux density B within it is made proportional to the load current. The moving coil is connected in series with a high resistance across the circuit under measurement, and the current I in the coil is thereby made proportional to the potential difference across the load. Since the force on the coil is proportional to $B \times I$ according to equation (164), it will be proportional to the product of the amperes in the load and the volts across it. Therefore, the instrument can be calibrated to read watts directly. The arrangement and connections of the wattmeter are shown in Fig. 259;

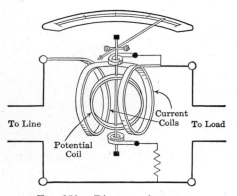

FIG. 259.　Diagram of a wattmeter

the "current winding" is shown by the fixed coils in series with the load, and the "potential winding" is shown by the movable coil bridged across the lines.

The metering of electrical energy for determining the cost of electric service is not accomplished by wattmeters, for these instruments indicate merely the instantaneous rate at which the energy is used; the meter that is used for this purpose is called a *watt-hour meter*. It is similar electrically to the wattmeter but the coil is arranged to rotate continuously at a rate dependent upon the power expended in the load circuit, and the cost of service is based upon the number of revolutions made.

271. Induced Electromotive Force.—In 1831, Faraday discovered that an emf. could be induced in an electric circuit by relative motion between the circuit and a magnet. This action was mentioned in § 265, and will be further illustrated by describing some fundamental experiments.

Fig. 260 shows a bar magnet NS and a coil of wire, the coil being in a vertical plane and having its circuit closed through a galvanometer G. No action is observed as long as the apparatus remains stationary, but when the magnet is moved horizontally toward the coil, the galvanometer deflects, showing that an emf. is being induced in the coil and sets up a current in its closed circuit. The faster the magnet is moved, the larger the deflection will be; if it is brought to rest, the deflection again becomes zero. Upon moving the magnet away from the coil, similar results are obtained, but the deflections are reversed, showing that the emf. is now in the opposite direction. The same effects may be produced by moving the coil instead of the magnet, by using an electromagnet instead of a permanent magnet, or by turning the coil. These tests lead to the conclusion that

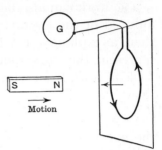

FIG. 260. Inducing an emf. in a coil

an emf. will be induced in a coil of wire whenever there is a change in the magnetic flux linked with it.

The magnitude of the induced emf. can be found by considering the energy relations in a circuit so arranged that a portion of it moves through a magnetic field. Fig. 261 is a plan view of such a circuit with the moving part located in a uniform field directed into the page. Two bare parallel rails MN and PQ in the plane of the paper are joined at the left by the stationary conductor MP. A bare wire CD extends perpendicularly from one rail to the other and may be moved along them without friction. An emf. is induced when the wire is moved and sets up a current in the loop $CMPD$, and it is desired to determine the value of this emf. Suppose that the wire CD has a length l between the rails and that a force F is exerted upon it. If the force acts for a time interval dt, moving the wire uniformly a distance ds, the work done is $dW = F\,ds$. Let the current in the

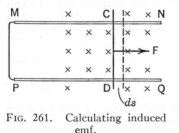

FIG. 261. Calculating induced emf.

loop, expressed in absolute units, be I; then the force acting upon the wire because of its presence in the field of flux density B is given by Ampère's Law (§ 266) as the product BIl, and the applied force F must have this same value in the opposite direction. Hence the work can be expressed as $dW = BIl\,ds$. But $l\,ds$ represents the amount by which the area of the circuit changes, and this area multiplied by the flux density B gives the change in the magnetic flux linking the circuit, namely $d\Phi$. Consequently $dW = I\,d\Phi$, where the work dW

is expressed in ergs, the current I in abamperes, and the change in flux $d\Phi$ in maxwells.

The work can also be expressed independently in terms of the emf. induced in the circuit; if this is represented in absolute units by e, then, as explained in § 230, $dW = Ie\,dt$. The two expressions for dW represent the same quantity of work and may be equated, yielding $I\,d\Phi = Ie\,dt$, from which

$$e = -\frac{d\Phi}{dt} \tag{167}$$

the negative sign being introduced to take care of direction, as explained in the following section.

This equation serves to define the electromagnetic unit of emf., or *abvolt*, as the emf. induced in a circuit while the flux linked with it changes at the rate of 1 maxwell (1 line) per sec. The volt is 100 million times as large as the abvolt, and therefore *the flux must change at the rate of 10^8 lines per sec. in order to induce an emf. of 1 volt.*

The foregoing expression applies to any circuit; for example, to a coil in which an emf. is induced by motion of a magnet. For a coil wound with several turns close together, so that all are subject to the same variation of flux, equal emf.'s would be induced in the several turns and these would be added to obtain the total induced emf. Consequently, the emf. induced in a coil of N turns while the flux through it is changing at the rate of $\dfrac{d\Phi}{dt}$ lines per sec. is given in volts by the expression

$$e = -N\frac{d\Phi}{dt} \times 10^{-8} \tag{168}$$

As a numerical problem, suppose a coil consisting of 6 turns wound close together to be arranged as shown in Fig. 260; find the emf. induced in the coil when the magnet is moved toward it in such a manner that the flux through the coil changes uniformly from 6000 lines to 10,000 lines in 0.2 sec. In this case $\dfrac{d\Phi}{dt} = \dfrac{10,000 - 6000}{0.2} = 20{,}000$ lines per sec., and the induced emf. is $-6 \times 20{,}000 \times 10^{-8} = -1.2$ millivolts.

Another way of regarding the process of induction is to consider that *an emf. is induced in a circuit whenever any of its conductors cuts magnetic flux.* By a rearrangement of the preceding equations expressing work done, it will be clear that $B\,Il\,ds = Ie\,dt$, whence $e = Bl\dfrac{ds}{dt}$. But $\dfrac{ds}{dt}$ is the velocity of the conductor CD in Fig. 261

and consequently the emf. induced in a circuit in which a conductor of length l cm. cuts magnetic flux of density B gausses with a velocity v cm. per sec. may be expressed as Blv abvolts. This expression will be modified as before by introducing a negative sign and converting the result to volts, giving the induced emf. as

$$e = -Blv \times 10^{-8} \qquad (169)$$

272. Direction of Induced Emf.; Lenz's Law.—Experiments on induced electromotive force conducted by the Russian physicist, H. F. Emil Lenz (1804–1865), led to the generalization called Lenz's Law. This law states, in effect, that whenever a current is set up by a change of flux through a circuit, *its direction will be such as to oppose the act which caused it*. The minus sign is used in the foregoing equations for induced emf. to indicate that the emf. is one of opposition. Under the conditions shown in Fig. 260 the act which induces the emf. is the movement of the N pole of the magnet toward the coil. In order to oppose this act, the adjacent face of the coil must also acquire N polarity, and lines of force must be established through the coil pointing toward the magnet. By the rule described in § 260 the current to produce this flux direction must be counter-clockwise as viewed from the magnet.

Again, under the conditions represented in Fig. 261, the act which caused the induced emf. was the motion of the conductor CD toward the right, a motion which increased the flux linking the circuit. To oppose this act, the induced emf. must be directed so that it tends to set up a current that would *decrease* the flux linking the circuit. This direction is from D to C in the figure.

273. Action of Magnetic Field on Moving Charge.—It has been shown that a conductor carrying a current experiences a force when located transversely in a magnetic field; this force is given by equation (164) as $F = \dfrac{BIl}{10}$, where B is the flux density of the magnetic field, I is the current in the conductor, and l is its length. Since a moving charge constitutes a current, it is evident that a force will act upon a charge while it is moving in a magnetic field. The magnitude of this force can be found by considering a charge Q to be transferred along a conductor of length l in the time t, the velocity of transfer being $v = \dfrac{l}{t}$ and the current being $I = \dfrac{Q}{t}$. The elimination of t

between these expressions gives $Il = Qv$, and therefore the force acting upon the moving charge can be expressed as $\dfrac{BQv}{10}$ dynes when B is in gausses, Q is in coulombs, and v is in centimeters per second. If Q is stated in electrostatic units of charge, the force in dynes is given by

$$F = \frac{BQv}{3 \times 10^{10}} \tag{170}$$

The direction of this force is at right angles to both the motion of the charge and the direction of the field.

The sidewise thrust upon such particles as electrons, protons, and alpha particles is utilized in the determination of electronic mass and in the acceleration of the heavier particles for bombarding atomic nuclei.

274. Electronic Measurements; Ratio of Charge to Mass.—The principles of electromagnetism and electrostatics enabled the English scientist, Joseph J. Thomson (1856–1940), to determine the ratio of

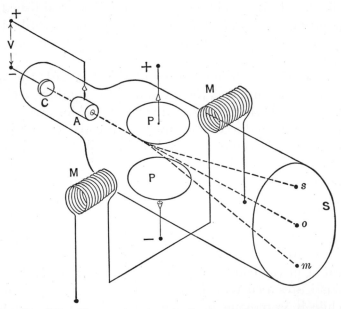

Fig. 262.   Thomson's apparatus for electronic measurements

the charge of the electron to its mass.   He used an evacuated tube of the form shown in Fig. 262, which contains a cathode C and an anode A near one end, the anode being pierced by a small hole at the center. Near the middle of the tube two charged plates *PP* are arranged to establish an electric field vertically directed in the view shown, and at the same region a magnet *MM* sets up a magnetic field horizontally directed. The front of the tube contains a fluorescent screen *S*.

When a potential difference *V* is applied across the electrodes *C* and *A*, electrons issue from *C*; while most of them fall upon the anode, a number pass through the hole in it. In the absence of the electric and magnetic fields, these electrons would travel undeviated to the screen, where they would produce a bright spot at *o*. With the plates *PP* energized, each electron passing between them would be subjected to an upward force of $\mathscr{E}e$ dynes (§ 210), $\mathscr{E}$ being the electric field intensity between the plates and *e* the charge of the electron. In consequence the spot on the screen would be displaced upward to some point *s*. Instead, with the magnet *MM* energized, each electron would experience a vertical force of $\dfrac{Bev}{3 \times 10^{10}}$ dynes according to equation (170), where *B* is the flux density of the magnetic field, and *v* is the electron velocity. The polarity of the magnet must be so arranged that this force would act in a downward direction, and would deflect the spot on the screen to some point *m*. Finally, with both the electric and magnetic fields acting simultaneously, their strengths can be adjusted so that the upward force on the electrons due to the one can be made equal to the downward force on them due to the other; under this condition the bright spot on the screen can be brought to the undeflected position *o*, the weight of the electrons being neglected. Then $\mathscr{E}e = \dfrac{Bev}{3 \times 10^{10}}$, from which the electron velocity can be determined as

$$v = 3 \times 10^{10} \frac{\mathscr{E}}{B}$$

An electron of mass *m* in moving from *C* to *A* has an amount of work *Ve* done upon it, which appears as kinetic energy when it leaves *A*, whence $Ve = \dfrac{mv^2}{2}$. With the foregoing value for *v*, this expression may be rewritten as

$$\frac{e}{m} = \frac{9 \times 10^{20} \mathscr{E}^2}{2VB^2} \tag{171}$$

which gives the desired ratio of the charge e of the electron to its mass m. The result is expressed in terms of the electric field intensity $\mathscr{E}$, the magnetic flux density B, and the potential difference V between the electrodes C and A.

The units used in the foregoing equations are: m = gm., v = cm. per sec., B = gausses, e = esu. of charge, V = ergs per esu. of charge, and $\mathscr{E}$ = dynes per esu. of charge. Conversion to other units may be made by noting that a potential difference of 1 erg per esu. of charge = 300 volts, and that an electric field intensity of 1 dyne per esu. of charge = 300 volts per cm.

The numerical value of e/m, based on a number of recent measurements, is approximately 5.28×10^{17} esu. per gm. When this result is combined with the value of the electronic charge $e = 4.80 \times 10^{-10}$ esu. as determined by Millikan's method (§ 217), the mass of the electron is found to be 9.11×10^{-28} gm.

It is customary to express the energy of such high speed particles in terms of the potential difference through which an electron must accelerate in order to acquire the particular energy value. *The energy represented by an electron accelerating through a difference of potential of one volt is called an electron-volt.* Since 1 erg of work per esu. of charge is equivalent to 300 volts, and since the charge of the electron is 4.80×10^{-10} esu. of charge, it follows that 1 electron-volt equals

$$\frac{4.80 \times 10^{-10} \text{ esu. of charge}}{1 \text{ electron}} \times \frac{1 \dfrac{\text{erg}}{\text{esu. of charge}}}{300 \text{ volts}} = 1.60 \times 10^{-12} \text{ erg}$$

*275. The Cyclotron.—The application of electromagnetic principles to the problems of modern research is illustrated in a machine developed by Professor Ernest O. Lawrence and called the *cyclotron*.

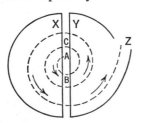

The purpose of this apparatus is to give charged particles very high speeds and a large amount of energy, so that they may be used for the bombardment of atoms in the investigation of nuclear structure and artificial radioactivity (Chapter XL).

FIG. 263. Path of particles in a cyclotron

Essentially the cyclotron consists of a pair of hollow semicircular segments X and Y, Fig. 263, like a large pill-box which has been cut in two, with the halves separated, and a source of positive ions, such as the nuclei of helium atoms, near the center. The segments are placed in an evacuated space within a uniform magnetic field at right angles to the plane of the segments; that is, perpendicular to the page in the figure. In operation, one segment is charged positively and the other negatively, and then the polarity of the charges is reversed again and again in rapid succession by connection to a source of alternating current.

The positive ions are released at A and are attracted into segment X when that segment is momentarily negative. Each ion is continuously deflected by the magnetic field and moves in a circular path until it leaves segment X at B. Suppose that at this instant the polarity of the segments is reversed; then the ion is accelerated by the difference of potential that exists between the segments, and enters Y at a higher speed, after which it travels again in a circular path until it emerges at C. By a repetition of these events the ion moves along the dotted path, traveling each half-revolution with higher speed, and finally leaves the apparatus at Z, where the material to be bombarded is located.

It is of interest to note that the ions travel around any semicircle of the path in the same time regardless of the radius. The force exerted by the magnetic field of flux density B upon a charge Q moving with a speed v is $F = \dfrac{BQv}{3 \times 10^{10}}$, the units being the same as in the preceding section; this force acts continuously at right angles to the direction of motion of the charge and becomes the centripetal force of its circular motion. It may be expressed as in earlier chapters, by $\dfrac{mv^2}{r}$, where m is the mass of the charged particle and r is the radius of its path; hence

$$\frac{BQv}{3 \times 10^{10}} = \frac{mv^2}{r}$$

But the speed of a particle which moves around a semi-circular path of radius r in a time t is

$$v = \frac{\pi r}{t}$$

This value when substituted in the foregoing equation yields as the time interval

$$t = \frac{3 \times 10^{10} \pi m}{BQ}$$

which is independent of r. Thus, as the ion moves, it completes each half-revolution in the same time interval. By properly regulating the magnetic field intensity B, the time interval may be varied so as to coincide with that elapsing between the polarity reversals of the segments. The apparatus builds up extremely high ionic velocities without the use of unduly high potentials.

The energy possessed by a particle of mass m gm. as it leaves the cyclotron segments of radius r cm. is clearly

$$E_k = \frac{1}{2} mv^2 = \frac{m\pi^2 r^2}{2t^2}$$

and is expressed in ergs when the polarity reversal time is in seconds.

As an illustration, consider a cyclotron which is adjusted for the acceleration of hydrogen nuclei, and suppose the machine to have segments of 40 cm. radius, upon which the polarity reverses 30×10^6 times per sec. It is desired to determine the energy of the issuing proton beam. Each proton has a mass of 1.673×10^{-24} gm.; when at the edge of the segment the radius of its path is 40 cm.; and the time for $\frac{1}{2}$ revolution is $1 \div (30 \times 10^6)$ sec. Hence by the equation of the preceding paragraph its kinetic energy is

$$E_k = \frac{1.673 \times 10^{-24} \times \pi^2 \times (40)^2}{2\left(\dfrac{1}{30 \times 10^6}\right)^2} = 1190 \times 10^{-8} \text{ ergs.}$$ This is equivalent

to $1190 \times 10^{-8} \div (1.60 \times 10^{-12})$ or 7,440,000 electron-volts.

PROBLEMS

1. A flat circular coil of 30 turns, having a radius of 8 cm., is placed flat on a table top, and a current of 5 amp. is set up in the winding in a clockwise direction as viewed from above. Determine the intensity of the magnetic field at the center of the coil due to the current.

2. It is desired to neutralize, at a particular point, the vertical component of the earth's magnetic field; this component has a value of 0.7 oersted and is directed downward. For this purpose a flat circular coil is mounted horizontally with its center at the reference point. If the coil has 6 turns and a diameter of 1 ft., what current is necessary and in what direction should it be established in the winding?

3. A magnet pole of 100 units strength is placed at the center of a flat coil of 8 turns having a radius of 10 cm. Compute the force acting on the pole due to a current of 4 amp. in the coil.

4. Two flat circular coils, one of 20 turns and 12 cm. radius and the other of 30 turns and 8 cm. radius, are placed concentrically on a level surface. They are connected in series and supplied with a current of 3 amp., which is oppositely directed in the two coils. At the common center of the coils, what is the magnitude of the field intensity due to the current?

5. A flat coil 18 cm. in diameter and composed of 30 turns of wire has its plane vertical and aligned to include a compass needle at the center of

the coil. What current will cause the needle to deflect through 20° if the horizontal intensity of the earth's field is taken as 0.20 oersted?

6. A pair of long parallel wires 5 cm. apart carry currents of 20 amp. and 30 amp. in opposite directions. Compute the magnetic field intensity due to these currents at a point half-way between the wires.

7. Two long parallel wires are 1 ft. apart and each carries 15 amp. Find the magnitude of the field intensity in oersteds at either wire due to the current in the other.

8. An iron toroid having dimensions as shown is closely wound with 2000 turns of wire. What current is necessary in the winding to produce a field intensity of 25 oersteds along the toroid axis shown dotted in the figure?

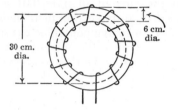

6 cm. dia.

30 cm. dia.

9. What is the value of the magnetic flux in the toroid of Problem 8 if the field intensity is considered uniform at 25 oersteds throughout its cross-section? Assume the permeability of the iron to be 600 under the conditions stated.

10. A straight wire, located within the gap between opposing magnet poles as in the diagram, carries a current of 25 amp. directed from *A* to *B*.

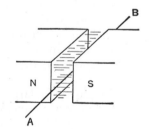

B

N   S

A

Each pole piece is 20 cm. high and 30 cm. wide, and the flux extending between them is 10,000,000 maxwells. Compute the force on the wire due to the magnetic field, both in magnitude and direction.

11. A magnet pole of 200 units strength is located at the center of a flat circular coil wound with 3 turns of 5-cm. radius. If the coil carries 10 amp., what force does it experience from the magnetic field set up by the pole?

12. Two long parallel wires are spaced 1 meter apart in air and a current of 1 amp. is established in each. Compute the force in dynes per meter of length that each wire will exert upon the other.

13. Two parallel wires are 1 ft. apart in air and the currents in them are 50 amp. and 70 amp. respectively. Compute the force which either wire exerts upon the other per foot of length.

14. A particular galvanometer produces a deflection of one division on its scale when 30 microvolts are impressed upon it. The resistance of the instrument is 500 ohms. What deflection will the galvanometer produce when it is connected in series with a dry cell having an emf. of 1.5 volts and a resistance of 1 megohm?

15. A galvanometer coil 3 cm. long and 1.5 cm. wide, wound with 500 turns, is supported as shown in Fig. 257. The magnetic field has an intensity of 800 oersteds and the suspension requires a torque of 0.09 dyne-cm. to twist it through 1 radian. What steady current maintained in the coil will cause it to deflect through an angle of 5°?

16. The moving coil of an ammeter has a resistance of 5.0 ohms and deflects full scale when the current in it is 0.01 amp. Compute the resistance of the shunt needed to make this instrument a 15-amp. ammeter.

17. The moving coil of an instrument has a resistance of 10 ohms and produces a full-scale deflection when the current in it is 0.005 amp. (*a*) Find the shunt resistance necessary to make this coil serve for a 5-amp. ammeter. (*b*) Find the series resistance necessary to make this coil serve for a 150-volt voltmeter.

18. A millivoltmeter of 1.2 ohms resistance yields full-scale deflection when 50 millivolts are impressed across it. What must be the resistance of an external shunt to convert this millivoltmeter into a 20-amp. ammeter?

19. The apparatus of Problem 10 is used to induce an emf. by moving a conductor through a magnetic field. Compute the value of the emf. induced in the wire when it is swept downward through the field in 0.05 sec.

20. In an experiment on induced emf., a bicycle wheel is placed within a magnetic field and at right angles to the flux; the wheel is then rotated, and the emf. induced in the spokes is measured. In a given test, the wheel, having spokes $11\frac{1}{2}$ in. long, was driven at 90 rev. per min., and the flux density of the magnetic field was 5000 gausses. Compute (*a*) the rate at which each spoke cuts magnetic flux, and (*b*) the emf. induced between the hub and the rim.

21. The flux density in the air gap of a large electromagnet is to be measured with the aid of an exploring coil connected to a ballistic galvanometer. The coil consists of 50 turns of fine wire wound as a flat winding having an average diameter of 3.2 cm. It is placed perpendicular to the magnetic flux in the gap and then quickly pulled out of the field. As a result, a quantity of electricity of 0.0015 coulomb is observed to flow through the galvanometer circuit of which the total resistance is 40 ohms. What is the flux density in the air gap? *Note:* The time of cutting the flux will not be involved in the result, but a symbol or any arbitrary number may be used for it in carrying through the solution.

22. To find the intensity of the earth's magnetic field at a particular location, a coil was pivoted on its vertical diameter and turned in the field, and the emf. induced in it thereby was measured. The coil used has a diameter of 24 cm. and is composed of 40 turns of wire. With the plane of the coil initially perpendicular to the earth's field, it was turned through one-quarter of a revolution in 0.012 sec.; this resulted in an average induced

emf. of 3 millivolts. What result does the test give for the horizontal component of the earth's field?

23. The N pole of a magnet is brought downward toward the coil described in Problem 1, changing the flux through the coil by 50,000 lines in 0.3 sec. (*a*) What is the magnitude of the emf. induced in the coil? (*b*) Will the induced emf. increase or decrease the current previously established in the coil?

24. A wire 5 meters long is wound in a flat circular coil of 10 turns, and the ends of the wire are connected to form a closed circuit of 0.12 ohm resistance. The N pole of a magnet is brought toward the coil, increasing the flux through it from 1200 lines to 8000 lines in 0.3 sec. Find the direction and the average values of the induced emf. and the resulting current.

25. What is the quantity of electricity which will flow through the coil of Problem 24 if the flux through the coil is changed from 500 lines to 5000 lines in 0.1 sec.; in 0.2 sec?

26. The coil of Problem 24 is suspended so that its plane lies in the magnetic meridian of the earth and is then turned through 90° about a vertical axis in $\frac{1}{60}$ sec. What is the average emf. induced in it if the horizontal intensity of the earth's field is 0.20 oersted?

27. Thomson's apparatus, Fig. 262, is used in a test with the plates PP uncharged. When a charged particle is projected into the magnetic field at right angles to the flux it experiences a lateral force and travels in a circular arc. Show that for a particle of mass m gm. charged with Q coulombs the radius of the arc in centimeters is

$$r = \frac{10^4}{B} \sqrt{\frac{20 Vm}{Q}}$$

where V is the accelerating potential in volts and B is the flux density in gausses.

28. Thomson's apparatus, Fig. 262, is used in a test with no magnetic field at the poles M. When a charged particle is projected horizontally into the electric field, it experiences a vertical force and travels in a parabola. Show that a charged particle (having mass m and charge Q) while traveling horizontally a distance l cm. in the electric field will be displaced vertically by an amount

$$s = \frac{\mathcal{E} l^2}{4 V}$$

where V is the accelerating potential in volts and $\mathcal{E}$ is the intensity of the electric field in volts per centimeter.

*29. In using a cyclotron to accelerate helium nuclei, what value of magnetic flux density should be used if the polarity of the cyclotron segments is reversed 15 million times per sec.? Assume the mass of a helium nucleus to be 6.644×10^{-24} gm.

Inductance and Capacitance

Chapter XXIV

INDUCTANCE

276. Mutual Induction.—A change of current in an electric circuit produces an alteration in the magnetic field around it, and the accompanying change in flux sets up an emf. in any circuit that may be located nearby. Such changes in current may occur from a variety of causes, such as closing and opening the circuit or varying the load; with alternating current even the maintenance of current without any alteration of the circuit involves changes of current value from moment to moment. The emf.'s induced in neighboring circuits by these current changes are often desired and the circuits are designed in such cases to develop particular emf.'s to suit the purposes intended; in other cases the emf.'s induced disturb the normal operation of the neighboring circuits, and provisions are made to minimize these disturbances.

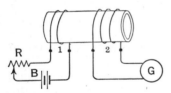

Fig. 264. Coils coupled magnetically to show mutual induction

Consider two coils, 1 and 2, to be wound side by side on a paper mailing tube, with a battery B connected to coil 1 and a galvanometer G connected to coil 2, as shown in Fig. 264; further, regard the neighboring materials to be entirely non-magnetic. So long as the current in coil 1 remains steady, the magnetic flux extending through coil 2 will be steady also, and the galvanometer will show no deflection. Now assume that the current is changed by moving the slider along the rheostat R; as a result the flux through coil 2 will change and the galvanometer will deflect. If, in a short interval dt, the current changes by the amount di_1, and meanwhile the flux linking coil 2 changes by the amount $d\Phi$, there will be induced in coil 2 an emf. that is proportional to $\dfrac{d\Phi}{dt}$, as expressed by equation (167). But the flux is proportional to the current that produces it and hence the time rate of change of flux is proportional to the rate of change of current, or $\dfrac{d\Phi}{dt} \propto \dfrac{di_1}{dt}$. Therefore the induced emf. in coil 2 will be proportional to the rate of current change in coil 1, or

$$e_2 = M\frac{di_1}{dt} \tag{172}$$

where M is a factor depending upon the magnetic coupling of the two coils and called the *coefficient of mutual induction*.

The expression above indicates that the more rapidly the current changes, the greater will be the emf. induced; this can be shown experimentally by moving the rheostat slider at different speeds. Further, if the battery (with rheostat) and galvanometer are interchanged, it will be found that an emf. is induced in coil 1 when the current is altered in coil 2. It develops that this emf. will be

$$e_1 = M\frac{di_2}{dt}$$

where M has the same value as before and $\dfrac{di_2}{dt}$ is the time rate of change of current in coil 2.

The coefficient of mutual induction, also called the *mutual inductance*, is expressed in terms of a unit called the *henry*; it is named after the American physicist, Joseph Henry (1797–1878). Two coils are said to have a mutual inductance of 1 henry when a current *change* of 1 amp. per sec. in one coil causes an emf. of 1 volt to be induced in the other.

If an iron core is inserted in the coils of Fig. 264 the results will be different in two respects: first, the mutual inductance of the coils will be greatly increased, and second, it will not have a fixed value, because a given change in current will not in general cause a proportional change in the magnetic flux in the iron (§ 282).

The direction of the induced emf. can be found by Lenz's Law. Thus, an increase of current in coil 1 is equivalent to a mechanical motion of this coil nearer to coil 2; an action that causes the emf. induced in coil 2 to be opposite in direction to the current in coil 1. Also, a decrease of current in coil 1 causes the emf. induced in coil 2 to have the same direction as the current in coil 1.

277. Self-induction.—When two circuits are close together, as illustrated by the coils in Fig. 264, a change of current in one of them produces an emf. in the second because of the accompanying change in flux linking the second coil, as already explained. It will be clear that the change of current in one of the coils will cause a change of flux not only through the other coil but also through the very coil in which the current is changing. Hence, by the process just described, a change of current *in one coil alone* will cause an emf. to be induced in that coil. As before, the emf. will depend upon the rate of current change; it may be expressed as

$$e = - L \frac{di}{dt} \tag{173}$$

where L is a factor, like M in the preceding equations, which is characteristic of the coil itself and its magnetic environment. The direction of this emf. is always such as to oppose the change of current which caused it; for this reason a negative sign is used in the equation and e is designated as the *counter emf. of self-induction*. Similarly, L is called the *coefficient of self-induction*, or simply *inductance*.

Inductance, like mutual inductance, is expressed in henries. *A circuit has an inductance of 1 henry if a current change of 1 amp. per sec. causes an emf. of 1 volt to be induced in it.* A circuit in which a large counter emf. of self-induction is set up for a given rate of current change is said to have a large inductance.

A coil of many turns of wire has more inductance than the same wire when unwound so as to form only a single loop, because the emf. induced depends not only upon the rate of change of flux but also upon the number of turns through which this change occurs. The inductance would also be increased by winding the coil upon an iron core.

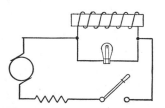

FIG. 265. Experiment to illustrate effect of inductance

The effect of inductance can be illustrated by the circuit shown in Fig. 265, in which a coil of wire with many turns around an iron core is shunted around a lamp and joined to a direct-current generator, some resistance being included in the circuit. The coil has vastly more inductance than the lamp, but much less resistance. When the switch is closed the lamp will flash brightly for a brief interval and then become dim. This action is explained by the fact that the magnetic field around the coil had first to be established and that during its formation the emf. of self-induction hindered the current growth in the coil, consequently the coil did not serve as an effective shunt on the lamp.   Again, when the switch is opened quickly, the lamp will flash even more brightly, because the large emf. induced in the coil by the rapidly decaying flux then establishes a strong pulse of current through the lamp.

For some purposes it is necessary to have coils of wire with very little or no appreciable inductance, and this means, of course, that there must be very little magnetic flux around them.   Such so-called *non-inductive coils* are wound by arranging the wire in a long "hair-pin" loop and winding the two conductors so formed side by side until the coil has the desired resistance; in this way the flux due to current in one conductor neutralizes that of the other.   The resistance coils of Wheatstone Bridges and similar apparatus for electrical measurements are usually wound non-inductively.

It is possible to state the mutual inductance of two neighboring coils in terms of their individual inductances L_1 and L_2 by means of the expression

$$M = k\sqrt{L_1 L_2}$$

where k is a constant that expresses the *closeness of coupling*.   If all the flux produced by the current in one coil links all the turns of the other coil, then there is no magnetic leakage and $k = 1$; this represents the tightest possible coupling.

*278. Inductance of a Solenoid.—The inductance of a coil of wire depends upon the number of magnetic lines that one ampere in the coil can produce.   This fact can be verified by considering the current in a coil of inductance L to change from one value to another, thereby inducing in its winding an emf. which at any instant is given by

$e = - L \dfrac{di}{dt}$ volts, as in the preceding section.   In reality the change

of magnetic flux through the coil of N turns induces an emf. having

an instantaneous value of $e = -N \dfrac{d\Phi}{dt} 10^{-8}$ volts (§ 271).   Obviously,

these equations express the same action in different ways, and therefore

$$L \frac{di}{dt} = N \frac{d\Phi}{dt} 10^{-8}$$

From this expression, $L = N \dfrac{d\Phi}{di} \times 10^{-8}$.   On the assumption that the flux grows uniformly with the current and that a value of flux Φ will be reached when the current is I, the inductance of the coil becomes

$$L = \frac{N\Phi}{I} 10^{-8} \qquad (174)$$

where the product of the number of turns N and the number of flux loops Φ linked with them is spoken of as *flux-linkages*.

This result provides a useful definition of unit inductance, as follows: *The henry is the inductance of a circuit which produces 100 million flux-linkages per ampere of current in that circuit.*

Equation (174) can be applied to a ring solenoid in which a coil of N turns is wound upon a ring-shaped core of length l and cross-sectional area A. The magnetic flux set up in this core by a current of I amp. in the coil is $\Phi = \mu HA$, where μ is the permeability of the core and H is the field intensity within it. The intensity is given in § 264 by $H = \dfrac{4\pi NI}{10l}$, and consequently the inductance, in henries, becomes

$$L = \frac{N}{I} A\mu \frac{4\pi NI}{10l} 10^{-8} = \frac{4\pi N^2 A \mu}{l} 10^{-9}$$

showing that the inductance of a solenoid varies directly with the square of its number of turns, and depends upon the cross-section, length, and permeability of the core.

279. Growth and Decay of Current in Inductive Circuits.—The rise of current in a circuit containing inductance and resistance when connected to a unidirectional source illustrates the application of equation (173). The full value of the current will not be attained instantly because of the counter emf. of self-induction. The current rises rapidly at first and then builds up more and more slowly as it approaches its final value, the entire growth occurring in a very short time.

Suppose a solenoid of 10 ohms resistance and 2 henries inductance to be connected across 120-volt direct-current supply mains. At an instant when the rate of current growth is 50 amp. per sec., the counter emf. will have a value of $e = -L\dfrac{di}{dt} = -2 \times 50 = -100$ volts, and hence the current in the solenoid at that instant will be $(120 - 100) \div 10 = 2$ amp. When the rate of current growth has fallen to 10 amp. per sec., the counter emf. will be momentarily $2 \times 10 = 20$ volts, and the current value at that instant will be $(120 - 20) \div 10 = 10$ amp. The final value of the current in this circuit is $120 \div 10 = 12$ amp.

The foregoing illustration also indicates that Ohm's Law in its simple form applies only to steady currents. A broader statement of the circuit conditions includes the counter emf. of self-induction as well as the emf. E impressed upon the circuit, as follows:

$$E = L\frac{di}{dt} + Ri \tag{175}$$

This equation may be regarded as a generalization of Ohm's Law or as an application of Kirchhoff's Second Law (§ 243) to the circuit being studied; it merely expresses symbolically the statements at the beginning of this section. At the instant when an inductive circuit is connected to an electrical source, all of the emf. causes the current to grow, for then the current i is zero and $E = L\frac{di}{dt}$; in contrast, when the current has reached its final value I, then $\frac{di}{dt} = 0$ and $E = RI$.

Equation (175) is a differential equation, and its solution for the current at any instant involves exponential functions. It will suffice to give the result, namely

$$i = \frac{E}{R}\left(1 - \epsilon^{-\frac{Rt}{L}}\right)$$

where i is the value of the current at an instant t seconds after an emf. of E volts is impressed upon a circuit having a resistance of R ohms and an inductance of L henries. In this expression ϵ is the base of natural logarithms, namely 2.7183.

When the applied emf. is withdrawn from the circuit by short-circuiting the source, the current falls to zero gradually. The current values during this period are given by that part of the foregoing equation which is subtracted from E/R.

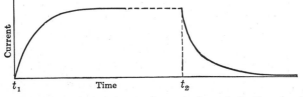

FIG. 266. Growth and decay of current in an inductive circuit

Fig. 266 shows a graph of current in an inductive circuit from the instant it is connected to a constant source of supply until the current subsequently falls to zero after short-circuiting the source. At instant t_1 a constant difference of potential is applied to the circuit and at instant t_2 the source is short-circuited.

⋆280. Energy of a Magnetic Field.—In order to establish current in an inductive circuit, work must be done against the emf. of self-induction in creating the magnetic field around the circuit. The rate at which this work is done at any instant during the period of current growth is the product of the current i already established and the instantaneous counter emf. $e = -L\dfrac{di}{dt}$. To establish the ultimate current I in the circuit the total energy expended in the magnetic field is determined by the method of integration in calculus as

$$W = \int_{t=0}^{t=t} ie\, dt = \int_{i=0}^{i=I} iL \frac{di}{dt}\, dt = \left[\frac{Li^2}{2}\right]_0^I$$

or

$$W = \tfrac{1}{2}LI^2 \tag{176}$$

The energy of the magnetic field will be expressed in joules when the current is in amperes and the inductance is in henries.

Equation (176) is analogous to the expressions for the kinetic energy of a moving mass (§ 68), and affords an energy concept of the unit of inductance. A circuit of 1 henry inductance and carrying a current of 1 amp. will have $\tfrac{1}{2}$ joule of energy stored in its magnetic field.

281. The Induction Coil.—The development of emf. in one winding by a change of current in another, as described in § 276, is the operating principle of the *induction coil*. Fig. 267 shows the two windings surrounding a straight core composed of soft-iron wires. The primary winding, represented by the heavy line, is connected in series with a battery, a switch S, and an interrupter; the secondary winding, represented by the light line, is a coil of many turns connected across a spark gap G. The interrupter is an armature mounted on a flat spring s which carries a hard metal contact a; this periodically touches a similar but stationary contact b when the spring is set into vibration. A condenser C is bridged across the contacts in order to eliminate sparking there, and thus hasten the breaking of the circuit by the interrupter, § 287.

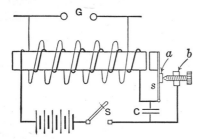

FIG. 267.   Circuit of an induction coil

When the switch is closed, the current through the primary winding establishes magnetism in the core, inducing an emf. in the secondary winding. The armature is soon attracted to the core and the contact between a and b is broken. Current in the primary winding is thus interrupted and the magnetism in the core falls to a low value (the residual magnetism), again inducing an emf. in the secondary winding. The armature is then released from the core and springs back, closing contact between a and b. This cycle is repeated as long as the switch is closed, at a rate determined by the stiffness of the spring and the mass of its armature. The emf.'s induced in the secondary produce a succession of sparks across the gap.

If no condenser were used, the opening of the interrupter contacts would cause an arc to form between them. This would be objectionable, partly because the contacts might be injured but principally because the primary current would decay less rapidly and the secondary emf. would be correspondingly smaller. With the condenser connected as shown, every time the contacts a and b separate, the electricity flows to the condenser and charges it, instead of bridging the contacts; the primary current falls off very rapidly and the secondary emf. is increased in proportion. The charge of the condenser is released a moment later when the contacts come together. The emf. induced in the secondary coil is much greater when the contacts open than when they close; as a result the discharge across the spark gap G is practically unidirectional. The discharge shows a short bright section near the negative terminal.

An electrolytic interrupter may be used instead of the mechanical one above described; it produces very rapid and sharp interruptions of current. It consists of a large lead electrode and a small platinum electrode in a solution of sulfuric acid. The intermittent formation and collapse of gas bubbles on the platinum +electrode interrupts the current. When the primary is supplied with alternating current no interrupter is needed; the induction coil is then made with a closed core of laminated iron and is called a transformer (§ 312).

282. Magnetic Substances.—The inductance of a circuit and the energy that can be stored in the magnetic field around it depend a great deal upon the properties of the region in which this field is built up. The permeability of this region to magnetic flux and the work involved in changing the flux from one value to another are both important.

Substances are classed into three groups according to their permeabilities. For *diamagnetic* substances the permeability μ is less than unity, for *paramagnetic* substances it is greater than unity, and for *ferromagnetic* substances it is very much larger. The values of μ for all known diamagnetic substances are but slightly less than unity; the most diamagnetic substance, bismuth, has a permeability of 0.99998. The values of μ for paramagnetic substances are but slightly greater than unity; for example, platinum has a permeability of 1.00002. Iron, nickel and cobalt are the ferromagnetic elements, and certain alloys are also ferromagnetic. Naturally, magnets are made of ferromagnetic substances.

To determine whether a substance is diamagnetic or paramagnetic, a rod of it is suspended between the poles of a powerful magnet. If the rod aligns itself so that its longer dimension lies in the direction of the field the substance is paramagnetic (or ferromagnetic); if it assumes a position crosswise to the field, assumed uniform, the substance is diamagnetic.

The permeability of any ferromagnetic substance is not a constant quantity but depends greatly upon the field intensity; this dependence of μ upon H is usually shown indirectly by curves, called magnetization curves, which coordinate the flux density B with the field intensity H.

A magnetization curve may be obtained for a sample of iron or other material by arranging the specimen in the form of a ring, equipped as shown in Fig. 253 with a primary winding connected to a battery and a secondary winding closed through a ballistic galvanometer. A rheostat, not shown, is connected in series with the primary coil for adjusting the current. To conduct such a test, the primary circuit is closed and the corresponding throw of the galvanometer is observed, and this procedure is repeated with constantly increasing values of primary current, starting each time with the specimen demagnetized. For each observation the field intensity H inside the specimen is proportional to the primary current, equation (161), and the flux density B can be shown to be proportional to the galvanometer throw.

Fig. 268 shows a typical magnetization curve for silicon steel, a material that is widely used in electrical apparatus and machinery. It will be observed that for low field intensities, the flux density B increases in direct proportion to H, but that for large field intensities the specimen becomes "saturated" with flux, and a large increase of H

causes only a slight increase of B. To find the permeability for a given field intensity, the corresponding value of the flux density is read from the curve, and these values are substituted in equation (163), $\mu = B/H$. Thus at 20 oersteds silicon steel has a flux density of 14,500 gausses, and a permeability of $14,500 \div 20 = 725$.

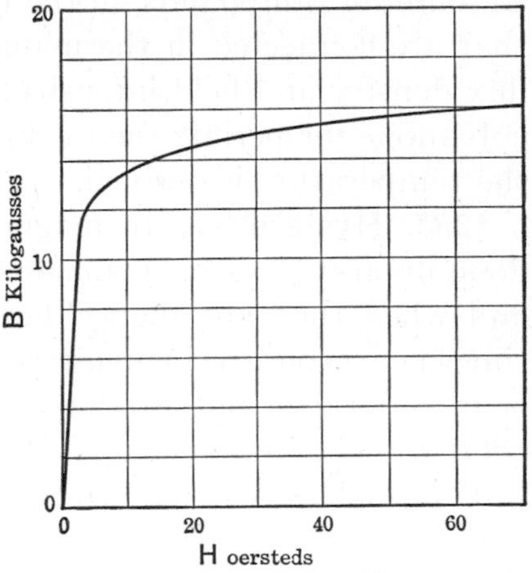

The table below lists a number of ferromagnetic materials with their maximum permeability values and the corresponding flux densities. The values are only approximate inasmuch as definite figures depend on the purity of the substance, the method of preparation, and the thermal treatment.

Fig. 268.   Magnetization curve of steel

The Heusler alloys (only one of which is tabulated) were discovered by F. Heusler, a German physicist, and are interesting in that the ingredients are non-magnetic. On the other hand, there are varieties of manganese steel which are practically non-magnetic. In these, the carbon content is about 1 per cent, while the manganese varies between 10 and 15 per cent. Iron ceases to be ferromagnetic at 770° C.

Permeabilities of Magnetic Materials

	μ_{max}	B, gausses
Cobalt...................................	170	3,000
Iron-cobalt alloy (Co 34%).................	13,000	8,000
Heusler alloy (Cu 60%, Mn 24%, Al 16%)....	200	2,000
Iron, purest commercial annealed...........	6,000 to 8,000	6,000
Nickel......................................	400 to 1,000	1,000 to 3,000
Permalloy (Ni 78.5%, Fe 21.5%)...........	over 80,000	5,000
Perminvar (Ni 45%, Fe 30%, Co 25%).......	2,000	4
Silicon steel (Si 4%).....................	5,000 to 10,000	6,000 to 8,000
Steel, cast................................	1,500	7,000
Steel, open-hearth.........................	3,000 to 7,000	6,000

An interesting application of paramagnetic substances occurs in the measurement of temperatures near the absolute zero. It is found that the factor $(\mu - 1)$ for such substances is inversely proportional to the absolute temperature, and the variation of this factor serves to specify a scale for these low temperatures. Measurements are made by placing a paramagnetic salt, like chromic alum or various gadolinium compounds, in the region under test within a pair of coils that are connected in the manner described for the measurement of flux density and field intensity. Readings of the associated ballistic galvanometer permit the evaluation of μ for the salt, and from this the temperature is derived.

*283. Hysteresis.—In magnetizing a piece of iron, work must be done upon its molecular magnets in order to change their alignment, and when they are aligned first one way and then the other many times per second, as in an alternating-current electromagnet, the work is considerable and produces appreciable heating. This waste of energy in the iron due to cyclic magnetization is called *hysteresis loss*.

The process of magnetization and demagnetization can be studied with an iron ring arranged as described in the foregoing section. If the primary current is varied, the field intensity within the iron will be altered; also, each variation of current causes a throw of the galvanometer from which the corresponding change in flux density can be determined. As the current is increased from zero to some desired maximum value, the field intensity H and the flux density B will increase as previously described, their relationship being indicated by a magnetization curve such as shown in Fig. 268.

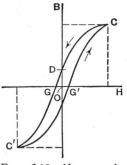

FIG. 269. Hysteresis loop

If the current is now decreased step by step the magnetization curve is not retraced but will have higher values as shown by curve *CD* in Fig. 269. When the current has been reduced to zero there will still be some flux in the ring, and the ordinate *OD* corresponding to this condition represents the residual magnetism. It would be necessary to reverse the direction of current and increase its strength to produce a field intensity *OG* in order to demagnetize the ring completely.

Next, the magnetization is increased further until the current has reached the same maximum value as before, causing the curve to continue from *G* to *C'* in the figure. The current is next reduced to zero, its polarity is reversed, and it is increased again to the initial maximum value, giving the rest of the magnetization cycle as indicated from C' through G' to C. The closed curve CC' is called a *hysteresis loop* for the sample under test, and its area can be shown to represent energy loss. If the sample were magnetized by an alternating current, then the loss represented by one loop would occur for each individual cycle of current values. Had the magnetization in both directions been carried to a lesser maximum value, the hysteresis loop would have been smaller and less loss would be represented by its area. Charles P. Steinmetz (1865–1923), American electrical engineer, showed that the hysteresis loss is proportional to the 1.6 power of the maximum flux density attained during the current cycle.

For the magnetic parts of electrical machinery, it is necessary to use soft iron or silicon steel because they have a low hysteresis loss and a high permeability under operating conditions. On the other hand, permanent magnets are made of tungsten steel, chromium steel, or Alnico, because in these materials the residual magnetism is high and because a large demagnetizing field is necessary to destroy the magnetism. A typical composition of tungsten steel is: tungsten 3 to 6, carbon 0.7, manganese and silicon 0.7 per cent, and the rest iron. The composition of chromium steel is the same except that all or most of the tungsten is replaced by 2 per cent of chromium. A typical Alnico alloy has the following composition: aluminum 10 to 12, nickel 17 to 28, cobalt 5 to 13 per cent, and the remainder iron.

284. Analogy Between Electric and Magnetic Circuits.—The fact that magnetic flux forms closed loops accounts for the application of the term *magnetic circuit* to the path that the flux loops follow. There are many points of similarity between electric circuits carrying current and magnetic circuits carrying flux. To produce a current in an electric circuit requires that it contain a source of electromotive force. Likewise, to produce a flux the magnetic circuit requires an agency called *magnetomotive force* (abbreviated mmf.). Furthermore, resistance in the electric circuit has a counterpart called *reluctance* in the magnetic circuit; its value depends upon the dimensions and material of the magnetic circuit. The unit of reluctance, to which no name is assigned, is the reluctance offered by a portion of a magnetic circuit 1 cm. long, 1 sq. cm. in cross-section, and of unit permeability.

The unit of magnetomotive force is named after the English physicist, William Gilbert (1540–1603). The *gilbert* is the magnetomotive force that would establish a flux of 1 maxwell in a magnetic circuit having a reluctance of 1 unit.   In keeping with this definition, reluctance is sometimes expressed in gilberts per maxwell.

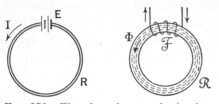

Fig. 270 illustrates the parallelism between electric and magnetic circuits. At the left is shown an electric circuit of resistance R, in which a battery of emf. E sets up a current I. At the right is shown a toroidal core of reluctance $\mathscr{R}$ and surrounded by a coil of wire carry-

Fig. 270.   Electric and magnetic circuits compared

ing a current; this magnetizing agency sets up a magnetomotive force $\mathscr{F}$ to establish a flux Φ in the toroid.   The circuits are compared in parallel columns:

Electric	*Magnetic*
$\text{current} = \dfrac{\text{emf.}}{\text{resistance}}$	$\text{flux} = \dfrac{\text{mmf.}}{\text{reluctance}}$
$I = \dfrac{E}{R}$	$\Phi = \dfrac{\mathscr{F}}{\mathscr{R}}$
$\text{amperes} = \dfrac{\text{volts}}{\text{ohms}}$	$\text{maxwells} = \dfrac{\text{gilberts}}{\text{reluctance units}}$
Resistance of a wire of length l, of sectional area A, and of resistivity ρ is	Reluctance of a flux path of length l, of sectional area A, and of permeability μ is

$$R = \frac{\rho l}{A} \qquad (147)$$

$$\mathscr{R} = \frac{l}{\mu A} \qquad (177)$$

While the parallelism between the two circuits is seemingly exact, there are important differences which make the calculation of magnetic circuits less direct.   In the electric circuit, the resistance does not depend upon the current, except insofar as it is influenced by heating.   In the magnetic circuit, on the other hand, the reluctance depends upon the magnetic flux, because the permeability is not constant.   Also, in the electric circuit, the current is practically confined to the conductors, whereas in the magnetic circuit there is usually more or less magnetic leakage through the surrounding medium, because no material serves as an insulator for magnetic flux.

285. Magnetic Circuit Calculations.—The amount of flux in a magnetic circuit can be computed when the dimensions and permeability of the circuit are given and when the characteristics of its magnetizing winding are known. Consider first a ring solenoid wound upon an iron core, and disregard any magnetic leakage. The field intensity in oersteds along the axis of such a solenoid was shown in § 264 to be

$$H = \frac{4\pi NI}{10l}$$

where N is the number of turns in the magnetizing coil, l is the length of the coil in centimeters, and I is the current in it in amperes. It has been found that the field intensity is practically uniform throughout the cross-section of the coil, and hence the flux established in the core is given in maxwells by

$$\Phi = \mu HA = \mu \frac{4\pi NI}{10l} A$$

where A is the cross-section of the core in square centimeters, and μ is its permeability. By a rearrangement of terms, the foregoing equation can be put in the form

$$\Phi = \frac{\dfrac{4\pi NI}{10}}{\dfrac{l}{\mu A}} = \frac{\mathscr{F}}{\mathscr{R}} \tag{178}$$

where the numerator represents the mmf. of the winding and the denominator represents the reluctance of the core. The product NI is called the *ampere-turns* of the winding.

Equation (178) is not limited to the ring solenoid but applies to magnetic circuits in general. The term l should be interpreted as the length of the entire core in case the winding does not cover it completely.

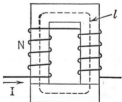

FIG. 271. Calculation of an electromagnet core

Suppose an inverted U-shaped magnet with its contacting member or armature, Fig. 271, to have a core length indicated by the dotted line of 34 cm., and a core cross-section of 8 sq. cm. The winding consists of 500 turns and the current in it is 1.5 amp. Assume the permeability of the iron core to be 540 under the stated magnetization, and compute the flux established in the core.

The mmf. of the winding is $\dfrac{4\pi NI}{10} = \dfrac{4\pi 500 \times 1.5}{10} = 942$ gilberts, and

the reluctance of the core is $\dfrac{l}{\mu A} = \dfrac{34}{540 \times 8} = 0.0079$ reluctance units;

hence the magnetic flux is $\mathscr{F} \div \mathscr{R} = 942 \div 0.0079 = 119{,}000$ maxwells.

The customary method of procedure when iron is present is to make use of the magnetization curve rather than to specify the permeability. For the magnet just considered the field intensity is $H = \dfrac{4\pi nI}{10} = \dfrac{4\pi}{10} \times \dfrac{500}{34} \times 1.5 =$ 27.7 oersteds. On the assumption that Fig. 268 applies to the iron, this field intensity yields a flux density of $B = 14{,}900$ gausses (making the permeability at this magnetization $14{,}900 \div 27.7 = 540$); consequently the total flux is $\Phi = BA = 14{,}900 \times 8 = 119{,}200$ maxwells.

CAPACITANCE

286. Capacitance of a Conductor.—A conductor isolated in space and charged with an amount of electricity Q will have an equipotential surface, § 211, and its potential V will be proportional to Q. The relationship between these two factors can be expressed as

$$Q = CV \qquad (179)$$

where C is a constant determined by the size and shape of the particular conductor and called its *capacitance*. For a charged sphere mounted so as to be undisturbed by neighboring charges, the capacitance can be evaluated easily. The field about such a body extends radially from the sphere and will have the same configuration as though its charge were concentrated at the center. The potential at any distance r from such a concentrated charge in a vacuum

($\epsilon = 1$) is given by equation (130) as $V = \dfrac{Q}{r}$, and this would necessarily be the potential of the surface of a concentric sphere of radius r. It follows that the capacitance of the sphere is

$$C = \frac{Q}{V} = \frac{Q}{\dfrac{Q}{r}} = r$$

In the electrostatic system of units the capacitance of an isolated conducting sphere is equal to its radius in centimeters. The capacitance of a conductor is increased by bringing a second conductor near it. Such a combination forms a *condenser* or *capacitor*.

287. The Capacitor.—Essentially a capacitor consists of two conductors separated by some insulating medium; the conductors are often called the *plates* and the insulation is called the *dielectric*. Capacitors are used to reduce arcing at contact points, to neutralize the effects of inductance, and to obtain pulses of current for various purposes. In an automobile ignition circuit the condenser is ordinarily composed of two long strips of tinfoil separated by treated paper. The type commonly used in radio reception consists of two sets of aluminum plates separated by air, the effective area of the plates being varied by turning one set with respect to the other.

A capacitor can be charged by connecting its plates to the terminals of a battery or other source of direct current. This will cause electrons to leave one plate and flow to the other until a state of equilibrium is reached in which the plates have a potential difference equal to the emf. of the battery. Assume each plate to receive a definite charge, one positive and the other negative, when connected across a particular battery. If a battery of higher emf. were used the charges would also be larger, but the ratio of the charge on either plate to the potential difference between the plates would remain the same. The *ratio of the charge on one of the plates to the potential difference between them is defined as the capacitance of the condenser;* it is given by

$$C = \frac{Q}{V}$$

In this expression, if Q is in electrostatic units of charge and V is in ergs per electrostatic unit of charge, C will be in electrostatic units of capacitance. Usually, however, the expression is used with the practical system of units, Q being in coulombs and V in volts; in this case C is expressed in a unit derived from the name of Faraday, the *farad*. *A condenser has a capacitance of 1 farad when a potential difference of 1 volt will charge it with 1 coulomb of electricity*. The farad is an enormously large unit of capacitance, and for convenience a smaller unit, the microfarad (abbreviated mf.), is generally used. A farad $= 10^6$ microfarads $= 9 \times 10^{11}$ esu. of capacitance.

Oceanic cables have large amounts of capacitance. The conductor at the center acts as one plate of a capacitor, and the sheathing together with sea water forms the other plate, the gutta percha and other insulating layers between them being the dielectric. Such a cable 2000 miles long has a capacitance around 0.001 farad; this is better expressed as 1000 mf.

*288. Energy of a Charged Capacitor.—When a condenser is connected across a battery, it charges very quickly and the current falls from an initially high value to zero within a fraction of a second. Its value at any instant during this brief period is

$$i = \frac{dQ}{dt}$$

dQ being the small amount of charge that was transferred in the time interval dt, when this interval is vanishingly small. From equation (179), this current can be written as

$$i = C\frac{dv}{dt}$$

showing that the momentary value of the charging current is proportional to the time rate of change of potential difference $\frac{dv}{dt}$ across the capacitor.

The energy that is supplied to a capacitor in charging it can be determined by evaluating the work dW done in transferring a small charge dQ from one plate to the other when the potential difference between them is v; this is found to be $dW = v\,dQ$ according to equation (131). If a series of amounts like this, or its equivalent $vi\,dt$, are summed up during the entire charging period t in which a potential difference V is being established across the condenser, the result is given by

$$W = \int_{t=0}^{t=t} vi\,dt = \int_{v=0}^{v=V} vC\frac{dv}{dt}\,dt = \left[\frac{Cv^2}{2}\right]_0^V$$

or

$$W = \tfrac{1}{2}CV^2 \tag{180}$$

an expression which shows the amount of electrical energy that is stored in the capacitor to set up an electric field in the dielectric. When the capacitance C of the condenser is expressed in farads and the potential difference V is in volts, the energy W will be in joules.

289. The Parallel-plate Condenser.—The capacitance of a parallel-plate condenser is determined entirely by the dimensions and properties of the dielectric, and is not affected, for instance, by the materials used for the plates, provided only that these are electrical conductors. Consider a capacitor, Fig. 272, which consists of a pair of conducting plates separated by a dielectric layer of thickness s, of effective area A, and of permittivity ϵ. Assume that the plates have charges of $+Q$ and $-Q$ and that the potential difference between them is V. The charges will be confined to the interior surfaces of the plates by

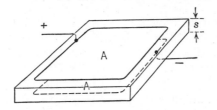

FIG. 272. Computing the capacitance of a condenser

mutual attraction, and will establish a uniform electric field in the region between them, the intensity of which is given by equation (132) as $\mathscr{E} = \dfrac{V}{s}$. In terms of dielectric flux, reference to § 210 will show that $4\pi Q$ flux lines extend from the positive plate to the negative plate, so that the number per unit area of dielectric is $\dfrac{4\pi Q}{A}$. The flux per unit area is also represented by the product $\epsilon\mathscr{E}$.

The electric field established between the plates can then be expressed not only by $\mathscr{E} = \dfrac{V}{s}$ but also by $\mathscr{E} = \dfrac{4\pi Q}{\epsilon A}$, consequently

$$\frac{V}{s} = \frac{4\pi Q}{\epsilon A}$$

Finally, since the capacitance of a condenser is the ratio of the charge on one of the plates to the difference of potential between them, that is $C = Q/V$, it follows that

$$C = \frac{\epsilon A}{4\pi s} \tag{181}$$

If the dimensions are given in centimeters, the result will be in electrostatic units of capacitance; this may be converted to microfarads by dividing by 9×10^5.

The ratio of the permittivity ϵ of a dielectric to the permittivity ϵ_v of empty space is known as the *dielectric constant* of the dielectric; the dielectric constant of a material is also commonly defined as the ratio of the capacitance of a condenser with that material as dielectric to its capacitance when the dielectric is a vacuum. Some typical values of dielectric constant are given in the following table:

Dielectric Constants

Glass, crown.......	5 to 7
Glass, flint........	7 to 10
India rubber.......	2.1 to 2.3
Mica.............	5.7 to 7
Paper, dry........	.2 to 2.5
Paraffin wax.......	2 to 2.3
Water (pure)......	81

Find the capacitance of a condenser formed of 21 square metal plates measuring 10 cm. along each edge, separated by sheets of mica 0.01 cm. thick and having a dielectric constant of 6. Alternate plates are connected to one terminal of the capacitor and the remaining plates are connected to the other terminal. The 20 dielectric sheets may be regarded as equivalent to a single one having an area of $20 \times 10 \times 10 = 2000$ sq. cm., whence the capacitance is $\dfrac{6 \times 2000}{4\pi \times 0.01} = 9.55 \times 10^4$ esu. of capacitance or 0.106 mf.

The capacitance of a condenser may be compared experimentally with that of a standard capacitor, by the use of a ballistic galvanometer (§ 268). The capacitors are charged separately from the same battery and each is discharged in turn through the instrument, the maximum throw being noted in each case. Since the deflections are proportional to the charges, and these in turn are proportional to the capacitances, it follows that the capacitances are in the same proportion as the deflections.

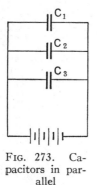

FIG. 273. Capacitors in parallel

290. Capacitors in Parallel and in Series.—Condensers are often connected in parallel in a circuit in order to increase the capacitance of that circuit. Let $C_1, C_2, C_3, \ldots$ be the capacitances of several capacitors that are connected in parallel as in Fig. 273, to form a condenser of equivalent capacitance C. The potential differences across the condensers will be represented by $V_1, V_2, V_3, \cdots$, and the charges on them by $Q_1, Q_2, Q_3, \cdots$. The corresponding potential difference and charge for the equivalent capacitor will be taken as V and Q respectively.

For the parallel connection, each condenser has the same potential difference as the source, or

$$V = V_1 = V_2 = V_3 = \cdots$$

and the total charge is distributed among them, or

$$Q = Q_1 + Q_2 + Q_3 + \cdots$$

Hence, by division

$$\frac{Q}{V} = \frac{Q_1 + Q_2 + Q_3 + \cdots}{V} = \frac{Q_1}{V_1} + \frac{Q_2}{V_2} + \frac{Q_3}{V_3} + \cdots$$

But $C = \dfrac{Q}{V}$, $C_1 = \dfrac{Q_1}{V_1}$, and so on, from equation (179), consequently

$$C = C_1 + C_2 + C_3 + \cdots \tag{182}$$

showing that the combined capacitance of several condensers connected in parallel is equal to the sum of the individual capacitances.

Condensers are sometimes connected in series in order to lessen the potential difference across them; the capacitance will be reduced by this arrangement. In the series connection of Fig. 274, the same momentary flow of electrons occurs in all of the condensers, thus giving each an equal charge, or

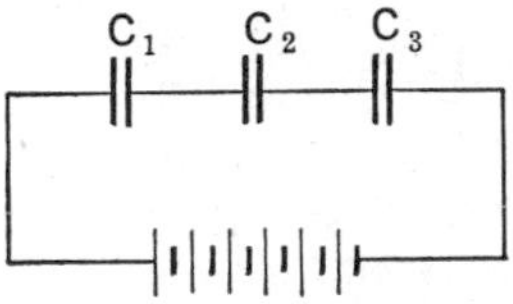

Fig. 274. Capacitors in series

$$Q = Q_1 = Q_2 = Q_3 = \cdots$$

and the applied potential difference is divided among the individual condensers, or

$$V = V_1 + V_2 + V_3 + \cdots$$

Then

$$\frac{1}{C} = \frac{V}{Q} = \frac{V_1 + V_2 + V_3 + \cdots}{Q} = \frac{V_1}{Q_1} + \frac{V_2}{Q_2} + \frac{V_3}{Q_3} + \cdots$$

or

$$\frac{1}{C} = \frac{1}{C_1} + \frac{1}{C_2} + \frac{1}{C_3} + \cdots \tag{183}$$

an expression which shows the relation between the capacitances C_1, C_2, C_3, $\cdots$, of the individual condensers and the equivalent capacitance C when these are connected in series.

Two condensers having capacitances of 3 mf. and 6 mf. are connected in series across a 12-volt direct-current source. Find the charge of each capacitor and the potential difference across each. The combination is equivalent to a single condenser of capacitance C such that $\dfrac{1}{C} = \dfrac{1}{3} + \dfrac{1}{6}$, whence $C = 2$ mf. The charge of this capacitor would be $Q = 2 \times 12 = 24$ microcoulombs, and this is the charge of each individual capacitor in the series connection. The potential difference across the 3-mf. condenser is $\dfrac{24 \text{ microcoulombs}}{3 \text{ microfarads}} = 8$ volts, and that across the 6-mf. condenser is obtained similarly as 4 volts.

In verifying experimentally the potential distribution in circuits containing condensers in series, it is necessary to use voltmeters that do not require current for their operation; a useful instrument for this purpose is the so-called *electrostatic voltmeter* in which the deflection depends upon the force action between charged plates.

PROBLEMS

1. An emf. of 5 volts is induced in a circuit when the current in a nearby circuit changes uniformly from 1000 to 200 amp. in 1 sec. What is the mutual inductance of the circuits?

2. A coil of wire has an inductance of 0.12 henry and a resistance of 4 ohms. What emf.'s will be induced in this coil when the current in it changes at the rates of 50 and 10 amp. per sec.?

3. Two coils are wound to have inductances, one of 20 and the other of 30 millihenries, and are placed so that their mutual inductance is 8 millihenries. What is the value of the coupling of the coils when so placed?

*4. A coil consisting of 400 turns of wire wound on a cardboard mailing tube has an inductance of 8 millihenries. How much magnetic flux is set up through the coil when the current in it is 3 amp.?

*5. Compute the inductance of the coil described in Problems 8 and 9 of Chapter 23.

*6. An iron ring solenoid of square cross-section has the dimensions in inches shown in the accompanying sketch. It is completely wound in the

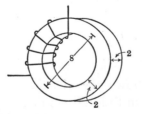

manner indicated and there are 800 turns of wire in all. If the permeability of the core under a definite magnetization is 900, what is the inductance of the solenoid?

*7. A coil formed of a single layer of wire on a wooden cylinder has an inductance of 4 millihenries. The wire is removed and the cylinder is rewound with a single layer of wire having one-half of the cross-section of the first. If the new winding has the same axial length as the first, how much inductance will it have?

8. Suppose there is a circuit which has exactly 1 ohm of resistance and 1 henry of inductance, and suppose that a unidirectional potential difference of 1 volt is impressed upon it at the instant $t = 0$. What will be the current in this circuit when $t = 0$ sec., 1 sec., and ∞ sec.?

9. How fast will the current grow in the coil of Problem 2: first, at the instant it is connected to a 12-volt storage battery, and second, when the current has reached half of its ultimate value?

10. Calculate the current in the coil of Problem 2 for an instant 0.04 sec. after connecting it to a 24-volt storage battery.

*11. One field coil of a certain bipolar dynamo has an inductance of 3.7 henries when carrying a current of 1.26 amp. Determine how much energy resides in the magnetic field of the dynamo when the current has the value stated.

*12. The energy associated with the magnetic field around a winding carrying a current is 1000 joules. The current is then reduced to half its former value, and this brings about an increase in the inductance of the coil to 40 per cent over its former value. How much has the energy of the field been reduced?

*13. The hysteresis loss in a core of sheet steel is 85 watts when there is a 25-cycle current (that is, one that reverses $25 \times 2 = 50$ times each second) in the winding around it which yields a maximum flux density of 7500 gausses. What loss will occur in this core when the winding is energized by a 60-cycle current which produces a maximum density of 10,000 gausses?

14. The core of a transformer forms a closed iron circuit having a cross-section of 20 sq. cm. and a mean length of 60 cm. for the flux path. What magnetomotive force must be provided to establish a flux density of 8000 gausses in the core?

15. If the current in the ring solenoid of Problem 6 is 1 amp., what will be the field intensity in the iron core and the total flux in it? Use Fig. 268 as the magnetization curve of the iron.

16. The magnet and armature described in § 285 are arranged to have an air gap between them of 1 mm. at each side. Neglect the change that this adjustment makes in the permeability of the iron, and compute the magnetic flux density in the core.

17. An iron rod 50 cm. long and 2.54 cm. in diameter is bent and welded to form a closed ring. Upon this core is wound a coil of 1600 turns. What current is needed in the winding to establish a flux density of 10,000 lines per sq. cm. within the core, if the permeability of the iron under these conditions is 2200?

18. Two metal spheres are isolated from each other and individually charged. One sphere, of radius 5 cm., is given a charge of $+20$ esu. and the other, of radius 10 cm., is given a charge of $+25$ esu. The spheres are next

brought into contact, so that they assume the same potential, in which process one transmits charge to the other. If care is taken that no charge is lost, what is the resulting charge on each when they are separated?

19. A ballistic galvanometer is used to measure the capacitance of a condenser. The galvanometer is first calibrated and found to produce a 160-mm. throw for a quantity of 0.001 coulomb. Then the capacitor is charged to 120 volts and discharged through the galvanometer, the throw being 78 mm. Compute the capacitance.

20. Two strips of tinfoil 3 in. wide, are placed on each side of paper 0.020 in. thick to form a condenser of 0.5 mf. capacitance. How long should the strips be, if the paper has a dielectric constant of 2.2?

21. A large plate of amber 0.15 cm. thick is placed between metal sheets measuring 15 x 24 cm. and the condenser so formed has a capacitance of 0.00060 mf. Find the dielectric constant of amber.

★22. A condenser consists of two brass plates each 20 cm. long and 8 cm. wide, separated by a layer of air 0.2 cm. thick. The condenser is permanently connected across a 4000-volt battery. Find (*a*) the charge on the condenser and (*b*) the energy stored in it. A large sheet of glass 0.2 cm. thick and having a dielectric constant of 8.5 is next inserted between the plates, completely filling the space between them. (*c*) How much additional charge will the condenser now take from the battery, and (*d*) what will be the total energy stored in it?

23. It is necessary to have a capacitor of 3 mf. in a certain test, but the capacitors on hand are only of 2 mf. capacitance. How many of these would be needed and how would they be connected to obtain the desired capacitance?

24. Two condensers of 4 mf. and 12 mf. capacitance are connected in parallel, and this combination is connected in series with a third condenser of 8 mf. capacitance across 240-volt direct-current supply mains. Find the charge of each condenser and the potential difference across each.

★25. A condenser of 1 mf. capacitance is charged by a 24-volt battery, which is then removed. This condenser is next connected across another condenser identical with the first, except that it is initially uncharged. Precautions are taken to prevent loss of charge by leakage during the experiment. Compare the initial and final states of the two condensers with regard to charge, potential difference, and stored energy. If there is a change in the total energy, how can the change be accounted for?

Alternating Currents *Chapter XXV*

291. Generation of Alternating Electromotive Force.—The production of an electromotive force in a conductor by the cutting of magnetic flux, as explained in § 271, is the basic principle of operation of all types of electric generators. Most generators at present are of the alternating type, and set up currents which traverse the circuit first in one direction and then the other, reversing their directions many times a second. An alternating emf. is produced when a conductor repeatedly cuts flux first in one direction and then in the other. The simplest way to accomplish this result is to place a coil of wire in a magnetic field between the two poles of an electromagnet, and rotate the coil about an axis in the plane of the coil and at right angles to the flux. Fig. 275 shows a simple *alternator* wherein the coil $ABCD$ rotates between the magnet poles N and S of

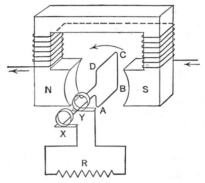

Fig. 275. Elementary alternating-current generator

the field structure. The ends of the coil are joined to *slip rings*, and *brushes* X and Y press against them, so that the coil while rotating may remain connected to the external circuit R.

At an instant during rotation when the coil is in the position shown, no emf. will be generated, since at this instant neither coil-side AB nor CD is moving across the magnetic flux. As the coil rotates in a counter-clockwise direction from this position, AB moves upward and CD moves downward through the flux, setting up small emf.'s directed from A to B and from C to D; these add together and make brush Y positive and brush X negative. The emf. keeps increasing in magnitude until the coil is horizontal, at which instant the conductors have their greatest velocity at right angles to the flux. As the coil turns farther, the emf. becomes smaller, finally reaching zero again when the coil-sides AB and CD have interchanged places.

During the second half-revolution the same effect is produced, but the emf. is in the opposite direction because AB is then moving downward and CD upward through the flux. This action continues and results in an alternating emf.

292. Sinusoidal Emf. and Current.—To investigate how the emf. of a generator varies from moment to moment, consider a coil in cross-section, Fig. 276, with the ends A and D of its two conductors facing the reader, and suppose it to re-volve at constant speed in a uniform magnetic field. As already stated, the emf. induced will be zero when the coil passes position AD, and will have a maximum value, say E_m, as it passes the axis of the poles NS, for there the conductors forming the sides of the coil move at right angles to the flux. At some intermediate coil posi-

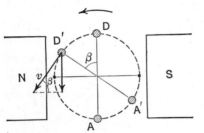

Fig. 276. Coil rotating in a uniform magnetic field

tion such as $A'D'$, making an angle β with the initial position AD, the induced emf. will have a value between these extremes of 0 and E_m; this can be found by resolving the linear velocity v of the conductor into two components. The effective component is the one that is perpendicular to the flux, namely $v \sin \beta$ as shown; hence the emf. at that position becomes $e = E_m \sin \beta$. If t is taken as the time in which the coil turns through the angle β, its angular velocity is $\omega = \beta/t$; consequently, the instantaneous emf. generated in it may be written as

$$e = E_m \sin \omega t \qquad (184)$$

This equation shows that the emf. generated by a coil rotating at constant speed in a uniform field can be represented by a sine curve with respect to time.

When such an alternating emf. is generated in a circuit, and when no other emf.'s are acting in it, the current established will undergo similar variations, and the instantaneous current i will be related to the maximum value I_m in the same way, that is

$$i = I_m \sin \omega t \qquad (185)$$

Hence a sine curve, as shown at the left in Fig. 277, may be used to represent either the alternating emf. of the generator or the alter-nating current in the circuit.

During the time that the coil rotates through 360°, a complete *cycle* of emf. or current values will be produced, and the curve will have a positive lobe from 0 to 180° and a negative lobe from 180° to 360°. The time required to com-plete 1 cycle is known as the *period*, and the number of cycles completed per second is called the *frequency*. For a coil rotating in a bipolar field and driven at 3600 rev. per min. (60 rev. per sec.), the period will be $T = \frac{1}{60}$ sec., and the frequency will be $f = 1/T = 60$ cycles per sec. The frequency and the angu-

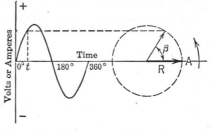

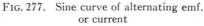

FIG. 277. Sine curve of alternating emf. or current

lar velocity of the coil are related by the expression $\omega = 2\pi f$, where the angular velocity ω is expressed in radians per second.

A sine curve can be constructed by considering a point which rotates uniformly around a circle, and projecting its successive posi-tions upon the vertical diameter of the circle (§ 92); the projections determine the corresponding ordinates of the curve. It is usual to represent an alternating emf. or an alternating current with the aid of a radius extending to such a rotating point. The radius is a vector having a length equal to the maximum value of the sine curve, and is assumed to turn counter-clockwise, making one revolution per cycle. The rotating vector R in Fig. 277 represents the sine curve shown at the left; its vertical projection after a rotation of β from the zero position at A gives the value of the emf. or current at in-stant t, as shown.

293. Effective Values.—One might well inquire how a definite numerical value can be given to an alternating current, when it actually has all values from zero up to the maximum value corre-sponding to the highest point on the sine curve. Such an evaluation is made possible through the heating effect of the current. Suppose that a direct current of 1 amp. is passed through a coil immersed in water, and that the heat produced in a given time is measured. If the test were repeated with alternating currents of different magni-tudes, a value would eventually be found for which the same amount of heat is produced in the coil over the same period. This alternating current is then said to have an *effective value* of 1 amp. Thus, in a particular conductor, *one ampere of alternating current will produce* *the same amount of heat in a given time as one ampere of direct current.*

Since the heating effect is known to be proportional to the square of the current, the effective value of an alternating current can be calculated from the sine curve by squaring all of the ordinates, taking the average of these values, and extracting the square root. The effective value, being the root of the mean square of the instantaneous currents, is also called the root-mean-square or rms. value of the current. This process is indicated in Fig. 278, wherein the instantaneous values of current i are plotted as a sine wave at the top, and the corresponding values of current squared i^2 are plotted below; the latter curve is observed to be a sine curve also, but one having doubled frequency and having its axis displaced by an amount equal to the amplitude. The ordinate of this axis is the average of the i^2 values, and the square root of this ordinate gives the effective current I.

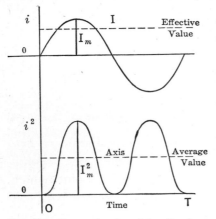

FIG. 278. Determination of the effective value of current

A definite relation exists between the effective value of a sinusoidal alternating current and its maximum or *peak* value I_m; it can be determined easily from the procedure represented in Fig. 278. Since the average of the current squared values is $\frac{1}{2}I_m{}^2$, the effective current is the square root of this amount, namely $I_m/\sqrt{2}$; whence the effective value is

$$I = 0.707\, I_m \tag{186}$$

Alternating emf.'s are related in the same manner. The maximum value of a sinusoidal emf. is represented by E_m, and therefore the effective value is

$$E = 0.707\, E_m$$

Whenever alternating quantities are expressed it is understood that effective values are meant; thus, an alternating current of 10 amperes means an effective current of 10 amperes (its maximum or peak value is 14.1 amp. if sinusoidal). Alternating-current ammeters and voltmeters are calibrated to indicate effective values.

A 25-cycle alternating current of sinusoidal wave shape has a maximum value of 30 amp. Find the effective value of this current, and also its momentary value at an instant 0.002 sec. after passing in a positive direction through the zero value. The effective value is $0.707 \times 30 = 21.2$ amp. Since the angular velocity $\omega = 2\pi \times 25$, the instantaneous current value for $t = 0.002$ is given by equation (185) as $i = 30 \sin (2\pi 25 \times 0.002)$

$$= 30 \sin \frac{\pi}{10} = 30 \sin 18° = 9.27 \text{ amp.}$$

294. Phase Relations.—In the circuits connected to alternating-current generators it frequently happens that the emf. of the source and the current established by it, although of the same frequency, do not rise and fall together. As a result there is a time interval between any point on the emf. cycle and the corresponding point on the current cycle. This interval represents an angular separation, called a *phase difference*, that may be expressed in degrees. The term phase is also applied in referring to two or more like quantities, either alternating currents or emf.'s.

Phase difference will be explained by supposing that two alternating-current generators develop the same emf. at the same frequency and that the machines are connected in series to a load circuit. If

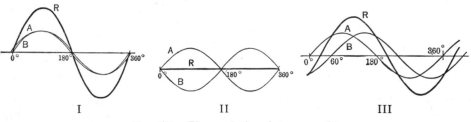

FIG. 279. Phase relations between emf.'s

the emf.'s pass through the zero value at the same instant, rise together, pass through the maximum value together, and so on, they are said to be *in phase*. The total emf. available is the sum of the two individual emf.'s. The emf. curves coincide as illustrated in part I of Fig. 279, in which the individual curves *A* and *B* are slightly displaced from each other to reveal their separate identities. The resultant emf. curve *R* is obtained by adding the ordinates of curves *A* and *B* point by point.

When the two emf.'s do not rise and fall together, they are *out of phase* with respect to each other. Part II of the figure represents the condition when one machine is generating its maximum positive emf. at the instant that the other has its maximum negative value. The curves *A* and *B* are displaced from each other by 180°, indicating that the two emf.'s are in opposition and annul each other; thus the resultant emf. is zero. In part III, the emf. *A* of one generator reaches every emf. value somewhat before *B*, the phase difference shown being 60° with *A leading B*, or *B lagging A*. The resultant emf. *R* is shown in each diagram.

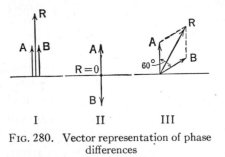

Fig. 280. Vector representation of phase differences

The phase relations shown above can be represented more simply by replacing the sine curves by appropriate vectors. These vectors are commonly drawn to represent the effective values of alternating quantities rather than the maximum values. The vector diagrams in Fig. 280 correspond respectively to the sine curve diagrams shown in Fig. 279. The vectors *A* and *B* represent two individual emf.'s of equal value and *R* represents the resultant. If *A* and *B* are in phase, the resultant *R* will be their numerical sum. This condition is represented by drawing *A* and *B* along the same line, and adding them; part I of the figure shows this addition, the vectors being separated for clearness. If the individual emf.'s are in opposition, as shown in part II, their resultant is zero. If they are out of phase as in part III, the resultant may be obtained by the Parallelogram Method; its magnitude and phase are correctly represented by *R* in the figure.

295. Circuits Containing Resistance Only.

—The current due to an alternating emf. in a circuit containing only resistance is determined by Ohm's Law (§ 231). At an instant when the emf. is zero, the current will also be zero; when the emf. has its maximum positive value, the current will also have its maximum positive value, and so on. Thus, *the current will be in phase with the emf.*, as represented in Fig. 281 by

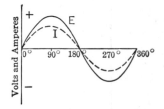

Fig. 281. Phase relations in a circuit having only resistance

the curves *I* and *E*. Also, if a part of any alternating-current circuit contains resistance only, the potential difference across that part of the circuit will be in phase with the current in that part.

At high frequencies, and particularly with conductors of large cross-section, it is found that a conductor presents more resistance to an alternating current than to a direct current. The increase is due to emf.'s which are set up by variations of flux within the conductor itself; these crowd the current toward the surface, giving rise to the so-called *skin effect*, and thereby render the inner portion of the conductor less effective than the outer layers.

296. Inductive Circuits.—It was pointed out in § 277 that whenever the current is changing in an inductive coil, an emf. is induced in it which depends upon the inductance of the coil and upon the rate of change of current. This emf., called the emf. of self-induction, has a value at any instant given by the expression $e = -L\dfrac{di}{dt}$, where L is the inductance of the coil, and $\dfrac{di}{dt}$ is the instantaneous rate of current change. With an alternating current in such a coil, the continuous changing of the current causes the emf. of self-induction to be alternating also. To show that such is the case, the expression for an alternating current will be substituted in the foregoing expression and then differentiated with respect to time. Since, from equation (185), the instantaneous current is $i = I_m \sin \omega t$, it follows that $\dfrac{di}{dt} = I_m \omega \cos \omega t$, and consequently the emf. of self-induction becomes

$$e = -\omega L I_m \cos \omega t$$

This equation represents a cosine curve, which has the same shape as the sine curve of current, but is displaced 90° from it. To verify this fact; observe that any value of time t which would make $\sin \omega t$ a maximum in the equation for current, would make $\cos \omega t$ zero in the equation for e, and vice versa. By Lenz's Law, the emf. of self-induction is directed in such a way as to oppose the change of current which produces it; thus, when the current is increasing, this emf. is opposite in direction to the current, and when the current is decreasing, this emf. has the same direction as the current. Therefore, the emf. of self-induction e lags the current i by 90°.

Evidently an inductive alternating-current circuit contains two emf.'s in series: E from the alternator that supplies the circuit, and e resulting from the inductance of the circuit. The current at any instant is equal to the resultant emf. divided by the resistance of the circuit. Vectorially, this statement may be written $i = \dfrac{E + e}{R}$ or $E = iR - e$. This is a vector equation and means that E is the resultant of iR and $-e$. The relations among these quantities can best be explained by a diagram like Fig. 282, in which the current vector i is taken as a datum or reference direction. The potential drop iR due to resistance is in phase with i; the emf. of self-induction e lags i by 90° as shown; $-e$ is equal and opposite to e and therefore leads i by 90°; and finally the resultant of iR and $-e$ gives the supply emf. E. It will be observed that the supply emf. leads the current; in other words, the current lags the supply emf.; if the circuit were

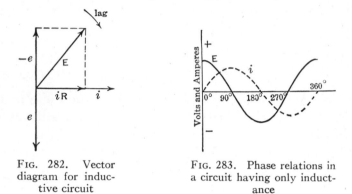

FIG. 282.   Vector diagram for inductive circuit

FIG. 283.   Phase relations in a circuit having only inductance

so inductive that the potential drop iR due to resistance could be disregarded, the current would lag the supply emf. by 90°. This result is pictured in Fig. 283.

Inductance in a circuit not only makes the current lag the emf. but *chokes it down to a smaller value* than if the inductance were not present. The choking effect will be computed by imagining a circuit to contain inductance only (resistance being neglected), in which case the emf. of the source will be $-e = \omega L I_m \cos \omega t$. This emf. will have its maximum value E_m when $\cos \omega t = 1$, whence $E_m = \omega L I_m$. A similar relation will be true for the effective values of emf. E and current I, or $E = \omega L I$. Since $\omega = 2\pi f$ (§ 292), it follows that the current in amperes established in an inductance of L henries by an emf. of E volts of frequency f cycles per sec. is

$$I = \frac{E}{2\pi f L}$$

The quantity $2\pi f L$ is called the *inductive reactance* of the circuit; in symbols

$$X_L = 2\pi f L \qquad (187)$$

where the inductive reactance X_L is expressed in ohms when the inductance L is in henries.

297. Capacitive Circuits.—A condenser that is connected across a source of alternating emf. becomes charged alternately in opposite directions, and electrons surge to and fro in the connecting wires. This means that there is an alternating current in them and for this reason alternating current is said to "flow through" a capacitor, even though the capacitor is supposed to have a perfectly insulating dielectric. An alternating-current ammeter placed in such a circuit would show a steady deflection. The condenser presents a certain reactance to an alternating current which is somewhat similar to the reactance of an inductance coil; it is called *capacitive reactance*. The value of this reactance can be derived from equations (179) and (184) in a manner similar to that followed in the preceding section; the result is

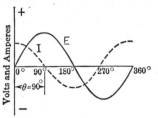

Fig. 284. Phase relations in a circuit having only capacitance

$$X_C = \frac{1}{2\pi f C} \tag{188}$$

and is expressed in ohms when the capacitance C is in farads and the frequency f is in cycles per second.

Suppose the circuit to have negligible resistance; then the current I in the capacitor will lead the emf. E of the source by $\theta = 90°$, for when this emf. starts to decrease from its maximum value the condenser will begin to discharge in the opposite direction. These relations are shown in Fig. 284, the current changing from $+$ to $-$ at the instant the emf. recedes from its maximum $+$ value.

298. The Alternating-current Series Circuit.—It has been shown that the alternating current in a circuit containing only resistance is in phase with the emf. of the source, that the current in a circuit containing only inductance lags that emf. by 90°, and that the current in a circuit containing only capacitance leads that emf. by 90°. Where all three of these elements of a circuit are combined in series, the current will be the same throughout and the potential drops IR, IX_L, and IX_C across the several parts of the circuit will add up vectorially to the emf. of the source. The relations of the potential differences in such a circuit are shown in the vector diagram of Fig. 285, wherein the datum represents the phase

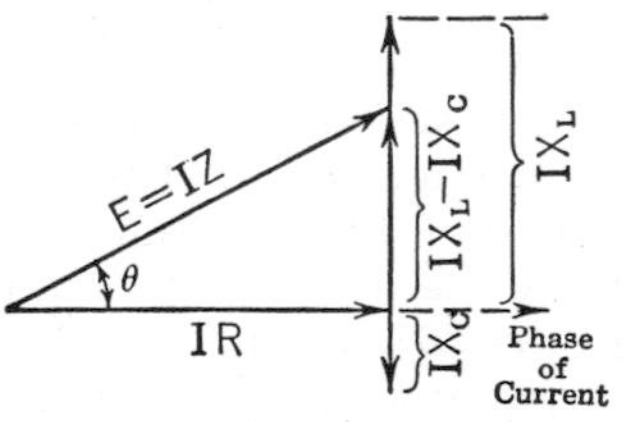

Fig. 285. Vector diagram for a series circuit

of current. The potential difference across the resistance R is *in phase* with the current and is shown as IR, that across the inductance L *leads* the current by 90° and is shown as IX_L, and that across the capacitor C *lags* the current by 90° and is shown as IX_C. The net reactive drop in potential is the difference between the capacitive drop and the inductive drop, and will be either $IX_C - IX_L$ or $IX_L - IX_C$, depending on which is the greater. This reactive drop added at right angles to the resistance drop will equal the emf. E of the source. The total opposition presented by the circuit may be expressed in a manner similar to Ohm's Law as

$$Z = \frac{E}{I}$$

where Z is called the *impedance* of the circuit, and is expressed in ohms. Its value can be obtained from the figure as

$$Z = \sqrt{R^2 + (X_L - X_C)^2}$$

The current in such a circuit is given by the general equation

$$I = \frac{E}{\sqrt{R^2 + (X_L - X_C)^2}} \tag{189}$$

and lags the emf. by an angle

$$\theta = \tan^{-1}\frac{X_L - X_C}{R} \tag{190}$$

It is interesting to note that in circuits having large values of L, X_L is large and the current is small, but that in circuits having large values of C, X_C is small and the current is correspondingly large.

To illustrate the solution of a circuit problem, consider a 20-volt, 1000-cycle source of alternating emf. acting in a series circuit having a resistor of 200 ohms resistance, an inductive coil of 20 millihenries inductance and negligible resistance, and a condenser of 0.36 mf. capacitance. The inductive reactance will be $X_L = 2\pi \times 1000 \times 0.020 = 125.6$ ohms by equation (187), and the capacitive reactance will be $X_C = 1 \div (2\pi \times 1000 \times 0.36 \times 10^{-6}) = 442.3$ ohms by equation (188); consequently the net reactance will be $442.3 - 125.6 = 316.7$ ohms. The impedance of the circuit will be $Z = \sqrt{(200)^2 + (316.7)^2} = 374.6$ ohms. The application of 20 volts to this circuit will establish a current of $20 \div 374.6 = 0.0534$ amp., or 53.4 milliamperes. It leads the emf. by the angle $\theta = \tan^{-1}\dfrac{316.7}{200} = 57.7°$.

If the capacitor were removed from the circuit, the current would be $20 \div \sqrt{(200)^2 + (125.6)^2} = 0.0846$ amp. If, instead, the inductive coil were removed, the current would be $20 \div \sqrt{(200)^2 + (442.3)^2} = 0.0412$ amp.

An inspection of equation (189) shows that when the inductive reactance and capacitive reactance are equal, that is, when

$$2\pi f L = \frac{1}{2\pi f C}$$

the current in the circuit will have its greatest value, namely $I = E/R$, and will be in phase with the supply emf. Such a condition is called *resonance*. The frequency at which resonance occurs is evidently

$$f = \frac{1}{2\pi\sqrt{LC}} \tag{191}$$

and is called the *natural frequency* of the circuit.

299. Power and Power Factor.—The power developed at any instant in an alternating-current circuit is the product of the instantaneous emf. and the instantaneous current. Consider first a capacitive circuit, in which the current I leads the emf. E by 90°, as shown in Fig. 286. From a to b, the emf. and current are both positive, and

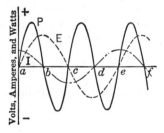

FIG. 286. Curves of emf., current, and power in a capacitive circuit

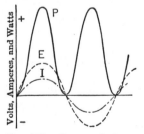

FIG. 287. Power relations in a resistive circuit

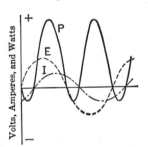

FIG. 288. Power relations in an inductive circuit

when their instantaneous values are multiplied point by point along the time axis, a positive lobe of the power curve is obtained; it is marked P and its area represents energy stored in the capacitor. From b to c, the emf. is positive but the current is negative, and their product gives a negative lobe in the power curve, the area of which represents energy being returned to the circuit as the capacitor discharges. During the second half of the emf. cycle from c to e, the situation is the same; consequently, the power curve is alternately positive and negative, and since the lobes have the same area, the net energy expended in the circuit is zero. A similar result is obtained in an inductive coil of negligible resistance; in this case the current lags the emf. by 90°. Evidently, a current that is 90° out of phase with the emf. represents no power expenditure.

A different condition exists in a circuit containing only resistance. The current and emf. in such a circuit are in phase, as shown in Fig. 287, and whether both instantaneous values are positive or both negative their product will have a positive value. The power curve is similar to that shown in Fig. 286 but is entirely above the axis and the area under it represents energy that is dissipated as heat.

For circuits in which the current is neither in phase nor 90° out of phase with the emf., the power curve will have positive lobes that are larger than the negative lobes as in Fig. 288; the difference between their areas represents the amount of energy expended.

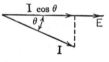

Fig. 289. Phase relations in computing power

The power supplied to a circuit can be determined most readily by representing the effective emf. and current as vectors and computing the component of current that is in phase with the emf. Thus in Fig. 289, the current I lags the emf. E by the angle θ, consequently the component of current that is in phase with E will be $I \cos \theta$. Therefore, the rate at which energy is expended in the circuit is

$$P = EI \cos \theta \qquad (192)$$

Since cos θ is a factor by which the product EI must be multiplied in order to give power, it is known as the *power factor* (abbreviated pf.) of the circuit. From the preceding equation,

$$\text{Power factor} = \frac{P}{EI} \qquad (193)$$

so that the *power factor of a circuit is defined as the ratio of the power to the product of the emf. and current;* that is, the ratio of the watts to the volt-amperes. Reference to Fig. 285 shows that the power factor of a circuit can be expressed also as the ratio of its resistance R to its impedance Z. For a circuit containing resistance only, the phase angle is 0, so that $P = EI$, as for direct currents, and the power factor has its maximum value of unity.

A highly inductive circuit has a low power factor, the current lagging the emf. considerably; a highly capacitive circuit also has a low power factor, in this case the current leading the emf. by a large angle. Low power factor is a disadvantage, because on the ordinary constant-potential circuit it necessitates a relatively large current in order to supply a given amount of power. Electrical machinery for alternating currents is always rated in kilovolt-amperes (abbreviated kva.) instead of kilowatts.

An inductive load takes 8 amp. when connected to 2200-volt, 60-cycle supply mains. The power factor has the low value of 0.75, and improvement is sought by connecting a 2-mf. capacitor in parallel with the load. Find the resulting power factor of the combination. To help in visualizing the problem, the student is advised to construct a vector diagram. Use the applied emf. E as a basis of reference, and show the current in the inductive load lagging this emf. by an angle $\theta = \cos^{-1} 0.75 = 41.4°$. Resolve this current into a component of 8 cos 41.4° = 6.00 amp. in phase with E and a component of 8 sin 41.4° = 5.29 amp. lagging E by 90°. The capacitor has a reactance of $X_C = 1 \div (2\pi \times 60 \times 2 \times 10^{-6}) = 1327$ ohms and takes a current of 2200 ÷ 1327 = 1.66 amp. which should be shown leading E by 90°. The resultant current has two components. One of these is 6.00 amp. in phase with E. The other is found by subtracting the capacitor current from the lagging component of the inductive load current; it equals 5.29 − 1.66 = 3.63 amp. and lags E by 90°. The resultant current thus lags E by the angle $\tan^{-1} (3.63 \div 6.00) = 31.2°$; this means that the power factor is now cos 31.2° = 0.855.

*300. Alternating-current Measurements.—The usual measurements in alternating-current circuits are those of current, difference of potential, and power. In particular applications and in research determinations of frequency and wave form are also needed.

In practical measurements, the effective value of an alternating current or emf. is desired and such values are indicated directly by commercial instruments that are properly calibrated. In the *hot-wire* ammeter, the current passes through a resistance wire which elongates upon heating, and this action is magnified mechanically to deflect a pointer across a scale.

The *iron-vane* instrument makes use of the fact that iron is attracted by a coil carrying current regardless of the direction of current, and hence will be attracted if the current is alternating. In an ammeter of this type the current in a stationary coil causes the attraction of a soft-iron vane, which, as it moves, swings a pointer over a scale. An instrument of similar construction is used as a voltmeter, the coil having a high resistance in series with it to permit direct connection across a supply circuit.

The *dynamometer* type of ammeter has two current coils in series, one of which is stationary. The other coil carries a pointer and is pivoted at right angles to the field of the first, being normally held in this zero position by a coiled spring. An alternating current through the instrument reverses simultaneously in both coils, and the resulting torque on the moving coil is, therefore, always in the same direction. When a high resistance is connected in series with the coils, this type of instrument can be used as a voltmeter.

The power delivered to a load connected in an alternating-current circuit cannot be measured with a voltmeter and an ammeter; for

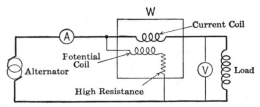

FIG. 290. Connections for measuring power factor

this purpose it is customary to use a wattmeter. This instrument is described in § 270 and operates with alternating as well as with direct currents. The torque producing the deflection is proportional to the instantaneous values of current and potential difference, and the deflection is proportional to the power delivered.

The power factor of a load circuit can be determined by measuring the power with a wattmeter *W*, the current with an ammeter *A*, and the potential difference with a voltmeter *V*, connected as shown in Fig. 290; and dividing the watts by the volt-ampere product.

The d'Arsonval type of galvanometer described in § 268 will not deflect when there is an alternating current through it, because the coil tends to turn first one way and then the other, and its moment of inertia is too great to allow it to follow the rapid reversals of the deflecting torque. The *oscillograph*, on the other hand, will respond to the variations of an alternating current and will follow its wave form. The moving element of this instrument is a single loop of fine wire, on which a tiny mirror is mounted; its moment of inertia is so small that it can respond to alternating currents of thousands of cycles per second. A beam of light reflected from the mirror permits the vibrations of the loop to be photographed on a moving film.

*301. Cathode-ray Oscillograph.—Another form of oscillograph makes use of the *cathode-ray tube*, which is somewhat similar to the evacuated tube used in Thomson's experiment for determining the charge-to-mass ratio of the electron, as discussed in § 274. The appearance of the cathode-ray tube is shown in Fig. 291 wherein the cathode C is a filament (§ 318), the anode A is a disk pierced by a hole, and the pairs of plates P_1 and P_2 are arranged in planes at right angles to each other. When the filament is heated and a difference of potential is maintained between it and the anode, an electron stream or *cathode ray* passes through the hole, travels straight ahead, and impinges upon a fluorescent screen S, producing a tiny luminous

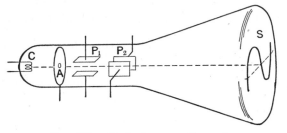

FIG. 291.   Cathode-ray oscillograph

spot. When the plates P_1 are charged, the electric field established between them acts on the electron stream and deflects it upward or downward, and when a field is established between plates P_2 the electron stream is deflected to one side or the other. If the potential differences on the deflecting plates vary, the electron stream will be deflected accordingly, and the spot on the screen will move about, tracing a luminous line that reveals the character of these potential differences.

When used as an oscillograph to show the wave form of an alternating emf., one pair of plates, P_2 in the figure, is periodically charged at a uniform rate from a capacitor and then suddenly discharged, each time sweeping the luminous spot across the screen along the dotted line and making it hop back to the starting point again. The alternating emf. is applied to the other pair of plates, thereby producing vertical displacements of the spot; the combination of the two displacements gives a picture showing the wave shape. The rapidity of the sweep motion is adjusted to the frequency of the alternating emf. in order to produce a steady image of its wave shape on the screen.

The cathode-ray oscillograph is inherently an instrument for measuring potential difference. It can be shown that the vertical deflection produced by the plates P_1 in Fig. 291 is proportional to the potential difference V between them. Let the horizontal length of these plates be l and their separation be s. The work done on an electron of charge e in moving it from C to A may be expressed as eV', where V' is the potential difference between these electrodes. This work will appear as kinetic energy of the electron as it leaves A, whence $eV' = \frac{1}{2}mv^2$, where m is the mass of the electron and v is its velocity. The time t required for the electron to travel the length l of the electric field between plates P_1 is $\dfrac{l}{v} = \dfrac{l}{\sqrt{2eV' \div m}}$. While in this field, the electron experiences a vertical force $F = e\mathscr{E}$, where $\mathscr{E} = \dfrac{V}{s}$ by equation (132). Finally, the electrons have a vertical acceleration $a = \dfrac{F}{m} = \dfrac{eV}{ms}$ and in time t will move vertically a distance $d = \frac{1}{2}at^2$. Hence,

$$d = \frac{1}{2} at^2 = \frac{1}{2} \times \frac{eV}{ms} \times \frac{l^2 m}{2eV'} = \frac{l^2}{4sV'} V$$

Consequently the displacement of the electron stream as it leaves the plates is proportional to the potential difference V between them, and this displacement determines the deflection of the spot on the screen.

PROBLEMS

1. What is the period of an alternating current that has a frequency of $16\frac{2}{3}$ cycles per sec.? If this current were passed through the coil of an electromagnet, how many times per sec. would the electromagnet tend to attract its armature?

2. A certain vacuum tube starts to operate when the potential difference applied to its input terminals rises to $+20$ volts and ceases when the potential difference falls to 0 volts. Over what fraction of a cycle does the tube operate when supplied with a sinusoidal emf. having a maximum value of 150 volts?

3. What is the maximum value of the current in an alternating-current circuit in which an ammeter indicates 10 amp.?

4. A 60-cycle alternator generates sinusoidal emf. having a maximum value of 160 volts. (*a*) What is the value of the emf. at an instant $\frac{2}{3}$ of a period after it passes through zero in a positive direction? (*b*) What would an alternating-current voltmeter read if connected across the alternator?

5. A certain immersion heater consists of a 12-ohm resistance wire encased in a metal shell. The heater is placed in 6 liters of water and an alternating current of 10 amp. is passed through it for 15 min. Assume that all of the heat produced is used in heating the water and compute the resulting temperature rise.

6. A resistor is desired to develop heat at the rate of 100 cal. per sec. when connected across 110-volt alternating-current mains. What should its resistance be?

7. Two alternating-current generators operating at the same frequency are connected in series. One generates 110 volts and the other generates 50 volts. What is the resultant emf. of the combination if the smaller emf. (a) is in phase agreement with the larger? (b) is in phase opposition to the larger? and (c) lags the larger by 90°?

8. Two alternating emf.'s *A* and *B*, of the same frequency, are in series. If *A* has the value 160 volts, and if the resultant of the two is 220 volts and lags *A* by 30°, what will be the value of emf. *B* and its phase relation with respect to *A*?

9. Three alternating emf.'s *A*, *B*, and *C*, all of the same frequency, are in series. *A* and *B* are each 120 volts and *B* lags *A* by 120°. Find the value and phase relation of *C* in order that the resultant of all three shall be zero.

10. An inductive coil of negligible resistance draws a current of 2 amp. when connected across 120-volt, 25-cycle supply mains. What will be the current in the coil when it is connected across 110-volt, 60-cycle mains?

11. A solenoid has an inductance of 0.18 henry. What is its reactance to an alternating current having a frequency of 1000 cycles per sec.?

12. Find the reactance of a 3-mf. condenser to an alternating current having a frequency of 1000 cycles per sec. What potential difference across the condenser will produce a current of 1 milliampere?

13. A 2-mf. condenser is used in a telephone set. Find its capacitive reactance (a) for the "ringing current" of $16\frac{2}{3}$ cycles per sec., and (b) for the "speech current" averaging 1000 cycles per sec.

14. (a) Compute the inductance of a coil that has an inductive reactance of 100 ohms when used on 60-cycle mains. (b) Compute the capacitance of a condenser that has a capacitive reactance of 100 ohms when used on 60-cycle mains.

15. A coil of 0.2 henry inductance and 20 ohms resistance is connected across a 220-volt, 60-cycle line. Find (a) the reactance of the coil, (b) its impedance, (c) the current in it, and (d) the angle by which this current will lag the applied potential difference.

16. A 60-cycle, 110-volt potential difference is impressed across a condenser of 20 mf. capacitance. Compute the reactance of the condenser and the current in the circuit.

17. Across a 60-cycle, 200-volt alternator there are connected in series a 50-ohm resistor, an inductive coil having a resistance of 30 ohms and an inductive reactance of 40 ohms, and a condenser having a capacitive reactance of 100 ohms. Compute the potential drops across the resistor, the inductive coil, and the condenser.

18. Across a 110-volt, 25-cycle line there are connected in series a resistance of 100 ohms, an inductance coil having a reactance of 60 ohms and a resistance of 30 ohms, and a condenser of 25 mf. capacitance. Find (*a*) the impedance of the circuit, (*b*) the current, and (*c*) the angle by which the current leads or lags the applied potential difference.

19. What inductance connected in series with a 10-mf. condenser will produce resonance at a frequency of 60 cycles per sec.?

20. Across 60-cycle supply mains are connected in series a condenser and an inductive coil which have reactances respectively of 100 and 150 ohms. What should be the capacitance of a series-connected condenser which, when added to the circuit, would establish resonance?

21. Compute the power developed in the circuit of Problem 15 and also the power factor of the circuit.

22. Find the power developed in a coil having a resistance of 100 ohms and an inductance of 0.50 henry when connected across a 220-volt, 60-cycle supply line.

23. A fluorescent lamp unit takes 0.3 amp. when connected across 115-volt alternating-current mains. If the unit draws 24 watts, what is its power factor?

24. A sodium vapor lamp is connected in a constant-current circuit in which the current is maintained at 6.6 amp. If the lamp takes 225 watts at a power factor of 65 per cent, what is the potential difference across it?

Elements of Electrical
Machinery   *Chapter XXVI*

302. Generators and Motors.—An electric *generator* is a machine that is driven mechanically, usually by an engine or turbine, and which is capable of producing an electric current in a circuit connected to it. This machine converts mechanical energy into electrical energy. An electric *motor*, on the other hand, is supplied with current from an electrical source and is able to exert a torque upon a shaft; that is, it can do mechanical work. The term dynamo is applied to either generator or motor.

The direct-current dynamo has the same physical construction for use as a generator or as a motor, except for minor differences of design and adjustment. Such a machine, if driven mechanically, will act as a generator and deliver unidirectional current to a circuit, or, if supplied with unidirectional current from a suitable electrical source, will run as a motor to operate a machine coupled to it.

303. The Direct-current Generator.—The simplest type of generator is the alternating-current machine described in § 291, consisting essentially of a coil rotated in a magnetic field and provided with slip rings for connection to the external circuit. To convert this machine into a direct-current generator of rudimentary form requires only that the slip rings be replaced by a *commutator*, to reverse the connections between the coil and the external circuit at the instants when the emf. reverses in the coil. The construction is represented in part I of Fig. 292, in which the commutator is shown as a split metal tube, one part connected to conductor AB and the other to conductor CD of the coil. Part II of the figure illustrates the action of the commutator by showing the emf. developed in the coil at different positions and the emf. available at the brushes.

When the coil moves from the position shown, the performance during the first half-revolution, represented between 0 and 1 in the figure, is the same as that of the alternator; this produces the positive lobe of the emf. curve. During this time, conductor AB has been connected to brush Y and conductor CD to brush X. Then the commutator interchanges these connections, joining AB to X and CD to Y; consequently during the second half-revolution, from 1 to 2

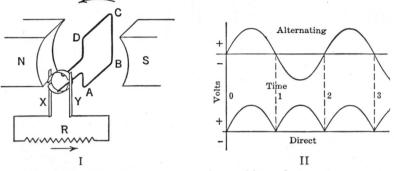

FIG. 292.   Elementary generator and its emf. curves

in the figure, another positive lobe is produced with the direct-current generator, instead of the negative lobe produced by the alternator. Therefore, as the coil is rotated, it supplies a pulsating but unidirectional current to the external circuit R.

304. Direct–current Generator Construction.—The modern generator used for furnishing large currents at constant potential is a development of the simple machine illustrated in Fig. 292. It consists essentially of a stationary *field* structure composed of electromagnets, and a rotating *armature* carrying a number of coils, together with a multi-segment commutator and brushes.

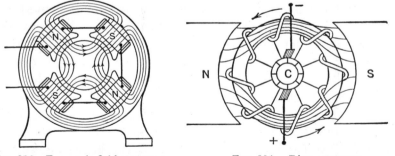

FIG. 293. Four-pole field structure   FIG. 294.   Ring armature

The field structure may have one or more pairs of poles. A bipolar field, with one N and one S pole, is shown in Figs. 275 and 292. A typical 4-pole construction is illustrated in Fig. 293; the poles are alternately N and S, and there are four flux paths as shown by the four groups of flux loops.

An early form of armature for a bipolar machine is shown in Fig. 294. The coils form a continuous closed winding upon an iron ring, and are connected as shown to the segments of the commutator *C*. Brushes press against the commutator at points midway between the pole pieces N and S, and constitute the positive and negative terminals of the machine. The magnetic lines follow the iron ring because of its low reluctance, leaving the space inside of the ring practically free from flux. When the armature is rotated, the conductors on the outer cylindrical surface of the ring cut the flux as they sweep past the poles. The conductors moving across the top and bottom are not cutting flux and no emf.'s are induced in them.

If the winding is traced from the top brush, two paths will be found leading to the bottom brush, each path containing the same number of active conductors with emf.'s so directed as to make the bottom brush positive and the other negative. These paths are in parallel and the total emf. generated by the armature is the sum of the emf.'s of the conductors on one side only. Incidentally, the armature coils as they reach positions at the top and bottom are momentarily short-circuited by the brushes, but this does no harm since emf.'s are not being induced in them at those positions.

A considerable part of the winding on a ring armature is ineffective because the conductors on the inside do not cut flux. In modern machines the ring is replaced by a drum-shaped iron core with the conductors laid in slots along the cylindrical surface, each conductor being joined to one nearly opposite it by an end connection. With this construction all of the conductors are active in cutting flux.

The generator in practical use has a large number of armature coils and a correspondingly large number of commutator segments. The advantage of this construction will appear from Fig. 295, which shows the effect of connecting in series two coils which are so located that when either coil has its maximum emf., the emf. in the other coil is zero. The instantaneous

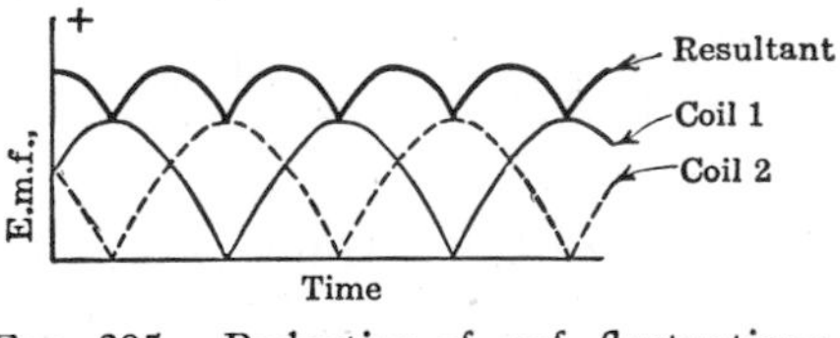

FIG. 295. Reduction of emf. fluctuations

values of these emf.'s are added and their resultant is represented by the heavy line in the figure. It will be seen that the fluctuation is less in the resultant emf. than in the emf.'s of the individual coils. By the use of a large number of coils, the fluctuation is nearly eliminated.

The number of paths in parallel through the armature of a generator is determined by the manner in which the armature is wound. For the usual type of winding the number of parallel paths is the same as the number of poles on the machine; this construction will be assumed. In any machine, the emf. will be the same as that generated in one of the parallel paths through its armature, and the total current will be the sum of the currents in these paths.

The iron structure which supports the armature coils is made of thin sheets or *laminations*, in order that the motion of the armature through the flux may not induce currents to any great extent in the iron itself. Currents induced by flux changes in metal masses are called *eddy currents*. They waste energy in heat, and thus reduce the efficiency of a dynamo.

Generator action is illustrated in the magnetic damping device shown as part of the analytical balance in Fig. 12. As the scale-pan oscillates, it causes an aluminum vane to move up and down in the field of some permanent magnets; the motion induces emf.'s in the vane and these in turn set up eddy currents in it. By Lenz's Law the induced currents are so directed as to oppose the motion that produces them and serve as an effective damper.

305 Electromotive Force of a Generator.—The emf. of any direct-current generator can be computed by finding the average emf. induced in each armature conductor and multiplying this value by the number of conductors in series in each path through the armature. When the machine is driven at n rev. per sec., it will complete 1 rev. in $\dfrac{1}{n}$ sec., and if it has P poles the entire flux Φ extending from each pole will be cut in $\dfrac{1}{P}$ of this time, or $\dfrac{1}{Pn}$ sec. The average rate of cutting flux is therefore $\Phi \div \dfrac{1}{Pn}$ lines per sec., and hence the average emf. induced in each armature conductor is $\dfrac{\Phi Pn}{10^8}$ volts. Let Z represent the total number of conductors and p the number of paths in parallel through the armature; then the number of conductors in series in each path will be $\dfrac{Z}{p}$, and hence the emf. of the generator in volts will have an average value of

$$E = \frac{\Phi PnZ}{p10^8}$$

For example, compute the emf. of a 4-pole generator driven at 1200 rev. per min., on the supposition that the machine has 120 armature conductors arranged in four parallel paths, and that 4,800,000 lines of flux extend from each magnet pole. Rather than solve the problem by substituting in the equation above, it will be more instructive to follow the steps in its derivation. For this generator, each conductor makes 1 rev. in $\frac{1}{20}$ sec. and cuts the flux of 4,800,000 lines in one-fourth of this time or $\frac{1}{80}$ sec. The average emf. per conductor is $48 \times 10^5 \div \left(\frac{1}{80} \times 10^8 \right) = 3.84$ volts, and since there are $120 \div 4 = 30$ conductors in series in each armature path, the average emf. of the generator is $3.84 \times 30 = 115.2$ volts.

Expressions such as the foregoing are of value in analyzing the action of a machine. Thus, for a given generator, the quantities P, Z, and p in this equation are fixed, showing that the emf. is determined by the speed and flux, or

$$E \propto n \times \Phi$$

The emf. induced in the armature conductors can be raised or lowered by driving them faster or slower, or by increasing or decreasing the flux which they cut. In practice, the speed of a generator is determined by that of the driving engine or other prime mover, and the emf. of the machine is adjusted by changing the flux. This is accomplished by varying the current in the field coils with a rheostat. To show the effect of field-current variation in a generator driven at constant speed, consider first the field circuit to be open; under this condition only a small emf. is generated by the armature conductors in cutting the residual magnetic flux. When a current is set up in the field, the emf. becomes greater, and as the field current is increased step by step the flux, and hence the emf., will increase in proportion. Finally, however, a value of field current will be reached for which the iron approaches saturation (see Fig. 268). Beyond this, an increase of field current will increase the flux density but little, and, therefore, saturation limits the emf. which can be generated.

*306. The Shunt Generator.—The field winding of a direct-current generator is usually supplied with current from the armature of the machine itself. This is done in the *shunt-wound* generator by shunting the field coils across the armature terminals B and D as shown in part I of Fig. 296, and in the simplified diagram, part II. With these connections, a small part of the current supplied by the generator is used to excite its own field.

Suppose that such a generator is producing an emf. E, and that its armature, of resistance R_a, is supplying a current I_a. A small drop in potential, I_aR_a, occurs in the armature itself. Consequently,

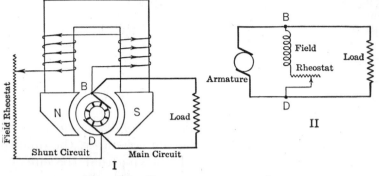

FIG. 296.   Shunt generator connections

the potential difference V_t across the machine terminals will be smaller than the emf. generated by this amount, or

$$V_t = E - I_aR_a \tag{194}$$

This equation shows that as the load on the generator increases' thereby increasing the armature current I_a, the potential difference across its terminals V_t must fall off.   It is also lowered by the reduction in the field current and by the magnetizing action of the current in the armature conductors, an effect which is treated in electrical engineering texts.

307. The Direct-current Motor.—The fundamental principle upon which every electric motor operates is stated in § 266; briefly it is that a conductor carrying a current and appropriately placed in a magnetic field experiences a sidewise thrust.   The magnitude of this force on a conductor of length l cm., carrying a current of I amp., and placed at right angles to a magnetic flux of density B lines per sq. cm. is given by equation (164) as $F = \dfrac{BIl}{10}$ dynes.   The direction of the force can be determined by reference to Fig. 255.   If the current in the wire is directed toward the observer, and the magnetic flux is directed from left to right, the wire will be forced upward.

Fig. 297 illustrates the armature conductors within the field of a bipolar motor.   A commutator (not shown) keeps the current in the right-hand belt of conductors directed toward the observer and that in the left-hand belt directed away from him.   It will be seen that the conductors at the right are forced upward and those at the left are forced downward. Each conductor experiences a torque determined by the force acting upon it and the lever arm of this force about the axis of rotation. These torques all have the same direction, counterclockwise in the present instance, and may be added to give the total torque developed by the armature which enables it to turn a shaft and drive a mechanical load.

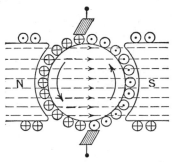

FIG. 297. Direction of torque in armature

For a given motor, the torque will depend upon two factors: first, the current in the armature conductors; and second, the density of the flux in which they are located, or, just as truly, the total flux extending from a pole face. Let these quantities be I_a and Φ respectively; then the torque is

$$T \propto I_a \times \Phi$$

The horsepower output of the motor can be determined as described in § 74 by measuring the torque with a band brake placed around a pulley and measuring the speed with a revolution counter or tachometer.

308. The Shunt Motor.—A direct-current motor in which the field coils are connected in parallel with the armature, as shown in Fig. 298, is called a *shunt motor*. Current is supplied through a starting device which first connects the field winding across the mains and then joins the armature to them through starting resistors that are gradually cut out of circuit. The field current can be computed directly by Ohm's Law, by dividing the potential difference V_t across the field by the field resistance R_f; that is, $I_f = V_t/R_f$. To find the current in the armature requires further consideration.

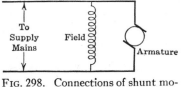
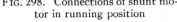

FIG. 298. Connections of shunt motor in running position

As the armature rotates, even though it turns by virtue of its own motor action, its conductors cut magnetic flux and an emf. is induced in them, just exactly as in the armature of a generator. To determine the direction of this emf., suppose the currents in the armature conductors to be directed as shown in Fig. 297, driving the armature

in a counter-clockwise direction. From Lenz's Law, explained in
§ 272, it will be found that the emf. induced in each conductor is
opposite to the direction of the current. As a motor rotates, therefore, a *counter emf.* is induced in its armature that depends primarily
upon its speed; its value can be calculated in the same way as for a
generator. If the motor is connected across supply mains which
provide a difference of potential V_t at the motor terminals, and if E_c
is the counter emf., the net potential difference acting to produce
current in the armature will be $V_t - E_c$, and the current through
the armature of resistance R_a will be

$$I_a = \frac{V_t - E_c}{R_a} \tag{195}$$

If the mechanical load on a motor is increased, the machine automatically develops a larger torque. This action may be explained
as follows: The increased load exerts an increased backward torque
on the armature, causing it to slow down somewhat, and thereby
reducing the counter emf. induced in it. As a result, the net potential
difference becomes greater, causing the armature current to increase,
and thereby a larger torque is developed. The motor, therefore, takes
more armature current and drives the greater load at a slightly
reduced speed.

As a typical example, suppose a shunt motor operating on a 230-volt
line to have a field resistance of 100 ohms and an armature resistance of
0.15 ohm, and to be rotating at a speed such that its counter emf. is 228
volts. The field current will be $I_f = \dfrac{230}{100} = 2.30$ amp. and the armature
current will be $I_a = \dfrac{230 - 228}{0.15} = 13.3$ amp. If the load is increased so
that the counter emf. falls to 223 volts, the armature current will become
46.7 amp. Thus, a drop from 228 to 223 volts increases the current from
13.3 to 46.7 amp.

Just as a motor when turning develops a counter emf., so also a
generator which is delivering current sets up an opposing torque.
This fact can be verified easily by noting that in a generator under
load, the armature conductors carry current and are located in a
magnetic field; a study of the distribution of flux will show that the
torque set up is opposite to the direction of rotation. This torque
must be overcome by the driving engine, and the engine must do
more work as the electrical load on the generator is increased.

Shunt motors operate at fairly constant speed and are applied to wood-working machinery, lathes, drills, printing presses, and installations where heavy mechanical loads are not applied until the motor is running. There are other types of direct-current motors having different operating characteristics; their description and fields of application are to be found in texts on electrical engineering.

309. The Alternating-current Generator.—The simple alternating-current generator, or alternator, was described in § 291 and consists essentially of a coil rotated as an armature in a stationary magnetic field and provided with slip rings for connection to the external circuit. The modern alternator is a development of this simple machine, but usually the field coils rotate and the armature is stationary. The desired emf. is obtained by having a sufficient number of armature coils connected in series, these coils being placed in slots along the inner surface of a laminated iron structure called the *stator*. Fundamentally, the operation is the same whether the field or the armature constitutes the rotating element or *rotor*.

The *synchronous speed* of an alternator is the speed at which the generated emf. will have its rated frequency. In a 2-pole machine a cycle of emf. values, representing 360 *electrical degrees*, will be produced in each revolution of the rotor. In a 4-pole machine two cycles will be produced in one revolution, and in general, in a machine having P poles there will be $P \div 2$ cycles generated per revolution. If the machine is driven at a speed of n rev. per sec., the frequency in cycles per second will be

$$f = \frac{Pn}{2} \tag{196}$$

In this country the standard frequencies are 25 and 60 cycles per sec. Alternators that are to be driven at slow speeds must be designed with many pairs of poles in order that they may have standard frequency.

The alternator shown in Fig. 275 generates a single alternating emf. and is called a *single-phase* machine to distinguish it from the more usual type of alternator which generates two or three alternating emf.'s at the same time, and which is called a *polyphase alternator*. These emf.'s have the same magnitude and have definite phase relations with each other.

The two-phase alternator consists of two independent sets of coils mounted 90 electrical degrees apart, so that in a bipolar field, they would be at right angles to each other. Upon driving such a machine, each set of coils generates an alternating emf., and because of the relative positions of the coils, the emf.'s are 90° apart in phase. These emf.'s are plotted with respect to time in Fig. 299. The ma-

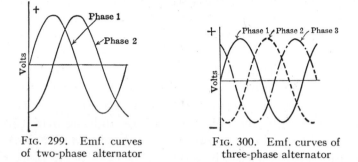

Fig. 299. Emf. curves of two-phase alternator

Fig. 300. Emf. curves of three-phase alternator

chine has four terminals so that it may supply a four-wire circuit, the potential difference across one pair of wires being displaced from that across the other pair as indicated. Sometimes one wire is common to the two phases.

The three-phase alternator consists of three like sets of coils, symmetrically placed on the armature so as to produce three equal emf.'s that are 120 electrical degrees apart in phase as shown in Fig. 300. Such a machine has three and sometimes four terminals, rather than six, because the armature coils are interconnected.

★310. Polyphase Connections.—There are two ways in which the windings of a three-phase machine are usually connected. In one of these, called the Y-connection, one end of each winding is joined

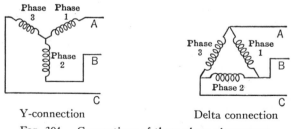

Y-connection

Delta connection

Fig. 301. Connections of three-phase alternators

to a common point, and the three line wires are connected to their other ends, as shown at the left in Fig. 301. With this connection the current in any line A, B, or C, is the same as that in the corresponding phase winding 1, 2, or 3; and the emf. acting between any two lines is $\sqrt{3}$ times the emf. in one of the phase windings. For instance, the emf. between A and B is found by combining the emf.'s in windings 1 and 2; these differ in phase by 120° but one is reversed with respect to the other and so must be subtracted from it.

The other method of connecting the armature windings of a three-phase alternator is to arrange them in a closed delta or triangle, from the corners of which the line wires are brought out. This so-called delta connection is shown at the right of the figure. The emf. acting between any two lines AB, BC, or CA, is the same as the emf. in one of the phase windings 1, 2, or 3, and the line currents are $\sqrt{3}$ times the currents in the phase windings.

The total power developed in a three-phase alternator is the sum of the amounts of power developed in its phase windings. Expressed in terms of the line values, which can be directly measured, the power developed in a three-phase generator is

$$P = \sqrt{3}\ EI \cos \theta \tag{197}$$

where E represents the emf. acting between any pairs of lines, I is the line current, and θ is the phase angle between E and I. This equation for the power developed by a generator assumes that the load is the same on all three phases.

*311. The Induction Motor.—The most widely used alternating-current motor is the *polyphase induction motor*. It consists essentially

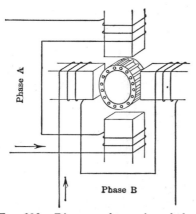

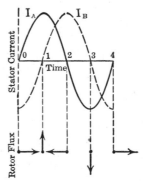

Fig. 302. Diagram of two-phase induction motor

Fig. 303. Current and flux relations in two-phase motor

of a stationary field structure and a rotating element as shown pictorially in Fig. 302. The rotor is usually formed of heavy copper bars welded to end rings and embedded in iron laminations; the latter are not shown in the figure. The resemblance of the rotor to a squirrel cage accounts for naming the machine a "squirrel-cage" motor. The windings on alternate poles are connected to one phase, and the windings on the others are connected to the other phase, of a two-phase supply circuit. The positive directions of the currents through the motor are indicated by the arrows.

The motor currents are shown graphically by curves I_A and I_B in Fig. 303, and the flux through the rotor produced by them is shown by the arrows at the bottom. At the instant indicated by 0 on the curves, $I_A = 0$ and I_B has its maximum negative value, and the flux will be horizontally directed toward the right. After $\frac{1}{4}$ cycle, $I_B = 0$ and I_A has its maximum positive value as indicated by 1 on the curves; the flux will now be directed upward. At the instant corresponding to 2 on the curves, $I_A = 0$ again and I_B is positive, directing the flux horizontally toward the left, and so on. In this manner, the same effect is produced upon the rotor as if the flux through it were rotating mechanically. The result is to induce currents in the rotor bars in such directions as to make the rotor follow the rotating field.

The rotor will not rotate as fast as the field, for if it did no magnetic flux would be cut by the rotor bars and no current would be set up in them. The difference between the actual rotor speed and the synchronous speed of the rotating field is called the *slip* of the motor. As the load on the motor is increased, the machine slows down a little, thereby increasing the slip and causing larger currents to be induced in the rotor; these larger currents set up a greater torque, enabling the motor to drive the increased load.

The three-phase induction motor is similar in construction and performance to the two-phase machine but has three sets of windings for connection to a three-phase supply circuit; it is the type most frequently used. The polyphase induction motor has characteristics similar to those of the direct-current shunt motor, but it does not require brushes.

The induction motor, operating close to synchronous speed, would continue to rotate if one phase were disconnected, for the alternations of flux at the poles still energized would be properly timed to give unidirectional torque. Such a machine would not start on a single-phase circuit. There are, however, induction motors specially designed to start and operate on single-phase supply lines; this type of motor makes use of a built-in starting device which is automatically cut out of circuit when the motor comes up to speed.

312. Transformers.—In transmitting electrical power over long distances, it is of advantage to use large potential differences, because a given amount of power can be transmitted with a correspondingly small current, thus reducing heating loss in the transmitting lines, and permitting the use of relatively small line wires. Transformers are used to change the potential difference from one value to another; in power transmission they step it up to a high value at the alternator end of a line and step it down at the other end to a suitable value for the apparatus in the consumer's premises.

The transformer consists essentially of two coils of wire, entirely separate electrically but wound upon the same core of laminated iron, as represented in the diagram, Fig. 304. The primary winding is connected to the power supply mains and the secondary winding is connected to the load circuit. The alternations of the primary current set up an alternating flux in the core, and the continual build-ing up and collapsing of this flux induces an emf. in the secondary coil. The value of this emf. depends upon the number of turns N_2 of the secondary coil and upon the rate of change of flux $\dfrac{d\Phi}{dt}$ through its turns, in accordance with equation (168), which gives

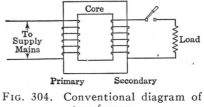

Fig. 304. Conventional diagram of transformer

$$e_2 = -N_2 \frac{d\Phi}{dt} \times 10^{-8} \text{ volts.}$$

The variations of flux which produce the secondary emf. also affect the primary coil of N_1 turns and induce in it an emf.

$$e_1 = -N_1 \frac{d\Phi}{dt} \times 10^{-8} \text{ volts.}$$ This emf., by Lenz's Law, opposes the impressed potential difference, in somewhat the same manner as the counter emf. of a motor. This explains the fact that a transformer under no load takes very little current from the supply circuit, for the emf. induced in the primary coil is very nearly equal to the potential difference of the supply; for practical purposes they may be considered equal. The foregoing expressions may be combined and changed to effective values of emf., yielding

$$\frac{E_1}{E_2} = \frac{N_1}{N_2} \tag{198}$$

which shows that the emf.'s in the transformer coils are directly proportional to the numbers of turns on their windings.

Upon connecting a load across the secondary winding, the emf.
induced in that coil will set up a current. This current will oppose
the magnetizing effect of the primary current, and will reduce the
flux in the transformer core slightly. As a result, the counter emf.
induced in the primary winding is lessened, and more current is taken
from the supply mains. In this manner the input to a transformer
automatically accommodates itself to the output.

The efficiency of transformers is very high, as might be expected
from the absence of moving parts, and values from 95 to 99 per cent
are usual. Most transformers have but little effect upon the power
factor of a circuit. Therefore, if losses are disregarded, the input
volt-amperes will equal the output volt-amperes, or $E_1 I_1 = E_2 I_2$,
whence from equation (198)

$$\frac{I_1}{I_2} = \frac{N_2}{N_1} \tag{199}$$

showing that the primary and secondary currents, I_1 and I_2, are inversely proportional to the numbers of turns on their respective
coils. The rating of transformers in kilovolt-amperes may be taken
for practical purposes to represent either the input or the output.

As an example, suppose that a 10-kva. transformer with 900 primary
turns and 90 secondary turns is connected across 2200-volt alternating-
current supply mains and that it is delivering its rated load. By equation
(198), $2200 \div E_2 = 900 \div 90$, whence the secondary emf. is $E_2 = 220$
volts. At full load, $E_1 I_1 = E_2 I_2 = 10,000$ volt-amperes; hence the primary
and secondary currents are respectively 4.55 amp. and 45.5 amp.

Transformers used in electric welding have massive secondary
windings of one turn or a few turns in order to produce large currents,
and the parts to be welded form a part of the secondary circuit.

313. Rectifiers.—It is frequently necessary to convert an alternating current into one that is unidirectional; for this purpose non-rotating
devices, called rectifiers, are commonly used. Rectifiers find application principally in charging storage batteries and operating low-
potential electrochemical processes from alternating-current supply
mains. Some rectifiers are electronic in action and their consideration is deferred to the following chapter. Others are based upon the
rectifying action of a "barrier layer," as in the selenium and the
copper-oxide types.

In the selenium rectifier, a thin coating of selenium is applied to one side of a supporting plate of steel, and the selenium is itself covered with an alloy except around the edges, which are left bare for insulation. The selenium and alloy serve as the two electrodes, and the barrier layer is the very thin film which exists at their interface.

When the rectifier is connected to an alternating-current circuit, the selenium and the alloy become alternately positive and negative. The alloy is a good conductor, and when it is negative its free electrons are driven through the barrier layer to the selenium with comparative ease. The selenium, on the other hand, is only a semi-conductor and has few free electrons, so that when it becomes negative the flow practically ceases. In this way conduction is established in one direction only.

The copper-oxide rectifier operates in a similar manner. In this device one electrode is of copper and the other is of cuprous oxide; electrons pass easily from the copper to the oxide but not in the reverse direction.

PROBLEMS

1. Construct a graph showing the relation between emf. and time for the generator in Fig. 292; suppose the coil to be a 10-cm. square and to be turned at 100 rev. per min. in a uniform field of 2000 gausses.

2. A bipolar generator has square pole pieces measuring 20 cm. on each edge and an armature 18 cm. in diameter with 150 conductors arranged in two parallel paths. The flux density in the air gap is 10,000 gausses. Compute the emf. of the generator when driven at 1200 rev. per min.

3. A 4-pole generator has pole pieces 100 sq. in. in cross-section and an armature with 120 conductors in 4 parallel paths. The flux density in the air gap is 50,000 lines per sq. in. At what speed will the armature generate an emf. of 230 volts?

4. Compute the instantaneous emf. induced in one of the armature conductors of the generator in Problem 2 at an instant when the conductor is moving perpendicularly through the flux; also the average emf. induced in the conductor during the half-revolution in which it sweeps past a pole face.

5. What is the flux density in the air gap of a bipolar shunt generator which has square pole pieces measuring 16 cm. on each edge, if the machine has 128 armature conductors and generates an emf. of 120 volts when driven at 1800 rev. per min.? The armature has a resistance of 0.12 ohm and is delivering its full-load current of 25 amp.; the field winding has a resistance of 100 ohms.

6. For the generator of Problem 5, how much heat is evolved per sec. in one of the parallel paths in the armature under the conditions stated?

★7. For the generator of Problem 5, compute (*a*) the potential difference across the terminals, and (*b*) the current in the field winding.

8. The armature of a bipolar shunt motor is 24 cm. in diameter and supports 100 conductors each carrying 20 amp. It revolves at 1200 rev. per min. between square pole faces measuring 25 cm. on each edge, in a field of flux density 8000 lines per sq. cm. Assume that each conductor moves at right angles to the flux, and compute (*a*) the torque developed by the armature, (*b*) the work done in 1 rev., and (*c*) the horsepower supplied by the motor.

9. If the machine described in Problem 2 operates as a motor, what torque will be developed by one of the armature conductors at a moment when it moves at right angles to the flux and carries a current of 20 amp.?

10. A shunt motor connected to 120-volt supply mains has an armature resistance of 0.20 ohm and a field resistance of 160 ohms, and is generating a counter emf. of 114 volts. Compute (*a*) the armature current, (*b*) the field current, and (*c*) the total current taken by the motor.

11. The armature of a shunt motor has a resistance of 0.25 ohm and takes 12 amp. from 120-volt supply mains when turning at 1080 rev. per min. If the motor slows down to 1070 rev. per min. when the load upon it is increased, what armature current will it then take?

12. A shunt motor having a field resistance of 180 ohms and an armature resistance of 0.15 ohm takes a current of 20 amp. when connected across 120-volt mains. Compute (*a*) the field current, (*b*) the armature current, (*c*) the counter emf., (*d*) the power wasted in heat in the field circuit, and (*e*) the power wasted in heat in the armature circuit.

13. If the output of the motor described in Problem 12 is 2.75 hp., what is its efficiency?

14. Compute the counter emf. of the motor described in Problem 8, under the conditions stated.

15. (*a*) What is the synchronous speed of a 6-pole, 25-cycle generator? (*b*) How many poles must an alternator have in order to generate 60 cycles per sec. while driven at 120 rev. per min.?

★16. An inductive load of 0.7 power factor is supplied by a 3-phase alternator which maintains 220 volts between each pair of lines. What is the power supplied to the load if the current is 25 amp. in each line?

★17. A three-phase, delta-connected induction motor operating on 440-volt supply mains has a power factor (lagging) of 0.75 and an efficiency of 0.80 when delivering 10 hp. What is the line current?

18. A transformer rated 20 kva. has 1900 turns on its primary coil and 55 turns on its secondary coil. When 4150 volts are impressed upon the primary winding, what is the secondary emf. and what are the full-load primary and secondary currents? Disregard losses.

19. A 10:1 step-down transformer operating on a 2200-volt primary circuit supplies a load which takes 8.5 kw. at a power factor of 0.85. Assume the transformer to operate at 100 per cent efficiency and compute the current in its primary winding.

Thermoelectricity and Thermionics

Chapter XXVII

314. Thermoelectric Effects.—It is known that two different metals placed in contact with each other assume slightly different potentials. This phenomenon, discovered by Volta, is now explained as a transfer of the free electrons that are present in all metals. These electrons in their rapid and haphazard motion cross the boundary between the metals and they pass more readily in one direction than the other, thereby making one metal negative and leaving the other positive. The difference of potential between the metals, spoken of as *contact potential difference*, depends upon the metals used, and is also influenced by the temperature of the junction.

It is this contact potential difference that explains three thermoelectric effects which have been known for many years. The most important of these, called the Seebeck Effect, is the production of an emf. in a circuit formed of two wires of different metals when their junctions are at different temperatures. Another, the Peltier Effect, accounts for the unequal heating of the junctions of a circuit formed of two different metals when a current traverses the circuit. The third, called the Thomson Effect, deals with the development of an emf. in a circuit formed of a single metal, when there is a temperature gradient along its length.

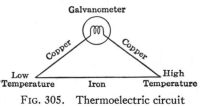

FIG. 305. Thermoelectric circuit

315. The Seebeck Effect.—When a circuit is formed of two wires of different metals and one of their junctions is at a higher temperature than the other an emf. is produced in the circuit; this effect was discovered by the German physicist, Thomas J. Seebeck (1770–1831). Fig. 305 shows an iron wire and a copper wire joined to form a thermocouple, with the circuit completed through a galvanometer to indicate the emf. produced. Assume the low-temperature junction to be kept at 0° C. while the temperature of the other junction is raised. Because of the thermo emf. a current will be observed which has a clockwise direction for the circuit shown in the figure. As the high-temperature junction is heated more and more, the thermo emf. increases to a maximum value, then diminishes to zero, and increases again in the opposite direction. Fig. 306 shows these values as computed from data given in the International Critical Tables; the resulting curve is approximately a parabola. For a given pair of metals, the thermo emf. depends upon the temperatures of the two junctions; it is also affected by structural changes in the metals such as are produced by heat treatment, rolling, drawing, and pressure.

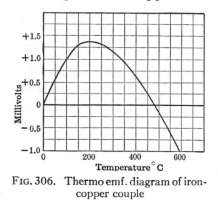

FIG. 306. Thermo emf. diagram of iron-copper couple

The temperature at which the thermo emf. of a couple has a maximum (or minimum) value is called the *neutral point*, and the temperature at which this emf. reverses is called the *inversion point*. For the iron-copper couple these temperatures are approximately 205 and 480° C. respectively. Other pairs of metals behave similarly and have their own characteristic neutral and inversion temperatures.

The slope of the thermo emf. curve at any temperature is called the *thermoelectric power* of the couple; it is the ratio of the emf. produced at that temperature to the temperature difference between the junctions of the couple. Thus, for the iron-copper couple the thermoelectric power is 13.7 microvolts per degree at 0° C. and 3.7 microvolts per degree at 150° C.

Electromotive forces that are produced by couples formed of any two metals can be ascertained from a knowledge of their thermoelectric powers with respect to some metal chosen as a standard, such as lead or platinum. For this purpose graphs of thermoelectric power against temperature are useful. Fig. 307 shows such graphs for a few metals against lead; they are straight lines over the temperature range shown. An example will clarify the procedure.

Consider an iron-copper couple over the range from 0 to 150° C. From the figure the thermoelectric power for iron falls from a value of 16.5 microvolts per degree at 0° to 8.1 at 150° C., and that for copper rises from a value of 2.8 microvolts per degree at 0° C. to 4.4 at 150° C. It follows that the total emf. generated by an iron-lead couple over this temperature range is the average of 16.5 and 8.1 microvolts per degree multiplied by 150 degrees, or 12.3 × 150 = 1845 microvolts; similarly the total emf. of a copper-lead couple over the same range is 3.6 × 150 = 540 microvolts. Consequently, the emf. of an iron-copper couple would be 1845 − 540 = 1305 microvolts; see also Fig. 306. The same result is obtained by computing the area between the graphs for iron and copper in Fig. 307 over the temperature range from 0 to 150° C. and observing that each square represents 5 microvolts. Over this range iron is positive with respect to copper.

Measurements of radiant heat energy are made with a multiplicity of couples formed of two metals and placed close together; such compact groups are called *thermopiles*. These are often constructed of

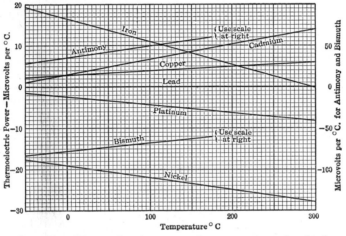

FIG. 307. Thermoelectric powers of some metals against lead

short lengths of bismuth and antimony connected in series alternately, and put together in zig-zag fashion so that every other junction can be exposed to the radiation while the intermediate ones are shielded from it.

The *thermo-ammeter*, which utilizes a thermo-junction in contact with a hot wire, is used in radio and research work for measuring small alternating currents. Heat is evolved in the wire by the current being measured and causes the thermocouple to generate an emf., thereby producing a deflection in a calibrated instrument connected across the couple. Increased sensitivity is secured by placing the wire and couple in a vacuum.

316. Thermocouples in Pyrometry.—The emf. of a thermocouple varies in a known manner with the temperature difference between its junctions. Consequently, if one junction is kept at constant temperature, the temperature of the other junction can be measured by observing the emf. produced. When so used, a thermocouple is called a *thermoelectric pyrometer*, the latter word indicating its particular applicability to measurements at high temperatures. A number of couples are used for this purpose. One of the most satisfactory for a wide temperature range has one metal of platinum and the other of an alloy of 90% platinum and 10% rhodium; a less expensive couple that is serviceable for ranges between 400° C. and the lowest temperatures has one metal of copper and the other of constantan (copper 60%, nickel 40%). The following table shows the emf.'s available with these couples at various standard temperatures (melting and boiling points of substances), the cold junction being at 0° C.

Millivolts Produced by Thermocouples

Standard point	Temperature, °C.	Platinum-Plat. Rhod.	Copper-Constantan
Water b.p............	100	0.643	4.276
Naphthalene b.p.......	217.9	1.585	10.248
Cadmium m.p.........	320.9	2.503	16.083
Aluminum m.p........	657	5.827	
Silver m.p...........	960.5	9.111	
Nickel m.p...........	1452.6	14.973	
Palladium m.p........	1549.5	16.144	

Temperatures of furnaces and of molten metals can be measured with the thermoelectric pyrometer, but the thermal junction must be protected from furnace gases and from direct contact with the molten substances.

317. Peltier and Thomson Effects.—The Peltier Effect is an inversion of the Seebeck Effect; it was discovered by the French physicist, Jean C. A. Peltier (1785–1845). When two dissimilar metals are connected in series with a source of emf. which establishes a current in the circuit, one junction will become heated and the other cooled. This effect is distinct from the heating of both metals by the current due to their resistance. The extent to which the junctions are heated or cooled by a given current depends solely upon the metals used. For an iron-copper junction at room temperatures about 4 calories are developed per hour per ampere of current. At ordinary temperatures when a current traverses the circuit of Fig. 305 in a clockwise direction, the left junction will become heated and the right junction will become cooled. A comparison of the Peltier and Seebeck Effects shows that the hot and cold junctions are interchanged for the same direction of current.

An analysis of the foregoing effects prompted William Thomson, later Lord Kelvin, to predict on theoretical grounds that an emf. must exist between different parts of the same metal if they are at different temperatures. He demonstrated that if a uniform metal bar is heated at the middle and a current is sent through it from end to end from an external source, the heat would be conducted unequally along the two halves. In a copper bar, Fig. 308, the region *A* where current is directed from a colder to a hotter part will be cooler than it would be if there

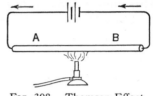

FIG. 308.   Thomson Effect

were no current, and the region *B* where current is directed from a hotter to a colder part will be warmer; thus *B* is warmer than *A*. The same is true for cadmium, silver and zinc, but the effect is reversed in iron and nickel, to mention but a few metals. This effect and the emf. involved are named after Thomson. Lead shows no appreciable Thomson Effect, and this accounts for its frequent use as a reference metal (see Fig. 307).

The evolution or absorption of heat at the junctions of a thermoelectric circuit demonstrates that there must be a difference of potential at places where two dissimilar metals are in contact. If both junctions are at the same temperature the thermo emf.'s at the two junctions are in opposite directions and annul each other; but if there is a temperature difference these two emf.'s do not balance, and their resultant, together with the Thomson emf.'s, establish a current in the circuit.

318. Thermionic Emission.—In 1883, Edison experimented with an evacuated tube containing a heated filament and a separate electrode, and discovered that a current would be set up between them if the electrode were positive with respect to the filament, but not if it were negative. In the light of present knowledge this current is explained by the passage of electrons from the interior of the filament into the space surrounding it and the attraction of these emitted electrons to the nearby electrode. The escape of electrons through the surface of a metal is comparable in many respects to the escape of molecules from a liquid during the process of evaporation. The situation is a little different, however, because an electron about to pass out of the metal induces a positive charge on the surface behind it and is pulled back. This action gives rise to a so-called *potential barrier*, somewhat like surface tension, which must be overcome before the electron can escape. When the metal is heated, the electrons in it are given more kinetic energy, which assists them in passing the potential barrier at the surface. For each metal, a definite amount of energy is needed to release an electron from the surface; this energy is known as the *work function* of the metal.

The emission of electrons by a hot body, called thermionic emission, is the operating principle of the modern electron tube. The simplest of these is the two-element tube, or *diode*. This device consists of a bulb or tube having a filament like that of an incandescent lamp and a separate metal plate, as shown in Fig. 309. The tube is evacuated and the filament is heated to incandescence by battery A. Electrons from the filament will be attracted to the plate when it is maintained positive by battery B as indicated, and the galvanometer will show a deflection. If the plate were made negative by reversing battery B, the electrons evaporated from the filament would be repelled by the plate and, since no electrons are emitted from the cold plate, the galvanometer would not show a deflection. Hence, the electrons can flow only from filament to plate, or what corresponds to the same thing, current can be directed only from plate to filament. Consequently this electron tube, containing the plate as anode and the heated filament as cathode, acts as a rectifier.

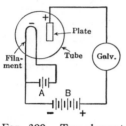

FIG. 309. Two-element electron tube

The number of electrons emitted per unit of time increases with the temperature of the filament and depends upon the substance of which it is made. The rate of electron emission is generally expressed as the current per unit of surface area of the hot body; at absolute temperature T it is:

$$J = A T^2 \epsilon^{-\frac{b}{T}} \tag{200}$$

as given by the English physicist, Owen W. Richardson. Herein J is expressed in amperes per square centimeter, T is in degrees K, ϵ is the base of natural logarithms, and A and b are constants. The work function is incorporated in constant b. The value of A is 60.2 for pure metals that may serve as the hot body; the values of b for three of the usual filament materials as found experimentally are: molybdenum 50,900, thorium 38,900, and tungsten 52,400.

319. Rectifier Tubes.—The current from plate to filament of an electron tube as expressed by the foregoing equation is the steady value that results when the plate potential is high enough to sweep all the electrons from the region around the filament as fast as they are liberated. At lower potential differences between the two electrodes of the tube the current will be less because some of the evaporated

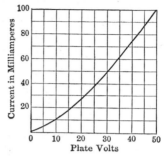

Fig. 310. Characteristic curve of thermionic rectifier

electrons will fall back into the filament, being repelled by a negative charge that builds up in the space around that electrode and called the *space charge*. In most types of electron tubes it is not expedient to measure the maximum emission or saturation current because its value is so large as to change the emitting conditions or to damage the tube.

The currents through the tube at the low potential differences are indicated by a curve such as Fig. 310, which shows the lower portion of the current-potential characteristic curve of a thermionic rectifier tube used in radio receiving sets for supplying direct currents

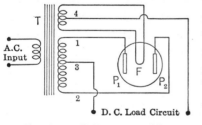

Fig. 311. Full-wave rectifier

to their other tubes. The filament is supplied with 5.0 volts and takes a current of 2.0 amp. This rectifier has two anodes and one filament so as to pass current during both halves of the alternating-current cycle.

The circuit of the full-wave rectifier is shown in Fig. 311; it comprises an iron-core transformer T with three windings, and a double-anode tube. The primary winding joins to the source of alternating current, the secondary winding 1–2 connects with the two anodes P_1 and P_2, and the third winding supplies current to heat the filament F. Mid-taps 3 and 4 on the latter windings lead to the load circuit. At an instant when terminal 1 of the lower winding is positive, the current is directed from P_1 to F, to 4, through the load, to 3 and back to 1. When terminal 2 is positive, the path of the current will be from P_2 to F, to 4, through the load, to 3 and back to 2. Consequently the load current will be unidirectional. Since this current would pulsate between zero and a maximum value, a *filter* is used to make the current steady. It usually consists of inductive coils connected in series with the load and condensers connected in parallel with the load. High alternating potentials can be rectified similarly, the tube for this purpose being often termed a *kenotron*.

Gases and vapors are used in some types of rectifier tubes in order to obtain large currents. The gas atoms are bombarded by the electrons emitted from the cathode and become ionized when electrons are knocked out of them. These gas ions are positively charged and tend to neutralize the space charge about the cathode, thereby increasing the emission of electrons from this electrode. The Tungar rectifier and the mercury-vapor rectifier are examples.

The *Tungar rectifier* tube contains argon or other inert gas at low pressure, a cathode of tungsten coiled into a closely wound spiral, and an anode of graphite having a relatively large area. Tungar rectifiers are available for half-wave as well as for full-wave rectification, and are often used for charging small storage batteries from alternating-current service mains.

The *mercury-arc rectifier* contains an electrode of mercury and one of graphite, within an evacuated container of glass or steel. To start the action, an auxiliary electrode is touched for a moment to the mercury pool and then withdrawn, striking an arc. Thereupon mercury vapor is formed which becomes ionized by electrons proceeding from the mercury surface, and causes conduction between the electrodes. When the rectifier is connected to alternating-current mains, there will be a current only during those intervals when the mercury electrode is negative, thus accounting for the rectifying action of the device. Two anodes are used for full-wave rectification from a single-phase supply; more are used when converting from polyphase systems. Steel-tank rectifiers, designed for currents up to several thousand amperes, are used in supplying power for traction systems.

320. Three-element Electron Tubes.—An American inventor, Lee De Forest, conceived the idea of adding another electrode to the two-element electron tube in order to control the number of electrons passing from filament to plate. The introduction of this so-called *grid* electrode has rendered the tube exceedingly useful as a sensitive detector of radio waves, as an amplifier of electrical signals, and as a generator of high-frequency alternating currents.

The effect of the grid is like that of a shutter which, opening and closing, controls the flow of electrons going through it from filament to plate. This control is accomplished by changing the potential of the grid. When the grid is positively charged, it attracts electrons and increases their flow from the filament to the plate. When negatively charged it repels the electrons so that they will not go to the plate. Consequently, when the grid G of a tube is made alternately positive and negative by joining the terminals TT' in Fig. 312 to a source of alternating current, the electron flow from F to P will be increased and decreased accordingly, thereby varying the direct current in the plate circuit; this variation can be detected by the telephone receivers shown. Actually,

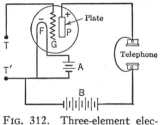

FIG. 312. Three-element electron tube

the grid is not made positive with respect to the filament, but only more or less negative; in this way there will be no current in the grid circuit and distortion and energy loss will be avoided. Thus, the grid serves as a gate-valve to control the plate current while taking practically no power itself.

The cathode of the tube is often a thin metal sleeve coated with thorium or other material having a low work function; a heating coil of tungsten wire is mounted within but separated from the sleeve. This construction makes it possible to heat the cathode with alternating current without introducing disturbing effects.

The behavior of a three-element tube or *triode* is best portrayed by curves of plate current plotted against plate potential. Such a family of curves is shown in Fig. 313 for a Type 6 SF 5 tube used in radio sets as a detector, oscillator, or amplifier, for a number of grid potentials ranging from $E_c = 0$ to $E_c = -4$ volts. The heater of the cathode takes 0.3 amp. at a potential difference $E_f = 6.3$ volts.

The *amplification factor* of a tube is defined as the ratio of a change in plate potential to a change in grid potential in the opposite direction such that the plate current will remain unchanged. An illustration will make the meaning of this factor clear.

For the triode having the characteristics shown in Fig. 313 assume -2.5 volts on the grid and $+300$ volts on the plate, both with respect to the filament; for these conditions the plate current will be 0.9 milliamp. Again, with −1.0 volt on the grid and +150 volts on the plate, the plate current will also be 0.9 milliamp. Thus, an increase of 1.5 volts on the grid yields the same output with a decrease of 150 volts on the plate. The ratio of 150 to 1.5 shows the amplification factor to be 150 ÷ 1.5 = 100.

As previously mentioned, the space between cathode and plate has a negative charge because of the presence of electrons. The more negative the grid the more it assists this space charge in limiting the electron flow. The curves show, for example, that with the plate potential maintained at 200 volts, the plate current is 0.9 milliamp.

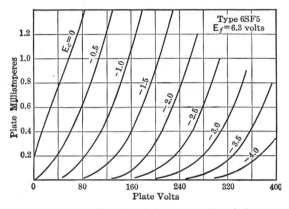

FIG. 313.   Characteristic curves of a triode

with −1.5 volts on the grid, 0.31 milliamp. with −2.0 volts on the grid, and 0.1 milliamp. with −2.5 volts on the grid. This illustrates the large variation in plate current that can be obtained by relatively small changes of grid potential.

*321. Thyratron and Ignitron Tubes.—A three-electrode electron tube containing mercury vapor, called a *thyratron*, is used for controlling currents of the order of amperes by varying the conditions of its grid potential. With some definite potential difference between filament and plate, ionization of the vapor begins at some particular grid potential. With the grid more negative than this critical value, no ionization will occur, but above this value a current will be established provided the plate is positive with respect to the heated cathode. After the plate current is once started, the grid cannot stop or control it. However, if the current stops sufficiently long for the vapor to deionize, the grid will resume control.

With alternating potentials on both plate and grid, the latter electrode can regain control once each cycle and delay establishment

of current in the plate circuit as long as the grid is sufficiently negative. Therefore, the phase relation between these two potentials
fixes the point in each cycle at which current is established and
thereby determines the average amount of current in the plate circuit. Fig. 314 shows the effect of shifting the phase between the
plate potential *P* and the grid potential *G*. The dotted curves show
the critical grid potentials and the shaded areas indicate the relative
currents in the plate circuit; note that the shaded area begins at an
instant *c* when the dotted curve has a particular ordinate. The
thyratron is useful chiefly in controlling contactors, solenoids, magnetic brakes, and rectifiers.

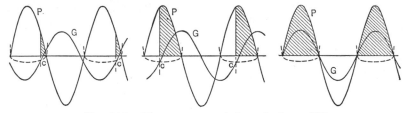

FIG. 314. Thyraton control through phase shift

The *ignitron* resembles a mercury-arc rectifier but utilizes an
auxiliary electrode of silicon carbide or other high-resistance material
for initiating ionization during each positive half-cycle. The tube
current is controlled by changing the point in the cycle when "ignition" occurs (that is, when ionization begins); this is done by connecting a thyratron to the auxiliary electrode and shifting the phase of
grid potential on the latter tube. Ignitrons are used for controlling
large currents such as are necessary in electric welding.

322. The Photoelectric Cell.—Experiments made around 1888
showed that freshly polished zinc would lose a charge of electricity
when illuminated by ultraviolet light, but only when the charge was
negative. This expulsion of electrons is now known to occur from
many substances when they are illuminated by ordinary or ultraviolet
light. This effect is called *photoelectric emission*, and the negative
charges emitted are sometimes called *photoelectrons* to indicate their
origin. It is found that with incident light of a given frequency of
vibration (color), a variation of light intensity does not cause a
change in velocity of the electrons emitted, but does change the
number expelled per unit of time. On the other hand, an increase
in the frequency of the incident light increases the velocity of expulsion, and a decrease in frequency decreases the velocity of expul-

sion down to a limiting frequency, characteristic of the metal used, at which the photoelectric effect disappears.

Einstein found that in order to explain these facts it was necessary to apply the quantum theory, § 202, to photoelectric emission, and to suppose that light in space is itself made up of discrete quanta of energy. Einstein's photoelectric equation states that the maximum kinetic energy of the electrons expelled from a metal is

$$\tfrac{1}{2}mv_m{}^2 = hf - w \tag{201}$$

Herein m is the mass of the electron, v_m is the maximum velocity of the electrons, h is Planck's constant, f is the frequency of the incident light, and w is the work function of the metal. According to this equation, each quantum of incident radiation, hf, is entirely absorbed by a single electron, an amount w being used to pull it out of the metal and the rest appearing as kinetic energy.

The low-frequency limit, or threshold value of f, is obtained when $hf = w$; this limit for such materials as caesium, sodium and potassium is in the infra-red, and therefore photoelectric emission occurs throughout the visible light range. Others show emission only for ultraviolet light. The foregoing facts have an important bearing upon the theory of light and radiation (§ 464). It is of interest here to observe that the number of electrons which are emitted per second is proportional to the intensity of light which causes the action.

The photoelectric cell is an electron tube that consists of a light-sensitive surface, most often of caesium, constituting the cathode, and a small wire or plate constituting the anode, both within a glass

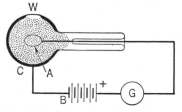

FIG. 315. Photoelectric cell circuit

tube. The diagram of such a cell appears in Fig. 315, its anode A and cathode C being connected to a battery B and a galvanometer G. When light enters at the window W it falls upon the cathode film on the inside surface of the glass, and the electrons emitted are drawn to the anode; this flow constitutes a current in the circuit and produces a deflection of the galvanometer. Experiment shows that over considerable ranges the current is directly proportional to the illumination at the cell. Photoelectric cells are of the vacuum type and of the gas-filled type; in the latter helium or argon is used at a pressure of a few millimeters. Much greater currents can be obtained in the gas-filled type than in the other because of the ionization of the gas molecules by collision with electrons and other molecules. The currents developed by photoelectric cells are of the order of microamperes for the usual range of illumination; to enlarge these currents use is made of three-electrode electron tubes as amplifiers.

Photoelectric cells are used particularly for color analysis and comparison, control of street lights and electric signs, counting operations, and for talking motion pictures.

323. X-rays and Their Production.—In 1895 the German physicist, Wilhelm K. Röntgen (1845–1923), discovered a type of invisible radiation which had great penetrating power and was capable of affecting photographic plates. He called these radiations *x-rays*, and nowadays they are also spoken of as *Röntgen rays*. These rays are similar to light but the vibrations which give rise to them are very much more rapid.

It has been found that x-rays are produced wherever cathode rays strike material substances, that they are produced more copiously if the substance upon which they impinge has a high atomic mass, and that they are more penetrating if the speed of the cathode particles is high. These particles are electrons; they are usually derived from a hot cathode and projected upon a target of heavy metal. A large difference of potential maintained between these electrodes gives the electron stream speeds from one-tenth to one-half that of light, which is 186,000 miles per second.

The general shape of an x-ray tube is depicted in Fig. 316. The anode *A* is a target of wrought tungsten attached to a molybdenum rod and supported by an iron sleeve which helps to radiate the heat evolved. The cathode *C* is a filament of tungsten wire wound into a spiral and heated by current supplied through a transformer as shown. These electrodes are connected to a source of high-potential direct current that is obtained from a high alternating potential by a mechanical rectifier or more effectively by a kenotron rectifier.

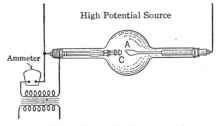

Fig. 316. Hot-cathode x-ray tube

When different substances are interposed between a photographic plate or film and a source of x-rays, the radiation penetrates them to different extents, according to their densities, and the plate or film, upon development, shows the shadows of the objects interposed. When the hand is so placed near an x-ray tube, the plate is affected less behind the bones than behind the flesh, because the bones are more opaque to the radiations. A print made from such a plate gives shadows of the bones and a faint outline of the flesh. Broken bones and foreign objects in the body can be located accurately in this manner. Equipments have been developed for high-speed x-ray photography, and for locating defects in thick metal objects.

X-rays may be used for the direct examination of objects by the use of a fluoroscopic screen. This screen consists of a piece of cardboard coated with certain crystals, as platinobarium cyanide or tungstate of calcium, which fluoresce under the action of x-rays. If the hand be interposed between such a screen and the tube, the shadow of the bones can be plainly seen.

Physicians use x-rays not only in making examinations but also for their curative action. Animal tissue undergoes a change in structure when exposed to x-rays and is destroyed by prolonged exposure. In x-ray therapy, the rays are concentrated upon abnormal or diseased tissue that is to be destroyed.

When a gas is exposed to x-rays it becomes ionized, and the amount of ionization produced serves as a measure of the intensity of the rays. Such a measurement is carried out with an ionization chamber and a charged electroscope. The chamber consists of a closed metal box, having a window of thin celluloid or aluminum, and containing an insulated metal electrode to which the electroscope is connected. When the rays are admitted through the window, and a difference of potential is maintained between the electrode and the box, the ions produced by the x-rays separate; those of one sign gather on the electrode while those of the other sign collect upon the chamber. The rate at which the electroscope discharges is an accurate measure of the intensity of the x-rays.

The radiation from an x-ray tube covers a wide range of frequencies, the range extending to higher frequencies as the potential difference between the target and cathode is increased. It has been shown that there is an upper limiting frequency f_m and that this is determined by the applied potential difference V according to the relation

$$Ve = hf_m \qquad (202)$$

where the product Ve represents the energy with which the electrons strike the target, and h is Planck's constant (§ 202). In this expression e is the charge of the electron, namely 4.80×10^{-10} esu., and V is the potential difference in ergs per esu. of charge. When V is reduced to volts (§ 233) and the value of h is introduced, the maximum frequency becomes $f_m = 2.41 \times 10^{14} V$. The higher the frequency of the x-rays, the greater will be their penetrating power.

When a beam of x-rays falls upon a substance it gives rise to other radiation which consists largely of x-rays also. This "secondary radiation" is partly of the same nature as the incident beam and partly of a character dependent upon the material from which it is emitted, § 463. A study of this radiation gives information regarding the structure of matter.

*324. The Betatron.—A machine was devised in 1941 by Donald W. Kerst for the purpose of giving a very high velocity to a beam of

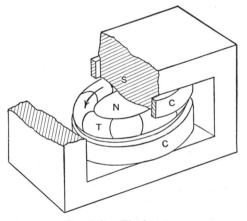

Fig. 317. The betatron

electrons, so that when directed upon a target they will produce x-rays of great penetrating power. This machine is called a *betatron* in keeping with the name "beta rays" given to electrons ejected at high velocities in radioactive changes. The essential elements of the betatron are shown in Fig. 317. It consists of an evacuated doughnut-shaped glass tube T placed between the poles N and S of a powerful electromagnet which is energized by alternating current in the circular coils CC. An electron gun, not shown in the figure, is arranged to project the electrons tangentially into the tube. Here they are acted upon by two forces: a radially inward force that makes them follow the curvature of the tube, and a tangential force that gives them higher and higher speeds.

The electrons are first projected into the tube for a few microseconds just as the magnetic field starts to build up, then they move at increasing speed around the tube, and finally, at a chosen instant, they are deflected from their circular path to the x-ray target. All this occurs within a quarter of a cycle, before the field has reached its maximum value, nevertheless, the electrons travel around the tube many thousands of times during this period. These operations are repeated over and over in succeeding cycles.

The radial force on an electron at any instant when it is moving with a speed v in the magnetic field is given in absolute units by equation (170) as $F = Bev$, where e is the electronic charge and B is the flux density at the electron orbit. This force acts toward the center of curvature and becomes the centripetal force of circular motion, causing the electron path to have a radius r such that $Bev = mv^2/r$, or

$$mv = Ber$$

In order that this path shall coincide with the curved axis of the tube, r in this equation must be constant at the appropriate value, and hence mv must be proportional to B. Consequently, as the momentum of the electron increases there is to be a proportionate increase in the flux density. Expressed mathematically, the condition which must be satisfied is as follows:

$$\Delta(mv) = er\,\Delta B \tag{203}$$

The tangential force on the electron is due to the fact that throughout the action the flux is increasing, so that with each revolution the electron acquires the same amount of energy as though it were subject to an induced emf. while traversing a single turn of wire. If a particular transit of an electron around the tube takes a time Δt and if the flux meanwhile changes by an amount $\Delta\Phi$, the induced emf., in absolute units, amounts to $E = \Delta\Phi/\Delta t$, as shown in § 271. The work done upon an electron during this transit is eE, by equation (139), and can be expressed as the product of some force F and the distance $2\pi r$. Hence $eE = 2\pi rF$, or $F = eE/2\pi r$. This force is tangent to the orbit, and in the time Δt represents an impulse $F\,\Delta t$ which causes an equal increase in the momentum of the electron, § 41, or

$$\Delta(mv) = \frac{eE}{2\pi r}\,\Delta t \tag{204}$$

Expression (203) and (204) may be equated, whence

$$er\, \Delta B = \frac{eE}{2\pi r}\Delta t = \frac{e\,\Delta\Phi}{2\pi r} \quad \text{and} \quad \Delta\Phi = 2\pi r^2\,\Delta B$$

If both the flux density and the flux are reckoned from an initial value of zero, then at an instant when the flux density at the orbit has increased to B the flux within the orbit must be

$$\Phi = 2\pi r^2 B$$

which is twice the value it would have if the flux density throughout the orbit were uniform at the value which exists at the tube. This particular flux distribution is necessary in the operation of the machine, and is obtained by special shaping of the pole pieces of the electromagnet.

To compute the energy of the issuing electron beam the principles of relativity are involved, § 466. In a large betatron each electron attains a speed which is close to that of light, and to compute its kinetic energy it is necessary to use the general expression, $E_k = (m - m_o)c^2$, as given by equation (293). In this expression m is the mass of the electron, m_o is its mass when at rest, and c is the velocity of light. The mass m may be expressed in terms of the momentum relation $mv = Ber$ whence $m = Ber/v$; further, because of the high speed, m becomes so large that m_o may be neglected by comparison, and at the same time, v may be placed equal to c. Consequently the kinetic energy is given by

$$E_k = Berc \tag{205}$$

The flux density B in this expression is in gausses and the radius r of the electron orbit is in centimeters. The electronic charge, 4.80×10^{-10} esu., is converted to $e = 1.60 \times 10^{-20}$ abcoulombs, and the velocity of light is $c = 3 \times 10^{10}$ cm. per sec. The kinetic energy of the ejected electron is in ergs.

In a General Electric betatron of recent design the maximum flux density is 4000 gausses and the radius of the circular tube is 33 in. or 83.8 cm. The maximum energy of the electron beam from this machine is $E_k = 4000 \times 1.60 \times 10^{-20} \times 83.8 \times 3 \times 10^{10} = 1.61 \times 10^{-4}$ ergs, which is equivalent to approximately 100,000,000 electron-volts.

The betatron finds application not only in the production of high-energy x-rays but also in the study of nuclear reactions resulting in the transmutation of elements (see Chapter XL).

PROBLEMS

1. What emf. is generated by a copper-nickel thermocouple when one of the junctions is at 0° C. and the other is at 175° C.?

2. Compute the emf. produced by an antimony-bismuth thermocouple, the junctions of which are at 20° C. and 150° C.

3. An iron-nickel thermocouple generates an emf. of 2760 microvolts when one of its junctions is at 0° C. and the other is at a temperature to be determined; compute this temperature.

4. A thermopile is composed of 50 antimony-bismuth junctions on one face and an equal number on the other. Radiation falls upon one face of the thermopile while the other is at the room temperature of 20° C., and the total emf. generated is 0.140 volt. What is the temperature of the thermopile face that receives the radiation?

5. A thermopile being designed for use in fire detection is to have a certain number of antimony-bismuth junctions on one face and an equal number on the other. It is desired to generate a total emf. of 90 millivolts when the exposed face of the thermopile reaches 150° C., the other face remaining at the room temperature of 20° C. What is the smallest number of junctions that may be used on the exposed face?

6. Compute the rate of electron emission per square centimeter from a tungsten filament operating at 2500° K.

7. Theoretical analysis shows that the constant b in Richardson's equation is equal to the work function of the metal divided by the gas constant per molecule, and is expressed in degrees K. Refer to the values given in this book for these quantities and calculate the work function for tungsten; express the result in electron-volts.

8. Calculate the amplification factor of the triode having the characteristic curves shown in Fig. 313 for the condition when the grid potential is varied from −0.5 to −1.5 volts and the plate current is maintained at 1.25 milliamp.

9. The so-called plate resistance of an electron tube is the ratio of a small change in plate potential to the corresponding change in plate current. Determine the plate resistance of the triode mentioned in the preceding problem for the following condition: plate potential = 200, grid potential = −1.5.

10. The ratio of a small change in plate current to the corresponding small change in grid potential which produced it (all other potentials remaining unchanged) is called the mutual conductance of the tube and is usually expressed in microamperes per volt. What is this constant for the triode of the two preceding problems at 100 volts when the grid potential is varied from −0.5 to −1.0 volt?

11. A surface of 1 sq. in. at a distance of 15 in. from a 60-watt frosted lamp receives about 0.2 lumen of light flux. About this much reaches the gate of the "sound-track" of a motion picture film. If the photoelectric cell passes 5 microamp. with this amount of light flux, what will be the change of photoelectric current when the film is inserted and varies the flux from 0.01 to 0.03 lumen?

12. If the photoelectric threshold for potassium is 3×10^{14} cycles per sec., what is the work function of this metal? What potential difference would be needed to remove one of the least firmly bound electrons from its surface?

13. What is the maximum frequency of the x-rays that can be obtained from an x-ray tube in which a potential difference of 50,000 volts is applied between target and cathode?

*14. Refer to the 100,000,000-electron-volt betatron described near the end of § 324 and compute the maximum flux through the circular tube.

Electronics in Communication

Chapter XXVIII

325. The Telegraph.—Many of the principles explained in the preceding chapters are utilized in the transmission of intelligence. Electric communication divides itself basically into telegraphy and telephony, and is accomplished through wire connection or radio waves. The present chapter outlines the physical aspects of these communication systems and stresses the application of electronics to them.

The system of telegraphy devised in 1837 by the American artist and inventor, Samuel F. B. Morse (1791–1872), is an application of electromagnetism. The circuit consists of a line wire, keys which serve as switches for opening and closing the circuit, instruments called sounders for receiving the signals, and batteries for supplying the current. Signals are transmitted by manipulating a key at one place in accordance with a code, and received at another place by listening to the clicks produced by the armature of the sounder as it is attracted and released by an electromagnet. On long telegraph lines the current received is small and consequently sensitive relays are used in the line circuits in place of the sounders. A relay has a light armature and functions merely to open and close a local circuit which includes a sounder, rather than to produce an audible response itself.

Fig. 318 shows the circuit of a Morse telegraph between two widely separated stations. When the line is idle, the circuit is kept closed by means of the by-passes s and s' associated with the keys K and K', and the current path includes generators B and B', relays R and R', line L, and ground from G to G'. When an operator wishes to send a message, he interrupts the circuit by opening s (as shown in the figure) and then establishes current pulses by depressing his key for long and short intervals to produce the so-called dashes and dots of the telegraph code. These current pulses through the relay windings cause the armatures A and A' to be attracted intermittently, thereby closing and opening the local circuits which include the generators g and g', and the sounders S and S'. When through sending, he again completes the circuit by closing s, thereby enabling the other operator to respond.

The system described provides a single channel of communication over the circuit. A number of systems have been devised and utilized

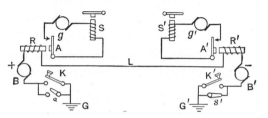

FIG. 318.   Single Morse circuit with relays

in extending the message-carrying capacity of a line, such as the *duplex, quadruplex,* and *multiplex* systems, names that suggest the number of channels provided.

326. The Telephone.—The transmission of speech by telephone was first accomplished in 1876 by Alexander G. Bell (1847–1922), American inventor and physicist. The elements of telephonic communication consist of a transmitter for producing a variable current having the same characteristics as the sound waves that impinge upon it (§ 359), and a receiver for converting this variable current into sound waves to reproduce the original sounds.

The transmitter consists of carbon granules confined between two electrodes, one being rigid and the other flexibly mounted on the diaphragm against which the voice is directed. Variations of air pressure on the diaphragm cause changes of resistance of the granules because their contacting areas are altered. The receiver comprises a small electromagnet combined with a permanent magnet, and a thin diaphragm of magnetic material. Variations of current in the electromagnet cause variations in the attraction of the diaphragm, thereby setting it into vibration to produce sound.

The simplest connection for demonstrating the transmission of speech is a series circuit including a transmitter, a receiver, and a battery. A sound impressed upon the transmitter causes its diaphragm to be moved with varying amplitudes and frequencies. Each push against the diaphragm lowers the resistance of the transmitter, causes a larger current in the circuit, and produces in the receiver an increased pull upon its diaphragm. The action of the transmitter is therefore to alter or "modulate" the current to conform to the incident sound waves.

Without the permanent magnet, the receiver diaphragm would produce sounds of double pitch. The reason for this will be evident if an alternating current is assumed in the receiver winding, for then the diaphragm would be attracted once for the positive lobe of the cycle and once for the negative, thereby producing two complete vibrations of the diaphragm for each current cycle.

Fig. 319 shows the connections of a modern telephone handset, with the transmitter and receiver mounted together in a shell of

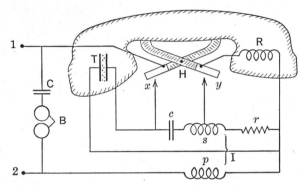

Fig. 319.   Connections of a subscriber's telephone set

molded insulation. The principal elements are the transmitter T, the receiver R, the switch H, the bell B, and the induction coil I. When the user lifts the handset from its support to engage in conversation, the switch makes contacts at x and y, closing the transmitter and receiver circuits respectively. These circuits are coupled magnetically by the primary and secondary windings p and s of the induction coil, and include a resistance r and a condenser c to match the average line constants.

When the user is talking, the vibration of the transmitter diaphragm varies the resistance in the circuit 1, x, T, p, 2 and produces corresponding variations of current in another telephone set to which the line wires lead. When he is listening to speech originating at the other set, the current variations produced by it occasion corresponding variations in the circuit just mentioned, as a result of which emf.'s are developed in the secondary winding of the induction coil. These produce corresponding current variations in the circuit s, y, R, r and operate the receiver accordingly. The connections are so designed that the receiver will respond very little to variations of current produced by its companion transmitter, thereby making it unresponsive to extraneous noises picked up at the home station and hence more effective as a receiver of incoming speech signals.

The bell serves in calling the subscriber to the telephone. It is connected in series with the condenser C across the line wires and is actuated by alternating current of about 16 cycles per sec. supplied from the central office.

★327. Repeaters.—The three-element electron tube (§ 320) is used with an appropriate circuit on long lines for amplifying the signal currents. The electrical energy to be amplified is applied to the input or grid circuit of the tube, and the amplified energy is made available in its output or plate circuit. Used in this manner, the tube constitutes a *repeater element* which permits of transmission in one direction.

The connection diagram of such a repeater element in a telephone circuit is given in Fig. 320. A high resistance is connected across the secondary winding of the input transformer T so that a portion of the emf. induced in this winding may be impressed between the filament F and the grid G. The battery A provides current to heat the filament, and the battery E_c maintains the grid negative to prevent current in the grid circuit. The circuit from the plate P of the

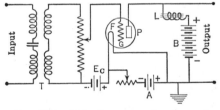

FIG. 320. Telephone repeater element

tube includes the battery B and the reactance coil L; the latter confines the voice currents to the output circuit indicated by the terminals at the right. Small variations in the voice currents in the input transformer cause proportional variations in grid potential, and these in turn produce similar but amplified variations in the output circuit. The additional energy is supplied by the battery in the plate circuit. For the usual two-way telephonic transmission over a single telephone line either one or two such repeater elements are needed, depending upon the manner of connection.

The gain in power produced by a repeater is expressed in terms of a unit called the *decibel* (abbreviated db.). One decibel represents a ratio between two power values of $10^{0.1}$ to 1. When the gain of a repeater is N db., the ratio of the output power P_2 to the input power P_1 is $10^{0.1N}$, or

$$\frac{P_2}{P_1} = 10^{0.1N}$$

Herefrom, the gain in decibels becomes

$$N = 10 \log_{10} \frac{P_2}{P_1} \tag{206}$$

The decibel scale is also used in the measurement of sound and noise levels, and is explained more fully in § 372.

As an illustration of the decibel scale in expressing amplification, suppose the input to an amplifier is 5 microwatts. A gain of 10 db. would give a power ratio $P_2/P_1 = 10^{0.1 \times 10} = 10$; consequently there would be a 10-fold increase and the output would be 50 microwatts. Similarly, a gain of 60 db. would signify a 10^6-fold power increase to 5 watts. Again, if the input is 5 microwatts and the output is 300 microwatts, then the gain in decibels is found from equation (206) to be $N = 10 \log_{10} 300/5 = 10 \log_{10} 60 = 10 \times 1.778 = 17.8$ db.

328. Electromagnetic Radiation.—In a circuit having capacitance and inductance distributed over zones of appropriate areas, it is found that some energy is emitted in the form of radiation whenever the current in the circuit changes. The discovery of this electro-magnetic radiation and its transmission through space was made about 1887 by the German physicist, Heinrich R. Hertz (1857–1894), who also showed that the radiations have measurable velocity and wavelengths. The Italian scientist, Guglielmo Marconi (1874–1937), made use of this discovery to bring about radio communication.

The waves are launched at the transmitting or broadcasting station from an aerial wire system or *antenna*, and are received at a similar antenna connected to the receiving set. At the transmitting station a high-frequency source is joined between the antenna and ground, and this forces electrons up and down, charging the upper end of the antenna alternately $+$ and $-$. The antenna and ground together act like the plates of a condenser and the region between them is under electrostatic stress. The antenna current is made as large as possible by adjusting the inductance or capacitance of the circuit so as to give resonance at the frequency desired. The region around the antenna may be pictured as shown in Fig. 321; at the left the antenna current i is upward and at the right it is downward. The electrostatic field is directed from the antenna to ground or vice versa, as depicted by the lines of force, and the magnetic field encircles the antenna as indicated by the dots and crosses.

The charges surge up and down the antenna as the current reverses, and since the lines of the electric field terminate on the charges themselves, the ends of these lines at the antenna also move up and down.

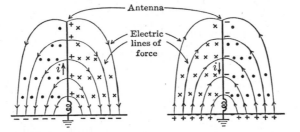

FIG. 321. Magnetic and electric fields around a vertical antenna

At the same time, both the magnetic and electric fields are pushed outward by successively new fields as the current changes with each cycle. Fig. 322 shows the propagation of the composite field in cross-section; the lobes embracing the electric lines are concentric with the antenna and the magnetic lines are horizontal circles, both expanding outward into space. The electromagnetic waves travel with a speed of 300,000 km. per sec.

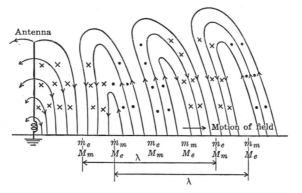

FIG. 322. Electromagnetic waves leaving a transmitter antenna

It is pointed out in § 202 that the wavelength of the radiation in space is given by

$$\lambda = \frac{V}{f}$$

where V is the velocity of propagation and f is the frequency of the oscillations. The frequency is determined by the inductance and capacitance of the transmitting circuit, and can be computed by equation (191), for resonance.

To illustrate these relations, consider a simple series circuit composed of a coil of 0.06 millihenry inductance and a variable condenser, and suppose that it is desired that the natural frequency of the circuit shall be 600,000 cycles per sec. The required capacitance of the condenser is

$$C = \frac{1}{(2\pi 600,000)^2\, 0.06 \times 10^{-3}} = 1.175 \times 10^{-9} \text{ farad} = 0.001175 \text{ mf.}$$

*329. The Electron-tube Oscillator.—The rapid oscillation of the electrons in a radio antenna can be produced by high-frequency

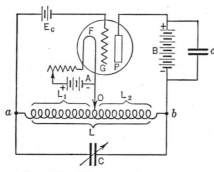

alternators, electric arcs, or electron tubes; the latter method is now the most common. The three-element tube is generally used for this purpose with the plate and grid circuits so coupled that some energy in the plate circuit is fed back to the grid circuit. Fig. 323 shows a simple form of such an oscillator, in which the condenser C and the coil L constitute the oscillating circuit.

FIG. 323.   Electron-tube oscillator

To explain the operation of the oscillator, consider the instant when the filament and plate circuits are closed. The filament F, heated by current from the battery A, emits electrons which pass to the plate P, establishing a current in the plate circuit and developing a magnetic field in coil L_2. The growing field about L_2 cuts the turns of the other half of the coil, inducing an emf. in L_1 exactly as in a transformer. The momentary direction of the counter emf. in L_2 is such as to make the intermediate point O positive with respect to b. Similarly the emf. induced in L_1 will be such as to make point a positive with respect to O, and therefore positive to b also. Hence, as the current in the plate circuit grows, it is aided by the positive potential pulse imparted to the grid G by L_1 (see § 320). However, as the plate current reaches a limiting value and no longer continues to rise, the emf. induced in L_1 becomes less, and very soon falls to zero. Under these conditions the plate-circuit current must decrease because the positive potential which was available at the grid is now lacking. As the plate current falls in value, the emf. induced in L_1 is reversed in direction and increased in magnitude. This reversal of the potential difference across L_1 aids the reduction of the plate current until it reaches zero. When this value is attained the emf.

induced in L_1 is again zero and the plate current begins to rise because the negative grid potential necessary to keep the plate current zero no longer exists. Once more the current rises in the plate circuit and produces an emf. in L_1 directed to make G positive; thereby aiding the current to grow, and this continues until the steady value is reached. Thereafter this cycle of events is repeated, and continuous oscillations are established.

The capacitor c is a by-pass around the battery B for the high-frequency pulses to the plate. The battery E_c is added to the circuit to permit selection of the most efficient operating condition, that is, one which results in a minimum loss in both grid and plate circuits.

*330. The Radio Transmitter.— The oscillations produced by an electron-tube oscillator can be transferred to the antenna of a *radio telephone transmitter* through a coupling device, as shown in Fig. 324 by the coil L'. The inductance of this coupler together with the capacitance and inductance of the aerial with respect to ground constitute the elements of an alternating-current

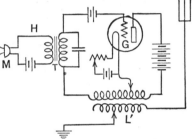

FIG. 324. Radio telephone transmitter

circuit that has a definite but adjustable natural frequency. A capacitor is shunted across the secondary winding of the transformer to by-pass the high-frequency currents.

The electromagnetic waves set up by the antenna may be used for radio telephony by modulating the generated wave to conform to the characteristics of the sound to be transmitted. The frequencies of sound waves range from about 16 to upward of 10,000 cycles per second, and the usual method of modulation may be looked upon as the superposition of such audio-frequency waves on the radio waves generated by the oscillator. This process of modulation is somewhat analogous to the superposition of the speech waves on the direct current used in wire telephony.

Modulation may be accomplished by inserting a microphone and a transformer in the grid circuit of the electron-tube oscillator, as shown. This arrangement is very simple and effective in low-power circuits. The sound waves impinging upon the microphone M are converted into corresponding electrical current variations in the local circuit H, and these voice currents impress suitably varying potentials upon the grid *G* by means of transformer *T*. Thus, the grid is subjected to two sets of potential variations, one being the very rapid radio-frequency oscillations or *carrier wave* as shown at the right in Fig. 325, and the other being the relatively slow audio-frequency variations as shown by the *voice wave* at the top. As a result the oscillations generated by the tube, which are constant in frequency, are varied in amplitude in accordance with the sound wave, as shown

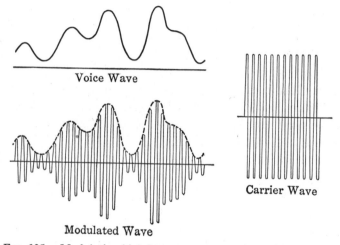

Voice Wave

Carrier Wave

Modulated Wave

Fɪɢ. 325.   Modulating high-frequency currents for radio telephony

by the *modulated wave* at the bottom of the figure. This procedure is known as *amplitude modulation* to distinguish it from another procedure to be considered in § 332.

Various types of microphones are used at present, but only two will be mentioned. The *electrodynamic transmitter* carries on its diaphragm a tiny coil located in the field of a stationary magnet, and emf.'s are generated in the coil when the pressure on the diaphragm changes. The *velocity microphone* has a light corrugated metallic ribbon between the pole pieces of an electromagnet, and emf.'s are induced in the ribbon when incident sound waves set it into vibration, the velocity of the ribbon being in phase with the velocity of the air particles.

The frequency of a radio transmitter can be controlled by utilizing crystals, like quartz, which exhibit the *piezoelectric effect*. If a plate is cut in a particular way from a quartz crystal, it is found that compressing the plate causes its faces to become charged, and then stretching it causes this charge to be reversed. Conversely, if the plate is located in an alternating electric field, it will contract and expand periodically and set up mechanical vibrations of constant frequency. The vibration rate will vary inversely with the thickness of the plate, its value for 1 mm. thickness of quartz being about 3×10^6 cycles per sec. When a quartz plate of appropriate thickness is placed between two electrodes that are connected to the grid circuit of an electron tube transmitter tuned to the frequency of the plate, the frequency of the tube may be kept constant regardless of load changes.

331. The Radio Receiver.—The function of the *radio receiving set* is to absorb energy from the electromagnetic waves available in its vicinity which are emitted from a radio transmitting or broadcast-

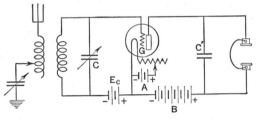

FIG. 326. Simple electron-tube receiver

ing station, to transform the weak high-frequency oscillations into amplified currents of lower and audible frequency, and from these currents to derive sounds having minimum distortion and sufficient volume. To receive waves from a particular station, the radio set is tuned to it by adjusting the capacitance or inductance of its antenna circuit, and the high-frequency currents induced in that circuit are rectified by a detector, usually an electron tube.

Fig. 326 shows the circuit of a simple electron-tube detector used in a receiver, in which the batteries A and B provide the power for the filament and plate circuits respectively. The variations of potential difference across the variable condenser C act upon the grid G of the tube through the battery E_c. The number of cells in this battery is adjusted to select the point on the characteristic curve of the tube for proper operation. Variations of grid potential produce amplified variations of current through the telephone receivers in the plate circuit, as explained in § 320.

The plate-current grid-potential characteristic of the tube is illustrated in Fig. 327, showing the extent to which rectification is carried out. The greatest rectification will result when the emf. E_c of the grid battery conforms to the bend of the characteristic curve. No rectification would be produced at the straight portion of the curve because equal positive and negative swings of the grid potential yield equal increases and decreases of plate current.

The wavy line at the bottom of the figure indicates the potential variation produced by an incoming signal on the condenser C of the tuned circuit. Successive points on this line are projected up to the tube characteristic and from there across to the right, giving a corresponding wavy line which represents the wave shape of current in the condenser C'. This condenser integrates the high-frequency impulses and discharges through the telephone receiver, giving a current pulse shown by the median line of this curve.

In another detector circuit the battery E_c is replaced by a condenser and a very high resistance connected in parallel, and called respectively a *grid condenser* and a *grid leak*.

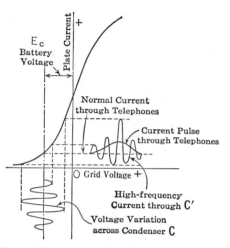

Fig. 327.   Action of a simple electron-tube detector

In order that an electron-tube detector may operate to the best advantage, it is necessary that the potentials upon its grid be reasonably large. Since the energy ordinarily received in antennas is insufficient to develop such potentials, it is almost always desirable to build up the received radio-frequency impulses before applying them to the detector. The process of increasing these radio-frequency potentials is termed *radio-frequency amplification*. This is accomplished by one or more electron tubes connected somewhat like that in Fig. 320. The detector then converts the radio-frequency oscillations into signals of audible frequencies and passes them to the telephones.

With one or more stages of radio-frequency amplification applied ahead of the detector tube of a receiver, the output of the detector may still be too weak to actuate the sound-reproducing devices. The output may then be increased by means of *audio-frequency amplifiers* which usually have two stages of amplification. The second stage often employs a tube of larger capacity, a so-called *power tube,* in order to yield sufficient volumes of sound in a loud speaker.

*332. Frequency Modulation.—One of the recent developments in radio broadcasting is frequency modulation, in which the frequency of the carrier wave, rather than its amplitude, is modified by the sound wave that is being transmitted. In this process, the amplitude of the radio wave emitted by the transmitter is always constant and is determined only by the power radiated by the station. Such stations operate at very high frequencies, say 50 megacycles per sec., at which there is relatively little interference from "static." Currents of audio frequencies up to 15,000 cycles per second may be transmitted readily with this system of modulation.

In frequency modulation the basic principles are: (1) the frequency of the carrier is varied over a range which is proportional to the intensity of the sound, and (2) the rate at which this variation takes place is equal to the frequency of the sound.

Fig. 328 represents a frequency-modulated carrier wave on a time axis. The frequency (and therefore wavelength) of the carrier varies with the intensity of the sound being carried, and the frequency range expands and contracts at a rate which depends upon the pitch of

FIG. 328. Frequency-modulated carrier wave

that sound. Thus, loud sounds produce a wide change of carrier wavelength, and high-pitched sounds produce a rapid stretching of the wave pattern.

Suppose a frequency-modulated transmitter operating at a nominal carrier frequency of 45,000,000 cycles per second to transmit a 1000-cycle tone of such intensity as to require a frequency change of 10,000 cycles per second above and below the nominal value. The frequency of the transmitter will then vary from 44,990,000 to 45,010,000 cycles per second, at the rate of 1000 times a second. This situation is depicted by a sine curve in Fig. 329 in which the ordinates show a frequency deviation of 10,000 cycles (or 0.01 megacycle) from the 45,000,000-cycle (45 megacycle) carrier to represent the chosen sound intensity. The abscissas indicate the time of sweeping through one complete set of frequency values to be 0.001 second, hence 1000 such sets of values are swept out per second, a rate which corresponds to a 1000-cycle tone. If the note were held for two seconds, the frequency of the transmitter would be varied from 44.99 to 45.01 and back to 44.99 megacycles exactly 2000 times in this interval.

Next suppose the intensity of the tone to be doubled. The deviation of the carrier frequency would be doubled, ranging from 44.98 to 45.02 megacycles. Should the original intensity of the tone be tripled, the frequency would vary from 44.97 to 45.03 megacycles. Thus, the frequency deviation for the three intensity values of the 1000-cycle note would be respectively 10, 20, and 30 kilocycles per second. In each case the frequency would

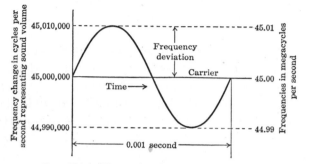

Fig. 329.   Illustrating frequency modulation
Note that the ordinates signify frequencies and not amplitudes

vary from its minimum to its maximum and back to the minimum frequency at the rate of 1000 times per second. Of course, the amplitude of the radiated wave would remain constant throughout.

Finally, suppose the tone being carried were to change from a pitch of 1000 to one of 4000 cycles per second, while maintaining the same intensity as originally employed. The radiated wave would vary over the same range (from 44.99 to 45.01 megacycles) as before, but now at a rate of 4000 times per second.

Reception of frequency modulated signals requires the use of specially constructed receivers. In addition to amplifiers and a detector, such a receiver includes two tubes, called a *limiter* and a *discriminator*. The first sets an upper limit to the plate current at a value which corresponds to a low signal potential on the grid of the tube and eliminates any amplitude variations in the incoming signals due to static or other causes. The discriminator transforms the frequency-modulated signals to corresponding ones of audio frequency. In the present allocation of channels, each station is allowed a band extending 100 kilocycles (0.1 megacycle) per second on each side of the carrier.

333. Television.—The problem of vision at a distance by electrical means has received much attention in recent years and several television systems are in experimental operation. The fundamental principles involve: 1, scanning the scene to be transmitted spot by spot in an orderly fashion; 2, establishing a current that varies with the light intensities of these spots; 3, amplifying these current variations and transmitting them over wire lines or by radio waves; 4, converting the electrical pulsations into corresponding light fluctuations at a receiving station; and 5, arranging these light patches upon a screen to form an image of the original scene. Further, the entire scene must be scanned repeatedly about 15 times or more per second in order that its successive images may merge to produce a steady result like that of motion pictures.

In the television system devised by Vladimir K. Zworykin, a narrow electron beam is used to scan an image of the scene in a photoelectric tube of special design called an *iconoscope*. This is an evacuated glass tube arranged as illustrated in Fig. 330. The electrons are emitted

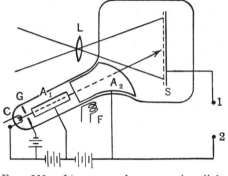

FIG. 330. Iconoscope for converting light image into varying current

by a heated cathode C, are controlled and focused by passing them through the grid G and the anodes A_1 and A_2, and are directed upon the screen S. This screen consists of a thin sheet of mica having a metal film on one side and a tremendous number of tiny photosensitive particles resembling a mosaic on the other. The scene to be transmitted is imaged upon the mosaic by a lens system L as shown, and as a result its particles are illuminated to various intensities. Each particle may be regarded as a tiny photoelectric cell that also forms a condenser with the metal film on the other side of the mica sheet, and therefore each one acquires a charge by photoelectric emission that depends upon the intensity of light upon it. The electron beam is deflected from one side to the other along a line, and then similarly from line to line by means of a magnetic field that is symbolized by F in the figure. In this way the entire image is scanned and the charges on the particles of the mosaic are released in succession, thereby establishing a current in the output circuit 1-2 that fluctuates in accordance with the light elements of the screen image. This current is amplified by electron tubes and transmitted to the distant station by methods already described in this chapter.

The television receiver comprises electrical receiving and amplifying tube circuits, together with a large vacuum tube resembling the cathode-ray oscillograph described in § 301.   The intensity of the electron beam in the tube is controlled by the fluctuating current that represents the incoming picture signals.   This beam is moved from side to side and from line to line by applying appropriate potentials to its deflecting plates as previously explained or by using a magnetic field for its deflection.   With proper synchronization of the scanning operation to that at the transmitter, an image of the original scene will be produced upon the fluorescent screen of the receiving tube.

334. Radar.—The method of ranging by radio waves, conceived before the recent war and developed tremendously during that conflict, is called "Radar," a contraction of *r*adio *d*etection *a*nd *r*anging. The technique is now being adapted to aerial and marine navigation. Aerial navigators use radar, when vision is obstructed, to determine altitude, to locate mountains, and to avoid aircraft in flight.   Marine navigators use the system at night or in fog to locate coastlines, icebergs, buoys, and ships.

The basic principle of radar is the reflection of radio waves from solid objects and the detection of the reflected waves at the same station from which the waves originated.   Since the velocity of the waves is known, it is only necessary to measure the time which elapses between the transmission of radio-frequency pulses and the arrival of the reflected waves in order to locate the object which caused the reflection.

The waves used in radar are very short, say from 3 to 10 cm. long, so that they can travel considerable distances without much diffraction, § 448.   The effective range of a marine radar extends from a circle of about 100-yard radius around the ship outward to the horizon, which may be from 10 to 15 miles away depending upon the height of the antenna.   Elevated areas, as well as tall structures beyond the horizon, can also be located as far away as 30 miles if they are in a direct line from the transmitting antenna.

Radar equipment includes an antenna, the transmitter and its modulator, the receiver and its indicator, and the usual power supply system and auxiliary circuits.

The antenna is a short conductor which has a parabolic reflector to focus the radio waves into a narrow beam, just as the parabolic reflector of a searchlight does with light.   The antenna assembly is rotated continuously when in use.

The transmitter has an oscillator of special design to generate the very short waves needed in radar; the frequencies range from 10,000 to 3000 megacycles per second. The modulator causes the transmitter to radiate its signals in short pulses, usually of 1 microsecond or less, with a recurrence rate of about 1000 pulses per second. The pulses are of high intensity; in fact, the power transmitted in each one may be of the order of several kilowatts.

When the transmitter is active, the radio-frequency power is conveyed to the antenna through an electronic switch which simultaneously short-circuits the input terminals of the receiver to protect that instrument from damage. Immediately after each pulse of power leaves the antenna, the switch removes the short-circuit and connects the receiver to the antenna so that the reflected pulse can be detected.

The electronic switch is essentially a needle spark gap within an enclosure containing gas under pressure. When a pulse is sent out from the transmitter, the high potential causes a spark at the gap and short-circuits the receiver; when the pulse ends, the gas de-ionizes in about four microseconds and the receiver is ready for any returning signal.

The receiver amplifies and rectifies the signal pulse and impresses it upon the cathode-ray oscilloscope of the indicator. Radial scanning is employed, in which the sweep starts from the center of the oscilloscope screen and spirals outward in a direction to match that of the radio beam from the antenna, and then returns quickly to the center. When the echo signal is received, the rectified pulse from the receiver is impressed on the grid which controls the intensity of the electron beam in the oscilloscope. In this way a bright spot appears on the screen for each echo received.

Since the time required for radio waves to reach an obstacle and return to the antenna is determined by the distance of this obstacle from the ship, the distance of a bright spot on the oscilloscope from the center of its screen bears a fixed relation to the distance of the obstacle. The range of the obstacle may be measured by turning a control on the set which moves an expanding circle on the screen to the position of the white spot which corresponds to that obstacle. The bearing or direction of the obstacle is determined generally by reference to a line from the center to the top of the screen; this line may represent either the lengthwise axis of the ship or the true north-south direction. Bearings from that line are read on a graduated circle around the edge of the screen.

The radar antenna rotates about a vertical axis at a speed up to 20 revolutions per minute, and scans the entire region about the ship with its wave beam. The electron beam of the oscilloscope is synchronized with the antenna and a corresponding trace is made on the screen. The retentivity of the screen material is such that the repeated scannings produce a picture of the region about the ship, obstacles appearing as bright spots on a dark background. Radars employing the higher antenna rotational speeds yield complete pictures, while those operating at lower speeds show only partial pictures

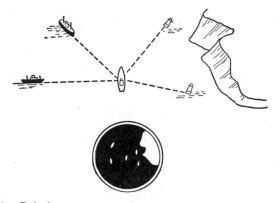

Fig. 331.   Relative appearance of a scene and its radar representation

which appear behind the scanning beam and fade almost completely before being reproduced again by subsequent scannings. Fig. 331 shows a typical scene and its appearance on the radar screen.

PROBLEMS

1. A 5-mile telegraph circuit consists of a line wire having at each end a 20-ohm sounder that requires 0.2 amp. for operation; the circuit is completed through a ground return of negligible resistance. If the circuit is to operate on 40 volts, what is the maximum allowable resistance of the wire per mile of line?

2. How far would it be possible to telegraph over a single Morse line having 8.4 ohms resistance per mile of length and having a 115-volt generator at each end? Assume that there are two 120-ohm relays in this series circuit, each requiring 0.05 amp. for actuation, and that the ground resistance is negligible.

3. The telephone circuit which joins a subscriber's instrument to the central office consists of a 60-ohm transmitter, two miles of line wire having a resistance of 44 ohms per mile, and a 24-volt battery. This series circuit also includes two windings of a "repeating coil" having 21 ohms each, two

"heat coils" (or fuses) of 3 ohms each, a "supervisory relay" of 9 ohms, and one winding of an induction coil having 14 ohms. (*a*) Determine the steady current in the circuit. (*b*) What percentage current change will be produced by a 15 per cent change in the resistance of the transmitter?

4. The gain of an amplifier is found to be 25 db. What is the ratio of the power output to the power input of the amplifier?

5. The input to a telephone repeater is 10 microwatts and its output is 2.5 watts. Calculate the gain of the repeater in decibels.

6. A telephone transmitter generates 10^{-11} watt of power when placed 1 ft. from a person speaking in a moderate tone of voice. If 15 watts are required to operate a loud-speaker system in a particular auditorium, what gain must be provided in an amplifier connected between transmitter and loud speakers to meet this requirement?

7. The oscillatory circuit of a vacuum-tube oscillator operating at 1 megacycle has an inductance of 0.1 millihenry. Calculate the capacitance of the condenser in this circuit.

8. How much inductance should be used with a 0.02-mf. condenser in order that the circuit so formed shall be tuned to a 25,000-cycle carrier current?

9. An antenna has a capacitance to ground of 0.00070 mf. and its circuit includes an inductance of 0.044 millihenry. What is the natural frequency of the antenna circuit?

10. A condenser of 0.00125 mf. is inserted in series with the antenna circuit of Problem 9. Determine the natural frequency under this condition.

11. A modern television picture is produced by 525 scanning lines, each of which may be regarded also as having 525 picture elements, on the assumption that the picture is square. Two such elements are scanned for each cycle of the video (vision) wave. If the entire picture is to be scanned 30 times per sec., what should be the frequency of the wave used in transmitting the video signals?

12. A radar echo is received at a ship's antenna 25 microseconds after the transmitting pulse leaves that antenna. How far from the ship is the obstacle that caused the echo?

13. (*a*) How many waves are there in a radar signal pulse lasting 40 microseconds when the station operates on 1750 kilocycles per second? (*b*) How many waves constitute a signal pulse lasting 1 microsecond when waves 10 cm. long are used in the transmission?

Electricity and
Magnetism Reviewed
with Mks. Units   *Chapter XXIX*

335. The Mks. System of Units.—In the foregoing chapters on Electricity and Magnetism use has been made of three separate systems of units. Two, the electrostatic and electromagnetic systems, are *absolute* systems, for they are based on the fundamental quantities length, mass, and time, together with an additional quantity, either the permittivity or the permeability of free space. The third system employs the so-called practical units, which are formed by multiplying the electromagnetic units by some power of 10 to make them easier to use. The student can now perceive the difficulties that arise from the multiplicity of unit systems, and appreciate the desirability of having a single system adopted. The present chapter introduces such a system and reviews the fundamental concepts of the subject in terms of the new units.

The system to be described embraces all of Mechanics together with Electrostatics and Electromagnetism, and was devised with a double purpose: first, to incorporate the practical electrical units such as the ampere, volt, ohm, joule, and watt; and second, to eliminate the powers of 10, such as 10^7, 10^{-1}, and 10^{-8}, that occur in many electrical expressions. This system was proposed by Professor Giovanni L. T. C. Giorgi in 1903 and was adopted by the International Committee on Weights and Measures in 1935. It is an absolute system based upon the meter, kilogram, and second as the fundamental units of length, mass, and time, and is known as the *meter-kilogram-second* or *mks. system*. The system is being used more and more in engineering, and it is expected that it will eventually replace the electrostatic and electromagnetic systems that are still in use after many years.

336. Applications to Mechanics.—Many of the concepts of Electricity are founded upon the principles of Mechanics, and therefore a brief consideration of the mks. system will first be given to this basic

subject.   The use of the meter as the unit of length and the kilogram
as the unit of mass means that area in mks. units is expressed in
square meters, volume in cubic meters, and density in kilograms per
cubic meter.   For example, the density of water, which in cgs. units
is given as 1 gm. per cm.^{3}, is given in the mks. units as 1000 kg. per
meter^3.   It is admitted that this particular unit is cumbersome.

The mks. unit of velocity is the meter per second, and that of
acceleration is the meter per second per second.   The unit of force
would be that needed to give a unit of mass a unit of acceleration; in
the mks. system the force unit is called the *newton*.   It is the only
new unit introduced in Mechanics, and is defined as follows: the
newton is the unbalanced force which will give a mass of 1 kg. an
acceleration of 1 meter per sec. per sec.   The application of Newton's
Second Law of Motion to the mks. system is expressed tersely as

$$\text{force} = \text{mass} \times \text{acceleration}$$

$$\text{newtons} = \text{kilograms} \times \frac{\text{meters}}{\text{second}^2}$$

To find the equivalent of the newton in cgs. units of force, consider
a 1-kg. mass to have its velocity changed every second by $1 \dfrac{\text{meter}}{\text{sec.}}$;
then, since 1 kg. = 1000 gm. and 1 meter = 100 cm., the force to
produce this acceleration is

$$1 \text{ newton} = 1000 \text{ gm.} \times 100 \frac{\text{cm.}}{\text{sec.}^2} = 100,000 \text{ dynes.}$$

The unit of work in the mks. system is the work done by a force
of 1 newton acting on a body through a distance of 1 meter in the
direction of the force, and is expressed as the newton-meter.   Since
the newton is 10^5 dynes, and the meter is 10^2 centimeters, the newton-
meter of work is equivalent to 10^7 dyne-cm. = 10^7 ergs, or 1 joule.
Consequently, the unit of work in the mks. system is the joule.   Thus

$$\text{work} = \text{force} \times \text{distance}$$

$$\text{joules} = \text{newtons} \times \text{meters}$$

Similarly, the mks. unit of power is the newton-meter per second,
which is the same thing as the joule per second, or the watt.

Many problems on work and energy with cgs. units require a conversion from ergs to joules by employing the factor 10^7.   These
conversions are not involved when mks. units are used.

337. Applications to Electromagnetism; the Ampere.—When two
wires are placed parallel to each other and current is established in
each, the force action between them depends upon the length and
separation of the conductors and upon the current strengths; further
it differs with the medium surrounding the conductors. This force
is given in equation (166) as

$$F = \frac{2\mu I_1 I_2 l}{r} 10^{-2}$$

where F is the force between the two parallel wires in dynes, μ is the
permeability of the medium, I_1 and I_2 are the currents in amperes,
l is the length of each conductor in centimeters, and r is the conductor separation in centimeters.

To adapt this equation to the mks. system of units, two changes
are necessary. First, the factor 10^{-2} is omitted. Second, the quantity μ is replaced by the product $\mu = \mu_v \mu_r$, where μ_v is the permeability
of empty space (vacuum) and μ_r is a factor known as the *relative
permeability* of the medium. The relative permeability is regarded
as a pure numeric and its value is the same as originally assigned to μ,
being unity for a vacuum, approximately 1 for air and non-magnetic
substances, and much greater for magnetic substances. With these
two changes, the force between the parallel wires becomes

$$F = \frac{2\mu_v \mu_r I_1 I_2 l}{r} \tag{207}$$

In order that the force may be given in newtons when I_1 and I_2 are
in amperes, and when l and r are in meters, an appropriate value is
assigned to the permeability of free space. This value of μ_v can be
obtained by computing the force between two conductors under
assumed conditions by means of equation (166), then converting the
result to newtons, substituting it in the mks. equation (207), and
finally solving for the permeability. Suppose that the two parallel
conductors are each 1 meter long, that they are 1 meter apart in a
vacuum, and that there is a current of 1 amp. in each. Under these
conditions, the quantities l and r are each 100 in equation (166),
while μ, I_1, and I_2 are each 1; whence the force between the conductors
is $F = 0.02$ dyne. This is equivalent to 2×10^{-7} newton. When
this value is substituted in equation (207), with the quantities μ_r,
I_1, I_2, l, and r each equal to 1, μ_v is found to be 10^{-7}. This will be
the result whatever conditions are assumed for the parallel wires.

Thus the value assigned to the permeability of empty space in the mks. system of units is 10^{-7}.

As a numerical illustration, consider the example solved in § 267 in which two wires carrying currents of 200 amp. each are located parallel to each other and 5 cm. apart in air (for which $\mu_r = 1$). The force acting between the wires per meter of length, by equation (207), is

$$F = \frac{2 \times 10^{-7} \times 1 \times 200 \times 200 \times 1}{0.05} = 0.16 \text{ newton}$$

This is equivalent to $0.16 \times 10^5 = 16,000$ dynes, which agrees with the previous answer.

The unit of current can be defined from equation (207) as follows: The *ampere* is that current which, when established in a pair of parallel wires each 1 meter long and spaced 1 meter apart in a vacuum, causes a force of 2×10^{-7} newton between them.

338. Other Applications to Electromagnetism.—In the mks. system the magnetic flux is expressed in a new unit, the *weber*, which is equivalent to 10^8 lines of induction or 10^8 maxwells. If a uniform flux Φ extends normally through an area A, the flux density in the region, as given by equation (162), is $B = \dfrac{\Phi}{A}$. The mks. unit for flux density is the weber per square meter and is equivalent to 10^8 maxwells $\div 10^4$ sq. cm. $= 10^4$ gausses.

The relation between flux density and field intensity was originally given as $B = \mu H$, by equation (163). This expression is modified in mks. units by replacing μ by $\mu_v \mu_r$ and becomes

$$B = \mu_v \mu_r H \tag{208}$$

where the field intensity H is necessarily expressed in a new unit if the flux density B is in webers per square meter.

From Ampère's generalization about the magnetic effect of the current, § 260, the equations for field intensity, expressed in mks. units, become:

At a point distant r meters from a straight wire carrying a current of I amp., $H = \dfrac{2I}{r}$.

At the center of a circular coil carrying a current of I amp., the coil having N turns and radius r meters, $H = \dfrac{2\pi NI}{r}$.

Along the curved axis of a ring solenoid of N turns and axial length l meters, with a current of I amp. in the winding, $H = \dfrac{4\pi NI}{l}$.

The flux in a ring solenoid can be evaluated by considering the flux density within it to be uniform. Suppose the solenoid to have an axial length of l meters and a cross-section of A square meters, and let it be wound with N turns carrying a current of I amp.; then if the flux density within it is B webers per square meter, the flux within it in webers is $\Phi = BA = \mu_v\mu_r HA$; whence $\Phi = \dfrac{4\pi\mu_v\mu_r NIA}{l}$, or

$$\Phi = \frac{\dfrac{4\pi NI}{l}}{\mu_v\mu_r A} \tag{209}$$

in which $4\pi NI$ is the magnetomotive force of the winding and $\dfrac{l}{\mu_v\mu_r A}$ is the reluctance of the magnetic path. The field intensity $H = \dfrac{4\pi NI}{l}$ is equal to the magnetomotive force of the winding divided by the length of the magnetic path; its unit in the mks. system is $\dfrac{1}{4\pi}$ ampere-turn per meter.

The force on a conductor located in a magnetic field can also be expressed basically in mks. units. Imagine a straight conductor in which the current is I_1 amp. and which therefore sets up a magnetic field having an intensity of $2\,I_1/r$ units at a distance r meters from the conductor. The flux density at this same distance in webers per square meter is $B = \mu_v\mu_r H = \dfrac{2\mu_v\mu_r I_1}{r}$. A second wire of length l meters placed parallel to the first at this location and carrying a current I amp. would experience a force in newtons of $F = \dfrac{2\mu_v\mu_r I_1 Il}{r}$, by equation (207). The combination of these equations shows that the force F in newtons on a conductor of length l meters, carrying a current I amp. and located in a region of flux density B webers per square meter, is

$$F = BIl \tag{210}$$

Related to the foregoing are the three expressions for induced emf., which in the mks. system are without powers of 10.   These are

$$E = -N\frac{d\Phi}{dt} \qquad E = -Blv \qquad E = -L\frac{dI}{dt} \qquad (211)$$

where E is in volts, L in henries, and other quantities are in the same units as previously explained for this system.

339. The Mks. Units in Electrostatics; the Coulomb.—The application of mks. units to electric charges may be considered in the same manner as with electric currents, § 337.   It is known that the force between two charges depends upon the magnitudes of the charges and the distance separating them, and differs with the surrounding medium.   Equation (126) gives the force in dynes as

$$F = \frac{Q_1 Q_2}{\epsilon r^2}$$

where Q_1 and Q_2 are the charges in electrostatic units, r is their separation in centimeters, and ϵ is the permittivity of the surrounding medium.   In the conversion to mks. units the quantity ϵ is replaced by the product $\epsilon = \epsilon_v \epsilon_r$, where ϵ_v is the permittivity of free space and ϵ_r is a factor called the *relative permittivity* of the medium.   The relative permittivity is regarded as a pure number and has the same value as that originally assigned to ϵ, being 1 for a vacuum and approximately 1 for air.   The expression for the mks. system becomes

$$F = \frac{Q_1 Q_2}{\epsilon_v \epsilon_r r^2} \qquad (212)$$

In order that the force F may be given in newtons when Q_1 and Q_2 are in coulombs and r in meters, an appropriate value is assigned to the permittivity of free space.

The value of ϵ_v is obtained from a fundamental expression in the subject of electromagnetic waves, which shows that the wave velocity in free space is determined by the permeability and permittivity of a vacuum.   The expression gives the velocity of electromagnetic waves as

$$c = \frac{1}{\sqrt{\mu_v \epsilon_v}} \qquad (213)$$

and this is true in any absolute system of units. In the mks. system, the wave velocity is 3×10^8 meters per sec., hence $\epsilon_v = \dfrac{1}{c^2 \mu_v} = \dfrac{1}{(3 \times 10^8)^2 \times 10^{-7}} = \dfrac{1}{9 \times 10^9}$, and this is the value assigned to the permittivity of free space in the mks. system.

To show that this value is consistent with others previously used, consider two charges of 1 coulomb each, which are separated 1 meter in a vacuum ($\epsilon_r = 1$). The force between them, from equation (212), is $\dfrac{1 \times 1}{\dfrac{1}{9 \times 10^9} \times 1 \times (1)^2} = 9 \times 10^9$ newtons. Since each of the charges is equivalent to 3×10^9 esu. of charge, the force between them is given by equation (126) as $\dfrac{3 \times 10^9 \times 3 \times 10^9}{1 \times (100)^2} = 9 \times 10^{14}$ dynes. This is equivalent to 9×10^9 newtons, as before.

340. Other Applications to Electrostatics.—The fundamental expressions for potential and for electric field intensity are the same in the mks. system as stated previously. The potential at a point in an electric field is given directly in joules per coulomb, or volts, by the basic equation (129), $V = \dfrac{W}{Q}$, where W is the work done upon a charge Q to bring it from an infinitely great distance to the point referred to. If two parallel plates spaced s meters apart are charged to a difference of potential V volts, the electric field intensity in the region between them is given by equation (132) as $\mathscr{E} = \dfrac{V}{s}$ in volts per meter.

Another unit for electric field intensity arises from the fundamental expression $\mathscr{E} = \dfrac{F}{Q}$, equation (127). If F is the force in newtons acting upon a charge of Q coulombs located in an electric field, then the field intensity is given in newtons per coulomb. This unit for electric field intensity is exactly equivalent to the more commonly used unit, the volt per meter.

The earlier expressions for the potential and field intensity at distances from a point charge are modified by the substitution of $\epsilon_v \epsilon_r$ for ϵ; whence, at a point r meters away from a charge of Q coulombs, the potential in volts is

$$V = \frac{Q}{\epsilon_v \epsilon_r r} \tag{214}$$

and the field intensity there in volts per meter is

$$\mathcal{E} = \frac{Q}{\epsilon_v \epsilon_r r^2} \tag{215}$$

At a point in an electric field where the field intensity is $\mathcal{E}$ volts per meter, the dielectric flux density is $\epsilon_v \epsilon_r \mathcal{E}$, and is expressed in lines per square meter. If this field is produced by a charge of Q coulombs, then the total flux extending from it in all directions is

$$\epsilon_v \epsilon_r \frac{Q}{\epsilon_v \epsilon_r r^2} \times 4\pi r^2 = 4\pi Q$$

Thus, 4π lines of dielectric flux extend from 1 coulomb of charge. It is to be observed that these lines have a different significance than in the electrostatic system, where 4π lines extend from 1 esu. of charge.

As an illustration, consider the work done in bringing one charge closer to another, as in the problem in § 211. In this example, two charges, one of $+600$ esu. and the other of $+500$ esu., are spaced 12 cm. apart in air initially and they are to have a final separation of 10 cm. The charges are respectively $\dfrac{600}{3 \times 10^9} = 2 \times 10^{-7}$ coulombs and $\dfrac{500}{3 \times 10^9} = 1.67 \times 10^{-7}$ coulombs. Suppose the larger one to remain at rest; the potential which it establishes at a point 0.12 meter away is $V_{12} = \dfrac{2 \times 10^{-7} \times 9 \times 10^9}{1 \times 0.12} =$ 15,000 volts, and at a point 0.10 meter away is $V_{10} = \dfrac{2 \times 10^{-7} \times 9 \times 10^9}{1 \times 0.10}$ $= 18,000$ volts. The work needed to move the other charge through the potential difference of 3000 volts is $1.67 \times 10^{-7} \times 3000 = 0.0005$ joule. This result is equivalent to 5000 ergs as found in the earlier solution.

341. Capacitance.—The capacitance of a condenser is given by the expression $C = \dfrac{Q}{V}$, equation (179), where Q is the charge on either of its plates when V is the potential difference between them. If s is the thickness of the dielectric separating the plates, then the electric field between them is $\mathcal{E} = \dfrac{V}{s}$.

In the mks. system the capacitance of the condenser will be in farads when the charge is in coulombs and the potential difference is in volts. With the dielectric thickness in meters, the electric field will be in volts per meter. The flux density in the dielectric of area A can be expressed in two ways: namely $\epsilon_v \epsilon_r \mathcal{E}$ and $\dfrac{4\pi Q}{A}$, as explained in the previous section. Hence, $\epsilon_v \epsilon_r \dfrac{V}{s} = \dfrac{4\pi Q}{A}$, and the capacitance of the condenser in farads becomes

$$C = \frac{\epsilon_v \epsilon_r A}{4\pi s} \tag{216}$$

In this expression, ϵ_r is the relative permittivity of the dielectric, and ϵ_v is the permittivity of free space; the latter has the value $\dfrac{1}{9 \times 10^9}$, as stated previously.

342. Applications to Electric Circuits.—The equations commonly used in electric circuits retain their form without change in the mks. system. Current I is expressed in amperes, emf. E and potential difference V in volts, resistance R in ohms, charge Q in coulombs, energy W in joules, and power P in watts, all of these being in agreement with the familiar practical units. In expressions involving time, the time t is in seconds. Consequently, in the following expressions the units used previously hold for the mks. system:

Current: $I = \dfrac{E}{R}$ or $\dfrac{V}{R}$

Charge: $Q = It$

Energy: $W = EIt$ or VIt

Energy expended in heat: $W = RI^2 t$

Power: $P = EI$ or VI

Power dissipated in heat: $P = RI^2$

343. The Rationalized Mks. System.—The foregoing sections show that the chief objectives of the mks. system of units have been met, in that the practical units are used directly in dealing with the electrical quantities and the powers of 10 are eliminated from the equations.

Through the years while the system has been developing, a somewhat different approach has been advocated as more rational than that described, and which leads to the "rationalized" mks. system as contrasted with the "unrationalized" form so far considered. The difference between these two forms can be explained by considering the equation for the flux in a magnetic circuit. Originally, magnetomotive force appeared in this equation as $\dfrac{4\pi NI}{10}$ gilberts, as in equation (178).   In the unrationalized mks. system, the magnetomotive force is stated as $4\pi NI$, and the permeability of free space, μ_v, is assigned the value 10^{-7} to give the flux in webers.   In the rationalized mks. system, the magnetomotive force is expressed simply as IN (ampere-turns) and the factor 4π is combined with the number 10^{-7} to make the value assigned to the permeability of free space $4\pi \times 10^{-7}$, so that the flux may still be in webers.

The permeability and permittivity of free space are related by equation (213) and, therefore, the product of these two quantities is a constant. It follows that a change in μ_v involves a corresponding change in ϵ_v. Consequently the expressions in which μ_v or ϵ_v appear will assume different forms when stated in terms of the rationalized and unrationalized units, but the two forms of the mks. system are otherwise the same.   The values for the permeability and permittivity of free space are given for the mks. and cgs. systems in the accompanying table.

Permeability and Permittivity of Free Space

Quantity	Mks.		Cgs.	
	Unrationalized	Rationalized	Electrostatic	Electromagnetic
μ_v	10^{-7}	$4\pi \times 10^{-7}$	$\dfrac{1}{9 \times 10^{20}}$	1
ϵ_v	$\dfrac{1}{9 \times 10^9}$	$\dfrac{1}{4\pi \times 9 \times 10^9}$	1	$\dfrac{1}{9 \times 10^{20}}$

The International Committee on Weights and Measures in adopting the mks. system did not specify a choice between the rationalized and unrationalized form.   A survey of the more advanced texts in Electrophysics shows a greater use of the rationalized form.   One of the principal reasons for this selection is the avoidance of the factor 4π in several of the more frequently used equations and the accompanying simplification of the units; thus the unit of magnetic field intensity is simply the ampere-turn per meter.

344. Tabulated Units and Conversion Factors.—Some of the more commonly used units are tabulated for the various systems in the following chart, and the relations among them are indicated by the conversion factors given in the last column.

Quantity	Symbol	Mks. unrationalized or rationalized		Practical	Cgs. Electrostatic	Cgs. Electromagnetic	Conversion factors
Length	l	meter		....	cm.		1 meter = 100 cm.
Mass	m	kg.		....	gm.		1 kg. = 1000 gm.
Time	t	sec.		....	sec.		
Force	F	newton		....	dyne		1 newton = 10^5 dynes
Work, energy	W	joule		joule	$\dfrac{\text{erg}}{}$ erg		1 joule = 10^7 ergs
Power	P	watt		watt	$\dfrac{\text{erg}}{\text{sec.}}$		1 watt = $10^7 \dfrac{\text{ergs}}{\text{sec.}}$
Charge	Q	coulomb		coulomb	esu. of charge	abcoulomb	1 coulomb = 3×10^9 esu. of charge = 0.1 abcoulomb
Current	I	ampere		ampere	$\dfrac{\text{esu. of charge}}{\text{sec.}}$	abampere	1 ampere = $3 \times 10^9 \dfrac{\text{esu. of charge}}{\text{sec.}}$ = 0.1 abampere
Emf; potential, potential difference	E, V	volt		volt	$\dfrac{\text{erg}}{\text{esu. of charge}}$	abvolt	1 volt = $\dfrac{1}{300} \dfrac{\text{erg}}{\text{esu. of charge}}$ = 10^8 abvolts
Resistance	R	ohm		ohm	esu. of resistance	abohm	1 ohm = $\dfrac{1}{9 \times 10^{11}}$ esu. of resistance = 10^9 abohms
Capacitance	C	farad		farad	esu. of capacitance	abfarad	1 farad = 9×10^{11} esu. of capacitance = $\dfrac{1}{10^9}$ abfarad
Inductance	L	henry		henry	esu. of inductance	abhenry	1 henry = $\dfrac{1}{9 \times 10^{11}}$ esu. of inductance = 10^9 abhenries
Electric field intensity	$\mathscr{E}$	$\dfrac{\text{volt}}{\text{meter}}$ or $\dfrac{\text{newton}}{\text{coulomb}}$		....	$\dfrac{\text{dyne}}{\text{esu. of charge}}$	....	$1 \dfrac{\text{volt}}{\text{meter}} = 1 \dfrac{\text{newton}}{\text{coulomb}} = \dfrac{1}{3 \times 10^4} \dfrac{\text{dyne}}{\text{esu. of charge}}$
Magnetic flux	Φ	weber		....	....	maxwell	1 weber = 10^8 maxwells
Magnetic flux density	B	$\dfrac{\text{weber}}{\text{sq. meter}}$		....	....	gauss	$1 \dfrac{\text{weber}}{\text{sq. meter}} = 10^4$ gausses
		Unrationalized	Rationalized				
Magnetomotive force	$\mathscr{F}$	$\dfrac{1}{4\pi}$ ampere-turn	ampere-turn	....	....	gilbert	1 unrationalized mks. unit = $\dfrac{1}{4\pi}$ rationalized mks. unit = 0.1 gilbert
Reluctance	$\mathscr{R}$	$\dfrac{1}{4\pi} \dfrac{\text{ampere-turn}}{\text{weber}}$	$\dfrac{\text{ampere-turn}}{\text{weber}}$	....	....	$\dfrac{\text{gilbert}}{\text{maxwell}}$	1 unrationalized mks. unit = $\dfrac{1}{4\pi}$ rationalized mks. unit = $\dfrac{1}{10^9} \dfrac{\text{gilbert}}{\text{maxwell}}$
Magnetic field intensity	H	$\dfrac{1}{4\pi} \dfrac{\text{ampere-turn}}{\text{meter}}$	$\dfrac{\text{ampere-turn}}{\text{meter}}$	....	....	oersted	1 unrationalized mks. unit = $\dfrac{1}{4\pi}$ rationalized mks. unit = $\dfrac{1}{1000}$ oersted

The mks. units are given in the third column, and it will be observed that there is no distinction between the unrationalized and the rationalized units until the last three entries are reached. In these the difference is only the factor 4π.

By way of illustration, imagine a parallel-plate capacitor having two plates 1 meter square spaced 1 cm. apart in air, and compute its capacitance. In rationalized units $\epsilon_v = \dfrac{1}{4\pi \times 9 \times 10^9}$ and the equation for capacitance is $C = \dfrac{\epsilon_v \epsilon_r A}{s}$. Hence, with a relative permittivity of unity ($\epsilon_r = 1$), the desired capacitance is $C = \dfrac{1 \times (1)^2}{4\pi \times 9 \times 10^9 \times 0.01} = 8.84 \times 10^{-10}$ farads. The same result would, of course, be obtained in the unrationalized units.

PROBLEMS

1. An automobile weighing 1700 kg. is accelerated uniformly from rest and acquires a speed of 65 km. per hr. in 10 sec. What force is necessary to produce this result?

2. Express the following constants in the mks. system of units:
(a) Surface tension of water = 75 dynes/cm.
(b) Stretch modulus of mild steel = 30×10^6 lb/sq. in.

3. An object of 1000-kg. mass is accelerated upward from rest and moves through a vertical distance of 20 meters in 10 sec. If the hoist has an efficiency of 60 per cent, what is its power input during the hoisting operation?

4. A cylinder contains compressed air at a gage pressure of 70,000 kg. per sq. meter when the temperature is 15° C. What will the gage pressure be when the temperature of the air is raised to 50° C. and its volume is reduced to $\frac{1}{3}$ the initial value?

5. Calculate the value of the gas constant for air in the mks. system.

6. Two electric power feeders, located parallel to each other and 0.08 meter apart, are fastened to cleats at distances of 2 meters along their length. On short circuit a current of 2000 amp. is directed in one feeder toward the fault and the same current is directed the other way in the second feeder. What force acts between the unsupported lengths of these feeders under these conditions?

7. Show that the mks. unit of magnetic field intensity in the unrationalized form is 1 millioersted.

8. In Problem 10 of Chapter 23, regard each pole piece as 0.2 meter high and 0.3 meter wide and take the flux extending between them to be 0.1 weber. What is the force on the wire when it carries 25 amp.?

9. A magnet is brought up toward a coil of 5 turns, increasing the flux through it from 10^{-4} to 2.5×10^{-4} weber in 0.3 sec. Compute the value of the emf. induced in the coil.

10. Show that the volt/meter as a unit of electric field strength is the same as the unit newton/coulomb.

11. Three point charges of 0.001 coulomb each are located at the corners of a triangle with sides 3 meters long. If two charges are + and the third is −, what is the magnitude of the electric field intensity at the center of the triangle? Assume the medium to have unit relative permittivity.

Sound

Wave Motion   *Chapter XXX*

---

345. Some Types of Waves.—In the study of wave motion it will
become apparent that waves are of many kinds and of common
occurrence. Water waves sweep across the surface of the ocean; distortional waves surge to and fro within vibrating bodies; sound waves
carry tones and noises through the air; and electromagnetic waves
transmit radio programs, light, and x-rays.

Probably everyone has thrown a stone into quiet water and
watched an ever-widening circular wave spread over the surface from
the point of impact. The water does not move as a whole, but some
particular configuration of the surface does. To set up such a configuration the individual particles of water must move in transmitting the wave, but their motion takes place over rather short paths.
Another example of wave propagation is the motion of a disturbance
along a rope stretched horizontally. If the rope is pulled by the
hand and the hand is moved up suddenly and then back again, a
wave will start along the rope. When launched in this way, the wave
consists practically of only one crest, and is called a *single-pulse* wave.
If the hand is moved up and down repeatedly, going through the
same motion each time, a *train* of waves will be set up in the rope.
These waves all have the same configuration and are called *periodic*
waves. Unless specially mentioned, all of the waves to be studied
herein are of this kind.

The motion of the prongs of a tuning fork sets up periodic waves
in the surrounding air. Each forward movement of a prong compresses the air in front of it, and each backward movement rarefies
the air. These conditions are transmitted outward from the fork
as a wave disturbance comprising so-called *condensations* and *rarefactions*. Upon entering the ear, these waves produce the sensation of
sound, and the waves themselves are called *sound waves*.

Waves can be produced by vibrations other than those of material
particles. The current in the antenna circuit of a radio station sets
up a magnetic field and an electric field in the region around it. As

the current oscillates, these fields continually build up and collapse, and in so doing set up electromagnetic waves which spread outward from the antenna. These waves are not transmitted by motion of air particles but by changes in the magnetic and electrical conditions of space.

Most waves can be classified as either longitudinal or transverse. A *longitudinal* wave is one in which the vibrating particles move forward and backward parallel to the direction in which the wave is propagated. The sound wave produced by the tuning fork alluded to ahead is longitudinal. In a *transverse* wave, the particles vibrate at right angles to the direction of propagation. The wave moving along the rope previously mentioned is transverse. Electromagnetic waves of all types act as transverse waves.

The progress of any wave involves two distinct motions. The wave itself in a homogeneous medium moves forward with constant speed, which means that the configuration advances equal amounts in equal periods of time. Meanwhile, the particles of the medium that conveys the wave vibrate to and fro in harmonic fashion. Their locations at successive moments depend upon the period, amplitude, and phase of the vibration. These terms have been used in the study of harmonic motion; their definitions are restated below, together with those of some other terms commonly used in wave motion.

The *period* of a vibrating particle is the time in which it completes one vibration, and the *frequency* is the number of vibrations completed per second. The *amplitude* of vibration is the maximum displacement from the undisturbed position. Two particles vibrating with the same frequency have definite *phase relations*. They are *in phase* when they continually pass through corresponding points of their paths at the same times. Otherwise, they are *out of phase;* for the particular condition where they reach their maximum displacements in opposite directions at the same instant, they are in *phase opposition*. The *wavelength* is the distance, measured along the direction of propagation, between two points which are in phase on adjacent waves.

346. The Mechanism of Wave Propagation.—The process by which a wave advances will be explained by reference to a mechanical model, Fig. 332, in which a long coiled spring with distributed small masses represents the medium and the small masses $A, B, C \ldots$ represent the vibrating particles. The spring is fastened at the distant end, and particle A is given harmonic motion along the path 0–1–2–0.

During the time that the end particle A is moving up to position 1, particle B is pulled upward by the spring tension, and proceeds in that direction, as shown in part I of the figure. Because of its inertia, B continues to move upward when A reverses its direction. As

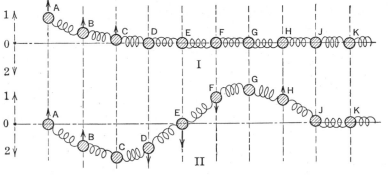

Fig. 332. Mechanical wave model illustrating a transverse wave

A moves to 2, a downward force acts on B which soon arrests its upward motion and causes it to move down. The same behavior is repeated at the lower end of the path, and it follows that B will have the same kind of motion as A, but will reach a corresponding point of the path a little later than A will. As a consequence of the inertia of the weights and the elasticity of the spring, similar motion will be imparted successively to all parts of the spring, and the weights will reach their maximum displacements in the sequence A, B, C and so on, causing the wave to advance toward the right. At the

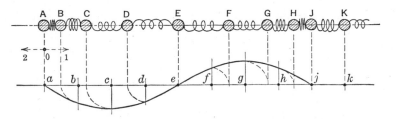

Fig. 333. A longitudinal wave and its transverse representation

instant represented in part II of the figure, A has been given a complete vibration and the wave has advanced to J; the wave along the spring has a crest at G and a trough at C.

The same model will also serve to illustrate the motion of a longitudinal wave, as represented in Fig. 333. Motion of A toward the right compresses the spring and motion toward the left extends it.

giving *B* the same kind of motion as *A*, except for a slight lag in phase. Similarly, *B* produces a corresponding motion of *C*, and so on. There results a series of condensations, in which the weights are close together, separated by rarefactions in which they are farther apart, both of which move to the right and constitute the advancing wave. In the condensations, the weights are moving in the same direction as the wave, while in the rarefactions they are moving in the opposite direction. At the instant shown in the figure, the wave in the spring has advanced to *J*.

In a longitudinal wave, the wave form is not apparent, but may be made so by laying off the displacements of the particles at right angles to the direction in which they actually occur. Such a construction is shown at the bottom of the figure. In this diagram the normal rest positions of the particles are indicated by corresponding lower-case letters and the displacements along the axis are shown turned through 90 degrees by means of arcs centered at these points.

From the behavior of the mechanical wave model, some general inferences may be made. Wave motion is evidently not due to bodily transfer of the medium through which the wave advances. It is caused by vibrations of individual particles over short ranges about normal rest positions, all the particles having the same kind of motion, but with a progressive change of phase along the direction of propagation. Moreover, mechanical wave motion requires that the transmitting medium possess both inertia and elasticity; for electromagnetic waves these properties are replaced by their electrical equivalents, inductance and capacitance.

347. Energy Transmission by Waves.—Waves transmit energy along the direction of propagation. This fact can be illustrated by the mechanical model of Figs. 332 and 333 which shows waves progressing to the right. For either type of wave, each section of the spring exerts a force on the weights at its ends, and the weights at the right move in the direction of this force, but those at the left are constrained to move in opposition to it. Each spring section thus *does work on* the weight *ahead* of it and *has work done upon it* by the weight *behind* it, § 65, and each weight, in turn, performs a similar action on the adjoining spring sections. Hence, a continuous transfer of energy takes place in the direction of wave travel. In the model described, if no energy were wasted as the wave advances, the amplitude of vibration would be the same for all of the weights. On the other hand, in a wave which spreads out as it advances, such as a circular wave on the surface of water, the amplitude of vibration would diminish as the wave progresses, since the energy is distributed over a larger and larger surface. The energy of a wave may be transformed in various ways; for example, that of a sound wave may be converted into mechanical energy in setting the ear drum into vibration.

When a wave encounters a medium of a different character, some of its energy will be *reflected* back into the initial medium, and the rest will be *transmitted* into the second medium; also, as the wave advances, part of its energy will be *absorbed*. For a light wave which impinges upon a sheet of glass, most of the energy is transmitted to the region beyond the glass, part being returned by reflection at the surfaces and a small portion being absorbed within the glass itself. When a light wave strikes black velvet, no light is reflected from it nor transmitted through it; the energy is absorbed by the velvet and its temperature is raised.

348. Equations of Wave Motion.—The relationship between the frequency of vibration of the source, the velocity of propagation of the wave, and the wavelength, § 202, is applicable to all wave motion.

Assume that a body is vibrating at a definite rate and that it produces a wave in the surrounding medium. In the periodic time T, the vibrating body completes one vibration, and the wave meanwhile advances uniformly a distance equal to its wavelength λ, whence the speed or velocity of the wave is $V = \lambda/T$. But the period T is the reciprocal of the frequency f, and hence the wave velocity is

$$V = f\lambda \tag{217}$$

The wave velocity V in this expression is determined completely by the properties of the transmitting medium and does not depend upon either the frequency of the source or the wavelength. It follows that whenever f changes there must be a corresponding change in λ to satisfy the equation.

To consider the relation between wave propagation and the motion of the particles in the transmitting medium, imagine a source vibrating with frequency f and amplitude r, so that its displacement at any instant is given by the expression

$$y_s = r \sin 2\pi ft \tag{218}$$

in which t is the time reckoned from the instant when the vibrating source passes through the midposition of its path in a positive direction. This motion is imparted to the particles of the surrounding medium; as the disturbance moves forward from the source it will reach these particles one after another and upon reaching each, will give it the same type of motion as the source. If the disturbance moves with a velocity V, then to travel a distance x will require a time $\dfrac{x}{V}$, and consequently the displacement of a particle in the medium at a distance x from the source will be

$$y_p = r \sin 2\pi f \left(t - \frac{x}{V} \right) \tag{219}$$

Although this expression gives the displacement of the particle in the medium, t is still reckoned from the time the vibrating source passes the midposition of its path. It will be clear that the displacement of the source at a given instant will be duplicated by the vibrating particle after a time interval $\dfrac{x}{V}$; thus, if t is given a particular value in equation (218) and is increased by $\dfrac{x}{V}$ in equation (219) the values of y_s and y_p will be identical.

The wave equation, (219), shows how the displacement of the vibrating particles vary with respect to their locations and also with respect to time. By selecting a particular value for t and plotting the values of y for different values of x, a sine wave is obtained which represents a snap shot of the wave in space; if this process is repeated for a slightly greater value of t, it will be found that the whole wave profile has moved away from the source.

To learn how the displacement of a particle of the medium varies from moment to moment, a particular value for x is selected to represent the distance of the particle from the source and y is plotted against t. This also yields a sine curve and represents the harmonic vibration of the particle in the medium with respect to time.

349. Wave in a Stretched Rope.—The velocity of a transverse wave in a stretched rope is determined by the mass of the rope per unit length and the force or tension with which the rope is stretched. To show how these quantities are related, suppose a rope is stretched horizontally and that it is given an impulsive blow at one place, thereby producing a dent having the shape shown in Fig. 334. The displacement sets up a distortional wave which will travel along the rope with some velocity V, substantially retaining the shape of the dent in its forward motion. To keep this dent stationary in space, imagine the rope to be of indefinite length and to be carried with the same speed V in the opposite direction. With this artifice, sections of the rope move continuously around the curve; perhaps the reader will have observed the maintenance of such shapes in the movement of belts between pulleys. The force acting upon the curved section

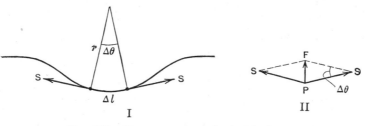

FIG. 334. Transverse wave in stretched rope

of the rope can be evaluated if the dent, or a small part of it, is regarded as circular, for the force then becomes the centripetal force of circular motion.

In part I of the figure, the short central portion of the dent Δl is considered as a circular arc of radius r subtending an angle $\Delta\theta$ at the center. If this portion of the rope has a mass Δm, the centripetal force acting upon it is $F = \dfrac{\Delta m V^2}{r}$, and is provided jointly by the forces S,S, each representing the stretching force in the rope. These forces are laid from a common point P in part II of the figure, and since $\Delta\theta$ is very small, it follows as a close approximation that $F:S = \Delta l:r$, whence

$$\frac{\Delta m V^2}{rS} = \frac{\Delta l}{r} \qquad \text{or} \qquad V^2 = \frac{S}{\dfrac{\Delta m}{\Delta l}}$$

The mass of the rope per unit of its length, namely $\dfrac{\Delta m}{\Delta l}$, may be designated as m_1. Consequently, the velocity of the rope, and its equivalent, the velocity of the wave along the rope, will be

$$V = \sqrt{\frac{S}{m_1}} \tag{220}$$

This expression as derived is suited to units of the absolute system. In metric units, S is expressed in dynes and m_1 in grams per centimeter; with these units V will be given in centimeters per second. In

British units, S is in poundals and m_1 in pounds per foot, and V will be given in feet per second.

As an illustration, suppose a wave to be established in a 40-ft. rope which weighs 5 lb. and which is stretched with a force of 50 lb. The force is 50 lb. $\times$ 32 ft/sec.^{2} = 1600 lb-ft/sec.^{2} = 1600 poundals, and the mass of the rope per unit length is 5 lb/40 ft. = 0.125 lb/ft. Therefore the wave velocity will be

$$V = \sqrt{\frac{1600 \text{ lb-ft/sec.}^2}{0.125 \text{ lb/ft.}}} = 113.1 \text{ ft/sec.}$$

and the time required to travel the length of the rope will be 40 ft. ÷ 113.1 ft/sec. = 0.354 sec.

*350. Propagation of Sound.—The longitudinal waves transmitting sound do not pass through a vacuum. This fact can be demonstrated by operating an electric bell within the chamber of an air pump and then withdrawing the air; the hammer can be seen striking the bell but no sound will be heard. The physical medium required for the propagation of sound may be in the state of a solid, liquid or gas. Consideration will first be given to propagation within a liquid, and the analysis will show that the velocity is determined by the elasticity and density of the medium. The expression for this velocity is found by comparing the pressure and velocity of the particles within a condensation with these characteristics of the particles in the undisturbed medium, and evaluating the force which produces the change of motion.

Fig. 335 pictures a longitudinal wave, represented by vertical lines, advancing toward the left with a speed V through a liquid

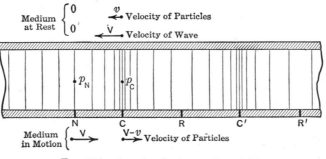

FIG. 335. Longitudinal wave in a fluid

medium. The liquid is assumed to have a constant cross-section. Rarefactions are shown at R and R', and condensations at C and C'; at point N just ahead of the foremost condensation the medium is as yet undisturbed by the wave. It will be remembered that in a condensation the vibrating particles are moving in the same direction as the wave; consequently the medium at C will have some velocity v toward the left when that at N is at rest, as indicated at the top of the figure. Also, it is evident that the pressure at C is greater than that at N, since C is at a condensation. In what follows, the conditions at these two points will be considered in further detail.

Imagine that the liquid as a whole is moving with the same speed V as the wave but in the opposite direction, so that the rarefactions and condensations remain stationary with respect to the surroundings. Let t be the time required for the liquid stream to flow from N to C; in this time interval a certain mass of liquid passes N at a speed V and an equal mass passes C at a reduced speed, namely $V-v$, as indicated at the bottom of the figure; the reduction of speed will be called ΔV. Suppose that in time t a mass of liquid m undergoes a speed reduction ΔV; that is, it has a negative acceleration equal to $\Delta V/t$. The reduction in speed may be attributed to the fact that the pressure p_C acting backward upon the liquid at C is greater than the pressure p_N urging it forward at N. Let Δp represent the unbalanced pressure $p_C - p_N$, and A the sectional area of the liquid; then from equation (31), the force on the liquid under consideration is

$$A \, \Delta p = m \frac{\Delta V}{t}$$

The mass m may be evaluated by considering the liquid passing point N, where the density of the undisturbed medium is d. The volume of liquid passing this point in time t is AVt by equation (86), and hence its mass is $m = AVtd$. If this value is substituted in the foregoing equation there results:

$$A \, \Delta p = AVtd \frac{\Delta V}{t}$$

whence

$$Vd = \frac{\Delta p}{\Delta V} \quad \text{or} \quad V^2 d = \frac{\Delta p}{\Delta V/V}$$

The equation will be modified further by expressing the denominator in terms of volume B (bulk) rather than velocity V. The liquid which at N would occupy a volume $B = AVt$ is compressed by an amount $\Delta B = At \, \Delta V$ upon reaching C. In consequence $\dfrac{\Delta B}{B} = \dfrac{At \, \Delta V}{AVt} = \dfrac{\Delta V}{V}$, and

$$V^2 d = \frac{\Delta p}{\Delta B/B} = E$$

where E is the bulk modulus of elasticity of the liquid, § 104. Hence the speed of the liquid, and consequently that of the wave, is

$$V = \sqrt{\frac{E}{d}} \tag{221}$$

In metric units, E is expressed in dynes per square centimeter and d in grams per cubic centimeter; then V will be in centimeters per second. Similarly, in British units, E is in poundals per square foot, d in pounds per cubic foot, and V in feet per second.

The foregoing treatment may also be applied to the transmission of sound along a solid rod. The result will be the same as that just obtained, except that E will be Young's modulus of the medium rather than its bulk modulus.

351. Velocity of Sound in Gases.—The method used in the preceding section for finding the velocity of a sound wave in a liquid which resulted in the equation $V = \sqrt{\dfrac{E}{d}}$ can also be used when the medium is gaseous. In order to interpret the elastic modulus E, it becomes necessary to inquire how the volume B of the gas is affected by changes in the pressure p. If the temperature remained constant during compression and expansion, then in accordance with Boyle's Law, § 137, a change of pressure Δp would cause a change of volume ΔB such that

$$pB = (p + \Delta p)(B - \Delta B)$$

The small $\Delta p\,\Delta B$ product is negligible, whence $p\,\Delta B = B\,\Delta p$, or $p = \dfrac{\Delta p}{\Delta B/B} = E$. Hence if the compressions and expansions were isothermal the velocity of the wave would be $V = \sqrt{p/d}$.

In the passage of a sound wave, the medium undergoes compression and expansion at a rapid rate, usually several hundreds of times each second. Throughout the range to which the ear responds, it has been found for gaseous mediums that the heat generated during compression does not escape quickly enough to maintain uniform temperature, and that the compressions and expansions should be considered adiabatic rather than isothermal. In an adiabatic process, the pressure change Δp corresponding to a given volume change ΔB is γ times as great as for an isothermal process, where γ represents the ratio of the specific heats c_p/c_v, § 176. Hence, for such a process

$$\frac{\Delta p}{p} = \gamma\,\frac{\Delta B}{B}$$

and the modulus of elasticity E in equation (221) should be replaced by γp. Consequently the velocity of a sound wave in gases becomes

$$V = \sqrt{\frac{\gamma p}{d}} \qquad (222)$$

the units being the same as before; see also § 377. For air under standard pressure and at a temperature of 0° C. the value of γ is 1.40 and the values of p and d are given in Chapter XIII; from these it is found that sound travels at a velocity

$$V = \sqrt{1.40 \times 1,013,000 \frac{\text{dynes}}{\text{cm.}^2} \div 0.001293 \frac{\text{gm.}}{\text{cm.}^3}} = 33,130 \text{ cm/sec.}$$

The velocity of sound in the atmosphere is unaffected by changes in the barometric pressure because the density is changed in the same proportion, thereby leaving the ratio p/d unchanged. Changes in the temperature of the atmosphere, however, affect the density without influencing the pressure, and hence cause a change in the wave velocity. An inspection of the General Gas Law, equation (107), shows that the density of a gas varies inversely with its absolute temperature T. From this fact, and from equation (222), it follows that $V \propto \sqrt{T}$. Consequently, for two conditions 1 and 2, the ratio of the velocities of sound becomes

$$\frac{V_1}{V_2} = \sqrt{\frac{T_1}{T_2}} \qquad (223)$$

Some values of sound velocity in various media are given in the following table:

Velocity of Sound

	Temper-ature °C.	Velocity	
		meters per sec.	ft. per sec.
Air, standard pressure......	0	331.3	1,087
Aluminum................	..	5,100	16,700
Copper..................	..	3,970	13,000
Hydrogen, standard pressure	0	1,286	4,220
Iron and steel............	..	4,900 to 5,100	16,000 to 16,700
Lead....................	..	1,230	4,040
Water...................	15	1,450	4,760

For calculations in which the effect of temperature is of no interest, the velocity of sound in air may be taken in round numbers as 1100 ft. per sec.

*352. Water Waves.—In surface waves, like those observed on water, the particles transmitting the disturbance move longitudinally as well as transversely. When the liquid is deep, the velocity of wave propagation depends upon the gravitational force on the liquid and upon its surface tension; it can be shown by extended analysis that the equation for the wave velocity is

$$V = \sqrt{\frac{g\lambda}{2\pi} + \frac{2\pi T}{\lambda d}}$$

where g is the acceleration due to gravity, T is the surface tension, d is the density of the liquid, and λ is the wavelength. In shallow liquids the wave velocity is found to depend upon the depth h rather than the wave length λ, and is expressed by the equation

$$V = \sqrt{gh}$$

being independent of the surface tension of the liquid.

353. Electromagnetic Waves.—Although many waves are transmitted by the mechanical vibration of physical particles, there are others in which the propagation is due to periodic variations in electric and magnetic fields; these are called electromagnetic waves. In the study of Electricity and Magnetism, it will be recalled that unit electric charge was defined in § 261 by entirely independent means in the electromagnetic and the electrostatic systems of units. A more detailed analysis shows that the ratio of the electromagnetic unit of charge (based on electricity in motion) to the electrostatic unit of charge (based on electricity at rest) has the dimensions of velocity. This ratio is found by direct measurement to have the value 3×10^{10} when the dimensions are reduced to centimeters per second. Furthermore, the velocity of light in empty space is almost exactly 3×10^{10} cm. per sec.; this coincidence suggested to Maxwell that light is propagated by electromagnetic waves.

Theory shows that the velocity of electromagnetic waves in a material medium is given by

$$V = \frac{c}{\sqrt{\mu_r \epsilon_r}} \qquad (224)$$

in which c represents the value 3×10^{10} cm. per sec., and μ_r and ϵ_r represent the relative permeability and the relative permittivity of the medium respectively, as explained in Chapter XXIX. The value of ϵ_r depends on the wavelength of the particular waves being transmitted. For empty space both μ_r and ϵ_r are taken as unity and so for a vacuum $V = c$ in the foregoing equation.

The velocity of light, radio, and other electromagnetic waves is approximately the same in air under standard conditions as in a vacuum. The value 3×10^{10} cm. per sec. or 186,000 mi. per sec. may be used for either air or vacuum without appreciable error for most purposes.

Many kinds of radiations are propagated by electromagnetic waves, their wavelength ranges being of the order listed in the accompanying table. These waves are all of the same character and differ only in frequency and wavelength.

The Electromagnetic Spectrum

Type of wave	Wavelength
Radio, low frequency............	30,000 to 1,000 meters
" high frequency...........	1,000 to 1 meter
" ultra high frequency......	100 to 1 cm.
Infra-red......................	0.030 to 0.000076 cm.
Visible light...................	0.000076 to 0.000040 cm.
Ultraviolet.....................	0.000040 to 0.0000013 cm.
X-rays.........................	10^{-6} to 10^{-9} cm.
γ-rays.........................	10^{-8} to 5×10^{-11} cm.

354. Wave-front Construction; Huygens' Principle.—A wave front is a surface of which all points are vibrating in phase. Fig. 336 illustrates a wave spreading outward from a source S, and the line W represents a wave front connecting particles of the medium which are momentarily at their greatest distances in a positive direction from the undisturbed positions. In a homogeneous medium the wave front from a point disturbance is spherical; however, at considerable distances from the source, small portions of such a wave front may be regarded as plane.

By studying the changes in wave front which occur as a wave advances, it is possible to predict the effects that will be produced when a wave encounters an obstruction or when it is reflected or refracted. This study is greatly assisted by use of a principle accredited to the Dutch scientist, Christian Huygens (1629–1695).

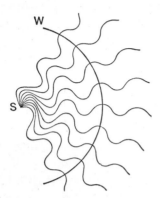

Huygens' Principle states that *every point on a wave front acts as though it were itself a center of disturbance, sending out little wavelets of its own, always away from the source, the collective effect of which constitutes a new wave front.* Starting with a wave front in any given position, these wavelets may be represented by arcs of equal radius drawn from various points on the wave front as centers, the radius representing the distance the wavelets would advance in some specified time. A line or surface tangent to these arcs on the side toward which the wave is advancing shows the new shape and location of the wave front at the end of the time interval selected.

FIG. 336. Illustrating a wave front

This construction is applied in part I of Fig. 337 to a plane wave front P and to a spherical wave front S, both advancing toward the right to new positions at P_1 and S_1 respectively. The progression

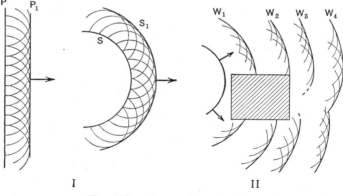

FIG. 337. Huygens' construction

of a wave around an obstruction is illustrated in part II of the figure. The same procedure is followed in constructing the successive wave fronts W_1 to W_4, but the time intervals between them are purposely made different.

355. Law of Reflection.—The behavior of a wave upon striking a reflecting surface can be determined by Huygens' construction. In Fig. 338, a plane wave front represented in cross-section by the line *AB* is shown impinging upon the surface *MN*, through which it cannot pass. If this surface had not been present, the wave would have advanced without change in direction, and in a certain time interval would have reached the position *CD*. The presence of the reflecting surface, however, causes a change in the direction of the wave front. In the particular time interval, different points on the

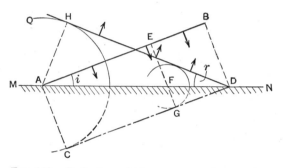

FIG. 338.   Reflection of plane wave at plane surface

wave front move as follows: *B* advances directly to *D*; *A* cannot move to *C* and travels an equal distance above the surface to some point on the arc *CQ* of radius *AC*; and any other point *E* advances without obstruction to *F* and, being unable to continue to *G*, travels an equal distance to some point on the arc of radius *FG*. The line *DH* tangent to the arcs is a cross-section of the wave front at the end of the specified time, the wave being reflected back into the region above the surface *MN*.

The line *AB* represents the *incident* wave front and *DH* represents the *reflected* wave front. The angles *i* and *r* that these wave fronts make with the reflecting surface are called the angles of incidence and of reflection respectively. To show the relation between these angles, draw the radius *AH* to the point of tangency *H*. Since *BD* = *AC* = *AH*, the right triangles *ADH* and *DAB* are equal, and consequently the angles *i* and *r* are equal. These angles are also coplanar, since the points *A*, *B*, *D*, and *H* lie in the same plane. These facts are embodied in the *law of reflection*, which states that *when a wave incident upon a plane surface is reflected, the angles of incidence and of reflection are equal, and lie in the same plane.*

356. Law of Refraction.—A wave which enters another medium obliquely will undergo an abrupt change in direction if the velocity of the wave in the second medium is different from that in the first. This phenomenon is called *refraction*.   In Fig. 339, the incident wave front AB, moving with velocity V_1 in medium 1, encounters the interface MN at an angle of incidence i.   Here it is partly reflected back into medium 1 and partly transmitted through medium 2. Consider the transmitted portion and suppose its velocity to be V_2. In the time required for B on the wave front to advance in the first medium a distance BD to the interface at D, point A does not move

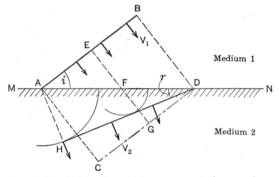

Fig. 339.   Refraction of plane wave at plane surface

an equal distance to C, but moves a distance $(V_2/V_1) \times AC = AH$ in the second medium to some point on the arc centered at A.   Any other point E advances to F in the first medium and then moves a distance $(V_2/V_1) \times FG$ in the second medium to some point on the arc centered at F.   The line DH drawn tangent to these arcs represents the refracted wave front at the end of this time interval, and the angle r which it makes with the interface is called the *angle of refraction.*

It was discovered by Willebrod Snell (1591–1626), Dutch astronomer and mathematician, that the ratio of the sine of the angle of incidence to the sine of the angle of refraction is constant for given mediums.   To find the relation between these angles draw the radius AH to the point of tangency H, and note that $\sin i = BD/AD$ and $\sin r = AH/AD$.   Consequently

$$\frac{\sin i}{\sin r} = \frac{BD}{AH} = \frac{BD}{(V_2/V_1)BD}$$

or

$$\frac{\sin i}{\sin r} = \frac{V_1}{V_2} \tag{225}$$

This relation expresses the *law of refraction*, which states that *when a wave travels obliquely from one medium into another, the ratio of the sine of the angle of incidence to the sine of the angle of refraction is the same as the ratio of the respective wave velocities in these mediums, and is a constant for two particular mediums.* The angles of incidence and refraction lie in the same plane.

357. Interference of Waves.—Two waves moving simultaneously through the same region will advance independently, each producing the same disturbance of the medium as though it were alone. The combined action of both waves can be pictured by adding the ordinates of the component waves algebraically, point by point.

Two waves of the *same frequency, in phase with each other*, and moving in the *same direction*, produce *reenforcement*. This result is

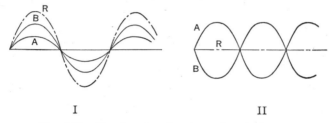

I   II

Fig. 340.   Reenforcement and annulment of waves

shown in part I of Fig. 340, in which the individual waves are represented by *A* and *B*. The resultant wave *R* is in phase with the component waves and has an amplitude equal to the sum of their amplitudes.

Two waves of the *same frequency, in phase opposition*, and moving in the *same direction*, produce *destructive interference;* if further they have *equal amplitudes*, the result is a complete *annulment*. An annulment is represented in part II of Fig. 340, the amplitude of the resultant *R* of the individual waves *A* and *B* being zero at all points. In the wave-front constructions in Figs. 338 and 339 the multiplicity of wavelets, typified by the two arcs in each diagram, also interfere with each other, and it can be shown that these wavelets annul one another except at the outermost points where the envelope representing the new position of the wave front is located.

Two waves of *slightly differing frequencies* produce a type of *pulsating interference* which is particularly noticeable ↙ith sound waves. The resulting sound is alternately loud and soft, giving pulses or throbs which are spoken of as *beats*. The effect is most pronounced when the individual waves have equal amplitude. Suppose two such waves A and B to originate from vibrating sources at M in Fig. 341, and let the frequency of the source generating A be 1 vibration per sec. greater than that of B. Each source sets up a train of waves; these are indicated in the figure at a particular instant by their transverse representations, and their resultant is shown by wave R. At the instant shown, the sources are vibrating in phase, and the waves produce reenforcement at M and P and an annulment at N. At an instant $\frac{1}{2}$ sec. later, the sources will be in phase opposition, and the waves A and B will be displaced with respect to each other by one-half wavelength from the positions shown, producing annulments at M and P and a reenforcement at N. At another instant

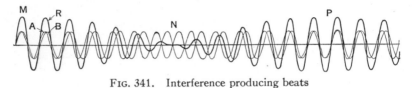

FIG. 341.　Interference producing beats

$\frac{1}{2}$ sec. later still, the sources will once more vibrate in phase, and the relative positions of the waves will again be as shown in the figure. These changes will continually recur as long as the sources are kept in vibration. An observer at any point along the path MNP will notice a reenforcement and an annulment of sound each second, that is, he will hear 1 beat per sec. If the difference in frequency of the sources were d vibrations per sec., then at a given point, a reenforcement would change to an annulment and back to a reenforcement again in $1/d$ sec., and the observer would hear d beats per sec.

358. Stationary Waves.—Two waves of *equal frequency and amplitude*, moving in *opposite directions* through the same medium, produce a *stationary* or *standing* wave. Such a wave has stationary *nodes*, or points of zero displacement, with intermediate *antinodes* at which the displacement varies between its widest limits. In Fig. 342, B and C represent two such waves and R is their resultant. In part I of the figure, the component waves coincide, yielding a resultant of double amplitude. In part II, representing the situation $\frac{1}{8}$ of a period later, both B and C have advanced $\frac{1}{8}$ wavelength in their respective directions; and in part III, for an instant $\frac{1}{8}$ period later still, a similar advance has occurred, bringing the component waves into opposition. As the waves progress, the nodes N of the resultant remain fixed in space $\frac{1}{2}$ wavelength apart, and the intervening antinodes A undergo a maximum variation of displacement.

The production of stationary waves can be demonstrated with a rope that is fastened to a wall at one end and moved transversely

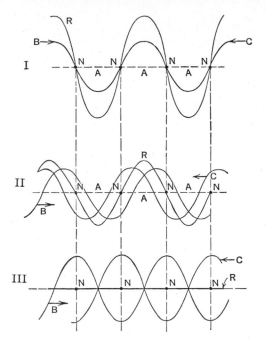

FIG. 342.   Location of fixed nodes in stationary wave

with appropriate frequency at the other end.   The outgoing waves are reflected at the wall with little reduction of amplitude, and consequently the two wave trains set up a stationary wave in the rope.

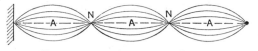

FIG. 343.   Stationary wave in rope

Fig. 343 illustrates the appearance when the rope vibrates in three segments with nodes at *N*, the rope whipping back and forth at the antinodes *A*.

In an experiment devised by Franz E. Melde, stationary waves were produced in a string fastened to one prong of a vibrating tuning fork. Assume that the string is 90 cm. long and has a mass of 0.1 gm., and that the fork is kept vibrating electrically at 264 vibrations per sec.   Find the stretching force that should be applied to the string when it extends along the direction of the prong so that the string will form 3 segments.   The

length of each segment is 30 cm., the wavelength is 60 cm., and consequently
the velocity of propagation is 264 $\times$ 60 = 15,840 cm. per sec. The required
stretching force in the string is found by equation (220) to be $S = m_1 V^2$

$$= \frac{0.1 \text{ gm.}}{90 \text{ cm.}} \times \left(15,840 \; \frac{\text{cm.}}{\text{sec.}} \right)^2 = 279,000 \text{ dynes} = 285 \text{ gm.}$$

Another interesting way in which the production of stationary
waves can be illustrated makes use of a flat dish with mercury and a
tuning fork with a stylus on each prong. When the fork is set into
vibration and each stylus is brought in contact with the mercury,

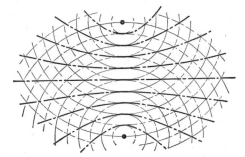

Fig. 344.   Interference pattern on mercury surface

circular waves will proceed from the points of contact. These are
represented at some particular instant by the concentric circles in
Fig. 344, the full lines representing the crests and the dotted ones the
troughs. At points where full lines intersect or dotted lines intersect,
the waves from the two sources meet in phase, and the disturbance
of the surface by one source is reenforced by that of the other. Between these points, however, are intersections of full lines with dotted
lines; these represent the meeting of a crest from one source with a
trough from the other and are, therefore, points where destructive
interference occurs. The surface of the mercury is thus divided into
regions of maximum disturbance (shown by the heavy lines), separated by lanes where the surface remains almost perfectly at rest.

PROBLEMS

*The numerical values of the moduli of elasticity and of densities of materials
will be found in §§ 105, 121, and 141.*

1. A reed vibrates back and forth 400 times a second and produces a
longitudinal wave that travels 100 meters in air in 0.29 sec. and travels the
same distance in water in 0.068 sec. Compute the period and wavelength
of the wave (*a*) in air, and (*b*) in water.

2. If the tip of the reed mentioned in Problem 1 vibrates with an amplitude of 3 mm., what is its displacement at an instant (*a*) 0.001 sec. after it passes through its midposition? (*b*) also $\frac{1}{800}$ sec. after it passes one of its end positions?

3. A string 200 yd. long weighs 4.0 oz. Determine the velocity of a transverse wave in this string when it is stretched with a force of 2 lb.

4. Derive an expression for the velocity of a transverse wave in a stretched wire in terms of the radius of the wire, the density of the material of which it is made, and the force with which it is stretched.

5. A stretching force of 18,000 dynes is applied to a long wire which has a mass of 5 gm. per meter of length. With what frequency should the wire be vibrated in order to set up a traveling wave in it having a wavelength of 10 cm.?

6. If a wire 4 ft. long which weighs 0.0014 lb. is stretched between two points, with what force must the wire be pulled in order that a transverse wave set up in it may travel from one end to the other in 0.003 sec.?

7. A rope weighing 2 oz. per ft. is fastened to a support at one end, and to the other end is tied another rope weighing 0.5 oz. per ft. The ropes are subjected to a tension of 400 lb. and the lighter one is set into vibration with a frequency of 4 vibrations per sec. There will be three distinct waves: one which advances toward the knot, another which is reflected back at the knot into the lighter rope, and the third which is transmitted onward into the heavier rope. Find the frequency, velocity, and wavelength of each.

*8. How far would a sound wave travel along a steel rod in 0.001 sec.? Take 7.8 as the specific gravity of steel.

*9. A longitudinal wave sent by a ship to the bottom of the ocean returns after a lapse of 1.87 sec. Consider the elasticity of sea water to be the same as for pure water, and calculate the depth of the ocean at this point.

*10. A brass pipe 200 ft. long is struck at one end, and sound waves travel to an observer at the other end both along the pipe and through the air. What is the time interval between the two sounds heard by the observer? Take the specific gravity of brass to be 8.5.

11. An auditorium 130 ft. long is equipped with a public address system having loud speakers at the front and back of the hall. An observer close to one of the speakers hears them both, but one signal is weaker than the other and sounds like an echo. What is the time interval between the loud signal and its "echo" as heard by this observer?

12. For sound waves of very high frequency it is found that the condensations and rarefactions are practically isothermal and not adiabatic. Find the velocity of such waves in air at standard temperature and pressure.

13. Find the rise in temperature above 0° C. that would cause an increase of 20 ft. per sec. in the velocity of sound through the atmosphere.

14. Compute the length of waves used in broadcasting a radio program at a frequency of 710 kilocycles per sec.

15. Compute the frequency in kilocycles per second of an ultra high frequency radio wave of 10-cm. wavelength traveling in empty space.

16. (*a*) How long would it take a sound wave to travel 90 ft. in an auditorium at 20° C.? (*b*) How far would a radio wave travel in the same time?

17. A V-shaped wave front is established by the bow of a boat when moving through the water. If the two portions of the wave front are 15° apart when the boat is traveling at 20 mi. per hr., what is the speed of the water waves?

18. A light wave traveling in air impinges on an amber plate making an angle of incidence of 60°, and the angle of refraction is 34°. Find the velocity of light in the amber.

19. A light wave in air strikes a glass plate 1 cm. thick at an incident angle of 50°. If the wave velocity in glass is $\frac{2}{3}$ that in air, what is the length of light path through the glass?

20. Two sources placed side by side are sounding simultaneously and an observer counts 50 beats in 14.7 sec. The sources produce sine waves, and one source vibrates 440 times per sec. What are the possible frequencies of the other source?

21. Two sounding sources having frequencies of 256 and 259 vibrations per sec. are mounted side by side and produce beats in the surrounding region. At a particular instant there is a reenforcement at the place where the sources are located. What is the shortest distance from the sources to a place where reenforcement also occurs at the same instant?

22. An electrically operated tuning fork making 264 vibrations per sec. is mounted with its prongs vertical. From one of these a string 150 cm. long and weighing 0.12 gm. hangs downward. What weight should be attached to the lower end in order that the string may vibrate in four segments?

23. Two waves, produced by bodies making 5 vibrations per sec., travel in opposite directions in a rope weighing 0.005 lb. per ft., which is subjected to a stretching force of 6 lb. How far apart are the nodes in the resulting stationary wave?

24. Two waves of equal amplitude are set up by pulses with a frequency of 60 per sec. The waves are moving in opposite directions in a string which has a length of 5 meters and a mass of 2.5 gm. With what force must the string be stretched in order that the nodes in the resulting stationary wave shall be 1 meter apart?

Sound Production *Chapter XXXI*

359. Characteristics of Sound.—The term sound is used in two senses: subjectively, it signifies the auditory sensation experienced by the ear, and objectively, it signifies the vibratory motion which gives rise to that sensation. It is used in the latter sense in Acoustics. This subject deals with the motion of vibrating bodies, the production and propagation of sound waves in different mediums, and the effect of discontinuities in the mediums. Some of these topics which are common to sound, light, and other wave disturbances are considered in the preceding chapter on Wave Motion; others, together with some of their applications, are discussed in the present and in the following chapter.

A variety of terms is employed in ordinary language to convey impressions of sounds; these include howl, whistle, squeal, rustle, rumble, and hum. Most of these would be classed as *noises*, in contrast with sounds that are spoken of as musical *tones*. The distinction is based largely upon the regularity of vibration of the source and the degree of damping, as well as the ability of the ear to recognize components that have a musical sequence. The sound made by a stick when dropped upon a table top is definitely a noise, but when a number of sticks of appropriate lengths are dropped in suitable order the effect of musical tones may be produced. The complicated sounds of speech are formed by grouping the more or less sustained tones of vowels and the impulsive launching and quenching of these tones by the consonants.

The ear can distinguish tones that differ in *pitch*, in *loudness*, and in *quality*. Each of these characteristics is associated primarily with a single property of the sounding body or of the waves which it produces. Thus, *pitch is determined chiefly by the frequency of vibration, loudness by the intensity of the sound, and quality by the nature of the vibrations as revealed by the wave shape.* In Fig. 345 are several curves depicting both the shapes of sound waves and the characteristics of the vibrations which produce them. The sine curves *A*

575

and *B* differ in frequency, *B* producing the tone of higher pitch. Curves *A* and *C* differ only in amplitude, *A* producing the louder sound; with the amplitude of *A* twice as great as *C*, the sound will have 4 times the intensity of the latter, although the loudness sensation will not increase in the same proportion. Curves *A* and *D* differ in shape, *D* having some components of higher frequency that are not present in *A*; the curves represent sounds of different quality.

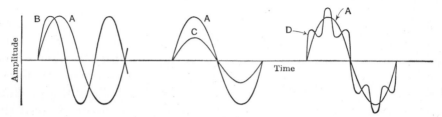

FIG. 345.   Differences in sound waves

The pitch of a tone is directly proportional to the number of condensations and rarefactions received per second, which in turn is determined by the vibration frequency of the sounding source. This relationship can be shown experimentally by means of a siren consisting of a disk with regularly spaced holes through which air is blown gently. As the disk revolves the air stream is interrupted, and the resulting puffs in the medium become condensations and rarefactions, which are transmitted to the ear. The rise in pitch with increased speed of the disk can be exhibited strikingly in this manner.

360. Intensity of Sound.—*The intensity of a sound is the time rate of transfer of vibratory energy per unit of sectional area of the sound wave.* To show that this intensity is dependent upon the amplitude and frequency of vibration of the sound, consider a plane wave in which the vibrating particles have harmonic motion, and ascertain the energy of a layer of the medium that is thin enough so that all of the particles in it may be assumed to have equal displacements. Assume a layer of thickness *x* and of unit area, and let the density of the medium be *d*; then the mass of this volume of the medium will be $m = xd$. Take *f* to be the frequency of the vibrating particles, *r* their maximum displacement, and *v* their greatest velocity (§ 93); it follows that the maximum kinetic energy of the portion of the medium under consideration is

$$E_k = \frac{1}{2} mv^2 = \frac{xd}{2} (2\pi f r)^2$$

The energy of the layer will all be of kinetic form as the particles sweep through their equilibrium positions and all of potential form when they have their maximum displacements; at other times they will have some of each kind of energy, but the total will always be as just expressed if losses are neglected. In consequence, the total energy per unit volume of the medium is

$$\frac{E_k}{x \times 1} = 2\pi^2 f^2 r^2 d \qquad (226)$$

and may be termed the *energy density* of the wave. When metric units are employed this equation will give the energy in ergs per cubic centimeter. If the velocity of wave propagation is V cm. per sec., the time rate of transmission of energy per unit of area of the wave front will be V times the foregoing energy density, and this product is a measure of the physical intensity of the sound wave. Therefore, the *intensity* of the sound in ergs per second per square centimeter is

$$I = 2\pi^2 V f^2 r^2 d \qquad (227)$$

This result shows that the intensity of a sound in a given medium is proportional to the square of the frequency of vibration as well as the square of the amplitude.

Equation (226) for energy density applies to a plane wave or to a spherical wave at a great distance from its source. At any distance from a point source, the energy density in the wave will vary inversely as the square of that distance (§ 200), consequently it may be concluded that the amplitude of vibration r will vary inversely as the distance from that source.

As a sound wave advances, variations in pressure occur at all points in the transmitting medium. The greater the pressure variations, the more intense the sound wave will be, and it can be shown that the intensity is proportional to the square of the pressure variation regardless of the frequency. Thus, by measuring pressure changes, the intensities of sounds having different frequencies may be compared directly, and instruments which make such measurements are preferred to those that measure amplitude.

361. Quality of Sound.—The tones produced by tuning forks have wave shapes approximating the sine waves *A*, *B* and *C* in Fig. 345 and are often referred to as pure tones. The tones produced by most sources can be represented by composite waves, in which the sound of lowest pitch, the fundamental, is accompanied by several overtones having frequencies 2, 3, 4, $\cdots$ n times that of the fundamental. Hermann L. F. Helmholtz (1821–1894), German physiologist and physicist, showed that *the quality of a tone depends upon the number of overtones present, and upon their frequencies and intensities relative to the fundamental.* It is this characteristic that distinguishes tones of like pitch and loudness when sounded on different types of musical instruments.

It is possible to produce a tone of any desired quality by combining pure tones in suitable proportions. For example, the various vowel sounds, which are known to have complicated wave forms, can be duplicated by combining the pure tones of particular organ pipes. Fig. 346 represents the compounding of three sine curves of different frequencies, the resultant curve at the bottom being obtained by adding the ordinates at each point along the time axis. The resultant can also be expressed as the sum of three terms, each having the form given by equation (218); for the amplitudes and frequencies noted in the figure the equation of the resultant is

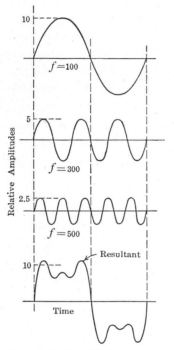

FIG. 346. Synthesis of wave shapes

$$y = 10 \sin (2\pi 100\,t) + 5 \sin (2\pi 300\,t) + 2.5 \sin (2\pi 500\,t)$$

in which y is the instantaneous displacement of the resultant at any time t, reckoned from the origin.

The reverse process, namely that of resolving a sound wave into its components, can also be carried out. Curves of sound wave shapes are obtainable experimentally in several ways (§ 373) and can be measured by suitable instruments. A mathematical analysis for determining the relative amplitudes and phases of the component pure tones is based upon a general principle stated by Jean B. J. Fourier (1768–1830), a French mathematician, to the effect that any periodic function can be represented by a trigonometric series, the terms of which involve frequencies that are integrally related to that of the original function. By Fourier's analysis, any periodic wave form can be resolved mathematically into component sine curves, of definite amplitudes and phases, and having frequencies in the proportion 1, 2, 3, $\cdots n$. There are several types of machines patterned after the planimeter that enable an operator to determine the sinusoidal components of complicated wave shapes; these are called *harmonic analyzers*.

362. Vibrating Strings.—The bowing of a string that is under tension sets up disturbances which travel to the ends of the string and are there reflected back again. At either end the incident and reflected waves have the same frequency and essentially the same amplitude and, since they move in opposite directions, establish a stationary wave in that portion of the string, forming nodes at intervals of one-half wavelength from that end. The same effect is produced at the other end of the string. Since the reflected waves travel from end to end of the string repeatedly, the nodes produced by reflection from both ends will coincide only for definite wavelengths. If the string were set vibrating with a multitude of frequencies at the same time, most of these vibrations would annul one another, and only a few would persist. These are called *free vibrations*; they are the ones for which the length of the string is an exact number of half wavelengths.

The free vibrations of a string are transverse and set up condensations and rarefactions in the surrounding air which proceed away from the string as a longitudinal sound wave. The pitch of the resulting tone heard by an observer is the same as the frequency of vibration of the string.

The simplest mode of vibration of a string is that for which the ends of the string are the only nodal points, and the center is the only antinode. This condition, producing the fundamental tone of the

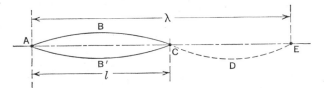

Fɪɢ. 347. Relation between string length and wavelength

string, is depicted in Fig. 347. Herein $ABCDE$ represents a sine wave of length λ, and AC represents the string of length l. During its vibration, the string travels periodically from its extreme upper position ABC to its extreme lower position $AB'C$, and forms a single loop which can be observed by the blurred pattern it makes. Thus, for the fundamental mode of vibration the string forms one loop and its length is a half wavelength.

The string may also vibrate at particular higher frequencies, depending upon the number of nodes between its ends. Fig. 348 illustrates the simpler modes of vibration, in which the string forms one,

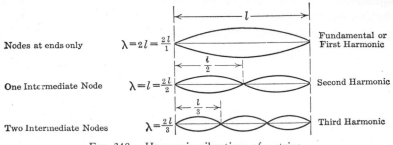

Nodes at ends only $\lambda = 2l = \frac{2l}{1}$ Fundamental or First Harmonic

One Intermediate Node $\lambda = l = \frac{2l}{2}$ Second Harmonic

Two Intermediate Nodes $\lambda = \frac{2l}{3}$ Third Harmonic

Fig. 348.   Harmonic vibrations of a string

two and three loops. The corresponding tones are called *harmonics*. In general, if the string of length l vibrates in n loops, the wavelength of the corresponding harmonic will be

$$\lambda = \frac{2l}{n} \tag{228}$$

The frequency of vibration of the string is obtained by combining this expression with the equation for the velocity of wave propagation, namely $V = f\lambda$, where f is the frequency of vibration. Thus, the frequency of a vibrating string is

$$f = \frac{nV}{2l} \tag{229}$$

If the velocity of wave propagation V in the string is in centimeters per second and its length l is in centimeters, then f will be in vibrations per second. For any vibrating body the free vibration having the lowest frequency is called the *fundamental* or *first harmonic*, a vibration having twice the frequency of the fundamental is called the *second harmonic*, and so on. The foregoing analysis shows that for a stretched string all harmonics may exist, and that the possible frequencies of vibration are proportional to the integers 1, 2, 3, 4, $\cdots$.

To express the vibration rate of a string in terms of its physical constants, the foregoing equation may be combined with equation (220). Thus, the frequency in vibrations per second becomes

$$f = \frac{n}{2l} \sqrt{\frac{S}{m_1}} \tag{230}$$

where n is the number of loops in the string of length l cm., S is the stretching force of the string in dynes, and m_1 is the mass of the string per unit of length in grams per centimeter.

To illustrate the application of the foregoing expression, determine the proper tension of the A-string of a violin to give it a fundamental vibration rate of 440 per sec. The string is 32.7 cm. in length, 0.0523 cm. in diameter, and its density (aluminum-covered steel) is 3.5 gm/cm.[3] Since $m_1 = \pi r^2 d$ in equation (230), the stretching force becomes $S = 4\pi d(lrf)^2 = 12.57 \times 3.5 \ (32.7 \times 0.02615 \times 440)^2 = 62.3 \times 10^5$ dynes $= 6.36$ kg.

Experimental verification of equation (230) can be carried out with a sonometer, which consists of a string mounted over a sounding board and rigidly fastened at one end. The other end of the string passes over a pulley and carries a weight to put the string in tension. By bowing the string at chosen places and by touching it lightly at appropriate points, the string can be set into vibration in a number of ways as illustrated by Fig. 348. The stretching force can be varied by altering the weight, and the length can be varied by shifting the movable bridges on which the string rests.

363. Vibration of Rods and Plates.—In order to set up a *longitudinal* vibration in a solid rod, it is stroked lengthwise with a small rosined pad. As a result, free vibrations will be produced, the possible modes of vibration depending upon the manner in which the rod is supported.

When the rod is supported at one end, it will vibrate in its fundamental mode with a node at that end and an antinode at the other. This longitudinal vibration is shown at the top of Fig. 349 in the usual transverse fashion. In this case the rod forms a half loop and the wavelength extends over four rod lengths or $4l$. The next higher mode of

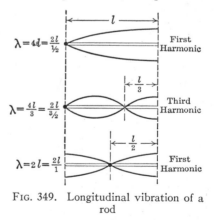

$\lambda = 4l = \dfrac{2l}{\frac{1}{2}}$ First Harmonic

$\lambda = \dfrac{4l}{3} = \dfrac{2l}{\frac{3}{2}}$ Third Harmonic

$\lambda = 2l = \dfrac{2l}{1}$ First Harmonic

Fig. 349. Longitudinal vibration of a rod

vibration introduces an intermediate node, which is located two-thirds the way out from the fixed end, as shown at the center of the figure; in this case the wavelength is $4l/3$. The bottom diagram shows a rod supported at the center so as to form two half loops; the corresponding wavelength will be $2l$. In general, if there are n loops, the wavelength of the vibration will be $\lambda = \dfrac{2l}{n}$. Theory shows that these results are true only when the wavelength is large in comparison with the thickness or width of the rod.

The frequency of longitudinal vibrations in the rod for the fundamental mode will be given with the aid of equations (217) and (221) as

$$f = \frac{n}{2l} \sqrt{\frac{E}{d}} \tag{231}$$

where E is Young's modulus of elasticity of the rod in dynes per square centimeter and d is its density in grams per cubic centimeter. A rod fixed at one end or at the center can give forth only the odd harmonics.

Suppose a rod fastened at one end vibrates longitudinally and produces a fundamental tone of 200 vibrations per sec. When the same rod is supported instead at the middle, the wavelength will be half its former value and the fundamental tone will be 400 vibrations per sec.

Consideration of transverse vibrations in a straight rod or bar is more complicated than that of longitudinal vibrations. The nodal points for the overtones are not evenly spaced, and consequently the frequencies of these overtones are not integral multiples of the 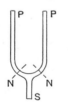 fundamental tone. Assume a rod to have two nodes and to be bent at the center. As the bending progresses, the nodes will approach each other, and in the final U-shape the nodes will be so close together that the rod vibrates practically as two separate bars, each fixed at one end. Fig. 350 illustrates such a bent bar with a stem at-

FIG. 350.
Tuning fork

tached to the center to form a *tuning fork*, the nodal points being indicated by NN. Transverse motions of the prongs PP cause an up-and-down motion in the stem S, and this motion can be arranged to impart vibration to a sounding board or to a column of air to intensify the sound produced by the fork. Tuning forks are usually made of steel, aluminum, or magnesium.

The vibrations of plates can be investigated experimentally by supporting them horizontally at the center or edge, sprinkling fine sand upon them, and setting them into vibration by mechanical or electrical means. The sand particles will hop about and accumulate in places of least motion, thereby indicating a series of nodal lines. Fig. 351 shows photographs of some patterns of such lines formed on plates clamped at the center. A great many modes of vibration are possible, depending upon the manner of supporting the plate and of setting it into vibration. The diaphragms of telephone transmitters and receivers can be tested similarly.

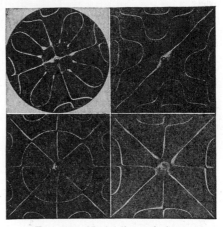

A bell may be regarded as a combination of a plate and a cylinder, with relatively more metal near the center. Many overtones accompany the fundamental tone of a bell when it is struck, and it is the aim of bell-founders to attain certain relationships between the frequencies of the principal overtones.

FIG. 351. Nodal lines of plates

364. Vibrations of Air Columns.—Disturbances in air or other gaseous mediums are propagated as condensations and rarefactions in all directions in open space. When the medium has the form of a column within a rigid tube, a disturbance produced at one end travels to the other end, is there reflected, travels back to the initial end, is reflected again, and so on. Stationary waves are set up in the gaseous column and one or more nodal points are established within the tube. Fig. 352 illustrates how an air column can be set in vibration by a jet of air impinging against one side of the tube at (a). The con-

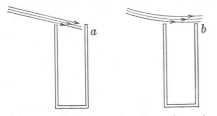

FIG. 352. Setting an air column into vibration

densation so produced travels down the tube, is reflected, and reaches the upper end again; there it pushes the air jet aside as shown at (b), and as a consequence, a rarefaction starts down the tube. This is reflected at the bottom and retraces its path; upon arrival of the rarefaction at the top of the tube, the condition represented at (a) is restored. This process is repeated over and over again. The closed end of the tube becomes a node, the open end becomes an antinode, and the tube length constitutes a quarter wavelength for the fundamental mode of vibration.

A somewhat similar behavior is observed for a tube open at both ends; in this case a condensation is reflected as a rarefaction and both open ends become antinodes. With one nodal point between these ends, the air column will vibrate in its fundamental manner, and the tube length constitutes a half wavelength.

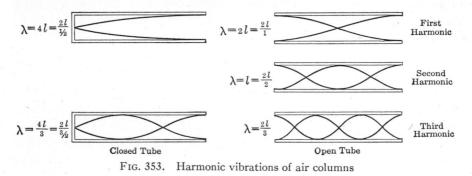

$\lambda = 4l = \frac{2l}{\frac{1}{2}}$ $\lambda = 2l = \frac{2l}{1}$ First Harmonic

$\lambda = l = \frac{2l}{2}$ Second Harmonic

$\lambda = \frac{4l}{3} = \frac{2l}{\frac{3}{2}}$ $\lambda = \frac{2l}{3}$ Third Harmonic

Closed Tube   Open Tube

FIG. 353. Harmonic vibrations of air columns

Some overtones produced by air columns and the relation between the wavelength λ and the length l of the column are indicated in Fig. 353. The frequencies of the various harmonics are given by the following expression:

$$f = \frac{V}{\lambda} = \frac{nV}{2l}$$

where V is the velocity of the sound wave in the gaseous medium and n is the number of loops formed by the vibrations. This equation is the same as (229). For closed tubes $n = \frac{1}{2}, \frac{3}{2}, \frac{5}{2}, \cdots$, while for open tubes $n = 1, 2, 3, \cdots$.

The equation above does not apply perfectly to air columns because reflection does not occur exactly in the plane of the open end but somewhat beyond it; with cylindrical tubes the plane of reflection may be taken as lying outside the tube by a distance about 60 per cent of the radius of the tube, on the assumption that this radius is small in comparison with the wavelength.

To compute the frequency of the fundamental tone of a tube 8 ft. long, take the velocity of sound in air to be $V = 1100$ ft/sec. and apply the equation ahead. If the end correction is neglected, the frequency will be $f = (\frac{1}{2} \times 1100$ ft/sec.$) \div (2 \times 8$ ft.$) = 34.4$ vibrations per sec. when closed, and $f = (1 \times 1100$ ft/sec.$) \div (2 \times 8$ ft.$) = 68.8$ vibrations per sec. when open. To apply the end correction the size of the tube must be known; if its diameter is 4 in., then the end correction is 0.6×2 in. $= 1.2$ in. or 0.1 ft. The effective tube length is 8.1 ft. when closed and 8.2 ft. when open, and the corresponding frequencies are 33.9 and 67.0 vibrations per sec.

365. Resonance.—The production of sound by some vibrating systems, such as strings, rods, and air columns, has been considered in the three preceding sections. These systems were assumed to be set into vibration without constraint to produce free vibrations, that is, vibrations having frequencies determined entirely by the constants and properties of the vibrating bodies themselves. Such bodies may also be set in motion by periodic impulses imparted by outside agents; then the bodies are said to execute *forced vibrations*. When conditions are so adjusted that the forced vibrations have the same frequency as the free vibrations of the body upon which they are impressed, the free vibrations reinforce the received ones; an effect which is known as *resonance*. When the impressed vibration has a different frequency from that of the free vibrations of a body, the received impulses sometimes help and sometimes hinder the free vibrations, and will not affect the free vibrations appreciably.

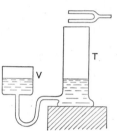

FIG. 354. Resonance of an air column

To illustrate the phenomenon of resonance, consider a tuning fork to be held over an air column, as shown in Fig. 354. The level of the water in the cylindrical tube T can be varied by raising or lowering the communicating vessel V. Upon sounding the fork and altering the height of the air column, resonance is established when the audible response is a maximum. This experiment affords a simple means of determining the velocity of sound in air; in such a test it is necessary to use a tuning fork of known frequency, to measure the length of the column at resonance, and to apply equation (229).

For example, a tuning fork vibrating 440 times per sec. is observed to produce resonance when held above an air column 18 cm. long. To compute the velocity of sound, the wavelength is taken as $4 \times 18 = 72$ cm., whence by equation (217) the velocity is $\dfrac{440}{\text{sec.}} \times 72$ cm. $= 31,700$ cm. per sec., according to the data provided. The result is low because the end correction was neglected; the error might be avoided by using an air column sufficiently long to resonate at two lengths, their difference being $\frac{1}{2}$ wavelength.

There are many applications of the phenomenon of resonance. Tuning forks are often mounted on top of wooden boxes closed at one end and open at the other; the length of such boxes is about one-quarter wavelength of the sound emitted by the fork so as to produce a loud response. Resonance is utilized in the tuning of a radio receiver by adjusting the inductance or capacitance of its circuits for the same frequency as that of the radiation from the desired broadcasting station, as described in § 331. There are instances where resonance may build up free vibrations of such amplitude in structures as to produce dangerous effects in them. Soldiers break step in marching across bridges, for example, in order to eliminate the possibility of setting up destructive vibrations in the various members of such structures.

366. Doppler's Principle.—A person standing near a railroad track can observe a distinct lowering of pitch in the whistle of a train as the train passes him. This observation illustrates a principle applicable to all wave motion; it was developed by the Austrian physicist, Christian Doppler (1803–1853). Applied to sound, this principle states that the pitch of the sound heard differs from the frequency of the vibrating source from which it originates whenever the observer or the source moves. This difference is quite marked even when the velocity of motion is only a few per cent of the velocity of sound, 1100 ft. per sec. in air. The pitch heard by the observer can always be obtained by dividing the velocity with which the waves pass him by their wavelength.

Source Moving.—To find the pitch heard by a stationary observer when the sounding source moves, let f be the frequency of the source, V the velocity of wave propagation, and S the velocity of the source. In one second it emits f waves, which spread out into the surrounding medium; in the region in front of the source these f waves will be crowded into a distance equal to $V - S$. To an observer in this region the wavelength will be $\dfrac{V - S}{f}$, and hence the pitch of the sound heard when the source moves toward the observer will be $V \div \dfrac{V - S}{f}$, or

$$p = f\left(\frac{V}{V - S}\right) \tag{232}$$

Similarly, when the source moves away from the observer, the observed pitch will be

$$p = f\left(\frac{V}{V + S}\right)$$

Suppose a whistle to be moving with a speed of 50 ft. per sec. toward a stationary observer, while emitting a sound of frequency 300 vibrations per sec. In 1 sec., the whistle will produce a train of 300 waves, the first of which will advance 1100 ft. while the last one is just being emitted from the source at a point 50 ft. away from the location it had when the first wave was emitted. This train of waves occupies a length of (1100 − 50) ft.; therefore, the wavelength of the sound is (1100 − 50) ÷ 300 = 3.5 ft. The observed pitch is the wave velocity divided by the wavelength, or 1100 ÷ 3.5 = 314.3 vibrations per sec. If the source had been stationary, the observed pitch would have been 300 vibrations per sec.

Observer Moving.—To find the pitch heard by a moving observer when the sounding source is stationary, suppose O to be the velocity of the observer, and the other symbols to retain their former significance. The velocity with which the waves pass him is $V + O$ if he is approaching the source, and the wavelength of these waves will be V/f. Hence the pitch of the sound heard by the observer when he approaches the stationary source will be

$$p = f\left(\frac{V + O}{V}\right) \tag{233}$$

Suppose that the 300-cycle whistle is stationary, and that the observer is approaching it with a speed of 50 ft. per sec. The velocity with which the waves pass him is (1100 + 50) ft. per sec., and since the wavelength of the sound in air is (1100/300) ft., the pitch heard by the observer becomes (1100 + 50) ÷ (1100/300) = 313.6 vibrations per sec. It is interesting to note that the increase in pitch in this case is different from that obtained with the source approaching the observer at the same speed.

Source and Observer Moving.—When both the source of sound and the observer are moving, the pitch heard will be changed in the proportion $\dfrac{V}{V \mp S}$ by motion of the source, and in the proportion $\dfrac{V \pm O}{V}$ by motion of the observer. The pitch heard by the observer is, therefore,

$$p = f\left(\frac{V \pm O}{V \mp S}\right) \tag{234}$$

In the choice of signs, use the upper of the double sign for O when the observer is moving toward the source, and the upper one for S when the source is moving toward the observer; use the lower signs if the respective directions are opposite to those just stated.

*367. Effect of Compressional Waves on Aircraft.—A body moving

through the air compresses the air in front of it and the compression spreads outwardly from this region with the velocity of sound, which is a compressional wave itself. If the body is moving slower

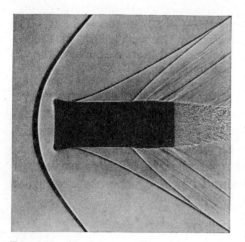

than this speed, it will follow the wave but will not catch up with it, so the presence of the wave does not influence the behavior of the moving body. A body traveling at *sonic speed* (about 1100 ft/sec. or 750 mi/hr.) moves forward just as fast as the wave does and is continuously impeded by a region of highly compressed air, termed a "shock wave." For a body moving at a higher speed than that of sound, such as a rocket or projectile, the shock wave produced is essentially conical in shape, but the camera shows this to consist of a detached

FIG. 355. Shock waves formed by moving projectile. (*Photograph by Ballistic Research Laboratories*)

shock front and other shock waves attached to the body, as shown in Fig. 355. The effect is the same as the V-shaped wave formed by a boat on the surface of water, except that it is three-dimensional.

In the field of Aeronautics, it is anticipated that travel at speeds approaching that of sound will present some problems of great difficulty. Engineers report that an airplane may be moving at a speed lower than this and yet, because of the curvature of the airfoil surface (§ 143), the air may reach sonic speed at places on top of the airfoil; the same may be true around corners of large curvature at other places on the airplane. Hence, a small shock wave or a series of them will often be formed locally. Since the shock waves move about considerably when there are small variations of velocity, they make the force on the wing top unsteady and can cause undesirable vibrations. Likewise the drag on the plane, or its resistance to motion, is greatly increased, and the lift of its wings is lessened. The subject is now under extensive study by aerodynamicists.

*368. Musical Scales.—The charm of music is based upon the

blending and the succession of sounds to give pleasing auditory sensations. The characteristics of the ear impose certain physical restrictions on the frequencies of the sounds to be combined to secure harmonious effects. The ear would interpret quite differently a frequency increase of 50 vibrations per sec. in an initial sound having a pitch of 200 vibrations per sec. than a like increase in a sound having a pitch of 400 vibrations per sec., but would give the same interpretation to an increase of 100 vibrations per sec. in the sound of higher pitch. Thus, the ear recognizes two sounds to have the same tonal interval as two others, if the frequency ratios, rather than the frequency differences, are the same for the two pairs.

Further, two simultaneous sounds that have nearly the same frequency produce pulsations in sound intensity. Two tuning forks that execute 200 and 205 vibrations per sec. would set up 5 beats per sec. if sounded together (§ 357), and produce an unpleasant musical effect. But if the frequency difference of two sounds is large, the beat frequency will be perceived as a new tone, called a *combination tone*. The complete sequence of tones used for musical selections constitutes a scale, and the tones are designated as notes of the scale.

Experience shows that tones having frequency ratios of 2 to 1, 3 to 2, 4 to 3, 5 to 3, 5 to 4, and 6 to 5 produce a pleasing effect; musical scales are based upon these ratios. The scales are formed by using three combinations called *triads*, each of which is a chord formed of three tones. In such a chord, the octave of a tone may accompany or replace the fundamental without altering the nature of the chord.

The major scale of eight notes beginning with middle *C* as the basic note includes notes *D, E, F, G, A* and *B* of successively higher pitches in reaching the octave *c*. The frequencies of these notes are determined by the major triads *CEG*, *FAc* and *GBd*, which notes have frequency ratios of 4:5:6, and also by the pitch of some one note regarded as standard. Based upon the present standard concert pitch of 440 vibrations per sec. for *A* in the treble clef, the notes of the major scale have the following frequencies and intervals:

Major Scale

	C	D	E	F	G	A	B	c	d
Triads	4		5		6				
				4		5		6	
					4		5		6
Name	do	re	me	fa	sol	la	si	do	re
Frequency	264	297	330	352	396	440	495	528	594
Intervals		$\frac{9}{8}$	$\frac{10}{9}$	$\frac{16}{15}$	$\frac{9}{8}$	$\frac{10}{9}$	$\frac{9}{8}$	$\frac{16}{15}$	

The intervals $\frac{9}{8}$ and $\frac{10}{9}$ are called full tones, and the interval $\frac{16}{15}$ is called a half tone. A study of the frequencies tabulated reveals that the tones of a triad as well as their harmonics will produce no disturbing beat notes. For example, the third harmonic of C coincides with the second of G, the fifth of C coincides with the fourth of E, the sixth of E coincides with the fifth of G, and so on.

The minor scale is built upon three minor triads for the same notes as the major scale, but having frequency ratios of $10:12:15$. The notes of this scale have the following frequencies and intervals over the range of values previously tabulated:

Minor Scale

	C	D	E	F	G	A	B	c	d
Triads	10		12		15				
				10		12		15	
					10		12		15
Frequency	264	297	316.8	352	396	422.4	475.2	528	594
Intervals		$\frac{9}{8}$	$\frac{16}{15}$	$\frac{10}{9}$	$\frac{9}{8}$	$\frac{16}{15}$	$\frac{9}{8}$	$\frac{10}{9}$	

The intervals have the same values as before, but have a different sequence. As a result, three additional notes are needed to produce the minor scale; these are below E, A and B of the major scale. Music rendered in the minor scale usually has a more plaintive character than that in the other scale.

To accommodate different instruments and voices, it is desirable to have sufficient tones to permit changing the tonic from C to some other keynote. If, for example, the successive notes were to be determined for the key of D, the same procedure followed above would indicate the successive frequencies for the major scale to be 297, 334, 371, 396, 445, 495, 557 and 594 vibrations per sec. These frequencies agree with those previously found for notes G and B as well as for the keynote, and approximate them for notes E and A; but two are quite distinct and these notes are designated as F sharp and c sharp.

Similar computations for other keys in both scales would reveal the necessity of having a large number of separate notes if it were desired to render a selection in any key. To avoid this situation and yet provide sufficient flexibility in musical instruments, like the piano and organ that produce sounds of fixed frequency, a scale has been developed which has 12 intervals and has the same frequency interval between consecutive notes. This so-called *tempered scale* has a frequency interval of the twelfth root of 2, namely 1.0595. The equal temperament scale is now universally used, and only those with well-trained ears can detect the slight errors of pitch from the natural scales.

*369. Musical Instruments.—Instruments for the production of music utilize various forms of vibrating bodies as the sound-generating elements, and some instruments have sounding boards or equivalents for the reinforcement of the tones produced. The following list gives some examples of the instruments that utilize the usual acoustic elements:

Air columns, conical	Bassoon, cornet, oboe, saxophone
" " cylindrical	Clarinet, flute, organ, piccolo, trombone
Plates and membranes	Cymbal, drum
Reeds and rods	Reed organ, xylophone
Strings, bowed	Violin, viola, violoncello, double bass
" plucked	Guitar, harp, mandolin, ukulele
" struck	Piano

The excitation of the air columns in some of the so-called wind instruments is accomplished by a thin stream of air or a reed which often has no definite frequency by itself, the air column responding by resonance. The column then vibrates at a constant rate as determined by its length, and reacts upon the exciter to keep its vibration rate unchanged. This method with reeds is utilized in the bassoon, clarinet, oboe, saxophone and some organ pipes, and with the human lips as reeds in the cornet and trombone. In other wind instruments, like the flute, piccolo and "flue" organ pipes, the air is set into vibration without reeds. The length of the air column is varied in the flute and clarinet by opening side holes in the tube, in the cornet by adding lengths of tubing by means of valves, and in the trombone by sliding one tube within another.

The stringed instruments have various numbers of strings that are constant or alterable in length. In the piano each string is of definite length; the string for the highest tone is usually from 5.0 to 5.5 cm. long, and the others are progressively longer. There are 88 notes extending over more than seven octaves from $27\frac{1}{2}$ to 4186 vibrations per sec. The strings of various diameters are set into vibration through key action by felt-nosed hammers at places approximately one-eighth the string length from one end. The lower tones have many harmonics while the high tones have few; the middle tones of the scale have at least ten harmonics of well-proportioned intensities.

In the violin family of instruments there are four strings of equal length stretched over a resonant box of particular shape and construction. The *G*, *D*, *A* and *e* strings are tuned to fifths, that is, the relative frequencies of two neighboring strings are 3:2. Other tones are produced by varying the lengths of the strings by pressing them against the flat fingerboard with the fingers. The strings are set into vibration by drawing a bow strung with rosined horsehair across them, the vibration being a succession of alternate forced and free movements as the string adheres to the bow because of the pressure applied, and slips back again by virtue of its elasticity. The third, fourth and fifth harmonics are particularly prominent in the tones of the violin.

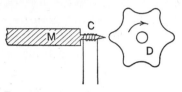

FIG. 356. Inducing element of the Hammond organ

Within the past few years there has been an interesting development of electrically operated instruments designed to give the musical effects of the organ. In the Hammond electric organ a series of toothed disks is driven by a constant-speed motor, one disk being provided for the fundamental tone corresponding to each key on the instrument. The action will be explained by reference to Fig. 356, which represents a disk *D* rotated near the tip of a permanent magnet *M*, on which there is a coil of wire *C*. The disk is made of steel, and as its teeth and slots move in succession past the magnet tip, variations of flux occur which induce an alternating emf. in the coil. An electron-tube circuit amplifies this emf. and operates a loud speaker. The instrument provides for superimposing additional emf.'s upon that of the fundamental to give desired tone qualities.

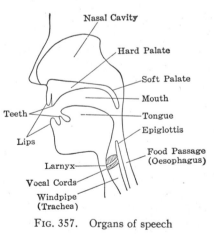

FIG. 357. Organs of speech

*370. Vocal Organs.—The organs of speech are composed of the vocal cords, through which the lungs force streams of air, and of the resonating chambers formed by the throat, mouth, and nasal cavities. Fig. 357 shows a sectional view of these parts of the neck and head. The larynx is the valve at the entrance of the windpipe and consists of a framework of cartilages connected by ligaments, including two fibrous bands which are called the *vocal cords*. These form a straight slit (*glottis*) from 11 to 15 mm. long, and when the breath passes through it the cords are set into vibration and send puffs of air to the chambers above it. The vibration rate is determined principally by the size of the glottis opening and to some extent by the tension of the vocal cords. The lips, tongue and teeth modify the shape of the vocal passages; certain tonal characteristics are impressed by this action upon the air puffs and they emerge from the mouth as speech or tonal sounds. When relaxed, the vocal cords are farther apart and form a V-shaped aperture; in this condition the passage of air to and from the lungs occurs without the emission of sound, as in normal breathing.

The sounds of speech are complicated tones that have many harmonics. As with musical tones, the quality is determined by the relative intensities of these harmonics. Fig. 358 illustrates the wave

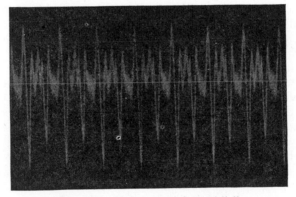

FIG. 358.   Voice wave of vowel "o"

shape of the vowel "o" as in tone. Measurements on the power of speech sounds show that the average power for conversational speech is about 10 microwatts. Talking as loudly as possible raises this average to about 1000 microwatts and talking as softly as possible without whispering lowers the average to about 0.1 microwatt.

The pitch of the voice in singing ranges generally from about 80 to 300 vibrations per sec. for bass voices, and from about 250 to 850 vibrations per sec. for soprano voices, but these ranges are extended considerably by many individuals.

PROBLEMS

1. Take the intensity of the wave represented by curve *A*, Fig. 345, as 100 units and estimate the intensity of the wave represented by *B*.

2. If the intensity of sound at the transmitter during a telephone conversation is 10 ergs per sec. per sq. cm., what is the amplitude of vibration of the air particles at the transmitter corresponding to a frequency of 800 vibrations per sec.? Assume the temperature to be 20°C.

3. Curve *D* in Fig. 345 is the resultant of curve *A* and a second curve having $\frac{1}{4}$ the amplitude and 5 times the frequency of curve *A*. Suppose the amplitude of curve *A* to be 10 units and its frequency to be 100 cycles per sec., and write an equation for curve *D* showing the relation between displacement *y* and time *t*.

4. Consider Fig. 346 to represent a sound wave in air, and take each unit on the amplitude scale to be equivalent to 0.0001 cm. Compute the intensities of the three component waves. Take the temperature as 0°C.

5. A string is stretched between supports 3 ft. apart and is set into vibration at a variety of frequencies. Of the vibrations that persist, compute the wavelengths of the three that have the lowest frequencies.

6. The *c′* strings of a piano are of steel and have a length of 19.3 cm. and a diameter of 0.089 cm. What should be the stretching force to produce a fundamental tone of 1056 vibrations per sec.?

7. What are the pitches of the fundamental and the second and third harmonics of a copper string 36 cm. long? Take the velocity of transverse waves in the string to be 180 meters per sec.

8. An aluminum rod 3 ft. long is clamped at the middle and is set into longitudinal vibration by stroking with rosined chamois. Compute the pitches of the two lowest tones which can be produced by the rod so clamped.

9. A slender rod 2 ft. long is clamped at one end and set into longitudinal vibration. Compute the wavelengths corresponding to the three lowest tones that the rod can give forth.

10. The fundamental frequency of a tuning fork having prongs of rectangular section of thickness *t* and of length *l* is given by the equation: $f = 0.161tV/l^2$, where *V* is the velocity of sound in the material of the fork, and where all units involve centimeters. An aluminum fork marked 524 vibrations per sec. has prongs 11.83 cm. long and 0.90 cm. thick. Calculate the theoretical frequency of this fork and compute the percentage difference between the theoretical and rated frequencies.

11. An organ pipe open at both ends is to produce a tone of 528 vibrations per sec. How long should it be?

12. Two organ pipes, each closed at one end, have lengths of 60 in. and 61 in. The pipes are sounded simultaneously, each producing its fundamental tone. Neglect the end correction, and determine the number of beats per minute.

13. A glass tube 30 cm. long and 5 cm. in diameter is thumped against the palm of the hand and withdrawn in rapid succession. The sound produced by this action is made up of two alternate tones; the lower is that

for an air column closed at one end, and the higher is that for the column open at both ends. Compute the frequencies of these tones.

14. At what rate should impulses be applied to the air column within a chimney 60 ft. tall in order to set it vibrating in its fundamental mode?

15. The velocity of sound is measured by the method illustrated in Fig. 354, using a glass tube 30 in. long and an electrically operated tuning fork which vibrates 396 times per sec. As the water is lowered in the tube, two points of resonance are observed, the heights of the water column being 22.3 in. and 5.7 in. respectively. Compute the velocity of sound in air from these data.

16. A tuning fork having a frequency of 440 vibrations per sec. is mounted on a wooden box to reenforce its sound. How long should the sounding box be if it is open at one end?

17. Compute the length of the shortest organ pipe, open at both ends, that would vibrate in resonance with the string of Problem 7. Suppose each of the sounding bodies to vibrate in its fundamental mode.

18. A locomotive approaching a crossing at 60 mi. per hr. is slowed down uniformly at 3 mi. per hr. per sec. beginning at a point 300 yd. from the crossing. If the locomotive whistle is sounding steadily with a frequency of 400 vibrations per sec., what is the pitch of the tone heard at the crossing when the locomotive is 200 yd. away?

19. An automobilist traveling at 50 mi. per hr. passes a car that is traveling along the same road at half that speed in the opposite direction. He is sounding his horn steadily, and it produces a tone of 280 vibrations per sec. Determine the pitch that will be observed by the other automobilist (*a*) as the faster car approaches him, and (*b*) after the faster car has passed him.

20. A man running away from a dentist at a speed of 30 ft. per sec. emits a shriek having a frequency of 500 vibrations per sec. What is the pitch of the tone heard by the dentist if he is chasing the man at 10 ft. per sec.?

*21. An organist wishes to produce a tone which is one octave lower in pitch than the lowest *C* on the keyboard. He obtains this result as a combination tone by playing the lowest *C* and another note at the same time. What is the other note?

*22. Compute the successive frequencies for the notes of the major scale, using *G* = 396 vibrations per sec. as the keynote.

Sound Reception and
Control

Chapter XXXII

371. The Ear.—In the process of hearing sound, the acoustic waves enter the auditory canal of the outer ear and fall upon the eardrum; the vibration of this membrane is transmitted through the middle ear to the inner ear and received by nerve endings, which in turn send nervous impulses to the brain that cause the sensation of hearing.

The principal parts of the ear are illustrated in Fig. 359, the inner ear being much enlarged with respect to the outer ear, and the sectional view of the end-organ (cochlea) being further magnified. The

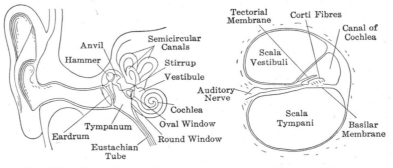

Fig. 359.   General view of ear and transverse section of cochlea

cavity beyond the eardrum, called the *tympanum*, connects with the upper part of the throat through the *Eustachian tube* which opens when swallowing occurs, enabling an equalization of pressure with the outside air to be effected. The tympanum houses the three tiny bones of the middle ear, the *hammer, anvil* and *stirrup*, and the base of the latter bone is applied to a membrane which closes an oval window, called the *fenestra ovalis*. There is also another membrane at that side of the tympanum which closes a round window, called the *fenestra rotunda*. Both of these membranes transmit incoming

596

vibrations to the inner ear. This part of the ear is encased in solid bone, and can be subdivided into three sections: the semicircular canals (which do not contribute to the process of hearing but serve as an organ of balance), the vestibule, and the *cochlea*. The latter has the form of a spiral of nearly three turns, and is the organ where the vibrations are translated into nerve impulses.

The cochlea is divided along its length into three parallel canals, as shown in the sectional view at the right, but the upper two, separated by a very thin flexible membrane, act mechanically as though they were one. The *scala vestibuli* and *scala tympani* have at their ends the oval and round windows respectively for communication with the tympanum, and are separated by a bony projection for about half their length and a flexible membrane, called the *basilar membrane*, for the other half. The terminal organs of hearing are the *Corti fibres* which are nerve terminals in the form of rods with small hairs that extend from one side of the basilar membrane into the canal of cochlea. Opposite them is a soft loose membrane called the *tectorial membrane*. In receiving sound, these two membranes move relatively to each other and stimulate the hair-like nerve endings, thereby causing the sound to be heard. That the cochlea is very small can be judged from the facts that the length is about 31 mm. when straightened out and that the greatest cross-section of any of its canals is less than 2 mm.[2] It is believed that the cochlea is responsive to different frequencies along the different parts of the length of its basilar membrane, so that its behavior may be likened somewhat to that of a harp. The reception of a complex sound on this basis would signify the agitation of certain of the resonating elements of the cochlea and the transmission of a corresponding pattern to the brain.

The range of sounds that can be heard varies with the individual, but the average range extends from about 20 to 20,000 vibrations per sec. If the ear is tested with tones of any one frequency and the intensity is changed, it will be found that the auditory sensation ceases when the intensity has been reduced to a sufficiently low level which is called the *threshold of audibility*; also that the sound produces the sensation of feeling and begins to be painful when the intensity has been increased to an appropriately high level which is called the *threshold of feeling*. Such a procedure carried out over a wide frequency range results in data from which a pair of curves, one for the minimum and the other for the maximum auditory response, can be plotted in terms of frequency, as shown in Fig. 360. These curves represent tests made on a number of persons with normal hearing and may be extrapolated to meet and thereby enclose a region termed the auditory sensation area.

The width of such an area would indicate the frequency range of normal ears; it should be noted that the scale is logarithmic. The height of the enclosed area indicates the intensity ranges for auditory response at various frequencies. The scale used is based on intensity

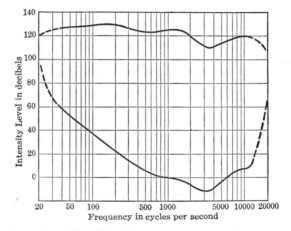

Fig. 360. Field of the hearing sensation
(*Courtesy of Western Electric Company*)

levels rather than intensities, in order to conform more closely to the sensation of loudness. The relation between these quantities is discussed in the following section.

372. Intensity Levels.—As the intensity of a sound wave is increased, the sound becomes louder, but there is no proportionality between wave intensity and loudness sensation. For this reason another concept has been found useful, that of *intensity level*, which is defined in such a way as to make its value roughly proportional to the sensation of loudness. A scale of such intensity levels is extensively used in acoustical measurements.

Just as ground elevations are measured from sea level as a datum, so intensity levels are measured from that of a particular sound intensity chosen arbitrarily as a reference standard: 10^{-10} microwatts per sq. cm. This is the value used for the zero level in Fig. 360. If the reference intensity is taken as I_0 and the intensity of a sound under consideration is taken as I, then the intensity level of that sound can be expressed by the logarithmic equation

$$\alpha = C \log_{10} \frac{I}{I_0}$$

where α is the intensity level and C is a constant that depends upon the units used. When C is taken as unity, the intensity level α is expressed in terms of a unit called the *bel*, named after Alexander G. Bell. In practice C is taken as 10 and α is then expressed in *decibels* (db); a decibel is one-tenth as large as the bel.

When it is desired only to compare one sound with another, it is not necessary to use the standard intensity as a reference level. If the reference sound is regarded as having an intensity of unity, then the level in decibels of another sound of intensity I is given by

$$\alpha = 10 \log_{10} I \tag{235}$$

above or below the reference level. The significance of 1 decibel can be gained from equation (235) by letting $\alpha = 1$ and solving for I; the result is $I = 10^{0.1} = 1.26$, showing that a 26 per cent increase of sound intensity corresponds to a 1-db. rise in intensity level.

To illustrate, if a particular sound is strengthened so that it has 10 times its original intensity, then the level has been increased by an amount given by equation (235), namely $10 \log_{10} 10 = 10 \times 1 = 10$ db. Again, if the sound is strengthened to 100 times its original intensity, then the level has been increased by $10 \log_{10} 100 = 10 \times 2 = 20$ db.

Consider the speech powers cited in § 370, namely 10 microwatts for average conversational speech, and ranging from 1000 to 0.1 microwatts for very loud and for very soft speech respectively. At a distance of one-half inch from the lips, the usual distance from a transmitter while telephoning, the area through which this power is radiated is about 10 sq. cm. At that zone the intensity of average speech is 10 microwatts ÷ 10 sq. cm. = 1 microwatt/cm.^{2}, and this value may be taken as the datum intensity. For a power of 1000 microwatts through this zone, the intensity is 100 microwatts/cm.^{2}, and the equation gives the intensity level of very loud speech as $+20$ db.; for very soft speech the level is -20 db., that is, 20 db. below the datum intensity level. Thus the average voice has a range of 40 db.

373. Some Measurements in Sound.—Systematic progress in sound control requires a knowledge of acoustic quantities based on

actual test.   Some of the experimental methods used are described
in the following paragraphs.

Pitch.—The pitch of a tone is usually measured by comparison
with a standard.   The standard tone may be generated by a card
held lightly against the rim of a rotating toothed disk, or produced
by a siren (§ 359), its frequency in either case being computed readily
for a particular speed of rotation.   By regulating the speed, the pitch
of the standard tone is made equal to that of the tone being measured.
The ear can detect this equality directly if the two sources are
sounded alternately, or by the elimination of beats if they are sounded
together.

An optical method is used for making precise comparison of the
pitches of two tuning forks, one being a standard.   This method
applies where the pitches are very nearly in simple proportion, for

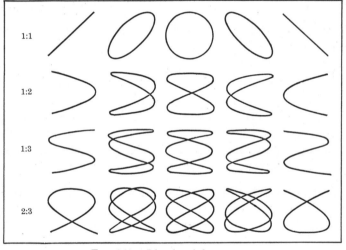

FIG. 361.   Lissajous' figures

example, 3:1.   The forks have their prongs polished to serve as
mirrors and are mounted in such a manner that one fork vibrates in a
horizontal plane and the other in a vertical plane, the vibrations being
maintained electrically.   A narrow beam of light projected upon one
fork is reflected to the other, from which it is reflected again to a
screen.   Thus, the spot of light is given two harmonic motions at
right angles, and traces a figure on the screen the shape of which
depends upon the frequency ratio of these vibrations.   If one of the
frequencies is an exact multiple of the other, the figure will appear
stationary, otherwise progressive changes of phase cause it to pass

through a succession of shapes, returning to the original shape when one fork has lost or gained one cycle with respect to the other. Fig. 361 shows some typical examples of these shapes, which are known as Lissajous' figures. Each row represents a particular value for the nominal frequency ratio, as indicated, and the diagrams across the row show the shapes for increasing phase differences up to $\frac{1}{2}$ cycle between the two sources. Suppose, for example, that the standard fork vibrates exactly 200 times a second and the other very nearly 600 times a second, and that the figure on the screen goes through a cycle of shapes in exactly 4 sec. Since the fork under test completes either 2399 or 2401 vibrations in the 4-sec. interval, its frequency is either 599.75 or 600.25 vibrations per sec. To determine which of these is correct, the test is repeated with a tiny bit of wax fastened to one prong of the test fork; this will lower its frequency.

Wave Shape.—Formerly the shapes of sound waves were measured by an instrument called a *phonodeik*. The sound was directed against a thin glass diaphragm and its motion was magnified mechanically and optically so that a trace could be formed on a film or on a screen. Present methods of wave shape measurement employ a cathode-ray oscillograph (§ 301) actuated by a microphone. The sound waves striking the microphone are converted into equivalent electrical vibrations and these are rendered visible upon the fluorescent screen of the oscillograph.

Intensity and Loudness.—The classical method for measuring sound intensity is due to Lord Rayleigh (John W. Strutt, 1842–1919), English physicist, who found that a suspended disk tends to set itself at right angles to the to-and-fro motion of the air particles transmitting a sound wave. The disk is supported by a torsion suspension and is placed where an antinode will be located in a resonating tube, its plane making an angle of 45° with the axis of the tube. When a sound is established in the tube, a torque will act on the disk and deflect it, the torque being proportional to the intensity of the sound.

The loudness of a noise can be measured by the *audiometer*, a device designed primarily for the measurement of deafness. The audiometer produces tones of numerous frequencies, the intensities of which can be adjusted to various sensation levels. The sound is produced in a telephone receiver supported at a fixed distance from the ear, and its loudness is regulated until it is just masked by the noise being measured. The difference between this setting and a similar setting made in a quiet place is a measure of the loudness of the noise.

374. Measurement of Velocity of Sound.—The velocity of a sound wave in the atmosphere can be determined by observing the motion which produces a distant sound, and measuring the time interval which elapses before the sound reaches the ear, as well as the distance between source and observer. The time required for light to travel that distance is neglected, and the velocity of sound can be computed directly, although the result is subject to considerable personal error. The distance to a lightning flash may be estimated in this way by counting seconds until its thunder is heard, allowing five seconds to the mile.

A better method for measuring the velocity of sound was devised by August A. E. Kundt (1839–1894), a German physicist. Longitudinal vibrations are set up in a metal rod placed so as to develop

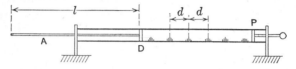

FIG. 362. Kundt's tube for measuring velocity of sound

stationary waves in air or other gas within a glass tube. Lycopodium powder or cork filings, spread over the interior of the tube, permit the location of the nodes and antinodes to be determined. The arrangement is shown in Fig. 362, wherein A represents the rod clamped at its center to one end of the tube, and P represents a plunger at the other end. The rod is set into longitudinal vibration by stroking with rosined chamois and the plunger is moved until the powder shows distinct differences in appearance along the tube. At the nodal points the powder will be lumped together, and at the antinodes it will assume sharply defined ridges across the tube. A node will form at P and there will be an approximate node at the disk D fastened to the end of the rod. The rod has a length l, and its pitch f is measured by comparison with a siren or equivalent means. When producing the lowest tone, the sound wave in the rod has a wavelength $\lambda = 2l$, and a velocity $V = f \lambda = 2fl$, as explained in § 363. If the average distance measured between successive antinodes is d, the sound wave in the gas has a wavelength $2d$, and a velocity $V = 2fd$.

375. Sound Recording and Reproduction.—In 1877, Edison arranged a diaphragm with a projecting point at the back, together with a cylinder of tinfoil which could be moved while in contact with the point; he conceived the idea that by speaking in front of the diaphragm he could produce indentations in the moving cylinder to record speech, and that upon returning the cylinder to its original position and moving it as before, the diaphragm would be set into vibration and reproduce the original sound. The success of this experiment led to the development of the *dictating machine* which employs cylinders of hard wax, and of the *phonograph* which operates with records in the form of disks.

In the ordinary phonograph record, the groove, when magnified, appears as a wavy line and represents a composite wave that is usually the resultant of many individual waves superimposed upon one another. In electrical reproduction of a phonograph record, the motion of the tracing point causes an iron armature to move within a coil of wire. The resulting disturbance of the magnetic flux induces an emf. in the coil and sets up an electric current which is amplified by electron tubes and operates a loud speaker.

The sound record of a talking motion picture usually consists of a narrow strip or "sound track" which extends along one edge of the film and is crossed by lines of varying intensity. In making the record, the sounds are received by a sensitive microphone and cause corresponding variations of the electric current in the microphone circuit. This current, suitably amplified, is caused to control a neon lamp, the intensity of which responds instantly to current changes. The light from the lamp is passed through a narrow transverse slit upon the moving film, and produces a series of lines of varying degrees of darkness in the finished film.

In reproduction from the film, a steady light shines through a similar slit upon the sound track, the transmitted beam varying continually in intensity. This beam strikes a photoelectric cell (§ 322) and causes proportional changes in the current through it. The varying current, properly amplified, operates a loud speaker and reproduces the original sound.

376. Sound Ranging.—Most persons can estimate with considerable accuracy the direction from which a particular sound comes, an ability called the *binaural sense*. The waves received by the two ears vary slightly in intensity and phase, and from early childhood these differences have come to be associated with particular directions. Improved accuracy may be obtained by use of an instrument which virtually increases the base line between the ears. This device consists of a pair of telephone transmitters mounted in positions corresponding to the ears on an imaginary head of large size. The transmitters are connected through separate circuits to corresponding receivers worn by the observer. The direction from which the sound comes can be located by turning the device until the source appears to be directly in front. The same result can also be attained by shifting the phase relation of the currents in the two circuits to balance the phase difference in the sound waves at the transmitters.

An extension of this procedure can be utilized to give the location of a sounding source as well as its direction. To locate the position of an enemy gun, for example, three or more receiving stations are

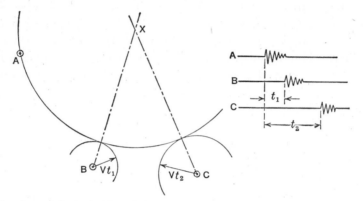

Fig. 363. Method of locating an enemy gun and form of electrical record

arranged at definitely known locations, and equipped with microphones that are connected with appropriate electrical apparatus at a central receiving point. This apparatus records accurately the time intervals between the reception of the sound impulses at the different stations. From this information, the location of the sounding source can be determined graphically, as illustrated with the aid of Fig. 363.

The three microphone stations are located at A, B and C, and it is supposed that the electrical record shows the impulse to reach B at an instant t_1 sec. after it arrives at A, and to reach C at an instant t_2 sec. after it arrives at A. At the moment the sound impulse reaches A, it is still a distance Vt_1 from B, V being the velocity of the wave, and is consequently at some point on the arc of radius Vt_1 centered at B. At the same instant the impulse is distant Vt_2 from C, and has reached some point on the arc of radius Vt_2 centered at C. A circle passing through station A and drawn tangent to the arcs around stations B and C shows the position of the wave front at the instant considered. The center of the circle, X, gives the location of the source sought for. The mathematical procedure for locating this point is quite involved, but graphical construction by trial can be carried out quickly.

377. Supersonic Vibrations.—Investigations of longitudinal vibrations have been extended into the so-called *supersonic* frequency region beyond the upper limit of hearing, and the resulting short waves have found a variety of applications. Such vibrations may be produced by a quartz crystal mounted between metal electrodes, making use of the piezoelectric effect described in § 330. The crystal has a natural frequency determined by its elasticity and density. When an alternating emf. of this same frequency is impressed upon the electrodes, the crystal will be set into mechanical vibration, which it will communicate to the surrounding medium. Supersonic vibrations may also be produced by slight periodic changes in length of an iron or nickel rod that is magnetized by a high-frequency alternating current through a solenoid around the rod; the variation in length due to magnetization is called *magnetostriction*.

Because of their relatively short wavelength, supersonic waves do not spread much by diffraction, § 448, but remain localized in narrow beams; this property makes them suitable for under-water communication between ships. The transmitting crystal is supported outside of the ship's hull and sets up a longitudinal wave in the water. This wave acts upon a similar crystal at the receiving station, setting it into vibration and causing it to generate an emf. of the same frequency between its electrodes. The water wave corresponds to the carrier wave in radio telephony, and the same methods of modulation and reception are used for both.

Supersonic waves, as well as those of somewhat greater wavelength, are also used for echo ranging and depth soundings. Instruments for these purposes are designed to transmit a signal and receive its echo, to repeat these operations many times per second, and to give visible indications of the distances sought. The system known as "Sonar" was effectively used in the War to determine the range and bearing of enemy submarines; it utilized crystals of ammonium dihydrogen phosphate and operated on frequencies of from 10 to 30 kilocycles per sec.

A depth-sounding instrument used at sea sends a signal to the bottom and receives the echo $\frac{1}{80}$ sec. later. If the velocity of the waves in sea water is 1500 meters per sec., then the depth at the place of observation is $\frac{1}{2} \times 1500 \div 80 = 9.38$ meters. Since 1 fathom = 6 ft. = 6×30.48 cm., the depth is $9.38 \times 100 \div (6 \times 30.48) = 5.13$ fathoms.

Biological and chemical effects are produced in many substances by exposure to strong beams of supersonic radiation; for example, particles of colloidal material in liquids are shattered and form extremely fine emulsions.

The passage of supersonic waves through a liquid sets up planes of condensation and rarefaction which may be so close together that the medium acts as a diffraction grating (§ 451), causing a beam of light perpendicular to the direction of wave propagation to be spread into spectra of several orders. This phenomenon has been used in the measurement of the moduli of elasticity of liquids and solids.

In gases, calculations show that as the frequency of supersonic waves is increased, say to the order of 10^8 vibrations per sec., bringing the wavelength close to the mean free path of the molecules, the compressions and rarefactions become more and more nearly isothermal. Under these conditions the velocity of the waves is given by the expression $V = \sqrt{p/d}$, as explained in § 351.

378. Reverberation.—Almost everyone has noticed the persistence of sound, particularly in a large empty hall. This effect is caused by echoes repeated in rapid succession, and is called *reverberation*. It may be explained by considering the effect of sustaining a tone within a room from which no acoustic energy escapes. When the source is set into vibration, the sound waves emitted travel to the walls and other surfaces, and are then reflected back and forth from one surface after another. If none of the acoustic energy were absorbed, the resulting sound intensity would increase indefinitely. Absorption does take place at the surfaces, however, and as a result, the intensity will reach a steady value when the rate of energy absorption equals the rate of emission. After this condition has been attained and the vibrating source is stopped, the sound does not cease instantly but dies away slowly as the acoustic energy within the room is absorbed. The intensity I at an instant t sec. after stopping a sound is given in terms of the maximum intensity I_0 by the equation:

$$I = I_0 \epsilon^{-kt} \tag{236}$$

where ϵ is the base of natural logarithms and k is taken as a constant for the room under consideration.

The time in which a sound diminishes until it can no longer be heard has been termed the *reverberation time*. Professor Wallace C. Sabine (1869–1919), an American pioneer in acoustics, regarded the reverberation time more definitely as the interval during which the intensity of the sound diminishes to one millionth of its initial value. A sound produced in a small room diminishes very rapidly because the reflections and absorptions at the walls are repeated at short intervals. In an auditorium, however, the reverberation time may be quite long, making it necessary for a speaker to talk very slowly to prevent confusion between the syllable being spoken and the echoes of the preceding one. On the other hand, the sound should not die away too quickly, for the room would be judged "too dead." Values of 1.0 sec. for a small auditorium and of about 2.0 sec. for a large one may be considered within the acceptable range. The reverberation time, according to Sabine's definition, can be found from the foregoing equation by taking I_0/I as 10^6; then its value is

$$t = \frac{1}{k} \log_\epsilon \frac{I_0}{I} = \frac{2.303}{k} \log_{10} \frac{I_0}{I} = \frac{2.303}{k} \log_{10} 10^6 = \frac{1}{k}(2.303 \times 6)$$

The reverberation time can also be defined as the time required for a sound to decay to a level 60 db. below that of the original sound.

*379. Acoustics of the Auditorium.—The suitability of an auditorium for the purposes of speaking or the presentation of music depends primarily upon two factors, reverberation and interference. Reverberation is responsible for the slowness with which sounds die away, and may be controlled by selecting wall materials and coverings which will absorb sound energy to the desired extent. Interference causes variations in intensity from point to point; excessive interference may be avoided by a proper choice of the dimensions and shape of the room.

The persistence of sound is due to incomplete absorption at successive reflections and the reverberation time t will be longer in a large room than in a small one; consequently the interval between reflections will depend upon the volume. For a similar reason this time will vary inversely with the velocity of sound. Furthermore, it is influenced by the character of the surfaces in the room, being reduced if they are good sound absorbers. Since an open window returns none of the energy that reaches it, the opening acts like a perfect absorber, and the *absorbing power* of a room is expressed as an equivalent number of square feet of open window. If the volume of the room in cubic feet is represented by B, the velocity of sound in feet per second by $V = 1100$, and the absorbing power of the room in effective square feet by a, these effects may be incorporated in the foregoing equation by taking $\frac{1}{k} = c\frac{B}{Va}$, where c is another constant. Theory and experiment show that this constant has the value 4 for the units employed; consequently, the reverberation time in seconds becomes

$$t = 4 \frac{B}{1100\,a} (2.303 \times 6)$$

or

$$t = 0.05 \frac{B}{a} \tag{237}$$

The absorbing power of the room, including furnishings and audience, is found by adding a number of terms for the various surfaces, each term consisting of the area s multiplied by an appropriate *absorption coefficient* β, thus

$$a = \beta_1 s_1 + \beta_2 s_2 + \beta_3 s_3 + \cdots$$

although a more exact appraisal of the absorbing power of a room must take account of the manner in which its various absorbing surfaces are distributed.

Absorption coefficients have been measured for many materials, and are expressed as fractions of the "absorption" at an open window of equal area. A felt surface is a good absorber because it contains many tiny channels in which the air vibrations are damped out and their energy dissipated as heat; its coefficient $\beta = 0.70$ indicates that 1 sq. ft. of felt is equivalent to 0.70 sq. ft. of open window space in quenching reverberation. On the other hand, glass and metals are poor absorbers. Absorption coefficients vary somewhat with the frequency of the sound and with the condition of the surface. Some values suggestive of the order of magnitude appear in the accompanying table.

Absorption Coefficients

Open window	1.00
Brick wall....................	0.03
Carpet, felt lined............	0.40
Draperies, cotton.............	0.50
Excelsior tile................	0.80
Felt.........................	0.70
Glass........................	0.025
Linoleum.....................	0.03
Plaster, smooth..............	0.03
Wood paneling...............	0.08

Absorbing Power (effective sq. ft.)

Auditorium chairs, wood, each..	0.3
Audience, each person.........	4.0

As an example of sound absorption, compute the reverberation time in an auditorium measuring $60 \times 90 \times 20$ ft., the absorbing materials consisting of 9500 sq. ft. of plaster, 7000 sq. ft. of wood, and 400 sq. ft. of glass, if the room has 800 seats and an audience of 500 persons. The absorbing power, based on the foregoing coefficients, is:

Plaster:	9500×0.03	$= 285$
Wood:	7000×0.08	$= 560$
Glass:	400×0.025	$= 10$
Seats:	800×0.3	$= 240$
Audience:	$500 \times (4.0 - 0.3)$	$= 1850$

Absorbing power   2945 effective sq. ft.;

whence, by equation (237), the reverberation time is

$$t = 0.05 \frac{60 \times 90 \times 20}{2945} = 1.83 \text{ sec.}$$

This value appears rather high for an auditorium of this size, and could be reduced by the use of more highly absorbing materials.

The second factor involved in the acoustics of an auditorium is that of interference produced by reflection of the sound waves from the walls and ceiling. As a result, the waves tend to reenforce one another at certain regions and to destroy one another at other places. Tests by Sabine showed regions within an auditorium where the intensity of sound was greater than at the source, separated by zones of almost complete annulment. In particular, large curved surfaces tend to focus the sound at definite spots. If such a surface is to be used in the architectural design of a room, it should be so shaped that the point of concentration will lie outside the room, thus avoiding the effects observed in so-called "whispering galleries."

The reflection of sound waves in an auditorium is strikingly shown by a method perfected by Professor Arthur L. Foley. The sound disturbance is produced by an electric spark at a chosen point within a model of the auditorium, and spreads outward as a single wave pulse. The advancing compression is illuminated for an instant by a second spark after any desired time interval, and casts a shadow on a photographic plate, showing the position then occupied by the wave front. The sound photograph shown in Fig. 364 was obtained in this manner, the outline A to F representing a horizontal section of a theatre. In the figure, SW is a sound wave, generated by the electric

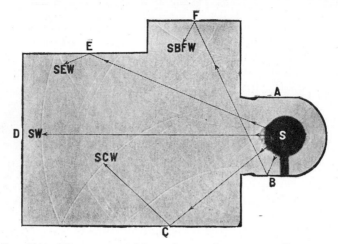

FIG. 364.   Momentary positions of a sound wave and its reflections

spark at S, that has not yet arrived at the rear wall D; SCW is one portion of SW that has been reflected from the wall C; and $SBFW$ is the portion of the original wave reflected from the wall B and then from the wall F. Every wave in the figure can be traced to the reflection from one or more of the walls of the model.

PROBLEMS

1. In measurements of sound intensity it is desired that the background noise should be at least 10 db. below the level being measured. If the sound under test has an intensity of 0.1 microwatt per sq. cm., to what intensity should the background noise be limited?

2. Noise levels out of doors reckoned above the standard reference intensity of 10^{-10} microwatts per sq. cm. have been given as follows: rustle of leaves in a gentle breeze, 16 db.; riveter 35 ft. away, 103 db. Compute the intensities of these noises.

3. A public address system raises the intensity level of a speaker's voice 20 db. If the average power of the speaker's voice is 10 microwatts, what is the power of the sound from the public address system?

4. Two sounds have intensity levels of 50 and 60 db. above the standard intensity of 10^{-10} microwatts per sq. cm. If these sounds are produced together, what is (*a*) the intensity of the resulting sound? and (*b*) the intensity level of that sound?

5. An observer 10 ft. away from a steady source of sound moves to a new position 5 ft. nearer the source. Compute the ratio of the sound intensity at the new position to that at the initial position, and also the increase in intensity level in moving to the new position.

6. To measure the pitch of a tone it is sounded simultaneously with that of a motor-driven siren and the beats produced by the two tones are counted. The siren disk has 120 holes; when it is driven at 499 rev. per min., 36 beats are produced in 15 sec., and when it is driven at the next higher available speed, 502 rev. per min., 54 beats are produced in 15 sec. What is the frequency of the tone under measurement?

7. The diagram shows a pendulum for combining two harmonic vibrations at right angles. The entire pendulum is set into vibration perpendicular to the page about line CD, and at the same time the lower part AB

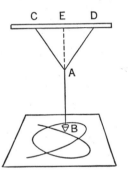

is set into vibration in the plane of the page about point A. Sand trickling from a funnel at B traces a Lissajous figure on a horizontal surface beneath the pendulum. If the length $EB = 20$ in., what should be the length AB to give a sand figure of the form shown?

8. An observer 1.5 mi. away from a gun sees the flash when it is fired and hears the report 7.0 sec. later. From these data and the fact that the air temperature at the time of the test was 20° C., compute the velocity of sound at 0° C.

9. In measuring the velocity of sound by Kundt's method, a brass rod 1 meter long clamped at the center produces the same pitch as that of a siren driven at 1012 rev. per min., the siren disk having 100 holes. The powder heaps within the tube are 9.9 cm. apart. Compute the velocity of sound in the brass rod and also that in the gas within the tube.

10. Two observers equipped with binaural detectors are stationed on an east-west line, observer A being 1 mi. east of observer B. A sound from a distant source approaches A from a direction 8° west of north and it approaches B from a direction 34° east of north. How far is the sounding source from observer A?

11. A plane supersonic wave traveling in water at 1470 meters per sec. is reflected upon itself and the stationary wave so formed has 5000 nodes per cm. Compute the frequency of the supersonic source.

12. If the reverberation time for an empty hall is 2.5 sec., in what time will the intensity of a sound in this room diminish by absorption to $\frac{1}{2}$ of its initial value?

*13. The reverberation time for the auditorium described in the solved problem of § 379 is to be reduced to $1\frac{1}{4}$ sec. by covering all of the plaster except the ceiling with absorptive material. What absorption coefficient should the material have?

*14. An auditorium has a floor area 40 x 60 ft. and is 15 ft. high. It has a linoleum floor and a plaster ceiling. The walls have a wood wainscot $3\frac{1}{2}$ ft. high, above which the windows have an area of 200 sq. ft.; the remaining surface is covered with acoustic material having an absorption coefficient of 0.75. Compute the reverberation time for the empty room.

Light

Sources and Velocity
of Light   *Chapter XXXIII*

380. Some Properties of Light.—Light is radiant energy which is capable of affecting the eye to produce vision. Its exact nature, as in the case of gravitation and electricity, is not fully understood, but much has been learned about the way it is produced and propagated. The character of light and the associated problems of atomic structure will be considered in detail farther on. For present purposes it will suffice to state that light energy, like other forms of radiation (§ 202), is apparently emitted in tiny quantities called quanta, and transmitted by electromagnetic waves having the various properties described in Chapter XXX.

Our everyday experiences with the behavior of light have to do largely with reflection and refraction; we see our images by reflection in mirrors or in other highly polished surfaces, and we observe the bending of light by refraction where it passes from one medium into another. The latter is usually accompanied by the splitting up of white light into the component colors of the spectrum, an effect called dispersion. Three other effects can be observed with simple facilities. On looking at a distant light source through a piece of silk, the patch of light appears to be made up of a group of small spots; this effect, called diffraction, is due to the slight bending of light in going through the small spaces between the silk fibres. The colors observed in soap or oil films are due to the interference of waves of light that are reflected from both faces of the films. Passing light through a crystal like tourmaline, or a film like polaroid, gives it a one-sidedness called polarization; this change in character is evidenced by the quenching action produced with another specimen placed crosswise to the first. These and other effects of light are considered in the chapters that follow; the present one deals with light sources, the illumination produced by them, and the velocity of light.

381. Rays and Waves.—It is generally stated that light travels in straight lines within a uniform medium. This statement is true to a close degree of approximation, as can be shown in many ways. For example, the shape of the shadow which an object casts when illuminated by a distant source is determined by the shape of the object. The straight-line transmission of light is made use of by practically everyone in sighting along edges and surfaces to verify their straightness or flatness.

The direction or path of propagation may be represented by a straight line, called a *ray*. This method of representation will be used frequently in the study of light; thus, the radiation from a point source is often represented by rays diverging from this spot. When such divergent rays enter the eye (§ 435) they are rendered converging by its lens system and are brought to a focus upon the retina; the image there formed stimulates the nerve endings of the retina and the resulting sensation is that of "seeing" the spot from which the rays appear to diverge.

Many of the effects of light can be explained in simple form upon the hypothesis that light travels in straight lines. The fact that light has certain wave properties often provides a more satisfactory explanation of these effects, and in some phenomena like diffraction and polarization, the wave theory alone can be relied upon. In the following chapters either rays or waves will be used, whichever will provide the more simple and straightforward analysis for the particular phenomenon involved.

382. Sources of Light.—The production of light is attributed physically to actions taking place within the atoms of the glowing source. When an atom in its normal state is excited by collision with another atom or by other means, the energy it receives causes the electrons to assume higher energy levels. The subsequent falling of electrons to lower energy levels is accompanied by loss of energy through radiation, and this radiation, striking the eye, produces the sensation of light provided its frequency is within the range of the visible spectrum.

Our great natural source of light is the sun. Its radiation is described in § 199, and curves are given in Fig. 201 which show that most of the energy falls outside the visible range. In a sense, the moon is also a natural source of light, but strictly speaking, it is merely a reflector of sunlight. Artificial sources of light, in the order of their development through the centuries, include the torch, the oil lamp, the candle, the gas lamp, the carbon arc lamp, the incandescent electric lamp, vapor lamps, the fluorescent lamp, and luminous gas tubes.

Arc Lamps.—The arc is now used only for picture projectors and searchlights. Ordinarily it consists of a pair of carbon rods connected in series with a resistance across direct-current supply mains. The arc is started by bringing the carbons into contact and then separating them. As the carbons burn away during operation, they must be fed toward each other manually or automatically to keep the gap between them fairly constant. Most of the light comes from a crater that is formed in the tip of the positive carbon; its temperature is about 3600° K. Arc lamps can also be operated on alternating-current circuits; when so connected both carbons of a lamp become equally bright and the result is not as satisfactory for projection purposes.

Incandescent Lamps.—The incandescent lamp consists essentially of a conducting filament enclosed within a glass bulb and heated so intensely by the electric current that it emits light. The original lamp of this type, brought out by Edison in 1880, used a filament of carbonized bamboo, mounted within an evacuated bulb to prevent oxidation. From this starting point, continued research has brought about numerous improvements, resulting in the tungsten-filament lamp of the present day. These lamps are commonly used for the illumination of streets and highways as well as for all sorts of interiors, and generally operate across 110-volt mains.

About 1910, when it became possible to draw tungsten into thin wires, lamp filaments were made of this metal and operated in a vacuum at temperatures around 2500° K. The early tungsten lamp was more efficient than those previously used because it could be operated at a higher temperature and still have the same life. Its principal drawback was a gradual blackening of the bulb due to deposition upon it of tungsten evaporated from the hot filament. Subsequent improvement brought about the gas-filled tungsten lamp, in which the bulb is filled with an inert gas, such as nitrogen, under a pressure of about an atmosphere. The presence of the gas retards the evaporation of the filament, as desired, but produces an undesirable cooling of the filament through convection currents. To offset the latter effect, the filament is arranged in the form of a closely wound helix, and practically all of the incandescent lamps used today have such filaments.

In the projection of moving pictures lamps are now used in which the filament is concentrated into a small space and aligned in one plane. Many projection lamps make use of doubly-coiled filaments.

Vapor Lamps.—The early vapor lamps were long tubes filled with mercury vapor at low pressure and were developed by the American inventor, Peter Cooper Hewitt. The present type of mercury vapor lamp operates at pressures of from $\frac{1}{2}$ to 6 atmospheres and is called the high-intensity lamp. Its construction is shown in Fig. 365. The inner or arc tube contains the two main electrodes, each consisting of a coiled tungsten wire coated with barium oxide; it also contains a starting electrode that is connected with a resistor to control the starting current. A small amount of argon is added to the mercury vapor to facilitate starting.

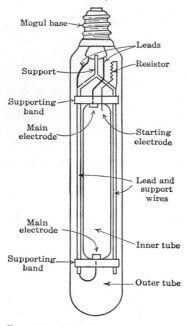

Fig. 365. High-intensity mercury vapor lamp

When the lamp is connected to alternating-current service wires, electrons are drawn from the upper main electrode by the starting electrode whenever the latter is positive. This stream of electrons ionizes the argon, and a blue glow fills the tube. The discharge serves to heat the mercury vapor to the point of ionization, and then conduction is established between the main electrodes. The heating process takes about 7 minutes. This unsatisfactory feature of the lamp is compensated for by its great brilliancy. Such mercury vapor lamps give off light of a greenish color and are used for street and industrial lighting.

The sodium-vapor lamp, used for highway lighting, has a double glass enclosure with a vacuum between. The inner bulb has two electrodes and contains some metallic sodium and a little neon gas. When the lamp is started, the neon ionizes and develops enough heat to vaporize the sodium. This accounts for the orange-red glow during the first few minutes of operation. When the lamp attains its rated output it emits the characteristic yellow light of sodium vapor.

Fluorescent Lamps.—One of the more recent developments in electric lighting makes use of fluorescence (§ 420), the fluorescent material or *phosphor* being applied in a thin layer on the inner walls of a long tubular glass bulb containing argon gas and mercury vapor. An electric discharge through the gas is initiated by the use of hot electrodes, and is rich in ultraviolet radiation. This energizes the phosphor, which in turn becomes a brilliant source of visible light, the color depending upon the phosphor used. The materials of some phosphors are: calcium tungstate for blue, magnesium tungstate for blue-white, zinc silicate for green, and cadmium borate for pink.

In starting a fluorescent lamp, current is first established in a small coil of tungsten wire at each end of the tube, but after a moment the connection is automatically broken between the two coils and they then serve as electrodes for the gaseous discharge. The lamp with its auxiliary equipment is designed for connection to 110-volt alternating-current supply mains and operates at a relatively low temperature. Circular tube lamps are being developed.

Luminous-tube Lighting.—Long tubes containing gas at low pressures are widely used for display lighting, neon being used to produce an orange-red light, argon and mercury for blue light, and helium for pinkish-white light. These units are usually operated from 110-volt alternating-current mains through step-up transformers. When the circuit is closed an initial potential difference up to 15,000 volts is impressed upon the tube and the gas becomes ionized at the electrodes, the ionization almost instantly extending throughout the tube as a result of the collision of electrons and ions with the atoms of the gas. Typical neon tube units have tubes 9 to 15 mm. in diameter, operating at gas pressures of 10 to 24 mm. of Hg., and taking currents of 15 to 50 milliamperes.

383. Luminous Intensity and Light Flux.—The luminous intensity of a source of light is expressed in terms of a source selected as a standard; originally the flame of a spermaceti candle burning at the rate of 120 grains per hour was selected for this purpose. This source was regarded as having an intensity of 1 international candle power (cp.) when viewed in a horizontal plane. In this country the candle was never actually used as a standard but was derived from a group of carefully calibrated incandescent lamps kept at the national laboratory.

A new primary standard of luminous intensity, effective January 1948, which was developed by the National Bureau of Standards at Washington, has been adopted by the International Committee on Weights and Measures. It consists of a glowing enclosure operated at the temperature of solidifying platinum, 2046° K., and arranged as shown in cross-section by Fig. 366. The platinum, contained in a crucible of fused thorium oxide surrounded by heat insulation,

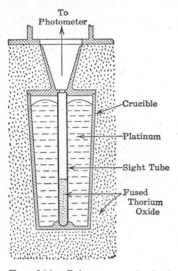

FIG. 366. Primary standard of luminous intensity

is placed in an alternating magnetic field and melted by the currents thereby induced in it; this method of heating is used because of its violent stirring action. A sight tube, also of fused thorium oxide and containing some of this material in a finely ground state, extends into the molten metal and serves as a black-body radiator, § 200. The brightness within this tube is taken as 60 cp. per sq. cm. when the metal, in cooling slowly, reaches its solidifying temperature. The new *candle* is therefore one-sixtieth of the luminous intensity of one square centimeter of a hollow enclosure at the temperature of solidifying platinum. The new candle is somewhat smaller than the international candle.

A 1-cp. source will produce a certain illumination of a surface near it. Any other source placed at the same point and which produces the same illumination of the surface is also rated 1 cp.; if it produces twice as much illumination it would be rated 2 cp., and so on. Measurements of illumination depend upon the response of the eye, and are influenced considerably by the color of the source, for the eye is more sensitive to some colors than to others. This fact is taken into account by the use of so-called luminosity factors when comparing sources of different color.

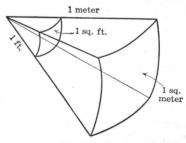

FIG. 367. Solid angle extending to unit area at unit distance

The rate at which a source emits light energy, evaluated in terms of its visual effect, is spoken of as light flux, and is expressed in lumens. One *lumen* is the amount of light flux radiating from a uniform 1-cp. source throughout a solid angle of such size as to surround a unit area at a unit distance from the source, as shown in Fig. 367. Such a 1-cp. source would radiate

1 lumen normally upon a surface of 1 sq. meter at a distance of 1 meter, or upon a surface of 1 sq. ft. at a distance of 1 ft. By imagining a spherical shell of 1-ft. radius around this source as center, it will be clear that each square foot of this spherical surface receives 1 lumen; since the total area of the shell is 4π sq. ft., the total light flux emitted by the 1-cp. source is 4π lumens.

Most light sources have different luminous intensities along different directions. The average of the candle powers measured in all directions about a light source as origin is called the *mean spherical candle power*. Since a source having a mean spherical candle power of 1 cp. emits 4π lumens of light flux, the total flux in lumens emitted by a source of mean spherical candle power I_0 is

$$F = 4\pi I_0 \tag{238}$$

Thus, a 100-cp. source produces $4\pi \times 100 = 1257$ lumens.

*384. Efficiency of Light Sources.—Electric lamps are commonly rated in terms of their power input in watts, and their outputs are stated in lumens. The efficiency, instead of being expressed numerically as a percentage, is given more usefully as the ratio of the output in lumens to the input in watts. Data on some modern lamps are listed in the following table. The incandescent lamps are of the

Efficiencies of Electric Lamps

Incandescent			Fluorescent		
Input to lamp, watts	Output, lumens	Efficiency, lumens per watt	Input to bulb, watts	Output, lumens	Efficiency, lumens per watt
15	140	9.3	Daylight Color		
25	260	10.4	15	495	33
40	465	11.6	20	760	38
60	835	13.9	30	1,230	41
100	1,620	16.2	40	1,800	45
200	3,650	18.2	White Color		
300	5,850	19.5	20	900	45
500	9,850	19.7	Blue Color		
1,000	21,000	21.0	20	460	23
			Green Color		
			20	1,300	65

tungsten gas-filled type for direct or alternating current at 110–120 volts. The fluorescent lamps are for alternating current at 110–120 volts, and the tube lengths are 18, 24, 36, and 48 inches respectively for the 15, 20, 30, and 40 watt sizes. The efficiencies of high-intensity mercury vapor lamps (250- and 400-watt sizes) and of sodium vapor lamps (100- and 200-watt sizes) are approximately 40 and 50 lumens per watt respectively.

385. Illumination of a Surface.—The illumination of a surface is defined as the amount of light flux it receives per unit area. For a surface of area A which receives a total light flux F, the illumination is

$$E = \frac{F}{A} \tag{239}$$

and may be expressed in lumens per square foot or lumens per square meter. The illumination will be uniform when the flux distribution is uniform. This will be true for a surface illuminated by a single lamp when all portions of the illuminated surface are equally distant from the source.

The amount of illumination produced by a light source upon a given surface is determined by the intensity of the source and its distance from the surface, provided the rays of light strike the surface normally. Upon increasing the intensity I of the source, there will be a proportional increase in the light flux falling upon the surface. Upon increasing the distance from the source, there will be a considerable reduction in the illumination of the surface; its value will be found to vary inversely with the square of the distance. This agrees with the behavior of radiation in general, as expressed by the Inverse Square Law, § 200. When both of these factors are considered, the illumination is found to vary as I/r^2, or $E = kI/r^2$, where r is the distance from source to surface, and k is a proportionality factor. Illumination is frequently expressed in foot-candles; *one foot-candle is the illumination of a surface 1 ft. away from a uniform 1-cp. source.* For this unit the factor k becomes unity, and the expression may be written

$$E = \frac{I}{r^2} \tag{240}$$

giving the illumination produced by a source of I cp. upon a surface at a distance of r ft. The numerical value of illumination is the same whether expressed in foot-candles or in lumens per square foot.

For example, a surface that is everywhere 8 ft. away from a 256-cp. lamp has an illumination of $E = I/r^2 = 256 \div (8)^2 = 4.0$ ft-candles. To compute the illumination of this surface in lumens per square foot, consider the total light flux issuing from the lamp to be distributed uniformly over a sphere of 8-ft. radius. The total flux is $4\pi \times 256$ lumens, and the spherical surface has an area of $4\pi(8)^2$ sq. ft.; consequently the illumination becomes $E = F/A = (4\pi \times 256) \div (4\pi \times 64) = 4.0$ lumens per sq. ft., as before.

The following table lists a few values of illumination which illuminating engineers regard as suitable figures for the purposes designated.

Illumination Values

Class of service	Foot-candles
Class rooms and laboratories........	20–30
Corridors and stairways..........	5
Drafting rooms..................	30–50
Flood lighting	4
Hospital operating tables..........	50–75
Library reading rooms............	20
Offices........................	20–30
Retail stores....................	30
Show windows..................	50
Tennis courts...................	15
Theatre and church auditoriums....	5–15
Waiting rooms..................	5–10

In calculating the illumination by equation (240), it is supposed that all parts of the surface are at the same distance r from the source. This expression is, therefore, true only for a spherical surface with the source at the center, as shown in part I of Fig. 368. It can also be used without appreciable error for a flat surface having dimensions that are small compared with the distance to the source, provided the light flux is approximately perpendicular to the surface, as shown in part II of the figure. In brief, the equation $E = I/r^2$ applies to normal illumination.

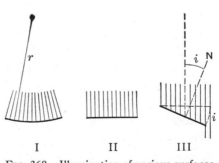

I   II   III

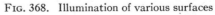

FIG. 368. Illumination of various surfaces

Suppose that a flat surface which would receive an amount of light flux F under normal illumination is inclined so that its normal N makes an angle i with the light rays, as indicated in part III of the figure. The light flux intercepted by the surface will be reduced from F to $F \cos i$, and the illumination will be lowered in the same proportion. A source of candle power I at a distance r ft. will produce upon such an inclined surface an illumination

$$E = \frac{I \cos i}{r^2} \qquad (241)$$

provided the surface dimensions are small in comparison with the distance to the source.

386. Measurement of Candle Power.—The eye is not capable of comparing the candle powers of two lamps by viewing them directly, but can determine quite accurately whether two surfaces side by side are equally illuminated. This is the operating principle of the *photometer*. In this device, two lamps are placed a suitable distance apart with a screen between them, each side of the screen being illuminated normally by one of the sources. The screen is moved laterally until the illumination is observed to be the same on both sides, and the distances from it to the lamps are measured. Then from equation (240) it follows that

$$\frac{I_1}{r_1{}^2} = \frac{I_2}{r_2{}^2} \qquad (242)$$

where I_1 and I_2 are the luminous intensities of the sources in candle power, and r_1 and r_2 are their respective distances from the screen. From this equation, either intensity can be computed if the other is known.

In the Bunsen "grease-spot" photometer, the screen consists of a small sheet of paper with a waxed spot near the center, and is provided with a pair of mirrors so that an observer may see both sides at the same time. The Lummer-Brodhun photometer has an improved optical system for accomplishing this purpose. Its elements, shown in Fig. 369, comprise a gypsum screen S, an observing telescope T, reflecting prisms P and P', and a compound glass cube C. The latter element consists of two prisms cemented together, one having a design etched in its principal face to give the field of view the appearance shown. The paths of light along which both sides of the screen can be observed in the telescope are also indicated in the figure.

From the side illuminated by source 1, the rays pass to P and are reflected to C (§ 403), the light passing through to the telescope without obstruction except where the cube is etched. From the other side, illuminated by source 2, the rays pass to P' and are reflected to C, where the light is reflected at the etched portions into the telescope. The field of view is thereby illuminated at zones a and b by lamp 1 and at zones c and d by lamp 2. When the screen is so placed as to be equally illuminated by the sources, the pattern

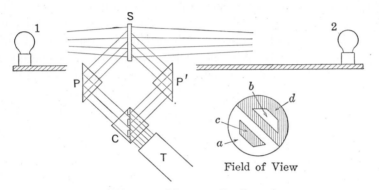

Field of View

FIG. 369.   Diagram of Lummer-Brodhun photometer

vanishes and the field appears uniform throughout. This arrangement, whereby a zone illuminated by one source is completely surrounded by another illuminated by the other source, makes it easy for the eye to judge equality of illumination, and permits the candle powers of the light sources to be compared with precision.

The procedure for determining the candle power of a lamp by comparison with the primary black-body standard (§ 383) utilizes a photometer to compare the illumination on two sides of a screen. One of these is illuminated by the lamp under test. The other receives the radiation from the primary standard after it passes through an aperture of known size placed near it, a lens being used to form an image of the source upon the screen. The illumination of this image may be found by the equation $E = I/r^2$, in which I is taken as the product of the brightness of the source (60 candles per square centimeter) and the area of the aperture in square centimeters, and r as the distance from the aperture to the screen.

To illustrate such a comparison numerically, suppose that equal illumination is produced when the lamp under test and the aperture of the primary standard are respectively 125 cm. and 340 cm. away from the screen, the aperture having a diameter of 1.7 cm. The illumination due to the lamp under test of candle power x is $x/(125)^2$, and that due to the primary standard is $60 \times \pi(1.7 \div 2)^2/(340)^2$. From these values, the luminous intensity is determined as $x = 18.4$ cp.

Difficulties are encountered when it is attempted to compare the candle powers of two lamps that have different colors, since the eye cannot judge accurately the equality of illumination of two surfaces unless their colors match approximately. In measuring incandescent lamps, it is sometimes possible to match their colors by altering the potential difference on the calibrated standard lamp, as the color is noticeably yellower when this is reduced. Lamps of different colors can be compared by means of a so-called *flicker photometer* which enables the observer to view first one side of the screen and then the other alternately in rapid succession. Upon increasing the frequency of alternation, a value will be found for which the flicker due to color difference disappears, the colors of the two sources appearing to blend into a single resultant hue. If the frequency is not too high, however, the flicker due to illumination difference remains. The photometer screen is then moved until this flicker also disappears, whereupon the candle power of the test lamp can be computed in the usual way. A rotating prism, or other optical arrangement, is employed to bring the two sides of the screen alternately into the field of view.

The photoelectric cell is often employed to compare the candle powers of two lamps, even though these sources have different colors. Cells are now available which, when used with suitable filters, have the same sensitivity characteristics as the normal eye, § 435. The cell is exposed to each lamp in turn and the corresponding currents are observed by a microammeter. Since the current is proportional to the illumination at the cell, as explained in § 322, the candle power of one lamp can be expressed definitely in terms of the other regarded as a standard.

387. Measurement of Illumination.—Since the object of artificial lighting is to produce adequate illumination, it is essential to have convenient means for measuring this quantity. One instrument for this purpose is the *illuminometer*; it is virtually a portable photometer for comparing the illumination of the surface under measurement with that produced by a small incandescent lamp of known candle power. The lamp is mounted within a light-tight enclosure and can be moved until it produces the same intensity of illumination as that existing upon the surface. Its value is then known to be $E = I/r^2$,

I being the candle power of the standard lamp, and *r* its distance from the surface. Since each position of the standard lamp corresponds to a particular value of illumination, a scale may be provided on the instrument to give the result in foot-candles directly.

Another device for measuring illumination is the *photovoltaic cell*, which generates an emf. under exposure to light. A plate of copper coated with a semi-transparent layer of copper oxide is exposed at the point where the illumination value is desired. Electrons pass from the copper oxide to the copper and the cell develops an emf. which is proportional to the illumination. The current is indicated on a microammeter, the scale of which usually is calibrated directly in foot-candles. No external source of emf. is necessary. The "Photronic" cell shown with indicating instrument in Fig. 370 is of this general type.

FIG. 370. Foot-candle meter. (*Courtesy of Weston Electrical Instrument Corporation*)

388. Measurement of Light Flux.—Candle-power measurements of light sources are now usually conducted to give the average illumination in all directions around a lamp rather than the value in only one direction as afforded by the photometers mentioned in § 386. Such measurements are made by placing the lamp under test within a large sphere, called a *sphere photometer*, and observing the illumination which it produces at the inner surface. The walls of the photometer chamber are painted dull white in order to scatter the light in all directions. While direct illumination of the surface by the light source may have different values at various points, the illumination produced by reflection is uniform over the surface and is proportional to the flux emitted by the source. This illumination is measured at a small translucent window in the spherical shell that is shielded against direct radiation from the source, the readings being made with an illuminometer, a photoelectric cell, or a photovoltaic cell.

Suppose that two lamps emit light fluxes F_1 and F_2, and produce illumination values E_1 and E_2 respectively; it follows that

$$\frac{E_1}{E_2} = \frac{F_1}{F_2}$$

and therefore, by equation (238), the ratio of the mean spherical candle powers I_{01} and I_{02} of these lamps becomes

$$\frac{I_{01}}{I_{02}} = \frac{E_1}{E_2}$$

showing that the mean spherical candle power of a lamp is proportional to the illumination which it produces on the window of the instrument.

*389. Illumination of a Room.—For correct interior lighting a sufficient amount of light should be provided to give the desired value of illumination, and the lighting units should be so designed and placed as to make it reasonably uniform, without glare.

Three methods of lighting are in common use, the so-called direct, indirect, and semi-indirect methods. With direct lighting, the lamps project light directly upon the desired working surfaces. With indirect lighting, the lamps are concealed entirely, and the illumination is produced by reflection from the walls and ceiling of the room. With semi-indirect lighting, the illumination is produced in part by light reflected from the walls and ceiling, and in part by direct transmission, usually through translucent glassware. In all of these methods, a large amount of light is absorbed by the walls and ceiling, particularly if these are dark colored, making it necessary to generate more light flux at the lamps than is received at the plane of utilization. This is particularly true for small rooms, where these

Coefficients of Light Utilization

Type of lighting unit	Color of both walls and ceiling	Floor area, sq. ft.			
		200	400	800	1600 and over
Direct	Light	0.30	0.34	0.38	0.41
	Dark	0.28	0.32	0.36	0.39
Semi-indirect	Light	0.16	0.20	0.23	0.26
	Dark	0.095	0.12	0.14	0.16
Indirect	Light	0.12	0.15	0.18	0.20
	Dark	0.045	0.065	0.080	0.090

surfaces are relatively large in comparison with the surface to be illuminated.

The usual method of determining the size of lamps to be installed is as follows: First, calculate the amount of light flux which must reach the working plane in order to produce the desired illumination. Next, apply a *coefficient of utilization* suitable for the installation, in order to obtain the number of lumens that must be generated in the lamps. Finally, from the efficiencies of the lamps, determine the size of lamp to be used.

The coefficient of utilization gives the proportion of the light produced by the lamps which reaches the plane of work; its value varies with the type of lighting unit, the color of walls and ceiling, and the size of the room. Such coefficients have been measured under a wide variety of conditions, and some values suggestive of their order of magnitude are given in the accompanying table. The values listed are based on average conditions of cleanliness of the lighting units, and are appropriate for a 12-ft. ceiling height.

The procedure will be illustrated by calculating the size of incandescent lamps needed to give an illumination of 12 ft-candles in a room measuring 20 × 40 ft. with light-colored walls and ceiling. Fig. 371 shows the room divided into eight sections, with a lighting unit at the center of each; this arrangement would afford reasonable uniformity of illumination. The desired illumination is equivalent to 12 lumens per sq. ft., and since the area to be illuminated is 20 × 40 = 800 sq. ft., it follows that 12 × 800 = 9600 lumens must reach the working plane. The coefficient of utilization for the conditions of the room is found from the table to be 0.23 for semi-indirect lighting units; this means that 9600 ÷ 0.23 = 41,700 lumens must be generated in the lamps. Therefore, each lamp must furnish 41,700 ÷ 8 = 5210 lumens. The table of lamp efficiencies in § 384 indicates that one 300-watt lamp should be used in each lighting unit.

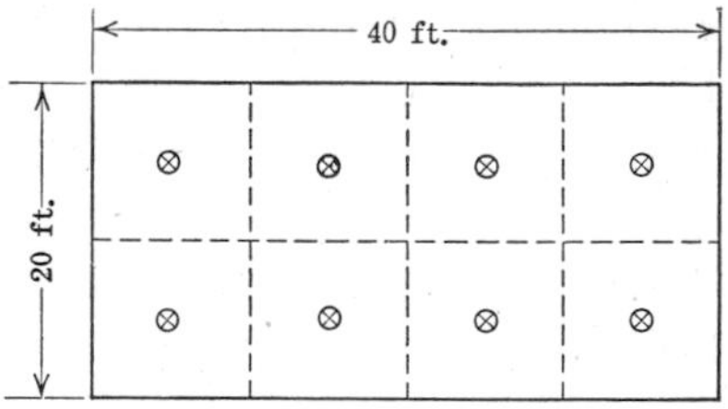

FIG. 371. Design of room lighting

390. Velocity of Light.—The velocity of light is so extremely great that early attempts to measure it were entirely unsuccessful. It is recorded that Galileo conducted an experiment in which two men, stationed some distance apart, flashed signals to each other with lanterns, a new signal being sent out at the instant one was received. It was hoped that after sending a number of such signals, the velocity of light could be found by dividing the total distance the light traveled by the total elapsed time. It is easy to recognize now that appreciable time intervals are bound to elapse between the receipt of a signal and the sending of a new one, and that the method must fail on this account.

The first successful measurement of the velocity of light was made by the Danish astronomer, Ole Roemer (1644–1710), from observations on the revolution of one of the moons of the planet Jupiter. This method is illustrated in Fig. 372, which represents Jupiter and the earth in their orbits about the sun. Roemer found that the time interval between two eclipses of the satellite (about 40 hr.) was the

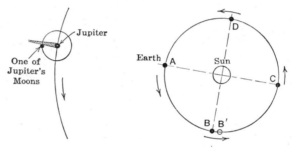

FIG. 372.   Velocity of light by Roemer's method

same when measured with the earth at *A* or at *C*, but that the interval was lengthened when the earth was at *B* and shortened when at *D*. These variations he judged correctly were not due to irregular motion of the satellite, but were caused by the fact that it takes time for light to travel. Thus, if the earth were at *B* at the beginning of a measurement, it would move away to some position *B'* during the 40-hr. interval between eclipses, and the light would have to travel the additional distance *BB'* to mark the conclusion of the test, thereby increasing the elapsed time.

From measurements made with the earth at *A*, Roemer predicted the time at which the moon in question would emerge from behind Jupiter for a particular transit when the earth had moved to *C* on the supposition that the velocity of light is infinite, and he found that this took place many minutes later than predicted on this assumption. He considered the difference between the observed and calculated times to represent the time required by the light to traverse the diameter of the earth's orbit. From more recent measurements the time difference is approximately 1000 sec. and the diameter of the earth's orbit is 186,000,000 mi., thus giving 186,000 mi. per sec. as the velocity of light.

391. The Rotating Mirror Method.—A terrestrial method for measuring the velocity of light was devised by the French physicist, Jean B. L. Foucault (1819–1868). He directed a narrow beam of light upon a plane mirror rotating at high speed, and the reflected beam flashed around accordingly. A distant mirror received a momentary flash of light and reflected it back to the rotating mirror, where it was reflected again. During the time interval in which the light beam traveled the measurable distance to the stationary mirror and back, the rotating mirror turned through some definite angle, and from observations of these quantities the velocity of light was computed.

The method just described was improved by the American physicist, Albert A. Michelson (1852–1931). The essential parts of the apparatus are indicated in Fig. 373. Light from an intense source X strikes one face of an octagonal mirror R, and is reflected to a distant plane mirror M; the ray which returns strikes another face of the octagonal mirror and is reflected into the observer's telescope T. When the octagonal mirror is set into rotation in a clockwise direction, flashes of light will strike the distant mirror and the reflected beam will fall to the left of the telescope. If the speed of rotation of the octagonal mirror is increased, a value will be reached such that in the time required for the light to travel to the mirror M and

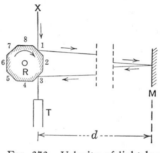

FIG. 373. Velocity of light by Michelson's method

back again, mirror face 2 will advance to the position shown at 3. Under this condition the light will be reflected into the telescope again for observation. If n represents the speed of the mirror in revolutions per second, the time required to turn through one-eighth of a revolution is $\frac{1}{8}$ of $1/n$ sec. In this time the light travels to mirror M and back, a distance $2d$; consequently the velocity of light becomes

$$V = 2d \div \frac{1}{8n} = 16nd$$

In Michelson's experiment, the revolving mirror was located at the observatory on Mt. Wilson, California, and the stationary mirror was at Mt. San Antonio, the distance between them (about 22 mi.) being measured with great precision by the U. S. Coast and Geodetic

Survey. The speed of the revolving mirror was determined by comparison with an electrically operated tuning fork, the fork in turn being calibrated against a free pendulum, which finally was compared with a standard astronomical clock. The velocity of light so determined becomes 299,776 ± 1 km. per sec. when reduced to a vacuum. Tests in an evacuated tube 1 mi. long gave results agreeing substantially with this value. In general calculations, the velocity is taken as 300,000 km. per sec. or 186,000 mi. per sec. The symbol c is generally used to represent the velocity of light in centimeters per second; $c = 3 \times 10^{10}$ cm. per sec.

So great is this velocity that light emitted by the sun reaches the earth in only 8.3 min., whereas an express train driven at 100 mi. per hr. would require over 100 years to travel the same distance. Even with this great velocity, the light from the stars takes years to reach the earth; for the nearest of them, α in the Centauri group, the time is about $3\frac{1}{2}$ years. The Great Nebula in Andromeda is more than 800,000 light-years distant.

The velocity of light in the atmosphere is so nearly the same as in a vacuum that the latter values apply without appreciable error. In other mediums, the speed is less than in a vacuum, and moreover, is different for different wavelengths, blue light traveling slower than red light.

PROBLEMS

1. A 60-watt lamp is supported at the center of a spherical enclosure 3 ft. in diameter. The luminous intensity of the lamp is 66 cp. Compute the average amount of light flux received per square foot of illuminated surface.

2. A fluorescent lamp has a tube 36 in. long. With a potential difference of 103 volts across the lamp, it takes 0.34 amp. at 0.86 power factor, and gives out 49 lumens for each watt of electrical input. Compute the luminous output of the lamp per foot of length.

3. A 150-watt spotlight equipped with a reflector and lens has a luminous intensity of 10,400 cp. along the axis of its beam. Compare the normal illumination produced by this lamp on a surface 15 ft. away with that produced by a lamp of the same rating which radiates uniformly in all directions and which delivers 17.2 lumens per watt of electrical input.

4. The illumination at a zone on a horizontal surface is 20 ft-candles, and is to be increased to 50 ft-candles by means of a supplementary incandescent lamp. Assume this lamp to have 780 cp. and to radiate uniformly in all directions; compute the height at which it should be placed vertically above the zone mentioned.

5. Imagine two horizontal planes on the earth's surface and in the same meridian, one being located at the equator and the other at a latitude of 41°. At a time when the sunlight has normal incidence upon the first of these, how does the illumination of that surface compare with the illumination of the other?

6. A horizontal surface measuring 3 x 5 ft. is illuminated by a single lamp placed 4 ft. above its center. Compare the illumination at the center of the surface with that at one corner.

◄ 7. A vertical sign 6 ft. high is illuminated by two floodlights placed 4 ft. in front of its upper edge and 6 ft. apart. Each floodlight has a rating of 500 watts and delivers 780 cp. Compute the illumination at a spot on the sign which is half way between top and bottom and which is equally distant from the lamps.

8. A simple form of photometer is shown in the diagram. The sources S_1 and S_2 illuminate the vertical wall W, upon which a rod R casts shadows at regions a and b. These regions are found to be equally illuminated for

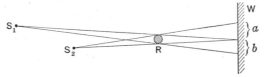

$S_1 = 66$ cp. when the rod is 1.0 ft. from the wall and the sources S_1 and S_2 are respectively 4.0 ft. and 2.7 ft. from the rod. Calculate the candle power of the source S_2.

9. A standard lamp calibrated to yield 37 cp. and a test lamp of unknown candle power are placed 200 cm. apart on a photometer bench and produce equal illumination on a screen between them when the screen is placed 86 cm. from the standard lamp. Compute (a) the illumination produced at the screen by each lamp, and (b) the candle power of the test lamp.

10. The luminous intensities of two lamps are compared by causing each in turn to produce normal illumination upon a photovoltaic cell and observing the corresponding current produced by the cell in a microammeter. When a standard lamp yielding 130 cp. is placed 180 cm. from the cell the current is 5.2 microamperes, and when a test lamp of unknown candle power is placed 150 cm. from the cell the current is 3.8 microamperes. Compute the candle power of the test lamp.

11. A photovoltaic cell 1.5 in. in diameter delivers 26×10^{-6} amp. to a microammeter when normally illuminated by a 40-watt lamp at a distance of 5 ft. The candle power of the lamp is 37. Compute the sensitivity of the apparatus in microamperes per lumen.

*12. A class room measuring 24 x 30 ft. has light-colored walls and ceiling and is equipped with six symmetrically spaced lighting outlets. Direct lighting units with daylight fluorescent lamps are to be installed. Compute the number of bulbs required at each outlet and the rating of each bulb to provide suitable illumination. What illumination value may be expected with the lamps selected?

13. The "astronomical unit" is defined as the mean distance of the earth from the sun. Take the distance to the nearest star to be $3\frac{1}{2}$ light-years and express this distance in astronomical units.

14. In designing the apparatus for measuring the velocity of light by the revolving-mirror method, what speed of rotation must be provided for a 16-sided mirror, if the distant stationary mirror is 33.0 km. away?

15. The velocity of light has been measured by means of a toothed wheel which has teeth that are just as wide as the spaces between them and which is revolved at high speed. A beam of light perpendicular to the wheel passes between two teeth and falls normally upon a stationary mirror, and the speed of rotation is adjusted until the reflected beam is intercepted by a tooth on the wheel. Assume such a wheel to have 520 teeth and the mirror to be 600 meters away; what is the minimum speed at which the wheel should be rotated?

16. (*a*) If rain is falling vertically with a speed of 5 meters per sec. and if a person is carrying an open tube along level ground at a speed of 1 meter per sec., at what angle should he incline the tube in order that a rain-drop entering at the top will follow the axis of the tube and emerge at the lower end? (*b*) If a star is directly above a telescope and if the telescope has a velocity of 18.5 mi. per sec. at right angles to this direction because of the earth's orbital motion, at what angle should the telescope be inclined in order that the star may be seen through it?

Reflection and Refraction

Chapter XXXIV

REFLECTION

392. Regular and Diffuse Reflection.—The behavior of a spherical wave front upon striking a plane surface has been considered in Chapter XXX, wherein Huygens' construction was used to determine the location of the reflected wave front. To apply this procedure to the reflection of light, consider a source of luminous flux at S in Fig. 374, located in front of the plane mirror M. At some

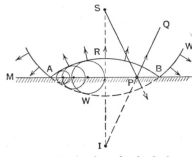

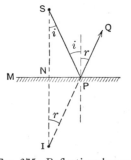

Fig. 374. Reflection of spherical wave at plane surface

Fig. 375. Reflection shown by ray

particular instant the wave front originating at S would have advanced to position WW had it not been for the reflecting surface. When points A and B on the wave front have reached the positions shown, each intermediate point has reached the reflecting surface and returned to some position along the arc of a secondary wavelet; several wavelets are represented by the circles in the figure. A curve tangent to these arcs shows the position of the reflected wave front R; the reflected wave appears to have come from I, and this point is said to be the *image* of S. By symmetry, the image I is located on a line through S normal to the mirror surface, and is as far back of the mirror as the object is in front of it. Thus a ray of light SP upon striking the mirror is redirected along *PQ* as though it had come from the image *I*.

These rays, together with the normal connecting the source *S* and the image *I*, are transferred to Fig. 375 for clearness. Since the object and image are equally distant from the mirror, *SN* = *NI*, and the triangles *SNP* and *INP* are similar, the side *NP* being common. It follows that angle *i* at *S* and angle *r* at *I* are equal, and these in turn are equal to the angles similarly marked at *P*. Thus the angle of incidence *i* between the incident ray and the normal is equal to the angle of reflection *r* between the reflected ray and the normal, as stated in the law of reflection.

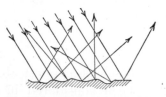

Fig. 376. Surface irregularities magnified to show diffuse reflection

Reflection of light from a smooth surface, like that of a mirror, takes place along a definite direction determined by the direction of the incident ray, and is called *regular* or *specular*. Reflection from a rough or mat surface, like that of plaster or blotting paper, occurs in a great many directions for any one direction of the incident beam, as indicated in Fig. 376, and is said to be *diffuse* or *scattered*. It is by diffuse reflection that non-luminous objects become visible. The law of reflection is evidently true for each tiny element of the reflecting surface in diffuse reflection.

393. Images Formed by Plane Mirrors.—The image of a point object formed by reflection in a plane mirror is known to be located the same distance behind the reflecting surface that the object is in front of it. For an extended object, each image point is similarly located and the complete image may be constructed readily. Fig. 377 shows an object *O* and its image *I* formed by reflection in the mirror *M*. Rays are also drawn for the extreme object points, extending to an eye at *E*. It will be observed that the angles of incidence, as at *i* and *i'*, are equal respectively to the angles of reflection,

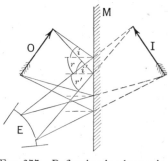

Fig. 377. Reflection in plane mirror

as at *r* and *r'*. The rays from each point enter the eye as a diverging pencil, and the image is at the point where the prolongations of these rays intersect.

Two plane mirrors which are inclined to each other yield multiple images of an object placed between them. These images can be found by the method just explained.

394. Rotation of Reflected Ray.—The rotation of a plane mirror upon which a ray of light falls causes the reflected ray to rotate also; moreover the rotation of the reflected ray is *twice* that of the mirror. This fact is used in amplifying the deflections of galvanometers and other sensitive instruments, and is mentioned in § 103. To prove this relation, consider an incident ray of light from a source S to fall upon a plane mirror M, Fig. 378, at an angle i with the normal N; it is reflected along Y at an equal angle r, and the angle $SOY = i + r = 2i$. Upon rotating the mirror through an angle β to M', the normal undergoes an equal rotation to N'; the angle of incidence increases

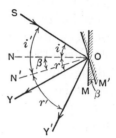

Fig. 378. Effect of rotating mirror

to $i' = i + \beta$, and the angle of reflection r' increases equally, the reflected ray being rotated to the position shown at Y'. The angle $SOY' = i' + r' = 2i'$, which may be written $2(i + \beta)$. The reflected ray, therefore, rotates through an angle

$$YOY' = SOY' - SOY = 2(i + \beta) - 2i = 2\beta$$

which is twice the rotation of the mirror.

In navigation it is necessary to measure the angle between the sun and the horizon as subtended at the observer's position on board ship, in order to determine the latitude of that position. This is accomplished by the *sextant*, a telescopic instrument which is held in the hand while the observer brings images of the sun and horizon into coincidence in the field of view of a small telescope. The sextant consists essentially of two mirrors called the index glass M and the horizon glass m, Fig. 379, supported perpendicularly to the

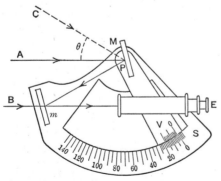

Fig. 379. Design of a sextant

plane of the sextant on a metal framework which also carries the telescope and a scale. Mirror m is fixed in position and is clear over half its surface so that the observer at E can see the horizon beyond B di-

rectly, that is, without reflection at mirror *m*. Mirror *M* is carried
by an arm which is pivoted at *P* and fitted with a vernier *V* at its
other end to enable the position of the index glass to be read accurately on scale *S*. When the two mirrors are parallel, the observer
will also see the horizon via the path *A Mm E*, and this image will
blend with the direct one obtained along *BE*; the vernier for this
position of mirror *M* will read zero. In viewing the sun at an angle θ
degrees above the horizon, the arm carrying the mirror will have to
be turned through an angle $\theta/2$ so that the rays from the sun coming
along the line *CM* will be reflected along the line *Mm*, and again
reflected into the telescope by the silvered portion of the horizon
glass *m*. The image of the sun then matches the image of the horizon,
and the altitude of the sun will be indicated by twice the angle through
which the vernier arm is turned. Each half-degree division on scale
S is marked as one degree, making it possible to read the angular
elevation of the sun directly.

395. Spherical Mirrors.—Curved mirrors are used to deviate a
beam of light and at the same time to render it more or less converging than before incidence upon the mirror. Spherical mirrors are
classified as *concave* and *convex*, depending on whether the reflecting
surface is on the inside or outside of the spherical shell.

Fig. 380 shows a concave and a convex mirror *M,M* with a parallel
beam of light incident upon each. The center of the spherical surface
is called the *center of curvature* of the mirror, and is designated by *C*.

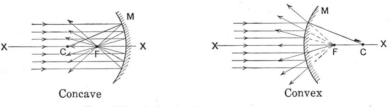

Concave   Convex

Fig. 380.   Reflection from spherical mirrors

A line connecting the middle point of the mirror surface and the
center of curvature is called the *principal axis* of the mirror; it is
marked *XX*.

Most spherical mirrors used for optical purposes are comparatively
flat, that is, the dimensions of the mirror are small in comparison with
the radius of the surface; such mirrors are said to have a small
aperture. With such a mirror, a bundle of rays parallel to the principal axis will pass through a common point *F* after reflection if the

mirror is concave, or will diverge as though they originated from a common point F if the mirror is convex. The point F is the *principal focus* of the mirror, and its distance from the mirror is the *focal length*. The concentration of parallel rays from the sun at the focus of a concave mirror can be shown experimentally by melting a bit of wax or scorching a piece of paper placed at that point.

The principal focus of a spherical mirror is located on the principal axis half way between the center of curvature and the mirror surface. This relation can be proved by reference to the diagrams in Fig. 381. In each of these, an incident ray AP, parallel to the axis XX, strikes the mirror M at P and is reflected along the line PF. Let θ be the

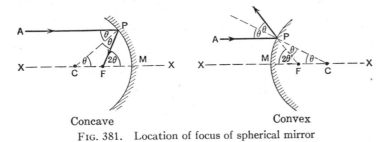

Concave   Convex

FIG. 381. Location of focus of spherical mirror

angle of incidence between the ray AP and the normal PC; the angle of reflection at P is equal to the angle of incidence θ; also, the angle made by the normal at C with the axis is equal to θ, since AP and XX are parallel. The angle between the reflected ray and the axis at F is 2θ, for the same reason. For mirrors of slight curvature, the angles θ are small, and PM may be considered perpendicular to the axis XX. Hence, as an approximation,

$$PM = CM \tan \theta = FM \tan 2\theta$$

But the tangents of small angles may be set equal to the angles themselves, hence $CM \times \theta = FM \times 2\theta$, or

$$CM = 2FM$$

showing that the focus F is half way between the center of curvature C and the middle of the mirror surface M.

396. Images Formed by Spherical Mirrors.—The images produced by spherical mirrors may be larger or smaller than the object, and may be either real or virtual. An image is called *real* if the rays after reflection actually pass through it, and *virtual* if they only appear to do so. Both types present the same appearance to the eye, but a real image can be caught upon a screen, whereas a virtual image can not.

A graphical method of image location, using rays of light, is indicated in Fig. 382 for a concave and a convex mirror of small aperture. In either case two rays are drawn from an object point O to the mirror M and are there reflected; one ray parallel to the axis passes through the principal focus F after reflection if the mirror is concave, or its prolongation does so if the mirror is convex; the other ray through the center of curvature C strikes the mirror normally and is reflected back upon itself. The intersection of these reflected rays (or their prolongations) is the corresponding image point I.

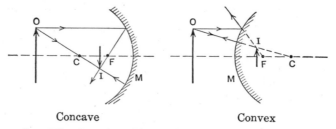

Concave   Convex

FIG. 382.   Location of images formed by spherical mirrors

Any other point of the image may be found in the same way. The figure shows the entire objects and images sketched in position by symmetry; the image formed by the concave mirror is real, inverted, and reduced, and that formed by the convex mirror is virtual, erect, and reduced.

Concave mirrors may produce images which are real or virtual, erect or inverted, magnified or reduced, depending upon the position of the object. Convex mirrors always produce virtual, erect, and reduced images. Although two rays are sufficient to locate the image of a point, it must not be inferred that only two are effective in forming the image. All other rays from the point which strike the mirror contribute to the image as well; consequently the larger the mirror the brighter the image will be.

The image of an object can be located analytically by means of the equation

$$\frac{1}{p} + \frac{1}{q} = \frac{2}{r} = \frac{1}{f} \tag{243}$$

in which p is the distance from the object to the mirror, q is the distance from the image to the mirror, r is the radius of the mirror, and f is its focal length. The equation can be made to apply to both concave and convex mirrors by considering distances back of the mirror to be negative; thus, r and f have *negative* values for a *convex* mirror. A negative value for q signifies that the image is behind the mirror and is, therefore, virtual.

To derive this equation, consider the concave mirror shown in Fig. 383, but regard it as considerably flatter than depicted. The object and image are located respec-
tively at O and I as in the previous figure, and the same two rays are shown joining their head-ends, one to P and through F, and the other through C and back upon itself. Also another ray is shown between these points; it extends from O to M and is reflected by the mirror along MI, the incident and reflected rays making equal angles with the axis XM. These rays form two pairs of similar triangles. From one pair, OXC and IYC, its follow that

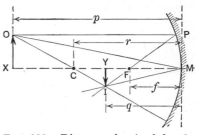

FIG. 383. Distances involved in the mirror equation

$$\frac{OX}{IY} = \frac{XC}{CY} = \frac{p - r}{r - q}$$

and from the other, OXM and IYM,

$$\frac{OX}{IY} = \frac{p}{q}$$

Hence $\dfrac{p}{q} = \dfrac{p - r}{r - q}$, or $qr + pr = 2pq$. If this expression is divided by pqr, there results

$$\frac{1}{p} + \frac{1}{q} = \frac{2}{r}$$

and the focal distance $f = r/2$, as before. The relation between the object distance p, the image distance q, and the radius r can be shown to apply to any spherical mirror, whether concave or convex, provided it has a small aperture.

The *magnification* produced by the mirror is the ratio of the image size to the object size and can be found by reference to the similar triangles OXM and IYM. The size of the image IY is to the size of the object OX as the image distance q is to the object distance p, the signs being neglected. Hence, for any spherical mirror

$$\text{Magnification} = \frac{IY}{OX} = \frac{q}{p} \qquad (244)$$

To illustrate, an object is placed 12 cm. in front of a convex spherical mirror of 15-cm. radius. Locate and describe the image, and find its size for an object 3.0 cm. high. To solve, transpose equation (243) and substitute numerical values as follows:

$$\frac{1}{q} = \frac{2}{r} - \frac{1}{p} = \frac{2}{-15} - \frac{1}{12} = -\frac{13}{60}$$

from which $q = -\frac{60}{13} = -4.6$ cm. Consequently, a virtual image will be produced 4.6 cm. behind the mirror. The right-hand diagram in Fig. 382, if drawn to scale, would serve as a graphical solution of this problem, and would show further that the image is erect. The height of the image, from equation (244), is

$$\frac{4.6}{12} \times 3.0 = 1.15 \text{ cm.}$$

397. Spherical Aberration.—The foregoing treatment of spherical mirrors applies to those of small aperture, the incident light rays being only slightly inclined to the principal axis. When such is not the case, the images formed are confused and imperfect. For example,

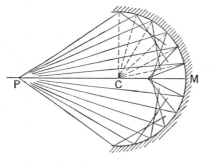

rays issuing from a point source on the axis do not come to a focus at a common point; instead, the rays reflected from the outer parts of the mirror cross the axis nearer to the mirror than those reflected from the central portion. This imperfection is called *spherical aberration*, and is illustrated in Fig. 384, where the symbols C and M have the same meaning as before. The image of the source P formed by

FIG. 384. Spherical aberration

this hemispherical mirror is not localized at a point but is drawn out along a surface generated by the intersecting reflected rays; a cross-section of this surface is a line called the *caustic* of the reflecting surface. A similar effect can be observed on the surface of milk in a glass when illuminated obliquely by a distant source, the glass acting as the reflector and the milk as a screen.

It is possible, of course, to design a reflecting surface of such shape that rays from a definite object point will be brought to a common focus. For an object point at infinity, the mirror would be a paraboloid. This form of mirror is often used with searchlights and automobile headlights. The lamp is placed at the focus and the light which is directed toward the mirror is reflected in a parallel beam.

REFRACTION

398. Refractive Index.—The phenomenon of refraction is described in § 356, where it is shown that a plane wave undergoes an abrupt change of direction upon passing obliquely into another medium wherein it travels with a different velocity. This result can be represented more simply with rays of light than by progressive positions of the wave front. *The ray will be deviated toward the normal when the velocity is reduced, and deviated away from the normal when the velocity is increased.*

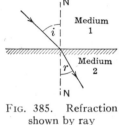

FIG. 385. Refraction shown by ray

In Fig. 385, suppose the light to pass from medium 1, where its velocity is V_1, into medium 2, where its velocity is V_2. The angle of incidence is i and the angle of refraction is r, both with respect to the normal N. In this case $V_2 < V_1$ and therefore the ray will be deviated toward the normal, making $r < i$. Some of the incident light will be reflected at the surface of separation, but the reflected ray is omitted in the figure for clearness.

The ratio of the light velocities V_1/V_2 in two contacting substances is a constant for those mediums known as the *refractive index* of the second medium relative to the first; it is represented by the symbol μ_{12}, the order of the subscripts indicating the direction of light travel. This concept may be combined with that expressed in equation (225), and the law of refraction may be expressed mathematically as follows:

$$\frac{\sin i}{\sin r} = \frac{V_1}{V_2} = \mu_{12} \qquad (245)$$

The (absolute) refractive index of a substance is its index with respect to a vacuum; the index against air has practically the same value. Thus, if the velocity of light is V_s in a particular substance, V_o in a vacuum, and V in air, the index of the substance is

$$\mu = \frac{V_o}{V_s} = \text{approximately } \frac{V_a}{V_s}$$

The refractive index of a substance can be measured fundamentally by passing a narrow beam of light into it in the manner suggested in Fig. 385, observing the angles of incidence and refraction, and applying equation (245). Methods are available for measuring the index of refraction of all kinds of substances very precisely.

The refractive index of a substance varies somewhat with the wavelength of light (§ 353); the following list gives a few representative values as measured with yellow light of wavelength approximately 0.00006 cm. It is natural that glass, being a synthetic product, should vary considerably in refractive index, depending upon the ingredients used; the table indicates the range of values to be expected.

Indices of Refraction

Gases and Vapors	
Air................	1.0002918
Carbon dioxide......	1.0004498
Mercury vapor......	1.000933
Liquids	
Carbon disulfide.....	1.6276
Water.............	1.3330
Solids	
Diamond...........	2.417
Glass (crown).......	1.48 to 1.61
" (flint)........	1.53 to 1.96
Ice...............	1.31
Rock salt..........	1.5443

To emphasize the physical meaning of the refractive index, consider the significance of μ for some particular substance. For ice $\mu = 1.31$, and this means that the velocity of light in vacuum (or air) is 1.31 as great as in ice; also that it will take the same time for light to travel through 1 cm. of ice as it takes to travel through 1.31 cm. of air. Thus, μ *indicates numerically the equivalent air distance of 1 cm. of a substance.*

399. Refraction in Parallel-sided Plates.—A ray of light in passing through one or more parallel-sided slabs and emerging into the original medium is displaced laterally but is not deviated. This result is shown in Fig. 386, where *a*, *w* and *g* represent any three different mediums such as air, water, and glass.

Consider, first, a single slab as in part I of the figure, and call the angles of incidence, refraction, and emergence x, y, and z respectively. From the law of refraction as applied to each surface of the glass,

$$\frac{V_a}{V_g} = \frac{\sin x}{\sin y} = \mu_{ag} \quad \text{and} \quad \frac{V_g}{V_a} = \frac{\sin y}{\sin z} = \mu_{ga}$$

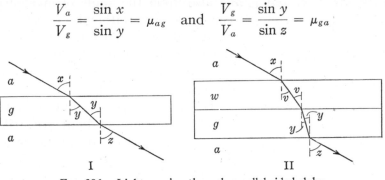

I   II

FIG. 386. Light passing through parallel-sided slabs

When these equations are multiplied member by member it is seen that, since the product of the first members is unity,

$$\frac{\sin x}{\sin y} \times \frac{\sin y}{\sin z} = 1$$

whence angles x and z are equal, making the incident and emergent rays parallel. It appears further that

$$\mu_{ag} = \frac{1}{\mu_{ga}} \tag{246}$$

showing, for example, that the refractive index of glass with respect to air is the reciprocal of the index of air with respect to glass.

When the same procedure is applied to two slabs, as indicated in part II of the figure, it is found that the angle of incidence x and the angle of emergence z are equal, and also that

$$\frac{V_a}{V_w} \times \frac{V_w}{V_g} \times \frac{V_g}{V_a} = 1$$

It follows from this expression that $\mu_{aw} \times \mu_{wg} \times \mu_{ga} = 1$, whence

$$\mu_{wg} = \frac{1}{\mu_{aw} \times \mu_{ga}} = \frac{\mu_{ag}}{\mu_{aw}} \tag{247}$$

showing that the relative refractive index of any substance g with respect to another substance w is equal to the absolute index of substance g divided by that of substance w.

400. Deviation by a Prism.—Prisms are often employed in optical devices to produce deviation in a beam of light. In a triangular prism, the amount of deviation depends upon the angle of the prism, upon its refractive index, and also upon the angle of incidence. It can be shown, either by experiment or by calculation, that for such a prism the deviation has a *minimum* value when the ray passes *symmetrically* through it as shown in Fig. 387.

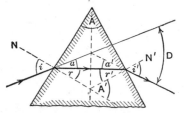

FIG. 387. Ray passing through prism

To prove this relation analytically, consider a beam of light to strike one face of the prism at an angle i with the normal N, and to be refracted at an angle r with this normal. It will proceed through the prism and emerge from the second face making angles of incidence r' and refraction i', with the normal N'. From geometric considerations the angle A of the prism is equal to the angle A' between the two normals, and since the latter angle is the exterior angle of a triangle of which r and r' are the opposite interior angles, it follows that $A = r + r'$. The angle of deviation between the incident and emergent rays is the sum of the deviations produced at the two faces individually, or

$$D = a + a' = (i - r) + (i' - r') = i + i' - A$$

If μ is the index of refraction of the prism relative to air, it follows from the law of refraction that $\sin i = \mu \sin r$ and $\sin i' = \mu \sin r'$, so that the deviation is

$$D = \sin^{-1}(\mu \sin r) + \sin^{-1}[\mu \sin (A - r)] - A$$

In order to find the relation between the angles r and r' which will make the deviation a minimum, differentiate the foregoing expression with respect to r; then equate the result to zero and solve. Thus,

$$\frac{dD}{dr} = \frac{\mu \cos r}{\sqrt{1 - \mu^2 \sin^2 r}} - \frac{\mu \cos (A - r)}{\sqrt{1 - \mu^2 \sin^2 (A - r)}} = 0$$

whence

$$\frac{\cos^2 r}{\cos^2 r'} = \frac{1 - \mu^2 \sin^2 r}{1 - \mu^2 \sin^2 r'}$$

and it follows that $r = r'$.

Whether demonstrated experimentally or analytically, it is found that the deviation is a minimum for a ray that passes symmetrically through the prism. For such a ray, the angles r and r' are equal, hence the angles a and a' are also equal. Then the angle of minimum deviation will be

$$D_m = a + a' = 2a = 2(i - r)$$

The index of refraction μ of the material constituting the prism can be expressed in terms of the prism angle A and the angle of minimum deviation D_m. This will be done by stating the angles of incidence and refraction in terms of these quantities, and applying equation (245). From the foregoing, the angle of refraction is $r = \dfrac{A}{2}$, and the angle of incidence is $i = \dfrac{D_m}{2} + r = \dfrac{D_m + A}{2}$. From the law of refraction, there results

$$\mu = \frac{\sin \frac{1}{2}(D_m + A)}{\sin \frac{1}{2}A} \tag{248}$$

which is the desired expression.

An accurate determination of the refractive index of a substance can be made from measurements of A and D_m taken on a prism of that substance. For liquids, a hollow glass prism is used to hold the liquid; the faces of the prism, being parallel-sided slabs, produce no

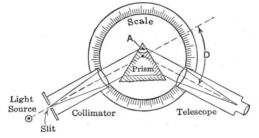

F<small>IG</small>. 388.   Deviation of light measured on a spectrometer

deviation and thus do not influence the result. The measurements are made with a spectrometer, the essential parts of which are shown in Fig. 388. The test is conducted most simply with light of a single wavelength, corresponding to a particular color of the spectrum. The light enters the instrument through a narrow slit, is formed into a parallel beam by a lens, and falls upon the prism. Here it undergoes refraction and upon emergence is received by a suitably placed tel-

escope, in which the observer sees an image of the slit. The prism
and telescope are turned by trial until the angle of deviation D is
observed to be a minimum; the value of this angle may be read from
the circular scale. The angle A is usually meas-

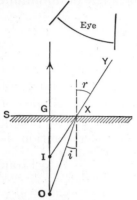

ured optically by reflecting light from one face
of the prism, as from a plane mirror, and then
rotating the prism until the second prism face
occupies the same position; the angle A is found
by subtracting the angle of rotation from 180°.

401. Apparent Depth of a Submerged Object.
—Refraction causes an object which is immersed in a medium of higher refractive index
than air to appear nearer the surface than it
actually is. Suppose O, Fig. 389, to represent
a stone in water a distance GO below the
surface S, with light rays extending upward

FIG. 389. Effect of refraction on apparent depth

to the eye as shown. For the ray OXY, the
angle of incidence i is equal to GOX and the angle of refraction r is
equal to GIX, therefore

$$\frac{\sin GOX}{\sin GIX} = \frac{1}{\mu}$$

where μ is the refractive index of water. For small angles the sine
may be equated to the tangent, whence

$$\mu = \frac{\tan GIX}{\tan GOX} = \frac{\dfrac{GX}{GI}}{\dfrac{GX}{GO}} = \frac{GO}{GI}$$

showing that the apparent depth, GI, is the quotient of the actual
depth, GO, by the refractive index of the medium, when viewed from
above. A small part of the incident light from O is reflected at the
surface S, but this effect is omitted since it has no bearing on the
result.

402. Atmospheric Refraction.—Probably most persons have noticed the apparent quivering of an object when observed across the
top of a hot radiator. Heating the air lowers its refractive index,
and the mixing of the warm air with the colder air in the process of
convection produces an irregular bending of the transmitted light
rays.

Light from outer space encounters air of increasing density and increasing refractive index as it approaches the earth. Consequently, a beam of light slanting downward through the atmosphere is bent more and more toward the vertical as it advances. For this reason, the stars are not seen in their true positions unless directly

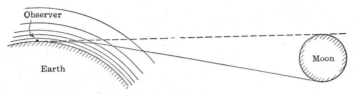

Fig. 390. Illustrating atmospheric refraction

overhead. The same phenomenon also explains the fact that the entire disk of the sun or moon may be seen for a short time when it is geometrically below the horizon where it would not be visible at all except for atmospheric refraction. This effect is pictured in Fig. 390.

403. Total Reflection.—A ray of light in a medium of high refractive index and directed toward one of lower index, passes into the second medium with refraction, provided the angle of incidence is not too large. If the ray is inclined more and more, however, a position will be reached in which it *does not pass into the second medium*, but is *totally reflected* at the surface of separation.

Suppose a source O, located in water of refractive index μ, to emit light rays in various directions, a few of which are indicated in Fig. 391. The light emitted along OA is mostly refracted into the air along AP in such direction that $\dfrac{\sin i}{\sin r} = \dfrac{1}{\mu}$, but a small part is reflected along AW. Similarly, the light emitted along OB is partly refracted along BQ and partly reflected along BX.

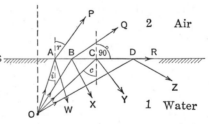

Fig. 391. Illustrating total reflection

The ray OC strikes the surface S at such an incident angle c that the refracted ray CR grazes the surface, the angle of refraction being 90°; the reflected part travels to Y. Any ray such as OD for which the angle of incidence is greater than c does not emerge into the air but is totally reflected along some line DZ.

The angle c is called the *critical angle* of incidence; it is the angle of incidence in the more highly refractive medium for which the angle of refraction in the other medium is 90°; its value is evidently given by

$$\sin c = \frac{1}{\mu} \tag{249}$$

In general, total reflection will occur at the boundary separating any two mediums having different refractive indices, when a ray in the medium of higher index is directed toward the other medium at an angle of incidence greater than the critical angle. For this general case, it can be shown in the same manner that the critical angle c is given by the relation

$$\sin c = \frac{\mu_2}{\mu_1} \tag{250}$$

when $\mu_2 < \mu_1$.

The principle of total reflection is frequently used in optical instruments. Fig. 392 shows three positions of a prism, having two 45° angles, in the path of the light rays forming an image. In the first

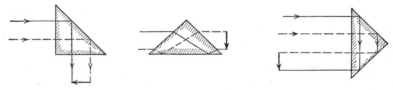

FIG. 392.   Total-reflecting prisms

position, the prism acts like a plane mirror tilted downward; when rotated into the second position it inverts the image; and when turned farther to the third position it displaces the rays and reverses their direction.

In one form of instrument for measuring the refractive index of liquids and crystals, a glass hemisphere of high refractive index is arranged with its plane face horizontal to receive the specimen under test, and a beam of light is caused to enter the hemisphere radially from below. The direction of the entering beam is adjusted so that when it impinges upon the specimen it will undergo total reflection. The reflected beam will emerge radially and is received by a telescope that can be moved along a scale for reading its position. In testing a liquid, a few drops of it are placed upon the hemisphere and the telescope is moved to the position which indicates the critical angle of total reflection. In testing a crystal, a few drops of a liquid of higher refractive index (like monobromnaphthalene) are placed between the hemisphere and the lower face of the crystal to provide optical contact and the same procedure is followed; the film of liquid has parallel faces and so does not introduce an error in the result.

A test is conducted with such an instrument to determine the refractive index of methyl methacrylate, commercially known as lucite. With sodium light, for which the glass hemisphere has an index of 1.9180, the critical telescope position is 51° 50′ away from the vertical. Upon analysis it will be clear that the reading is unaffected by the presence of the contact liquid and that the refractive index of the lucite specimen is 1.9180 × sin 51° 50′ = 1.5080. With the specimen removed but the liquid remaining in place the telescope position reads 59° 54′. From this value, the refractive index of the contact liquid mentioned is found to be 1.9180 × sin 59° 54′ = 1.6594.

*404. The Refractometer.—A number of instruments called *refractometers* have been designed for the rapid and precise measurement of refractive index. One of these, due to C. Pulfrich, is illustrated diagrammatically in Fig. 393. It consists of a right-angle prism P upon which the specimen X is placed, a lens L for converging a beam of monochromatic light along the interface, and a telescope T which is moved around a graduated quadrant (not shown) to obtain the direction of the emergent rays. The prism has

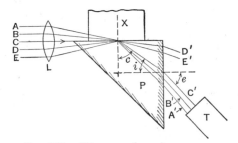

Fig. 393.   Diagram of a refractometer

a known refractive index, which is higher than that of any material to be tested. Rays such as A and B will be refracted to positions A' and B' respectively in the telescope, giving a band of light which is terminated sharply by the limiting ray CC' that makes grazing incidence. Rays such as D and E will be totally reflected along D' and E' and will not enter the telescope, which is set on the boundary of the refracted beam.

The refractive index μ_X of the test specimen can be found in terms of the angle of emergence e and the refractive index μ_P of the prism. To discover this relation, apply the law of refraction, and note that the critical angle c is complementary to the angle of incidence i on the vertical face, whence

$$\mu_P = \frac{\sin e}{\sin i} = \frac{\sin e}{\sin (90° - c)} = \frac{\sin e}{\cos c}$$

from which

$$\cos c = \frac{\sin e}{\mu_P}$$

Also for grazing incidence, by equation (250),

$$\sin c = \frac{\mu_X}{\mu_P}$$

But $\cos^2 c + \sin^2 c = 1$, and consequently

$$\frac{\sin^2 e}{\mu_P{}^2} + \frac{\mu_X{}^2}{\mu_P{}^2} = 1$$

from which the index of refraction of the specimen becomes

$$\mu_X = \sqrt{\mu_P{}^2 - \sin^2 e}$$

For measuring the refractive index of liquids by this method, a short glass tube is cemented to the prism. The liquid under test is poured into this cup and the measurement is made as for a solid.

*405. Loss in Reflection and Absorption.—The amount of light that is reflected from a transparent substance depends upon the angle of incidence and the refractive index of the substance. The French physicist, Augustin J. Fresnel (1788–1827), first derived an expression for the ratio between the intensity of the reflected beam and that of the incident beam. For natural (unpolarized) light perpendicularly incident within a medium of refractive index μ_1, upon a transparent substance of refractive index μ_2, the ratio of the intensity I of the reflected light beam to the intensity I_o of the incident beam is given by

$$\frac{I}{I_o} = \left(\frac{\mu_2 - \mu_1}{\mu_2 + \mu_1}\right)^2 \tag{251}$$

For light reflected in air against glass of refractive index 1.5, the ratio of intensities is $(0.5/2.5)^2 = 0.04$, showing that 4 per cent of the incident light is reflected where there is perpendicular incidence upon an air-glass boundary.

The amount of absorption of light in its passage through a transparent substance depends upon the nature of the absorbing medium and its thickness. If the entire medium is regarded as made up of a number of equally thin layers, each one will absorb the same fraction of the light entering it. Thus, if 100 lumens impinge upon the first layer and if each absorbs $\frac{1}{10}$ of the light which reaches it, the amount incident upon the second layer will be 90 lumens, upon the third layer 81 lumens, upon the fourth layer 72.9 lumens, and so on.

It has been established by experiment that for light of a given color an infinitesimally thin layer cuts down the intensity by an amount which, expressed as a fraction of its value, is directly proportional to the thickness of the layer. Let I be the intensity at a particular layer of infinitesimal thickness dx and $-dI$ the change of intensity in this layer, then the foregoing statement can be expressed mathematically in the form

$$-\frac{dI}{I} = k\,dx$$

where k is a constant of the material called its absorption coefficient. This expression may be integrated to give the intensity of a light beam after passing through a thickness x of a medium having an absorption coefficient k in terms of the intensity I_e of the entering beam by the equation:

$$I = I_e\,\epsilon^{-kt}$$

ϵ being the base of natural logarithms.

PROBLEMS

1. When an object is placed between two parallel plane mirrors which face each other, a series of images is formed behind each one. Two such mirrors are 4 ft. apart, with a lamp between them 1 ft. away from one mirror. Determine the locations of the first two images behind each mirror.

2. A room 12 ft. square has a plane mirror mounted at the center of one wall. How wide should the mirror be to allow an observer facing it and standing at the middle of the room to see the entire width of the wall behind him by reflection?

3. Two plane mirrors are mounted at right angles and an object is placed 3 cm. in front of one mirror and 4 cm. in front of the other. Locate the images formed and show the rays by which they would be seen by a suitably situated eye.

4. In an opaque picture projector, rays from an illuminated object pass vertically upward to an inclined plane mirror and thence extend horizontally 30 ft. to form an image on an upright screen. Through what angle should the mirror be rotated to elevate the image 6 in. on the screen?

5. In the so-called vibration galvanometer, the coil is operated by alternating current and oscillates rapidly. Light from a narrow vertical slit located directly in front of the instrument is reflected at a plane mirror carried by the coil and falls upon a fixed scale parallel to the mirror. With

no current through the instrument, the coil is at rest and the light spot on the scale may be regarded as a line of negligible width. In a given test the line on the scale is spread out into a band 4 mm. wide; if the scale is 50 cm. from the mirror, through what angle is the coil oscillating?

6. A concave spherical mirror has a radius of 30 cm. Determine analytically the image location for an object placed at each of the following distances from the mirror surface: ∞, 60 cm., 30 cm., 20 cm., 15 cm., 10 cm., 0 cm.

7. For a concave spherical mirror of 10-in. focal length, find analytically two locations of an object for which the image will be 3 times as high as the object. Verify the results graphically with diagrams carefully drawn to scale.

8. An object is placed 18 in. away from the surface of a polished metal sphere 12 in. in diameter. (*a*) Locate the image analytically. (*b*) Verify the result graphically by a carefully drawn diagram to scale. (*c*) Describe the image fully. (*d*) Determine the height of the image for an object 6 in. high.

9. Magnification is often expressed in "diameters" to imply that reference is made to length rather than area. If a circular object is 1 mm. in diameter and its image is $\frac{1}{2}$ in. in diameter, what is the linear magnification in diameters, and what is the surface magnification of the area?

10. To determine the focal length of a convex mirror C, an object O is placed in front of it and a plane mirror P is placed between them, as in the diagram. Each mirror forms an image of the object and the plane

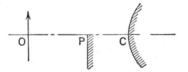

mirror is moved along OC until these images coincide. Suppose that after such an adjustment $OP = 24$ cm. and $PC = 16$ cm.; compute the focal length of the convex mirror.

11. From the data supplied in Problem 18 of Chapter 30, compute the index of refraction of amber.

12. A ray of light in air impinges upon a slab of glass, the angle of incidence being 45°. Assume the refractive index of the glass to be 1.6 and find (*a*) the angle of refraction within the glass, and (*b*) the velocity of light in the glass.

13. If the glass slab of Problem 12 is 2 cm. thick, what lateral displacement does the ray of light undergo in passing through it?

14. A ray of light slanting downward 30° from the horizontal passes through water and enters glass having a refractive index of 1.65. Find the direction of the ray in each of these mediums.

15. Compute (*a*) the refractive index of water with respect to glass of absolute index 1.5, and (*b*) the refractive index of the glass with respect to water.

16. It is found by test that a certain flint-glass prism of 60° angle produces a minimum deviation of 51° 30' for yellow light. Determine the index of refraction of the glass for this light.

17. What is the minimum angle of deviation produced by a glass prism of 45° angle if the glass has an index of refraction of 1.70 for the light used in conducting the test?

18. A ray of light is directed at an angle of incidence of 45° upon a 60° prism made of glass which has a refractive index of 1.65 for the light used. Compute the angle that the emerging ray makes with the normal at the point of emergence.

19. A certain prism of 60° angle is found to produce minimum deviation for yellow light when the ray of light strikes it at an angle of incidence of 53°. For the light used, determine (*a*) the angle of minimum deviation, and (*b*) the refractive index of the prism material.

20. A prism has an apex angle of 60° and a refractive index of 1.8. At what angle of incidence should light be directed upon the prism in order that it may undergo minimum deviation in passing through it?

21. The prism *ABC* shown in the diagram is backed by a mirror placed along the prism face *AB*. A ray of light shines upon the face *AC* and its

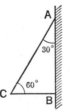

direction is varied until after reflection it returns upon itself. If the angle of incidence is then 50.2°, what is the refractive index of the prism material for the light used?

22. A flaw within a diamond appears to be 1 mm. behind the surface when the surface is viewed normally. Where is the flaw actually located?

23. To an observer looking straight down into a tub with water, the tub appears to be half full. How nearly full is it actually?

24. Light falls normally upon the short face of a 30–60–90° prism and after reflection at the hypotenuse emerges from the third face at an angle of 60° with the normal. (*a*) Compute the index of refraction of the prism material. (*b*) Determine whether the reflection at the hypotenuse is total reflection.

25. In the prism type of binocular, light is totally reflected within a glass prism, the ray incident upon the glass-air boundary being at right angles to the ray reflected from it. What limiting value might the refractive index of the prism material have and still cause the reflection at this boundary to be total reflection?

26. A ray of light shines upon a 60° prism, the refractive index of the prism material being 1.6 for the light used. Show by a diagram the passage

of the ray through the prism and compute the angle between the emerging ray and the normal (*a*) when the incident ray grazes the surface, and (*b*) when the incident ray is normal to the surface.

★27. A beam of light falls normally upon a smooth water surface. Compare the intensity of the beam just below the surface with that just above it.

★28. A beam of light of intensity 100 lumens per sq. ft. impinges normally upon a parallel-sided slab of plastic material which has an index of refraction of 1.5. If 10 per cent of the light entering the slab is absorbed in passing through it, what is the intensity of the emerging beam?

Dispersion, Spectra and Color

Chapter XXXV

406. Dispersion.—White light, such as that produced by the glowing carbons of an arc lamp, is in reality composed of many colors blended together. When a narrow slit is illuminated by such white light and the issuing beam is refracted through a prism, the colors are spread out into a brilliant array, merging insensibly into one another and forming a *spectrum*. Although there are hundreds of distinct hues in the spectrum, they may be grouped broadly into six

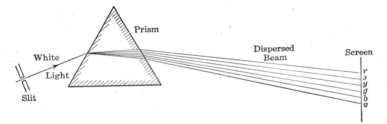

FIG. 394.   Dispersion of light by a prism

principal colors. These are red, orange, yellow, green, blue, and violet, in the order of increasing deviation, and are indicated by their initial letters in Fig. 394. Color is determined by the frequency of vibration and the associated length of the light wave, the wavelength being greatest for red and least for violet. Passing the light through a second prism, identical with the first and arranged to produce deviation in the same direction, will yield a spectrum of greater length. If the second prism is opposed to the first, the colors will be recombined almost perfectly into white light. The spreading out of a light beam into its component colors is known as *dispersion*. In examining spectra it is customary to place a lens in the light path so as to form a sharp image, or group of images, of the illuminated slit.

It has been observed that the deviation produced by a prism is greater for the shorter wavelengths of white light. No definite relation exists between wavelength and deviation, however, and prisms of different substances spread out the component colors of the spectrum to somewhat different extents. If two such prisms are arranged one above the other in such a manner that their spectra match exactly at two colors, say at the extremes of the red and violet portions, it will be found that the intermediate colors do not register point by point. A few substances exhibit what is known as *anomalous* dispersion; prisms of such substances do not disperse white light in the regular color sequence. Thus, fuchsine deviates red and orange light more than blue and violet, and absorbs the middle portion of the spectrum.

The spectrum extends at both ends into regions which are invisible to the eye, the *infra-red* being beyond the red end, and the *ultraviolet* being beyond the violet end of the visible spectrum.

407. Emission Spectra.—The spectrum produced by a glowing object is termed an *emission* spectrum. Its appearance depends primarily upon the composition and state of the luminous object.

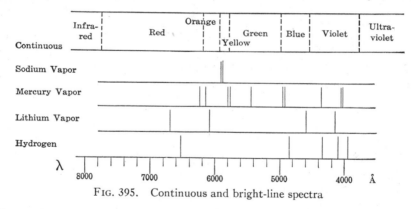

FIG. 395.   Continuous and bright-line spectra

Incandescent solids, liquids, and gases under high pressure produce continuous spectra extending from color to color without interruption. Such a spectrum is represented at the top of Fig. 395. Since the colors blend imperceptibly into one another, the boundaries between them, marked by dotted lines in the figure, are only approximate.

Luminous gases and vapors under moderate or low pressure yield spectra consisting of definitely placed bright lines. Each is an image of the slit through which the radiation is received. Every gas emits radiation of particular wavelengths, and each spectrum is characteristic of the radiating substance. Sodium vapor yields two bright lines in the yellow part of the spectrum; they are so close together that unless the slit is very narrow they appear as one line. Mercury vapor yields several bright lines, the most conspicuous being in the green and blue regions. The figure shows the bright-line spectra of several elements over the range of the visible spectrum; for many of them, other lines may be found in the ultraviolet and infra-red regions. The continuous spectrum is an uninterrupted series of images of the illuminated slit.

In a quantitative study of the spectrum, it becomes necessary to refer to each particular part of it with definiteness. This is done by specifying any hue by the vibration rate f of the light source, or its corresponding wavelength λ, the relation between these quantities being given by equation (217), namely

$$c = f \lambda$$

where c is the velocity of light. The wavelengths may be designated in centimeters, but are more commonly expressed in terms of the *Ångström unit*, named in honor of the Swedish physicist, Anders J. Ångström (1814–1874). One Ångström unit (Å) $= 10^{-8}$ cm. For example, the green line of the mercury spectrum has a wavelength $\lambda = 0.00005461$ cm. or 5461 Å. The wavelengths are indicated in the latter manner in Fig. 395.

The number of lines in a bright-line spectrum depends not only upon the nature of the source, but also upon the amount of energy with which its atoms are excited to produce glowing. Atoms may be excited by imparting energy to them, usually by heating in a flame or by supplying electrical energy in an arc or spark, or in a discharge tube, § 214. The excitation produced by heating a substance in a Bunsen or in a hotter flame is not as intense as by heating it in an electric arc, and more lines will appear in its spectrum when excited in the latter manner. When the excitation is produced by a disruptive discharge or spark, formed between electrodes made of the material under investigation, the potential needed is much higher than in the case of the electric arc. As a result the excitation is increased, and the spark spectrum will contain more lines than the arc spectrum. Intense excitation of gases at low pressure may be obtained within a discharge tube energized by an induction coil or electrostatic generator.

408. Absorption Spectra.—When the light from a glowing solid or other source yielding a continuous spectrum is passed through an absorbing medium before being dispersed, the spectrum is usually crossed by dark spaces which show that radiations of particular wavelengths have been absorbed. If the absorbing material is solid or liquid, these dark spaces appear as broad, structureless bands. If it is gaseous, they consist of dark lines which occupy the same positions as the bright lines in the corresponding bright-line spectrum.

The production of a dark-line spectrum is illustrated by a well-known experiment showing the reversal of the sodium lines. An arc lamp is arranged to project an intense beam of light upon a prism, the beam being directed through a cloud of glowing sodium vapor produced by heating common salt in a Bunsen flame. A narrow slit is provided near the prism in the light path. In conducting the experiment, the glowing sodium vapor is first used alone; the resulting spectrum consists of the two bright yellow lines characteristic of sodium. Upon starting the arc lamp and shining its rays through the sodium vapor, a continuous spectrum is formed, having two dark lines at exactly the positions previously occupied by the bright lines. This reversal of the lines is explained by supposing that the sodium vapor, which emits these particular lines when excited, responds to the corresponding frequencies of vibration, and absorbs the energy of these particular vibrations from the beam proceeding from the arc. This vapor considered as a source has low luminosity as compared with the arc because of its relative coolness, and hence the spectral lines which it produces are dark in comparison with the rest of the spectrum.

The absorption spectrum of a gas may also take the form of fluted bands, which under sufficient dispersion are found to consist of closely spaced dark lines arranged in an orderly manner. *Band spectra* are emitted only by molecules, and may be contrasted with *line spectra*, since these are emitted only by single or uncombined atoms. From the study of band spectra much has been learned about the structure of molecules and the forces acting within them. Bands occasionally appear in bright-line or emission spectra, but less commonly than in absorption spectra, because the intense excitation used in producing emission spectra is likely to break up the molecules into their component parts.

409. The Solar Spectrum.—The spectrum produced by passing sunlight through a prism appears continuous from a casual inspection; a more critical examination, however, shows that it is crossed by numerous dark lines. No doubt the radiation from the sun com-

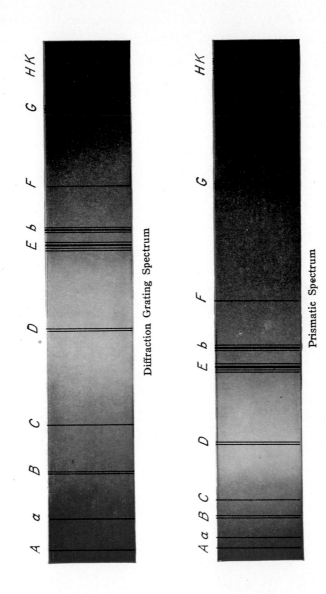

Diffraction Grating Spectrum

Prismatic Spectrum

prises all wavelengths throughout the visible range, but in passing through the sun's atmosphere, certain ones are absorbed; therefore the spectrum observed is in reality an absorption spectrum of that atmosphere. The dark lines indicate which gases are present around the sun and also reveal its own composition. The first careful study of these absorption lines was made by the German optician and physicist, Joseph von Fraunhofer (1787–1826), who assigned letters to several of the more conspicuous ones. These lines are shown in

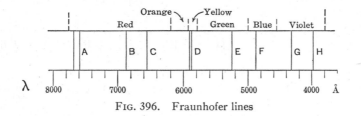

FIG. 396. Fraunhofer lines

the accompanying colored plate and their locations are indicated to scale in Fig. 396. They are located in definite color zones, and are frequently specified when reference is made to particular hues. The following table gives additional data for some of the lines more commonly used:

Fraunhofer Lines

Designation	Color	Wavelength, Å	Produced in the spectrum of
A	red	7630	Oxygen
C	red	6563	Hydrogen
D	yellow	5893	Sodium
F	blue	4861	Hydrogen
K	violet	3934	Calcium

410. Variation of Refractive Index.—It is known that lights of different color travel with different speeds in a transparent medium, a fact which explains why a beam of light comprising many colors is dispersed in passing through a prism. This is illustrated in Fig. 394, where the angles of refraction are different for the several colors, although the angle of incidence is the same for all. In consequence, the refractive index of the medium has a definite value for each color. The accompanying table lists the indices of refraction of a few common materials for light of particular wavelengths corresponding to the *C*, *D*, and *F* Fraunhofer lines. The index for the *D* line is often used as a reference value because this line is near the middle of the spectrum.

Variation of Refractive Index with Color of Light

	Index of refraction		
	C line	*D* line	*F* line
Carbon disulfide (20° C.).....	1.6182	1.6276	1.6523
Crown glass, sample.........	1.5145	1.5172	1.5240
Flint glass, sample..........	1.6221	1.6270	1.6391
Water (20° C.).............	1.3312	1.3330	1.3372

411. Dispersion by a Prism.—The amount of dispersion is expressed quantitatively by the angular separation of particular colors of the spectrum. Thus the angle ψ (psi) in Fig. 397 indicates numerically the dispersion of white light produced by a prism from the red to the violet region. This angle is clearly the difference between the deviations of the violet and red components of the incident light

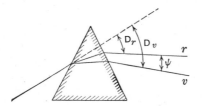

FIG. 397. Deviation and dispersion, with angles exaggerated for clearness

beam. If these deviations are called D_v and D_r respectively, the dispersion becomes

$$\psi = D_v - D_r$$

The deviation produced by a prism is definitely related to the angle of the prism by equation (248), which gives the refractive index as

$$\mu = \frac{\sin \frac{1}{2}(D_m + A)}{\sin \frac{1}{2}A}$$

where A is the prism angle and D_m is the angle of minimum deviation of the ray through the prism. When the prism angle is small, the sines of the angles may be replaced by the angles themselves, and when the rays pass through the prism with approximate symmetry the difference between the deviation D and the minimum deviation D_m may be neglected. Hence the index is

$$\mu = \frac{\frac{1}{2}(D + A)}{\frac{1}{2}A}$$

from which the deviation is

$$D = A(\mu - 1) \tag{252}$$

This expression shows that for a prism of small angle, the deviation is directly proportional to the angle of the prism and to the amount by which the refractive index exceeds unity. The equation can be used for prism angles up to $A = 30°$ without exceeding about 5 per cent error in the deviation.

The dispersion between any two colors may be found for a small-angle prism by using the foregoing equation to compute the respective deviation values. The dispersion between violet and red is $D_v - D_r = A(\mu_v - 1) - A(\mu_r - 1)$, or

$$\psi = A(\mu_v - \mu_r) \tag{253}$$

The amount of dispersion depends not only upon the angle of the prism but also upon the *dispersive power* of the material of which it is made. Dispersive power is the ratio of the dispersion which a small-angle prism would produce to the deviation of the median ray of the spectrum. The dispersion is commonly taken between violet and red, and yellow is considered as the middle color of the spectrum; whence the dispersive power is the ratio of ψ to D_y, or

$$\delta = \frac{\mu_v - \mu_r}{\mu_y - 1} \tag{254}$$

Note that the prism angle has been eliminated; dispersive power is a property of the substance and not of the shape of a dispersing agent.

When more definite values of deviation, dispersion, or dispersive power are needed, these quantities may be calculated with reference to particular Fraunhofer lines in the desired regions of the spectrum. For example, crown glass, having the indices listed in § 410, has a dispersive power over the region from blue to red (F line to C line) of

$$\delta = \frac{1.5240 - 1.5145}{1.5172 - 1.0000} = \frac{0.0095}{0.5172} = 0.0183$$

Deviation of light without dispersion can be produced by the use of two prisms placed so as to deviate the light in opposite directions; the prism materials must have different dispersive powers and the prism angles must be so proportioned that the dispersion due to one will annul that due to the other.

For example, the dispersion produced by a 12° crown-glass prism between the C and F spectral lines is 12° (1.5240 − 1.5145) = 0.114°, as found from equation (253) and the refractive indices mentioned. To annul this dispersion with a flint-glass prism, it must have an angle of 0.114/(1.6391 − 1.6221) = 6.7°. The deviation produced by the prism combination, computed for the D line, is 12° (1.5172 − 1) − 6.7° (1.6270 − 1) = 2.005°.

412. Spectrum Analysis.—The detailed study of emission and absorption spectra is termed spectrum analysis or *spectroscopy*, and is of great importance. Perhaps the best-known application is the identification of the elements present in a sample of unknown composition by the recognition of their characteristic spectra. Spectra disclose not only what elements are present but show whether the atoms are parts of molecules or exist by themselves, and in addition furnish evidence as to the conditions of ionization, temperature, and pressure under which they exist.

Analysis of the light from the sun and stars reveals the presence of the same elements as occur upon the earth; helium derives its name from having been first discovered in the atmosphere of the sun (Greek, *Helios*). In the spectra of certain stars, the expected lines appear, but are displaced slightly from their normal positions. This displacement indicates an apparent change in frequency, as explained by Doppler's Principle (§ 366), and reveals the fact that there is relative motion between the star under examination and the earth. A shift toward the red end of the spectrum, for example, means an apparent increase in wavelength or lowering of frequency, and shows that the star and earth are receding from each other. It is from measurements of this kind that the motion of the solar system mentioned in § 29 was computed.

413. Types of Spectroscopes.—Many kinds of instruments are used for the examination of spectra; it will suffice to describe briefly one type for each of the ultraviolet, visible, and infra-red ranges.

A spectrograph for the ultraviolet region is arranged as in Fig. 398. It consists of an equilateral prism of quartz mounted between two quartz lenses L_1 and L_2, together with an adjustable slit and a photographic plate holder. Light coming through the narrow slit is made parallel by a collimating lens L_1, and after dispersion by the prism is brought to a focus upon the sensitized plate by a camera lens L_2 (see Chapter XXXVI). The plate is inclined considerably to the dispersed beam in order to accommodate the different focal lengths of the lens for radiations of wavelengths from 2000 to 10,000 Å. The exposure time is suited to the intensity of the source and

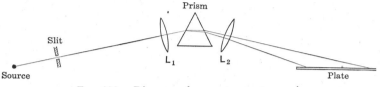

FIG. 398. Diagram of a quartz spectrograph

to the width of the slit. Provision is often made for photographing a scale calibrated in wavelengths next to the spectrum, so that the wavelengths of its individual lines can be read off directly. A spectrogram of a copper arc showing the lines down to 2150 Å appears in Fig. 399.

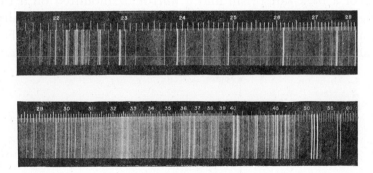

FIG. 399. Spectral lines of copper arc in ultraviolet and visible regions

A spectroscope for the visible region is illustrated in Fig. 400. It consists of a glass prism mounted on a table which can be rotated over a small angular range, two glass lenses L_1 and L_2 which serve the same purposes as in Fig. 398, a slit of adjustable width, and either a telescope for visual observation of the spectrum or a camera for making a photographic record of it. The prism has the following angles: $a = 90°$, $b = 75°$, $c = 135°$ and $d = 60°$. Its action can be explained by drawing the line ac and dropping a perpendicular to this line from b; this divides the prism into two 30-60-90° prisms and one 45-45-90° prism, the latter serving as a mirror by total reflection.

A little study will show that the incident and emergent beams are at right angles to each other, and that for all positions of the prism the center of the emergent beam will have minimum deviation. A

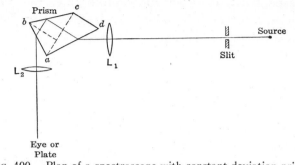

FIG. 400.   Plan of a spectroscope with constant deviation prism

calibrated scale is fitted to the prism table for reading directly the wavelength of the spectral line that appears at the center of the field of view.

Fig. 401 illustrates a spectrometer for the infra-red region. It consists of a rock-salt prism and a mirror M mounted on a table so that the two can be rotated as a unit, a concave spherical mirror C_1 for forming the incident radiation into a parallel beam, another concave mirror C_2 for focusing the emerging radiation upon the receiving

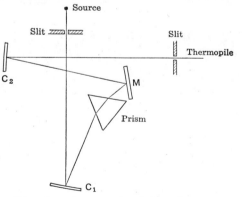

FIG. 401.   Arrangement of an infra-red spectrometer

slit, and a thermopile behind the slit in which the radiation sets up an electric current that is measured with a galvanometer. The prism table is moved by a drum carrying a scale, so that the wavelength of the radiation falling upon the thermopile can be read directly. The range of a typical instrument of this type is from 3800 to 170,000 Å. A study of the distribution and intensity of the radiation emitted by a black body over this range of wavelengths led to the quantum theory, § 203.

414. Spectral Series.—The definiteness of the spectral lines of the elements has long been regarded as the key to an understanding of atomic structure. Much experimental evidence on spectra has been accumulated and correlated with the quantum theory, as a result of which it is now known that the atom has definite energy levels, and that it assumes a higher energy level upon absorbing energy and assumes a lower one upon emitting energy through radiation.

Johann J. Balmer (1825–1898), a Swiss physicist, found that the spectral lines of hydrogen formed a *series* that could be expressed by the equation

$$\lambda = 3646 \frac{N^2}{N^2 - 4}$$

where λ is the wavelength of the lines in Ångström units and N is an integer having values greater than 2. For the four most prominent lines in the visible portion of the spectrum, the wavelengths are 6563, 4861, 4340 and 4102 Å. The foregoing equation gives these values when N is taken successively as 3, 4, 5 and 6. For progressively shorter wavelengths, the values of N become larger and larger, the limiting value being for a wavelength of 3646 Å in the ultraviolet region.

Other spectral series for hydrogen have been found beyond the visible region of the spectrum. Professor Theodore Lyman, an American physicist, discovered a simple equation for the lines in the extreme ultraviolet, and Friedrich Paschen, a German scientist and spectroscopist, originated a similar equation for a series of lines in the infra-red region. Later two other series extending farther into the infra-red zone were established. Lines of the various series are usually expressed in terms of the number of waves per centimeter, the so-called *wave number*, rather than the wavelength, and when so expressed can be merged into the single equation

$$\nu = 109,737 \left[\frac{1}{k_2{}^2} - \frac{1}{k_1{}^2} \right] \tag{255}$$

where ν is the wave number or the reciprocal of the wavelength in centimeters, and k_2 and k_1 are integers having the following values:

Lyman series	$k_2 = 1$	$k_1 = 2, 3, 4, \cdots$
Balmer series	$k_2 = 2$	$k_1 = 3, 4, 5, \cdots$
Paschen series	$k_2 = 3$	$k_1 = 4, 5, 6, \cdots$

When these integers are applied, the limiting wave numbers of hydrogen are found to be 5,334 and 12,193 for the Paschen series, 15,241 and 27,434 for the Balmer series, and 82,303 and 109,737 for the Lyman series. Expressions similar in character to the foregoing equation have been developed for many other elements.

The mathematical relationship between the wave numbers of spectral lines, as expressed by equation (255) for hydrogen, was explained on a physical basis by Professor Bohr in 1913. He applied the planetary picture of the atom, comprising a positively charged nucleus with external electrons revolving about it in shells or orbits, and postulated that an electron could occupy any one of a definite number of orbits or *stationary states* without radiating, each of these representing a definite energy level. For the hydrogen atom, with its single planetary electron, the normal state corresponds to the electron residing in its innermost orbit. When this atom receives energy, the revolving electron moves to a larger orbit in opposition to the attractive force of the nucleus. When the atom loses energy by radiation, the electron falls to definite inner orbits. and the amount of energy radiated is given by

$$E_h - E_l = hf \tag{256}$$

where E_h represents the higher energy level of an outer orbit, E_l represents the lower energy level of the inner orbit, h is Planck's constant (§ 202), and f is the frequency of the radiation given off. Each spectral line produced by an excited atom, therefore, corresponds to a specific change of energy as the electron falls from some definite outer orbit to a particular inner one. The spectral lines of any series are produced by the electrons of excited atoms falling back to a common inner orbit.

The relation between the wave number ν, the wavelength λ (cm.) and the frequency f of the radiation is indicated by equation (217) as

$$\nu = \frac{1}{\lambda} = \frac{f}{c}$$

where c is the velocity of light in centimeters per second. When this expression is combined with equation (256), the wave number becomes

$$\nu = \frac{1}{hc} (E_h - E_l)$$

which has the same form as equation (255). If now corresponding terms are compared, it appears that the energy levels of the hydrogen atom are given by

$$E_h = 109{,}737 \frac{hc}{k_2{}^2} \quad \text{and} \quad E_l = 109{,}737 \frac{hc}{k_1{}^2}$$

From the numerical values $h = 6.62 \times 10^{-27}$ erg-sec. and $c = 3.00 \times 10^{10}$ cm. per sec., it follows that the entire numerator for either expression becomes a constant having the value 21.8×10^{-12} ergs. If the symbol A is used to represent this value, the energy levels can be expressed by

$$E = \frac{A}{k^2} \tag{257}$$

where k represents successive integers that have the values of k_2 and k_1 previously tabulated for the three spectral series.

Fig. 402 represents the energy levels of the hydrogen atom by horizontal lines for values of k up to 6. If such an atom changes its energy from level 3 to level 2, it will radiate energy amounting to $E = \dfrac{A}{2^2} - \dfrac{A}{3^2} = 21.8 \times 10^{-12}\left(\dfrac{1}{4} - \dfrac{1}{9}\right) = 3.03 \times 10^{-12}$ ergs, and will produce only the spectral line having the wave number $109{,}737 \times (\tfrac{1}{4} - \tfrac{1}{9}) = 15{,}241$ waves per cm.; it is represented by the heavy vertical line in the figure. This wave number gives close agreement with the wavelength of the red line, $\lambda = 6563$ Å, found by experiment. The vertical lines connecting levels $A/2^2$, $A/3^2 \cdots A/6^2 \cdots$ with level $A/1^2$ represent the spectral lines of the Lyman series; lines connecting $A/3^2$, $A/4^2 \cdots A/6^2 \cdots$ with $A/2^2$ represent the spectral lines of the Balmer series; and similarly for the Paschen series.

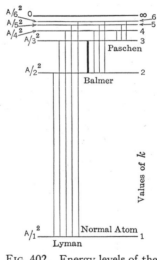

FIG. 402. Energy levels of the hydrogen atom

*415. Resonance and Ionization Potentials.—The emission of the line of lowest wave number in a spectral series involves the least energy. As more energy becomes available from the source of excitation, additional lines will appear; thus, the number of lines of a series that are present in the spectrum of an element is a measure of its energy of excitation. All the lines of a series will be present when the energy is just great enough to cause an electron to leave the atom, an action which constitutes ionization. These energy values may be expressed in ergs, as in the preceding section, but are more commonly stated in electron-volts, § 274. Since 1 electron-volt is 1.60×10^{-12} erg, the expression for the energy levels becomes

$$E = \frac{13.60}{k^2}$$

The energy required to excite the first line of a spectral series, expressed in electron-volts, is called the *resonance potential* for that series. The energy required to excite all the lines of the series is called its *ionization potential*, for it corresponds to the complete removal of an electron from an atomic system. Resonance and ionization potentials may be determined experimentally with gaseous discharge tubes and such measurements confirm the atomic energy levels computed theoretically. Values of these potentials for a few atoms are given in the following table:

Resonance and Ionization Potentials

	Electron-volts to produce first spectral line	Electron-volts to cause ionization
Helium..................	19.74	24.54
Hydrogen (Lyman series)...	10.20	13.60
Mercury.................	4.67	10.42
Potassium...............	1.58	4.33
Sodium.................	2.09	5.13

416. Color.—The term *color* is used in two senses. Physically, color is determined by the spectral distribution of energy in the light beam; that is, the frequencies of the component waves and their intensities. Physiologically, color refers to the sensation produced by these waves entering the eye. The sense of sight is such that the component waves proceeding from a given point are integrated or combined, and produce a single resultant effect of color.

Colors may be compared not only as to hue; red or green, for example, but also as to saturation or purity. Thus, the dilution of saturated red with white light gives a pink tint. The intensity of the beam or the illumination it produces also influences the resulting color sensation.

417. Mixture of Colored Lights; the Additive Process.—When a spectrum is produced by passing white light through a prism, and then all the colors of the spectrum are caused to overlap, their effects are added together and produce the sensation of white light. This result may be observed by allowing the composite beam to enter the eye directly, or by projecting it upon a white screen. However, it is also found that by combining only the yellow and blue-violet portions of the spectrum, a white light is produced which the eye cannot distinguish from the other. There are several pairs of colors which yield white light when added; they are called *complementary* colors. Yellow and blue-violet are complementary, as are also red and blue-green. Furthermore, the light from a sodium vapor lamp appears much like that of illuminating gas, but the former has primarily the yellow spectral lines while the latter has the continuous spectrum of carbon. Evidently a particular color sensation can be produced in a variety of ways, and the composition of the radiated beam cannot be determined by its appearance but only by an analysis of its spectrum.

It is possible to match any color by the addition of red, green, and blue-violet lights in suitable proportions. Consequently, these three are called the *additive primary colors*. This property can be demonstrated by the Maxwell color triangle, Fig. 403.
A white triangular surface is illuminated by three overlapping beams of the primary colors just mentioned, issuing from colored lamps at the corners. The illumination due to the red lamp at R is regarded as varying from a value of 100 at that corner to zero all along the opposite side BG; similarly the green and the blue-violet each vary

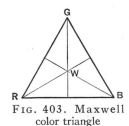

Fig. 403. Maxwell color triangle

from 100 at the corresponding corner to zero all along the opposite side.

At the corners of the triangle appear the saturated hues of the primary colors. Along the upper sides are the spectral colors in their regular order, with yellow midway between R and G and green-blue midway between G and B. At the center of the base BR, where only blue-violet and red are present, are the hues of purple, which are not present in the spectrum. It will be seen that the complement of each primary color appears at the center of the opposite side. Throughout the central part of the figure lighter tints appear than at the corners, the saturation being reduced by the addition of white light. The central point W where the three primary colors are added in equal proportions is white.

418. Selective Absorption; the Subtractive Process.—The light incident upon a non-luminous object may be partly *reflected* and partly *absorbed*, and the remainder will be *transmitted*. The color of the object depends upon the composition of the incident light and the extent to which the various component colors are reflected, absorbed, and transmitted.

A sheet of ordinary glass held in front of a source of white light appears colorless by light transmitted through it, because it transmits practically all of the light falling upon it. On the other hand, a sheet of red glass appears red because the complement of red, namely blue-green, has been subtracted by absorption. Similarly, a blue-violet transmitting medium absorbs yellow, and one of green absorbs purple. These colors, blue-green, yellow, and purple, are called the *subtractive primary colors*; they are the complements of the additive primaries.

The property of absorbing certain colors and transmitting others is called *selective absorption*. Ordinary uncolored glass transmits the entire range of wavelengths of the visible spectrum, but is comparatively opaque to most ultraviolet and infra-red radiation, and thus exhibits selective absorption outside of the visible range. In a greenhouse, the glass transmits energy over the entire visible range to the plants within, where it is largely converted into heat and chemical energy. The radiation from the interior is principally in the infra-red region (so-called radiant heat), and since but little of this is transmitted outward by the glass, the interior of the enclosure remains warm.

The light given out by the ordinary incandescent electric lamp is redder than sunlight, that is, the spectrum is relatively more intense toward the red than toward the violet end as compared with that of sunlight. The incandescent *daylight lamp* has an envelope of blue glass which, by selective absorption, removes some of the radiation from the red end of the spectrum, and the transmitted light, although slightly dimmed, conforms more closely to sunlight in the relative proportions of the component colors.

The principles of selective absorption are applied in a lamp which is used for destroying bacteria. This source of radiation, called a "Sterilamp," consists of a long closed tube containing inert gas and mercury vapor, and having coated electrodes at its ends. An electric discharge is maintained within the tube and produces radiation mostly in the ultraviolet region. The tube is made of special glass which absorbs the radiations not desired, and transmits over 80 per cent of the total radiation in the region of 2537 Å, which has been found effective in destroying micro-organisms. The lamp is used in sterilizing food and food containers, and also articles subject to mold or fungus growths. A 20-in. tube operating at 375 volts takes approximately 12 watts, and the temperature is but a few degrees above that of the surroundings.

419. Color by Reflected Light.—Opaque bodies are seen by light diffusely reflected from them. Suppose an object to be examined in white light containing all wavelengths of the visible spectrum. If the object reflects no light, it appears black; if it reflects all of the light incident upon it, it appears white; and if it reflects only part of the light, but reflects all wavelengths in equal proportions, it appears gray.

Most objects which appear colored when viewed by reflected light do so because of selective absorption. Reflection is not strictly a surface phenomenon, as the light seems to penetrate a short distance beneath the surface before reflection. A board painted blue-green absorbs the complementary red and reflects blue and green (see Fig. 403). Similarly, a board painted yellow absorbs blue-violet and reflects red and green. If blue-green and yellow paints are mixed, the only color reflected by both will be green; the blue-green paint will absorb the yellow and orange, and the yellow paint will absorb the blue and violet. This result is quite different from that produced by mixing yellow and blue lights, as described in § 417.

An object has its true color when examined by light which contains all the wavelengths of the visible spectrum. If certain colors are absent from the incident light, the apparent color of the object may be quite different from its true color. Thus, dark blue cloth appears nearly black when examined under an incandescent electric lamp because of the deficiency of blue in the incident light. The light from the mercury vapor lamp contains no red radiations; a red object appears black under such a lamp. Mercury vapor lamps are sometimes used in combination with neon lamps, the red light from the glowing neon offsetting the deficiency of red light in the glowing mercury vapor.

A few instances occur in which bodies exhibit a *surface color* which is apparently due to *selective reflection*, like the luster of metallic surfaces. Gold exhibits a yellow surface color, but this is not because the other colors are absorbed; in fact, the surface color itself is the one that is absorbed most strongly. This can be shown by passing white light through a sheet of gold foil, for it will be found that the transmitted light is bluish green, the yellow having been absorbed.

The rainbow is caused by the dispersion of sunlight within raindrops. The light that falls upon a drop is refracted at its surface, reflected within it, and refracted again upon emergence. Much of the light is scattered in various directions, but the rays near the path of minimum deviation from a series of drops merge into a fairly intense beam along the directions shown in Fig. 404. The dispersion resolves the incident white light into the spectral colors, the angle between the incident and emergent rays being about 40° for violet and 42° for red. An eye at E receives light of different colors from a multitude of drops, the red color appearing uppermost. Drops similarly located with respect to sun and observer but not in the plane of the page produce a corresponding effect, the collective action yielding the familiar rainbow. A secondary rainbow is sometimes formed outside of the first; it is produced by two reflections of the rays within the drops.

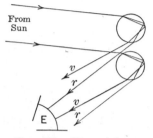

FIG. 404. The rainbow

The light from the sky is due to the scattering of sunlight by the molecules of air, as well as by dust and other impurities contained in the atmosphere, as the sun's rays pass through it. It has been established that the intensity of scattered radiation varies directly as the fourth power of the frequency of the incident light, and for this reason the short waves, corresponding to the blue and violet colors, are scattered more than the longer waves of red light; this accounts for the prevailing blue color of the sky. Without the atmosphere, the sky would appear black. The light coming directly from the sun when it is near the horizon is predominantly red, because the blue portion has been scattered to a large extent from the direct beam in traversing relatively long paths through the atmosphere.

420. Fluorescence and Phosphorescence.—Many crystalline substances are found to glow when stimulated by the bombardment of electrons or alpha particles, or by exposure to radiations like ultraviolet light and x-rays. With some substances the light is emitted only while the incident excitation is maintained, and in others it persists for a short time after the excitation is removed; these effects are called *fluorescence* and *phosphorescence* respectively. Among fluorescent substances may be mentioned fluorspar, willemite, some lubricating oils, alcohol solutions of chlorophyll, and uranium glass; among phosphorescent substances zinc sulfide and calcium sulfide exhibit luminescence for several hours after the exciting radiation is removed.

In general, when the excitation is induced by radiation, the luminescent material emits light of longer wavelength than that to which it was exposed. This principle is utilized in the fluorescent lamp (§ 382) in which phosphors when excited by ultraviolet radiation, principally of wavelength 2537 Å, emit visible light of various colors. The phosphors used in the lamps yielding soft white and daylight are combinations of zinc beryllium silicate and magnesium tungstate. In the fluoroscope, used for x-ray examinations (§ 323), the screen against which the shadows are seen is a card coated with platinocyanide of barium. This phosphor gives off a pale greenish light where it is exposed to the x-rays. For the fluorescent screens of iconoscopes, used in television, a variety of substances have been studied; the requirements are exacting for this service because of the steady electron bombardment.

421. Seeing in the Dark.—Strange as it may seem, it is possible to see objects in the dark. This result has been accomplished largely by research due to the War, and some of the methods used have now been disclosed. One of these employs a device called a sniperscope, which consists essentially of an infra-red light source and an image tube having a light-sensitive cathode. The sniperscope is attached to a rifle and projects upon objects in front of it a beam of infrared radiation from which all visible light has been filtered out. The reflected rays are caught upon a caesium cell, which is sensitive to infra-red light and which forms the cathode of the image tube. The radiation impinging upon the cell causes it to liberate photoelectrons and these are focussed on a fluorescent screen, as in a cathode-ray oscillograph, to form a visible image.

The same principle finds a peacetime application in the field of optometry. Examinations of the eye can be made with the infra-red light, which being invisible does not induce disturbing fluctuations and movements of the eye under observation.

*422. Color Photography.—The art of color photography depends upon the fact that any color occurring in nature can be matched by merging the additive primary colors in appropriate amounts. Latent images are formed on a light-sensitive emulsion separately for the

red, the green, and the blue portions of the subject being photographed, each showing the variations in the intensity of the light of
that particular color emitted or reflected by the subject. Positives
or negatives of the images, dyed the appropriate colors, can be combined in proper register to form a natural color photograph. A simple
way of doing this would be to dye the positive of each picture the
respective primary color and then to throw pictures of the three
positives from separate projectors upon a screen. Such a procedure
would be unwieldy, and other methods are more commonly used in
photography. One of these will suffice for illustration.

The colors are separated by using photographic materials that are
sensitive to different parts of the spectrum, and arranging them in
three separate layers. A cross-section of the film is illustrated in

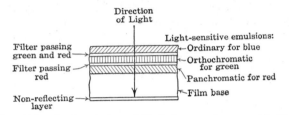

FIG. 405.   Sectional view of Kodachrome photographic film

Fig. 405. The upper emulsion (ordinary type) is affected by blue
and violet light, the next (orthochromatic type) by blue and green,
and the lowest one (panchromatic type) by all colors. Between the
first and second emulsions is a filter which transmits green and red
but no blue, and between the second and third is a substance which
is transparent only to red light. When the film is exposed in the
camera three separate latent images are produced, one in the top
layer formed by the blue light from the subject, one in the intermediate layer by the green, and one in the bottom layer by the red light.

By rather complex processing operations the filters are bleached
out and the film is made to yield three negatives (the image being
least transparent where most light reached the film), each in a color
complementary to the color of the light by which the original latent
image was produced. Thus, the top layer is converted into a transparent material which does not transmit blue-violet light at places
corresponding to regions where blue was missing from the subject.
It will appear as a yellow negative because yellow is complementary
to blue-violet. Similar changes are effected in the other two emulsions; the second subtracts green from those parts where it was absent

in the subject, and the third subtracts red in the same way. When white light passes through a part on the film that corresponds to a blue portion of the subject, it passes through the top emulsion with practically no absorption, it has green removed from it in the second, and red in the third; thus the emergent light through that part of the film will be blue. If the original exposure was correct the absorption of each of the layers will be proportional to the intensity of the incident light having the appropriate color, and hence the resulting transparency will be in the original colors. The Kodachrome process uses this method.

To produce a picture upon paper instead of a transparency, three separate negatives must be made, one by the light of each of the primary colors. Images from these are dyed in complementary colors, the red-filter negative image being dyed blue-green, the green being dyed purple, and the blue-violet being dyed yellow; these are then transferred in register to a sheet of white paper. The picture is observed by light transmitted through the dyes to the paper, and reflected by it back through the dyes.

PROBLEMS

In problems referring to crown glass and flint glass, use the refractive indices tabulated in § 410.

1. What information is obtained from the fact (a) that the background of the solar spectrum is continuous? (b) that one of the dark lines crossing the solar spectrum corresponds to the wavelength 5893 Å.?

2. A beam of white light is passed through a 60° crown-glass prism, the angle of incidence of the beam being such that the deviation is a minimum for the D spectral line. Compute the dispersion between this line and the F line.

3. A ray of white light is directed upon a plate of flint glass at an incident angle of 30°. Compute the angle between the C and F spectral lines in the refracted wave within the glass.

4. When white light is passed through a 10° flint-glass prism, what is the minimum deviation of the D spectral line and what is the dispersion between the C and D lines?

5. Compute the angle of a crown-glass prism which yields a dispersion of 0.1° between the C and F spectral lines. What minimum deviation of the D line would this prism produce?

6. Compute the angle of a carbon-disulfide prism that will produce the same dispersion between the C and F spectral lines as that due to a water prism of 10° angle.

7. Compute the angle of a crown-glass prism that will annul the dispersion due to an 8° flint-glass prism between the C and F spectral lines.

What deviation will be produced by the prism combination as computed for the *D* line?

8. It is desired to combine a flint-glass prism with a 10° crown-glass prism so that when light is passed through the combination the *D* spectral line will not be deviated. Compute the angle of the flint-glass prism needed, and also the dispersion between the *C* and *F* lines due to the combined prisms.

9. From the tabulated data for flint-glass, plot a curve showing the relation between index of refraction and wavelength, and determine the index corresponding to a wavelength of 5461 Å. What deviation would be produced for light of this wavelength by a flint-glass prism of 12° angle?

10. Ultraviolet light is passed through a 60° prism of fused quartz. The indices of refraction of this substance for three lines are:

$$1.4750 \text{ for wavelength } 3610 \text{ Å}$$
$$1.4963 \text{ for wavelength } 2750 \text{ Å}$$
$$1.5339 \text{ for wavelength } 2140 \text{ Å}$$

(*a*) If the light of the middle wavelength passes symmetrically through the prism, what are the angular dispersions between these spectral lines? (*b*) What is the dispersive power of fused quartz over this range with respect to the intermediate spectral line?

11. A hydrogen spectrum is formed by a crown-glass prism of 10° angle, and is received by a screen 20 cm. away from the prism. Compute the separation on the screen between the lines corresponding to wavelengths 6563 and 4861 Å. Assume that the rays are approximately symmetrical within the prism and that they fall almost normally upon the screen.

12. The wavelength of the green line in the mercury spectrum is 5461 Å. Compute the corresponding frequency and wave number.

13. Calculate the wave numbers of the first three lines of each of the three spectral series of hydrogen.

*14. To what velocity must an electron be accelerated in order that it may acquire 1 electron-volt of energy?

*15. Construct an energy-level diagram for atomic hydrogen using electron-volts as ordinates, placing 0 volts at the top and the ionization potential of 13.60 volts at the bottom, and showing the next four levels above the latter.

16. Approximately what wavelength of light would be complementary to light having a wavelength of 0.000059 cm.?

17. Two projectors throw spots of light upon a white screen. One projector lens is covered with red glass and the other is covered with blue-violet glass. Explain what hue will be produced on the screen where the two spots of light overlap.

18. Explain the result of painting a surface with a mixture of yellow and purple paint.

Lenses   *Chapter XXXVI*

423. Types of Lenses.—A transparent material shaped to converge
or diverge a beam of light transmitted through it is called a lens.   It
is usually a circular disk of glass that varies in thickness from the
center to the rim, one or both surfaces being spherical.   If a glass
lens is thicker at the center than at the rim, it converges a parallel
beam of light and is called a *converging* or *positive lens*.   If it is thinner
at the center than at the rim, it diverges such a beam and is called a
diverging or *negative lens*.

The development of a lens from a prism can be shown graphically
with the aid of equation (252), which shows that the angle of light

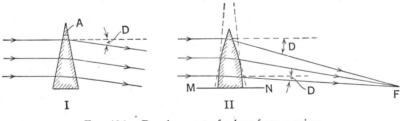

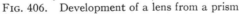

Fig. 406.   Development of a lens from a prism

deviation produced by a prism of angle A is equal to $A(\mu - 1)$ if the
prism angle is small.   Consider a parallel beam of monochromatic
light to fall upon the prism as shown in part I of Fig. 406.   The three
rays depicted will be parallel upon emergence, each being deviated
by the same angle D from the initial direction.   To converge the
beam at some point F requires that the upper ray be deviated more
and the lower one less than the center one, as shown in part II of
the figure.   Since the refractive index μ of the prism is the same
for all of the rays, the only way to change D is to make a corresponding change in A.   Thus, the prism angle should be larger for the upper
ray and smaller for the lower ray, as indicated.   To bring all possible
rays of the incident beam to the same point of convergence, the angle
of the prism should change continuously from point to point; that is,
one or both faces should be curved.   The prism may now be regarded

as a semi-section of a lens by which the cylindrical beam of parallel light is brought to convergence at F on the principal axis MN of the lens.

Fig. 407 shows six shapes of converging and diverging lenses. The first is called double-convex, the next plano-convex, the third concavo-convex, and the others are named

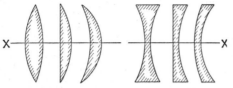

Converging Lenses   Diverging Lenses

FIG. 407.   Positive and negative lenses

similarly. The center line XX for any lens is called its *principal axis*; it is a line that passes through the centers of curvature of the lens surfaces.

424. Focal Length and Conjugate Distances.—When a parallel beam of light is incident upon a lens along its principal axis, the point of convergence or of divergence of the beam after passing through a lens is called the *principal focus* of the lens. In Fig. 408 the two upper diagrams show such parallel rays of light refracted in passing through a double-convex and a double-concave lens. The rays converge to point F in the first lens and diverge from point F in the second; the distance from the principal focus F to the lens in either case is called the *focal length* of the lens, the symbol for which is f. Should parallel

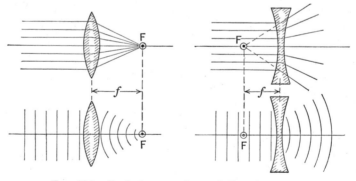

FIG. 408.   Foci of converging and diverging lenses

light be incident upon these lenses from the right, instead of from the left as shown, the focal points would be on the other side of the lenses at the same distances f from them.

In the simpler theory of lenses the thickness of a lens is assumed to be negligibly small in comparison with its focal length, and this assumption will apply to this and to the sections that follow up to § 433. With *thin lenses*, therefore, distances may be measured to either lens surface. In diagrams, it is customary to show the lenses with appreciable thickness in order to indicate their shapes more clearly, and particularly to show whether they are converging or diverging. In drawing lines to represent rays of light in such diagrams, the procedure is to deviate the lines at the transverse plane which actually shows the position of the ideally thin lens, instead of showing the refraction that occurs at each surface. The upper diagrams of Fig. 408 indicate this procedure.

The lower diagrams of this figure show the same results using wave fronts instead of rays of light. Plane waves normal to the principal axis are incident upon a double-convex lens at the left, and, because the retardation is greater at the center than near the edge of the lens, the waves converge upon the principal focus at F. With the double-concave lens at the right, plane incident waves diverge after refraction through the lens as though they had originated at F.

Fig. 408 represents the behavior of all six types of lenses; the left-hand figures typify converging lenses, and the right-hand figures typify diverging lenses.

When a point source of light is situated at some place along the principal axis of a lens, an image of it will be produced by the lens at some other point on the axis. Let the object distance be p and the image distance be q as measured from the lens; the relation between these distances will be demonstrated in the following sections to be

$$\frac{1}{p} + \frac{1}{q} = \frac{1}{f} \qquad (258)$$

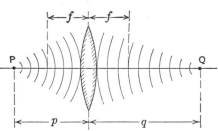

FIG. 409. Conjugate distances of a lens

where f is the focal length of the lens. Fig. 409 shows a spherical wave issuing from the point source at P, falling on the lens of focal length f, and converging to form an image at Q. The distances p and q are called *conjugate distances* of the lens. For every value of the object distance p there is a particular value of the image distance q. If q becomes negative, then a virtual image will be formed at Q, located on the same side of the lens as P. If p is ∞, q will be equal to f. Since the equation is symmetrical in p and q, it follows that object and image may be interchanged; that is, if the object is located at Q, the image would be formed at P.

425. Relation between Focal Length and Radii of Curvature.—
Before equation (258) is applied to lenses of particular shapes, it will
be expressed in terms of the physical constants of the lens itself.   It
is easier to accomplish this by using wave fronts
rather than rays of light, but it will be necessary
first to establish a geometrical relation between
the length of a chord, the radius of the associated
arc, and the maximum radial distance from chord
to arc.   The latter distance is called the *sagitta* of
the arc, and is shown as s in Fig. 410.   In the
diagram the radius OM of length r is intersected
by the chord from L perpendicular to OM.   Let
the chord have a length $2y$; then $r^2 = y^2 + (r - s)^2$,
or $y^2 = 2rs - s^2$.   For chords that are short in
comparison with the radius, s^2 will be negligibly
small with respect to $2rs$, and consequently the length of the sagitta
becomes

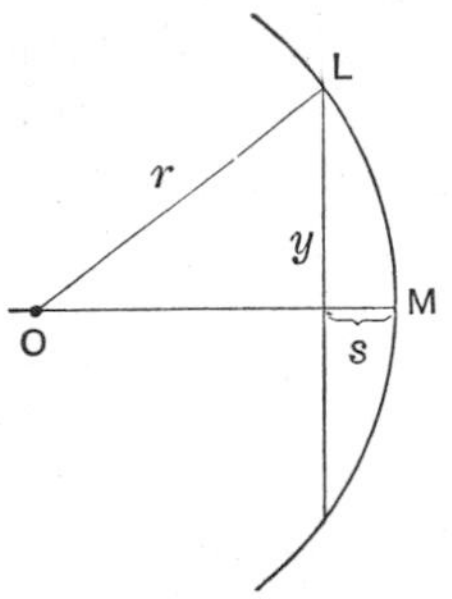

FIG. 410.   Sagitta of
an arc

$$s = \frac{y^2}{2r} \tag{259}$$

This is the desired relation between the radius and semi-chord of an
arc and its sagitta.

In order to derive the relation between the conjugate distances of
a lens and its radii of curvature, a diverging spherical wave front will
be considered to fall upon a thin converging lens and to be brought
to convergence after refraction.   A relationship will be set up between the sagittas of the incident and emergent wave fronts and of
the two surfaces of the lens; this will be stated in terms of equation
(259), and the desired expression will result.

Consider light to issue from a source at P in Fig. 411 on the principal axis PQ of the converging lens, which produces an image of
the source at Q.   The lens has surfaces of radii r_1 and r_2, as shown,
and the distance from its axis to its edge E is represented as y.   Incident and emergent wave fronts, W_1 and W_2, are shown just touching
the lens surfaces at M and N, and the extreme rays PE and EQ are
drawn to the edge of the lens, intersecting these wave fronts at A
and B respectively.

The wave advances from any point on the wave front W_1 to the
corresponding point on W_2 in the same time.   Consequently, at the
edge of the lens the distance AEB (entirely in air) is traversed in the

same time that is required at the center to traverse MN (entirely in the lens of refractive index μ). From the meaning of refractive index, it follows that

$$AE + EB = \mu(MN)$$

Suppose the extreme rays to make small angles with the principal axis, so that points A' and B' on the wave fronts at a distance y from the axis can be substituted for A and B without appreciable error. With this approximation, the lens surfaces and the wave fronts can be represented by arcs having the same semi-chord y. The sagittas

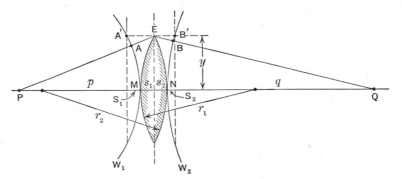

FIG. 411. Determining relation between conjugate distances and surface curvature of a lens

of these arcs are marked in the figure as s_1 and s_2 for the lens surfaces, and S_1 and S_2 for the wave fronts. With these substitutions the foregoing equation becomes $A'E + EB' = \mu(MN)$, or

$$S_1 + s_1 + s_2 + S_2 = \mu(s_1 + s_2)$$

whence

$$S_1 + S_2 = (\mu - 1)(s_1 + s_2)$$

Each of the sagittas may be expressed in terms of the semi-chord and radius in accordance with equation (259), giving

$$\frac{y^2}{2p} + \frac{y^2}{2q} = (\mu - 1)\left(\frac{y^2}{2r_1} + \frac{y^2}{2r_2}\right)$$

where $p = PM$ is the object distance, $q = NQ$ is the image distance, and r_1 and r_2 are the radii of the left and right lens surfaces as shown in the figure. Finally, each term is divided by $y^2/2$, and the relation between the conjugate distances becomes

$$\frac{1}{p} + \frac{1}{q} = (\mu - 1)\left(\frac{1}{r_1} + \frac{1}{r_2}\right) \tag{260}$$

When the object distance is infinitely great, the image will be at the focus; this means that $q = f$ when $p = \infty$, and equation (260) becomes

$$\frac{1}{f} = (\mu - 1)\left(\frac{1}{r_1} + \frac{1}{r_2}\right) \tag{261}$$

Equations (260) and (261) are the fundamental equations for lenses and apply to all forms of thin lenses, but for correctness the distances p, q and f should be such that the rays to the rim of the lens will subtend small angles at both object and image.

Opticians express the focal power of spectacle lenses in terms of a unit called the *diopter*. A lens having a power of 1 diopter has a focal length of 1 meter. The focal power of a lens is the reciprocal of its focal length f measured in meters; thus, the power in diopters becomes $D = 1/f$. Consequently, the shorter the focal length of a lens the greater will be its focal power.

426. Image Constructions.—It is frequently desired to verify the solution of a lens problem by constructing graphically the image which the lens produces of a given object. Such construction requires a knowledge of the focal length of the lens, and this may be procured by applying equation (261) if the radii of the lens and its refractive index are known.

The procedure is illustrated in Fig. 412, wherein a number of rays are shown extending from the head-end of the arrow as object O to various points on the lens and thereafter refracted to a common

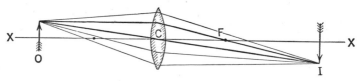

FIG. 412. Rays from object to image

point which forms the image of that object point. The same kind of picture applies to every other point of the object, and the complete result will be the image I. Thus, every portion of the lens contributes its share to the production of each part of the image. A fragment of a broken lens, with portions of its refracting surfaces in good condition, will produce a clear image, but it will not be as bright as the image that could be produced from the same object with the entire lens, if unbroken.

Only two rays are necessary to locate a point of an image, and it is natural to choose the two that can be drawn most conveniently. These are shown in heavier lines than the others in Fig. 412. One is drawn from the head-end of the object parallel to the principal axis XX as far as the lens, and thereafter through the principal focus F, as in § 424. The other is drawn from the same point of the object straight through the center C of the lens; it is undeviated because planes tangent to the lens surfaces where this ray meets them are parallel and the lens merely acts as a parallel-sided slab of glass. The intersection of these lines (or their prolongations backward) locates the image of the head-end of the object.

The procedure is the same whatever may be the shape of the lens and the location of the object. For converging lenses the focal point on the side of the lens opposite the object is used, while for

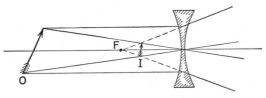

Fig. 413. Image construction for diverging lens

diverging lenses the focal point on the same side is used. If the construction is carried out for both ends of a straight object, the entire image can be definitely located with four rays. Fig. 413 illustrates the image construction for an object inclined to the axis of a diverging lens. The horizontal rays from the object O appear after refraction to come from F, but they do not actually do so; in consequence the image I is virtual.

427. Application of Lens Formula.—The relation between the conjugate distances, the focal length, and the surface curvatures of a lens, as expressed by equations (258), (260) and (261), applies to all types of thin lenses, provided correct signs are chosen for the various quantities involved. The combined equation and the rules governing the choice of signs are as follows:

$$\frac{1}{p} + \frac{1}{q} = \frac{1}{f} = (\mu - 1)\left(\frac{1}{r_1} + \frac{1}{r_2}\right)$$

Focal length (f) is taken *positive* for *converging* lenses and *negative* for *diverging* lenses. Radius (r_1 or r_2) is taken *positive* for *convex* surfaces and *negative* for *concave* surfaces. Object distance (p) or image distance (q) is *positive* when object or image is *real*, and is *negative* when object or image is *virtual*. The significance of a virtual object is mentioned in § 429.

The following examples illustrate the application of these rules in locating the image I of an object O formed by a lens having its foci at F, F as shown in Fig. 414.

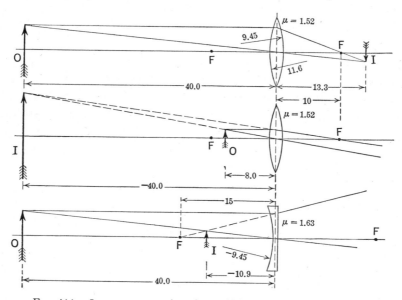

FIG. 414.   Image constructions for verifying numerical illustrations

I. A double-convex lens of crown glass has radii of 11.6 and 9.45 cm., and a refractive index of 1.52.   Calculate the focal length and determine where images will be located when the object is first 40 cm. and then 8 cm. from the lens.   Since $r_1 = 11.6$ cm., $r_2 = 9.45$ cm., and $\mu - 1 = 0.52$, it follows that

$$\frac{1}{f} = 0.52 \left(\frac{1}{11.6} + \frac{1}{9.45} \right) = 0.100;$$

whence $f = 10.0$ cm.   For an object distance $p = 40$ cm., $\dfrac{1}{40} + \dfrac{1}{q} = \dfrac{1}{10}$, and the image distance will be $q = 13.3$ cm.   Similarly, when $p = 8.0$ cm., the value of q will be -40.0 cm.   The first of the images is real, and the second is virtual.   The graphical constructions are shown to scale at the top and center of Fig. 414; rays are drawn only from the upper end of the object to avoid confusion.

II. A plano-concave lens of flint glass has a radius of 9.45 cm. and a refractive index of 1.63.   Determine its focal length, and the location of the image of an object placed 40 cm. from it. Here $r_1 = -9.45$ cm., $r_2 = \infty$, and $\mu - 1 = 0.63$; it follows that $f = -9.45/0.63 = -15.0$ cm. Further, for an object distance $p = 40$ cm., $\dfrac{1}{q} = \dfrac{1}{-15} - \dfrac{1}{40}$ and, therefore, the image distance will be $q = -10.9$ cm. The construction of this virtual image appears at the bottom in Fig. 414.

In both illustrations, computation will show that the same results are obtained if the lens is turned to present its other face to the object; this is true for all thin lenses. The diagrams indicate whether the images are erect or inverted.

428. Magnification.—The image produced by a lens may be made any size desired if there is freedom of choice in the object and image distances. The diagrams of Fig. 414 indicate that when the object is nearer the lens than its image, the image will be larger than the object, and vice versa. The magnification produced by the lens is the ratio of image size to object size. When these sizes are equal, the magnification is unity.

Fig. 415 shows two locations of a lens between object and screen. In position L_1, the lens produces an image $A'B'$ that is larger than the object AB, while in position L_2, it produces a reduced image $A''B''$. To gain clarity, only the rays through the lens centers are

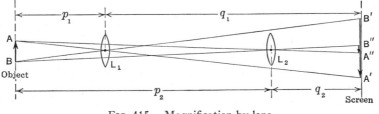

Fig. 415. Magnification by lens

shown in the figure. The two triangles formed at the center of the lens by the object and its image in either position are similar, consequently the ratio of image size to object size is the same as the ratio of image distance to object distance. Thus, the magnifications for the two lens positions become

$$M_1 = \frac{A'B'}{AB} = \frac{q_1}{p_1} \quad \text{or} \quad M_2 = \frac{A''B''}{AB} = \frac{q_2}{p_2} \tag{262}$$

The magnification produced by a lens of focal length f can also be expressed as the ratio $(q - f)/f$ by merging equations (258) and (262).

429. Lens Combinations.—Often the image formed by one lens serves as the object for another. The computation or construction for the location and size of the final image is carried out for the first lens and then for the second, as described previously. If the rays from the first lens to the image are intercepted by the second lens, that image then serves as a *virtual object* for the second lens; in the calculation for the final image the object distance for the second lens is regarded as negative.

To illustrate, consider an object placed 15 cm. in front of a converging lens having a focal length of 10 cm., and suppose that the rays to the image are intercepted by a second converging lens having a focal length of 8 cm. located 14 cm. from the first lens. Fig. 416 shows the image constructions

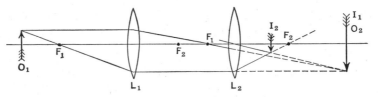

FIG. 416.   Construction of image formed by two lenses

to scale. An image I_1 is formed of object O_1 by lens L_1; the foci being located at points F_1. Since the focal distance $f_1 = 10$ cm., and the object distance $p_1 = 15$ cm., an application of equation (258) shows that the image distance $q_1 = 30$ cm. The image serves as a virtual object O_2 for lens L_2, which has its foci located at points F_2. The object distance $p_2 = -(30 - 14) = -16$ cm., and the focal distance $f_2 = 8$ cm., hence a second application of the lens equation yields $\dfrac{1}{8} = \dfrac{1}{-16} + \dfrac{1}{q_2}$; from which the image is found to be located at a distance $q_2 = \frac{16}{3} = 5.3$ cm. to the right of lens L_2.

The construction lines for the graphical determination of the image I_2 are shown in the figure only for the head-end of the object. The intermediate image I_1 is found by two rays from the tip of the object O_1; one of these is parallel to the principal axis and passes through F_1 on the farther side of the lens, and the other passes through the nearer focus F_1 and is parallel to the principal axis after passing through lens L_1. The latter ray will converge upon F_2 after passing through the second lens. It will be observed that a ray is shown passing from the center of lens L_2 to the tip of the image I_1; this ray is unchanged by the introduction of the lens and serves to locate the final image I_2.

When two lenses are in contact, they may be regarded as a single lens of appropriate focal length. Let f_1 and f_2 be the focal lengths of the component thin lenses, and let the object distance be p as before. The first image will be located at a distance q_1 from the lenses, so that $\dfrac{1}{p} + \dfrac{1}{q_1} = \dfrac{1}{f_1}$. This image will serve as a virtual object for the other lens at a distance $-q_1$ from it, and the final image will be located at a distance q from the lenses, so that $\dfrac{1}{-q_1} + \dfrac{1}{q} = \dfrac{1}{f_2}$.

Add these equations, and take $\dfrac{1}{p} + \dfrac{1}{q} = \dfrac{1}{f}$ for the equivalent single lens, and it will follow that

$$\frac{1}{f} = \frac{1}{f_1} + \frac{1}{f_2} \tag{263}$$

where f is the focal length of the equivalent lens formed of two lenses that have focal lengths of f_1 and f_2 and are placed close together. This equation applies only to lenses that are in actual contact. It is sometimes used where lenses are close but not touching, as, for example, a spectacle lens used in conjunction with the lens of the eye. In such instances the results should be regarded as approximate.

The foregoing equation can be expressed in simple form when each term is expressed in diopters, for then it can be said that the focal power of a combination of two lenses is equal to the sum of the focal powers of its components. Thus, a converging lens of $+5$ diopters combined with a diverging one of -2 diopters results in an equivalent converging lens having a power of $+3$ diopters.

430. Spherical and Chromatic Aberration.—Rays of light parallel to the principal axis of a lens that pass through zones near its rim are

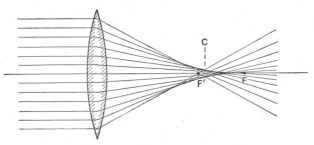

Fig. 417. Spherical aberration of a lens

not brought to a focus at exactly the same point as those that pass through the center of the lens. This imperfection, called *spherical aberration*, is not due to inaccuracies in the spherical surfaces of the lens. The effect with a converging lens is exaggerated in Fig. 417.

The parallel rays from a distant source intersect at various points along the principal axis from F to F'. If a screen is placed at these points a blurred image of the source will be obtained, and a position can be found for the screen where the least blurring will occur. The figure shows this position to be at C; the rays there constitute a *circle of least confusion*. The amount of spherical aberration produced by a lens is usually measured by the axial distance FF' between the intersections of the central and marginal rays.

In the design of lenses, spherical aberration can be reduced by a proper choice of radii for the surfaces. The minimum will be attained when, for a given ray, the deviation is the same at both refracting surfaces. It can be shown that a lens of refractive index μ will have minimum aberration for parallel incident light when the surface radii are in the proportion:

$$\frac{r_1}{r_2} = \frac{\mu + 4 - 2\mu^2}{\mu + 2\mu^2} \tag{264}$$

In a good photographic lens this aberration is less than $\frac{1}{2}$ per cent of its focal length. A plano-convex lens when used with the light incident upon the curved face gives relatively little spherical aberration.

So far in this chapter, no mention has been made of the influence of the color of light upon the action of a lens. Since the refractive index is greater for the violet end of the spectrum than for the red end, it follows from equation (261), namely

$$\frac{1}{f} = (\mu - 1)\left(\frac{1}{r_1} + \frac{1}{r_2}\right)$$

that the focal length of a lens will be less for violet light than for red. Fig. 418 shows a beam of white light incident upon a converging lens;

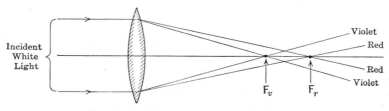

Incident White Light

Violet
Red
Red
Violet

F_v F_r

FIG. 418.   Chromatic aberration of a lens

every pencil of the beam will be dispersed in the same manner as the two shown, and the collective effect will be the convergence of the several colors along individual points on the principal axis from the focus of violet light at F_v to the focus of red light at F_r. The color distribution can be observed by moving a screen along the axis; at F_v a concentric color pattern will be observed with violet at the center, and at F_r red will be at the center. This dispersive effect produced by a lens is called *chromatic aberration*.

*431. Achromatic Lenses.—In designing lenses to avoid dispersion, it is necessary to combine two (or more) lenses so that the dispersion produced by one will be annulled by the other. Such a combination, called an *achromatic lens*, employs lenses placed in contact and made of substances having different dispersive powers. The principle employed in the design of an achromatic doublet will be explained for a converging component lens of crown glass and a diverging component of flint glass.

Equation (261) can be applied to either lens using light of any color. If violet and red are the extreme colors for which the doublet is to be achromatized, and yellow is taken as the central color of the spectrum for specifying the focal length of either lens, the reciprocals of the focal lengths of the crown-glass lens will be

$$\frac{1}{f_{vC}} = (\mu_{vC} - 1)\left(\frac{1}{r_1} + \frac{1}{r_2}\right) \qquad \frac{1}{f_{rC}} = (\mu_{rC} - 1)\left(\frac{1}{r_1} + \frac{1}{r_2}\right)$$

and

$$\frac{1}{f_C} = (\mu_{yC} - 1)\left(\frac{1}{r_1} + \frac{1}{r_2}\right)$$

The second parenthesis is eliminated from these expressions, yielding

$$\frac{1}{f_{vC}} = \frac{\mu_{vC} - 1}{f_C(\mu_{yC} - 1)} \qquad \frac{1}{f_{rC}} = \frac{\mu_{rC} - 1}{f_C(\mu_{yC} - 1)}$$

Similarly, for the flint-glass lens

$$\frac{1}{f_{vF}} = \frac{\mu_{vF} - 1}{f_F(\mu_{yF} - 1)} \qquad \frac{1}{f_{rF}} = \frac{\mu_{rF} - 1}{f_F(\mu_{yF} - 1)}$$

When the two lenses are placed together, the focal length of the doublet can be ascertained by applying equation (263) for each color. For violet, the focal length is f_v such that

$$\frac{1}{f_v} = \frac{1}{f_{vC}} + \frac{1}{f_{vF}}$$

For red, the focal length is f_r such that

$$\frac{1}{f_r} = \frac{1}{f_{rC}} + \frac{1}{f_{rF}}$$

To achromatize over this color range, the focal lengths f_v and f_r of the doublet should be equal; consequently

$$\frac{1}{f_{vC}} + \frac{1}{f_{vF}} = \frac{1}{f_{rC}} + \frac{1}{f_{rF}}$$

Next, these fractions are replaced by the foregoing values, whence

$$\frac{\mu_{vF} - \mu_{rF}}{f_F(\mu_{yF} - 1)} = -\frac{\mu_{vC} - \mu_{rC}}{f_C(\mu_{yC} - 1)}$$

an expression which reduces to

$$\frac{\delta_F}{f_F} = -\frac{\delta_C}{f_C} \qquad\qquad (265)$$

where δ_F and δ_C are the dispersive powers of flint and crown glass respectively, § 411.   This is the condition for achromatism.

Equations (263) and (265) enable one to specify the focal lengths of the component lenses of an achromatic doublet that shall have a particular focal length, provided the dispersive powers of the lens substances are known.

Suppose an achromatic lens of 30.0-cm. focal length is to be made of two lenses of crown and flint glass, for which the dispersive powers are taken as 0.018 and 0.027 respectively.   The component focal lengths must be such that

$$\frac{f_F}{f_C} = -\frac{0.027}{0.018} = -1.50$$

also, from equation (263), when the two component lenses are in contact,

$$\frac{1}{30.0} = \frac{1}{f_F} + \frac{1}{f_C}$$

These equations solved simultaneously yield the following values: $f_C = 10.0$ cm. and $f_F = -15.0$ cm.

These relations hold for the two lenses mentioned in § 427; consequently these could be combined to form an achromatic lens.

It is possible to make an achromatic lens of two components that have the same dispersive power.   This is done by using lenses of the same kind of glass and placing them coaxially a distance apart equal to one-half the sum of their focal lengths.   The Huygens eyepiece, Fig. 419, illustrates this construction.   It consists of two plano-convex lenses, one having a focal length about three times that of the other, with both plane faces directed toward the eye. The lens nearer the eye, called the *eye lens*, has the shorter focal length, and the other, called the *field lens*, is twice that distance from the eye lens. At the field lens the violet light is deviated more than the red, as shown by the rays marked *v* and *r* in the fig-ure, but the eye lens receives the first of these rays at a point nearer the center and for this reason deviates it less than the other. With lenses of correct proportions and spacing the total deviation can be made the same for both colors, rendering the eyepiece achromatic.

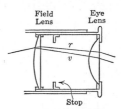

FIG. 419. Section of a Huygens eyepiece

*432. Astigmatism.—In addition to spherical and chromatic aberration, there are several other defects of a spherical lens which cause indistinctness in the image. An important one of these is called *astigmatism*; rays of light that pass through the lens obliquely from an object point remote from the principal axis do not converge upon a common image point.

Fig. 420 shows side and top views in part I of several rays from the upper end of a long slender object *O* in their passage through a con-verging lens. Viewed from the side, the rays converge upon A_1, and

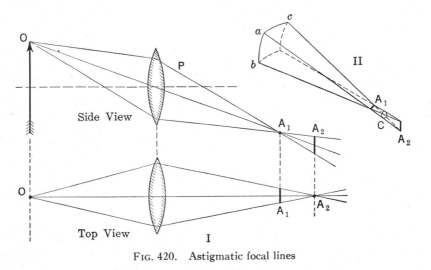

FIG. 420. Astigmatic focal lines

viewed from the top, they converge upon A_2. This shows that the emergent wave front possesses different curvatures in the two planes of view, the curvature in the vertical plane (side view) being the greater. Part II of the figure gives a perspective view of a pencil of the beam around ray P. It shows that the rays in vertical planes such as ab intersect at points along a line at A_1, while those in horizontal planes such as ac intersect along a line at A_2. These lines, at right angles to each other (see part I), are called *focal lines*. If a screen is placed at either focal line, an elongated patch of light will be observed, but somewhere between the two focal lines, as at C, there will be a patch of light roughly circular in shape. This is the nearest approach to a point image that the lens produces of an astigmatic beam of light. Rays of light that are incident obliquely upon a spherical mirror behave similarly upon reflection.

The amount of astigmatism of a lens or mirror for any object point is indicated by the distance between its focal lines as measured along the middle ray from that point. Astigmatism can be corrected by the use of two lenses with appropriate separation.

*433. Thick Lenses.—The lenses considered thus far were assumed so thin that no appreciable error would be introduced in calculations for focal lengths or conjugate distances by reckoning these quantities

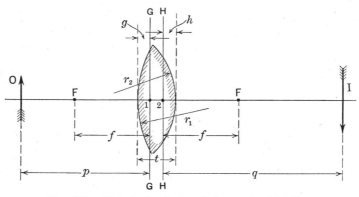

Fig. 421. Principal points and planes of a thick lens

to either lens surface. For lenses that have thicknesses comparable to their focal lengths such calculations may also be made by the usual equations if, instead of reckoning distances to the lens surface, the distances extend to two definite points that can be located easily. For the usual case where the rays enter a lens from some medium and reenter the same medium upon emergence, these points are called the *principal points* of the lens. They are shown at 1 and 2 in Fig. 421, located within a double convex lens of thickness t; and lines G and H drawn through these points perpendicular to the principal axis represent the *principal planes*.

The figure shows that object and image distances, p and q, extend respectively from O and I to the nearer principal point. The focal distance f, from either of these points to the principal focus F, is called the *equivalent focal length* of the lens. When p, q and f are measured in this way, equation (258), namely $\dfrac{1}{p} + \dfrac{1}{q} = \dfrac{1}{f}$, applies also to thick lenses. Equation (261) can be modified so that the equivalent focal length of a thick lens may be computed from its dimensions. For this purpose the equation proves to be

$$\frac{1}{f} = (\mu - 1) \left(\frac{1}{r_1} + \frac{1}{r_2} - \frac{(\mu - 1)t}{\mu r_1 r_2} \right) \qquad (266)$$

which reduces to the simpler form when $t = 0$.

The distance of a principal point from its associated lens surface depends upon the thickness of the lens, its refractive index, and both radii of curvature. An extended analysis shows that this distance for the left surface of the lens of Fig. 421 is

$$g = \frac{r_1 t}{\mu(r_1 + r_2) - t(\mu - 1)}$$

where r_1 is the radius of that surface, r_2 is the radius of the other surface, and t is the axial thickness of the lens. The corresponding distance h for the right surface of the lens is given by the same equation except that r_1 and r_2 are interchanged. If g and h are positive quantities, they are measured inward (as in the figure), and when negative they are measured outward.

To illustrate finding the positions of the principal points of a thick lens, consider a plano-convex lens, 1.0 cm. thick at its middle point, to have a radius of 10 cm. and a refractive index of 1.5. The foregoing equation gives the following distances for g and h when $r_1 = \infty$ and $r_2 = 10$:

$$g = \frac{t}{\mu + \mu \dfrac{r_2}{r_1} - \dfrac{t}{r_1}(\mu - 1)} = \frac{1.0}{1.5} = 0.67$$

and

$$h = \frac{t}{\mu + \infty - \dfrac{t}{10}(\mu - 1)} = 0$$

Consequently, one principal point is within the lens 0.67 cm. from the plane surface, and the other is on the curved surface. The same will be true for a diverging lens of the same thickness, radii, and refractive index.

The procedure in constructing graphically the image produced by a thick lens is illustrated in Fig. 422. A ray from the head-end of object O is drawn to the first principal point, 1, and upon emergence is continued in a parallel direction from the other principal point, 2.

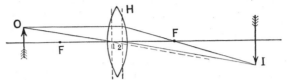

Fig. 422. Construction of rays for thick lens

The other ray is drawn parallel to the principal axis as far as the second principal plane, H, where it is shown refracted to pass through the focus F. The intersection of these rays at I locates the head-end of the image. This construction assumes the same medium on both sides of the lens.

PROBLEMS

1. An illuminated lamp is 12 ft. from a screen, and a converging lens is placed between them with its axis directed toward the lamp. When the lens is 7.5 ft. from the screen it produces an image of the lamp on the screen. If this lens is used to produce an image of a distant steeple upon a screen, how far from the screen should the lens be placed?

2. A reading glass converges the sun's rays at a point 8 in. from the lens. If this lens is placed 6 ft. from an illuminated lamp, how far behind the lens should a screen be placed to receive the image of the lamp?

3. A thin plano-convex lens of flint glass has a focal length of 25 cm. and the radius of its curved surface is 16 cm. From these data determine the refractive index of the glass of which the lens is made.

4. If the lens described in Problem 3 was ground from a glass disk 4 cm. in diameter, what is the thickness of the lens at its center?

5. Light from glowing hydrogen vapor passes through a prism, falls normally on a converging lens, and continues to a photographic plate, where it produces a photograph of the spectral lines. The C line is sharply focused at a place on the plate which is 12 in. from the lens; how far should the plate be from the lens at the F line in order that it also may be sharply focused? Assume that the lens is of flint glass having refractive indices as tabulated in § 410, and that the beam incident upon it is practically parallel.

6. A thin double-concave lens is to be constructed of glass having a refractive index of 1.65 for light of a particular wavelength, and its focal points are to be 10 cm. from the lens. If the surfaces are to have equal curvature, what should their radii be?

7. An object is placed at the following distances in front of a converging lens of 30-cm. focal length: ∞, 60, 45, 30, 20, and 10 cm. Determine analyti-

cally the corresponding image locations, and plot a graph showing the relation between object distances as abscissas and image distances as ordinates.

8. Verify the results of Problem 7 for the 45-cm. and 20-cm. object distances with carefully drawn diagrams to scale.

9. Where should an object be placed with reference to a converging lens of 10-cm. focal length in order to produce an image 25 cm. from the lens and on the same side as the object? Verify the result by a diagram drawn carefully to scale.

10. An object is mounted 80 cm. in front of a screen. At what two positions would a thin lens of 15-cm. focal length yield a distinct image of the object on the screen?

11. Sketch the four possible thin lenses that can be formed having surfaces of 10-cm. and 20-cm. radius. What is the focal length of each lens if made of glass of refractive index 1.5?

12. A certain telescope has a converging lens of 20-ft. focal length. Light from a star falls upon the lens along a direction that makes an angle of $\frac{1}{2}°$ with the principal axis. Make a sketch with this angle exaggerated for clearness and show two parallel rays from the star, one through the center of the lens and one through the focus in front of the lens, in order to determine the location of the image. (*a*) How far is the image from the lens, as measured along its axis? and (*b*) how far is the image from that axis?

13. An object is located a distance *a* outside of the principal focus of a converging lens, and the image is a distance *b* outside of the other principal focus of the lens. Show that the focal length of the lens can be expressed as $f = \sqrt{ab}$.

14. A thin plano-convex lens of refractive index 1.60 is placed horizontally with its plane surface uppermost and a beam of parallel light, directed vertically upon it from above, is found to converge at a point 30 cm. from the lens. If now the region below the lens is filled with water, how far from the lens will the beam converge?

15. Where should an object be placed with respect to the lens of Problem 6 in order that the image may be $\frac{1}{4}$ as high as the object? Verify the analytical solution by a carefully drawn diagram to scale.

16. An object is placed 200 cm. from a screen. A converging lens is placed between them and forms an image of the object on the screen when the lens is 160 cm. from the object. Find another position of the lens at which it would also form an image of the object on the screen. How would the second image compare in height with the first one?

17. A tiny object is placed in front of a converging lens of 16-mm. focal length and the position of the lens is adjusted until the image is 19.7 cm. behind the lens. This image, in turn, is examined by a second lens, the position of which is varied until the final image is virtual and at a distance of 25 cm. from the second lens. The latter has a focal length of 27.8 mm. Compute the magnification due to each lens and also the magnification due to the lens combination.

18. Another lens is to be used with that described in Problem 3 and placed in contact with it to yield a combination having a focal power of 3 diopters. Compute the focal length of the supplementary lens.

19. Two converging lenses, each of 15-cm. focal length, are arranged coaxially and an object is placed 60 cm. in front of the first lens. Determine the location of the final image formed by the lens combination, when the second lens is placed behind the first lens a distance of (a) 40 cm., and (b) 30 cm.

20. Place the second lens of Problem 19 a distance of 10 cm. behind the first one, and show a complete graphical construction for the image locations. Check the result analytically.

21. A converging lens is to be ground to have a focal length of 8 in. and to have minimum spherical aberration. If the index of refraction is 1.627, what should be the radii of the lens?

22. A converging crown-glass lens is to be combined with a diverging flint-glass lens in contact with it to form an achromatic combination having a focal length of +12.0 cm. What are the focal lengths of the crown- and flint-glass components, if their dispersive powers are 0.0162 and 0.0276 respectively?

23. An achromatic lens combination of +40-cm. focal length is to be formed by placing a plano-concave crown-glass lens in contact with the lens described in Problem 3. The dispersive power of crown glass is 0.0162 and that of flint glass is 0.0276. If the crown-glass component has a refractive index of 1.52, what should be the radius of its curved surface?

★24. A plano-convex lens of 5-cm. focal length is 0.9 cm. thick at the center and has a refractive index of 1.5. (a) What is the radius of its curved surface? (b) If an object is placed 15 cm. in front of the curved surface of the lens, how far behind its plane surface will the image be?

★25. If the lens of Problem 24 is turned around and the object is placed 15 cm. in front of its plane surface, how far behind the curved surface will the image be?

Optical Instruments   *Chapter XXXVII*

434. Optical Aids to Vision.—When objects are viewed at such close range that the eye, even if exerting its greatest effort, cannot focus sharp images of them upon its retina, or when the objects are so remote that their details are indistinguishable, instruments may be used to magnify the objects so that the eye may view them with maximum comfort and sufficient resolution of detail. Such instruments employ mirrors or lenses of appropriate design and location, and have a variety of forms. They include magnifying glasses and microscopes, astronomical and terrestrial telescopes, transits and levels for surveying, and binocular field and opera glasses, as well as low-power telescopes for such instruments as photometers, sextants, refractometers and spectroscopes, already described. The essential elements of some magnifying instruments and their magnifying powers will be considered in this chapter, while the factors governing their resolving power will be deferred to the next.

435. The Eye.—The human organ of vision consists of the eyeball cushioned in a bony socket, a muscular system for moving it, and lachrymal glands and ducts for moistening its anterior portion. The eyeball comprises a lens system for producing images of objects under observation, a *retina* for the reception of the images and their conversion into nervous impulses, and the *optic nerve* for transmitting these impulses to the brain to produce the sensation of vision.

The eyeball has two coatings outside of the retina, as illustrated in part I of Fig. 423. The outermost is the white fibrous envelope which, because of its toughness, is called the *sclerotic* coat. Its front portion, transparent and more curved than the "white of the eye," is called the *cornea* because of its horny texture. The inner layer or *choroid* is composed of numerous blood vessels which nourish the eye, and pigment cells that shield the retina from stray light. This dark coat extends forward to the colored *iris* diaphragm which, by involuntary muscular control, regulates the amount of light admitted through its circular aperture or *pupil*.

Within the eye is the *crystalline lens* comprising flexible layers of different refractive indices. The chamber in front of the lens contains a watery substance (a weak solution of sodium chloride) called

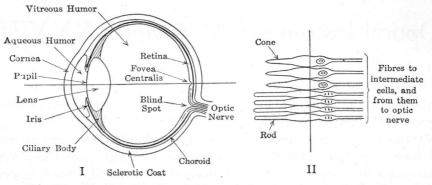

Fig. 423.　Horizontal section of right eyeball and section of retinal surface

the *aqueous humor,* and the chamber in back of it contains a gelatinous substance called the *vitreous humor.* The approximate dimensions and refractive indices of the optical parts of the normal eye are as follows:

Constants of the Eye

	Radius in mm.		Thickness along axis in mm.	Index of refraction
	Front	Back		
Cornea......................	7.8	7.3	0.5	1.351
Lens, for near objects...........	6.0	5.5	4.0	} average
for distant objects............	10.0	6.0	3.6	} 1.437
Aqueous humor, for near objects..			3.2	} 1.337
for distant objects............			3.6	}
Vitreous humor.................		12.0	15.9	1.337

The ability of the eye, not possessed by any other optical instrument, to focus automatically upon objects at different distances from it, is called *accommodation.* This result is accomplished by changing the shape of the lens, chiefly the curvature of its front surface, through the action of the muscles of the *ciliary body.* It is believed that in accommodating for a near object these muscles contract and relax the ligaments around the rim of the lens, thereby allowing the lens to thicken by its own elasticity. With increasing age the faculty of accommodation diminishes. When the eye is focused for parallel rays, that is, upon remotely distant objects, it is said to be unaccommodated.

The end organs of sight on the retina are microscopic elements called *rods* and *cones*, shown greatly enlarged in part II of Fig. 423. At the central point of the retina, the *fovea centralis*, only cones are present, and this is the place of acutest vision. At points more remote from the center the proportion of cones to rods decreases and in the peripheral portions there may be but one cone to ten rods. It is believed that only the cones are responsive to color. No sensation of vision is produced by light which falls upon that part of the retina known as the *blind spot*, where the optic nerve extends through the eyeball.

Experiment shows that the eye is most sensitive to light in the green-yellow region having a wavelength about 5560 Å. If the response at that wavelength is taken as 100 per cent, the response for the same luminous energy at various wavelengths will be substantially as indicated in Fig. 424. Because the eye is so selective, luminous flux is evaluated in terms of the visual effect (§ 383) rather than by energy content. The quickness of perception upon exposure to light and the persistence of vision for a time after its removal are important properties of the eye; the operation of the flicker photometer and motion pictures depends upon these factors. It is well known that the projection of 16 or more images per second in motion pictures produces a continuous impression, each "frame" of the film being held stationary while being projected.

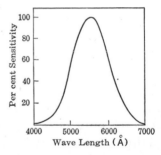

Fig. 424. Relative sensitivity of eye at average illumination

436. Some Defects of Vision and Their Correction.—In considering the passage of light through the cornea, aqueous humor, lens, and vitreous humor to the retina of the eye, the greatest deviation occurs at the front surface of the cornea because this interface separates the two mediums of the lens system that have the greatest difference of refractive index. In the diagrams of Fig. 425, which show beams of light entering the pupils of typical eyes, all the refraction is regarded for simplicity as occurring at this surface.

Diagram I represents an eye which, when entirely relaxed, forms an image of a remotely distant object point upon the retina; it is called a normal or *emmetropic eye*. Nearer object points can be focused upon the retina by making the lens system more converging through accommodation.

Diagram II represents at the left a *myopic eye* that is entirely relaxed; the parallel rays from a remotely distant object point focus in front of the retina, usually because the eyeball is too long. Such

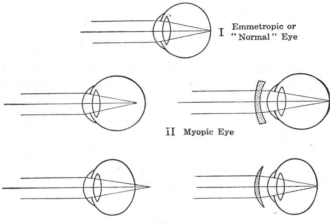

I Emmetropic or "Normal" Eye

II Myopic Eye

III Hypermetropic Eye

Fig. 425. Correction of myopia and hypermetropia by spectacle lenses

an eye cannot focus a distant object without a correcting glass and can see only near objects distinctly. The vision is said to be near-sighted, and a diverging lens is needed to diminish the refracting power of the eye, as shown at the right. The opposite effect is shown in diagram III for the *hypermetropic eye*; a converging spectacle lens is needed to improve vision.

If the lens system of the eye is more converging in one plane than in another, an object point will be imaged along two focal lines as with an astigmatic pencil of light through a lens, § 432. This defect of vision is called astigmatism and is generally due to unequal curvature of the front surface of the cornea. It is corrected by cylindrical lenses so arranged that the convergence produced by eye and spectacle lens together is the same in all planes.

437. The Camera.—A picture of an object can be produced on a photographic plate or film merely by interposing a screen having a tiny aperture. Rays of light from each object point proceed through the aperture in straight lines to a corresponding point on the plate, as illustrated in part I of Fig. 426. This arrangement is termed the *pinhole camera.* If the aperture is made larger to let more light fall upon the plate, a diverging pencil will proceed from each object

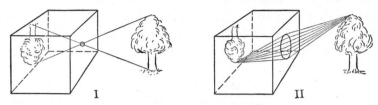

Fig. 426. Action of the photographic camera

point and produce a patch of light upon the plate; these patches will overlap and yield a blurred picture. Thus, brightness of the picture is attained at the expense of definition.

With a lens placed in the aperture, all the rays from each object point through the lens will be brought to a focus upon a corresponding image point, as shown in part II of the figure. The usual photographic camera makes use of this arrangement, and includes facilities for varying the distance between lens and plate to permit focusing objects at different distances, and for regulating the aperture of the lens by stops.

The brightness of the image upon the plate will depend upon the aperture of the lens or objective, that is, upon the diameter of the stop in the diaphragm placed at the lens. This diameter is expressed as a fraction of the focal length of the objective; thus a lens set at $f/8$ is stopped down to a diameter one-eighth of its focal length. If the stop is changed to $f/4$, the aperture will be doubled and four times as much light will reach the plate; the corresponding exposure time will be one-fourth the previous value.

Fig. 427. Anastigmat lens

There are several types of objectives for cameras which are so well corrected for spherical and chromatic aberration, astigmatism and other defects that they give splendid definition and may be used for such exacting service as photo-engraving. Most so-called *anastigmat* lenses are of this type; Fig. 427 shows a section of the well-known Tessar objective formed of four lenses, the two inner ones having lower indices of refraction than the others.

438. Projection Apparatus.—A *projector* for lantern slides or motion picture films consists optically of a *condensing lens* for illuminating the glass slide or film, and a *projection lens* for forming an enlarged image of that object upon the screen. A typical arrangement is illustrated in Fig. 428, wherein the condenser C consists of two plano-convex lenses, and the projection lens P consists of two lenses also, although shown as one for simplicity of ray construction. The lantern slide or film frame O is placed upside down in order that the image I will be erect. In projecting objects that cannot be inverted, such as cells of liquids for demonstrating capillarity and electrolysis,

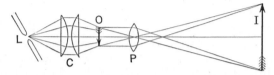

FIG. 428. Optical system of a projector

it is customary to use an erecting prism just beyond the projecting lens. The magnification I/O is the ratio of image distance to object distance, and depends upon the focal length of the projection lens. The source of illumination L may be an incandescent lamp with its filament concentrated in a small flat zone, or an arc lamp operated manually or automatically.

A motion picture projector in an auditorium throws a picture upon a vertical screen distant 100 ft. horizontally from the projection lens, which has a focal length of 4.5 in. = 0.375 ft. To find the magnification produced, it is necessary first to find the object distance for an image distance of 100 ft., by equation (258); thus $\dfrac{1}{p} = \dfrac{1}{f} - \dfrac{1}{q} = \dfrac{1}{0.375} - \dfrac{1}{100} = \dfrac{1}{0.376}$, showing that the film is practically at the principal focus of the lens. The magnification, by equation (262), is $q/p = 100/0.376 = 266$.

Suppose now that the projector is located in a booth directly above its earlier position and is inclined downward 20° from the horizontal. To determine the distortion introduced by this inclination, imagine a slide marked with a circle $\frac{1}{2}$ in. in diameter to be substituted for the film and compute the dimensions of the image that would be produced on the vertical screen. The distance from the lens to the screen is 100 ft. horizontally and is therefore $100/\cos 20° = 106.4$ ft. along the lens axis; consequently the width of the image is $\dfrac{106.4}{0.376} \times \dfrac{1}{2}$ in. = 141.5 in. or 11.79 ft. A rough sketch will suffice to show that because of the projection angle the vertical dimension of the image is increased to approximately $11.79/\cos 20° = 12.55$ ft. Hence the screen image is elongated vertically, its height being greater than its width by about $12.55 - 11.79 = 0.76$ ft. or 9 in. Further distortion will occur if the picture is not viewed directly from the front; its amount for various points of observation can be calculated similarly.

In television, a reflection system devised by B. Schmidt is at present used to enlarge the picture formed on the fluorescent screen of the receiving tube (§ 333). The arrangement is shown in Fig. 429; the picture surface of the cathode-ray tube C is directed downward toward a spherical mirror M, and a flat mirror is used to direct the image upon a vertical screen S. Light from an object point O is collected by the spherical mirror and focused at I on the screen, only the extreme rays being shown. In the process the light passes through a non-spherical ring-shaped lens, usually molded of a transparent plastic material, which corrects for the spherical aberration of the curved mirror. Apertures equivalent to about $f/0.9$ are possible.

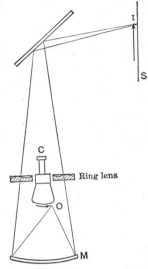

Ring lens

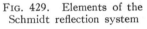

439. The Magnifying Glass.—The extreme rays from an object form an angle at the eye which is called the *visual angle* of that object. This angle determines the *apparent size* of the object. In the upper part of Fig. 430, α is the visual angle subtended by the

Fig. 429. Elements of the Schmidt reflection system

object O at the distance d, and also by the inverted retinal image I. An object twice as long and located twice as far away would have the same visual angle and produce the same retinal image, consequently it would have the same apparent size. As the object is brought nearer to the eye its visual angle and apparent size increases, but a limit is reached by the accommodation of the eye. This limiting distance for the normal eye at middle age is about 10 in. or 25 cm., and is spoken of as the *distance of distinct vision*.

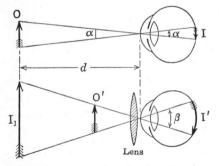

Fig. 430. Increasing visual angle with magnifier

The visual angle of an object can be increased by bringing the object near the eye and interposing a converging lens to yield a virtual image of the object where it can be accommodated easily. The object O at the distance of distinct vision d is moved to position O' in the lower part of the figure, thereby increasing the visual angle from α to β. Assume the lens to produce an image I_1 of O' at the initial distance d; the magnification afforded by the lens will be the ratio of the apparent sizes of the object in the two positions, that is

$$M = \frac{I'}{I} = \frac{\beta}{\alpha} = \frac{I_1/d}{O/d} = \frac{I_1}{O} \tag{267}$$

The converging lens thus acts as a *simple magnifier*, having a magnification that may be expressed either as the ratio of image size I_1 to object size O, or as the ratio of the angles β and α that these sizes subtend at the eye.

The magnification of the magnifying glass can be expressed in terms of its focal length by applying the procedure of §§ 426 and 428. Assume the object O to be located at a distance p from a converging lens of focal length f. With p numerically less than f, a virtual image I_1 will be formed on the same side of the lens at a distance q from it such that

$$\frac{1}{p} = \frac{1}{f} + \frac{1}{q}$$

Consequently the magnification will be

$$M = \frac{I_1}{O} = \frac{q}{p} = q\left(\frac{1}{f} + \frac{1}{q}\right) = \frac{q}{f} + 1$$

For the eye accommodated to the distance of distinct vision, the lens of focal length f cm. will have a magnification of

$$M = \frac{25 \text{ cm.}}{f} + 1 \tag{268}$$

The lens system of the eye can be used as a magnifier to produce an enlarged image of the retina for examination. For this purpose an *ophthalmoscope* is used, consisting essentially of a concave mirror with a hole at the center; the observer reflects light upon the retina and then views it at close range through the hole.

440. The Compound Microscope.—The *microscope* is an instrument for obtaining greater magnification than can be provided by the magnifier. It is generally called a compound microscope because it comprises two lenses or lens systems; the first or *objective* forms a real enlarged image of the object under observation, and the second or *eyepiece* forms an enlarged virtual image of this image just as in the simple magnifier. Fig. 431 illustrates in convenient proportions the construction of images formed by the microscope.

The object O is just outside the principal focus F_o of the objective, and the lens produces a real image of it at I_1. This image falls between the eyepiece and its principal focus F_e, and the eyepiece forms the final image I_2 at the distance of distinct vision.

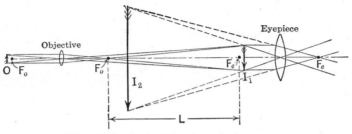

FIG. 431. Optical diagram of microscope

The magnification produced by the objective is commonly stated in terms of the *optical tube length*, which is taken as the distance between the facing focal points of the objective and eyepiece, marked L in the figure; this distance is usually made 18 cm. Since the image I_1 is close to the focal point F_e of the eyepiece, the magnification due to the objective of focal length F can be found as in § 428 to be approximately $M_o = \dfrac{L}{F}$. Also, the magnification produced by the eyepiece of focal length f is given by equation (268) as $M_e = \dfrac{25 \text{ cm.}}{f} + 1$. The total magnification of the microscope is the product of M_o and M_e, or

$$M = \frac{L}{F}\left(\frac{25 \text{ cm.}}{f} + 1\right) \tag{269}$$

Microscope objectives are corrected for spherical and chromatic aberration over the entire aperture; Fig. 432 shows a section of a typical objective having six lenses.

Microscopes are used chiefly in biological, chemical and metallographic investigations. Fig. 433 gives microscopic views of the surface of electrolytic iron formed by powder metallurgical processes with applied pressures of 20,000 lb. per in.[2] The left view shows extreme distortion of particles with little re-

FIG. 432. Typical objective lens system

crystallization, the black areas being oxide or voids; that at the right shows absence of particle boundaries and a completely recrystallized structure.

To secure maximum illumination in high-power microscopes their objectives are designed to use a liquid, such as cedar oil, that has about the same refractive index as glass, between the object and the lowest lens of the objective. This lens is hemispherical like that

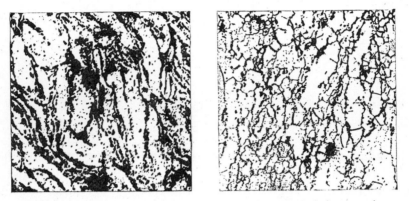

FIG. 433. Photomicrographs of hot-compacted electrolytic iron powder
(*Courtesy of Professor O. H. Henry*)

Magnification	500 diameters	Magnification	1000 diameters
Temperature	500° C.	Temperature	780° C.
Application time	50 sec.	Application time	450 sec.
Tensile strength	26,000 lb/in.^{2}	Tensile strength	53,000 lb/in.^{2}

shown in Fig. 432, but the one above it has its lower surface concave instead of plane. An objective of this type, called an *oil-immersion* objective, permits rays over a wide angle to be collected by the lower lens and to be refracted for normal incidence upon the one above.

High-power microscopes enable an observer to recognize objects down to about 0.0005 mm. in size; smaller particles (to about 0.000005 mm.) can be discerned by scattered light against a dark background, the particles being illuminated by rays that are too oblique to enter the objective. When so used the instrument is called an *ultra micro-scope*. Minute organisms, colloidal particles, and Brownian movements (§ 124) can be rendered visible in this way; the method is also used in the Millikan oil-drop experiment, § 217.

441. Astronomical Telescopes.—The apparent size of a distant object can be magnified by a *refracting telescope*, an instrument which consists of two lenses or lens systems, one the objective and the other the eyepiece. The objective has a long focal length and produces a real image of the object, while the eyepiece has a relatively short focal length and produces a virtual image of the first one for visual inspection.

The optical arrangement is shown in Fig. 434; the dotted lines represent rays from the head-end of the distant object converging

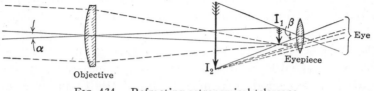

Objective

FIG. 434. Refracting astronomical telescope

upon image I_1 by action of the objective. These rays continue and are deviated by the eyepiece, so that they appear to come from the head-end of image I_2.

The full lines represent the extreme rays from object and image through the lens centers; they will aid in evaluating the magnifying power of the telescope. Without the telescope, the distant object would produce an image on the retina subtended by the visual angle α, and with the telescope the larger retinal image will be subtended by the angle β. Consequently the magnification is $M = \beta/\alpha$. Since image I_1 is located at the principal focus of the objective of focal length F, and since this image is practically at the principal focus of the eyepiece of focal length f, it follows that $\alpha = I_1/F$, and $\beta = I_1/f$; consequently the magnifying power of the telescope is

$$M = \frac{F}{f} \qquad (270)$$

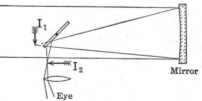

FIG. 435. Reflecting astronomical telescope

The objective of an astronomical telescope is a carefully corrected achromatic lens; the eyepiece is usually a compound one like the Huygens eyepiece.

The *reflecting telescope* has a large mirror for collecting light, and uses lens systems as eyepieces. Fig. 435 shows such a telescope of the Newtonian type, in which a small plane mirror (or a prism) on the axis shifts the real image formed by the concave mirror from position I_1 to position I_2 for the eyepiece to enlarge. In the Cassegrainian type, also widely used, the rays from the objective are doubled back by a convex hyperbolic mirror on the telescope axis and pass through a central hole in the mirror itself to the eyepiece.

Refracting telescopes are in use that have objectives up to 40 in. in diameter; some reflecting telescopes are much larger. The 100-in. telescope at Mount Wilson Observatory in California has a mirror of 42.3 ft. focal length. The largest is a 200-in. mirror at Mount Palomar Observatory, also in California. This mirror was cast of a special Pyrex glass having a coefficient of linear expansion of only 0.00000245 per centigrade degree. It can gather four times as much light as the 100-in. instrument and provide greater resolution of detail; it is expected to penetrate hundreds of millions of light-years into space.

When a telescope is used for making photographic records, the eyepiece is removed and the sensitized plates are located at the place where the images are formed by the objective. The optical arrangement is then the same as in the camera except that the focal length is much greater.

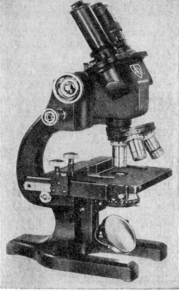

FIG. 436. Binocular microscope (*Courtesy of American Optical Company*)

442. Binocular Vision.—Vision in three dimensions is based primarily upon the fact that both eyes give their impressions simultaneously, each eye viewing the scene from a slightly different angle than the other. The familiar *stereoscope* simulates this effect upon a flat surface. In this device two photographs taken from slightly different positions are viewed at the same time, the arrangement being such that the right eye will see the scene as photographed from the right, and the left eye will see it from the left. As a result the objects in the scene "stand out" in correct perspective, giving so-called depth to the picture.

Numerous optical instruments employ binocular vision. In the *opera glass* the eyepieces are diverging lenses; each is placed so as to intercept the rays to the image that would be formed by the objective, thereby producing an erect virtual image of the object for observation. This construction has the advantage of providing a relatively short tube length for a given magnifying power. Short tube length is secured in the *prismatic field glass* by the use of two total-reflecting prisms (as shown at the right in Fig. 392), which double back the rays twice between the objective and the converging eyepiece and yield an erect image. A *binocular microscope* is illustrated in Fig. 436.

*443. The Electron Microscope.—An entirely new approach to the problem of high magnification has been made by applying the deflecting action of electric and magnetic fields upon charged particles. The experiments of H. Busch in 1926, using cathode rays in fields that were symmetrical axially, showed that such fields could focus a beam of electrons very much as a lens focuses a beam of light. For this reason such symmetrical fields are spoken of as electrostatic and magnetic *electron lenses*, and the subject itself, dealing with the study of such lenses and their application, is termed *electron optics*. Its principles have been utilized in an apparatus styled the electron gun for accelerating electrons to high velocities for experimental purposes, in television apparatus for electronically reproducing distant scenes, and in the electron microscope for achieving tremendous magnification.

The law of refraction has its counterpart in electron optics. An electron that moves in an equipotential region is not acted upon by any forces and naturally its path will be straight, but when it travels from one such region to another which is at a different potential, the path will change abruptly.

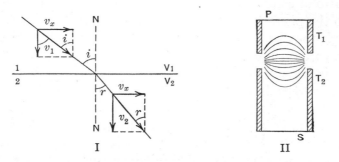

Fig. 437. Electronic refraction and electrostatic electron lens

Consider an electron beam to travel as shown in part I of Fig. 437 from a region of constant potential V_1 to another of value V_2. Suppose the latter region to be more highly positive than the first; then an electron will change its direction toward the normal NN in crossing the potential boundary, because the component of its velocity along the normal will be increased while the component along the separating plane will be unchanged. Let the electron velocities in regions 1 and 2 be designated respectively as v_1 and v_2 and call their unchanged velocity component v_x; then $\sin i = \dfrac{v_x}{v_1}$ and $\sin r = \dfrac{v_x}{v_2}$, where i and r are respectively the angles of incidence and refraction of the electron beam at the plane separating the two equipotential regions. Consequently

$$\frac{\sin i}{\sin r} = \frac{v_2}{v_1}$$

Now, let e represent the charge of an electron and m its mass; then the work done on the electron in crossing the boundary will be

$$e(V_2 - V_1) = \tfrac{1}{2}mv_2{}^2 - \tfrac{1}{2}mv_1{}^2$$

Suppose the work done upon the electron in bringing it initially into the zone of potential V_1 to be $eV_1 = \tfrac{1}{2}mv_1{}^2$; it follows that $eV_2 = \tfrac{1}{2}mv_2{}^2$, and by division $V_2/V_1 = v_2{}^2/v_1{}^2$. This result may be merged with the earlier one to yield

$$\frac{v_2}{v_1} = \sqrt{\frac{V_2}{V_1}} = \frac{\sin i}{\sin r}$$

showing that the ratio of electron velocities in the two regions is proportional to the square root of the potential ratio and to the inverse ratio of sines of the angles the electron beam makes with the normal to the plane separating the potential regions.

Although the abrupt bending of an electron beam as described is analogous to the refraction of light on entering a medium of greater refractive index, in practically all arrangements applying electron optics the potential zones change gradually, and consequently the electron paths shift gently from zone to zone. Thus, part II of Fig. 437 shows a simple arrangement, consisting of two cylindrical tubes T_1 and T_2 charged to different potentials, which is equivalent optically to a converging lens and serves as an electron microscope of low power. The curved lines are sections of symmetrical equipotential surfaces which spread into the tubes, the potential gradient being greatest at the midplane of the gap where these surfaces are closest together. To explain the action, suppose a light image to be projected from above onto the semi-transparent photoelectric surface P, causing it to release electrons from each spot in proportion to the intensity of light incident upon it. The beam of electrons from each spot diverges and reaches the electrostatic lens between the tubes; this converges the beam upon a particular spot on the fluorescent screen S at the lower end. In this way an inverted image may be produced on the screen in a manner analogous to the formation of an image on a photographic film with a camera lens. The magnification can be made quite large and the focusing more precise by placing near the electron emitting surface several anode rings that are charged to appropriate potentials.

Magnetic lenses are more powerful than those of the electrostatic type just described, but their action is more difficult to visualize. An electron slanting into a uniform magnetic field has two component

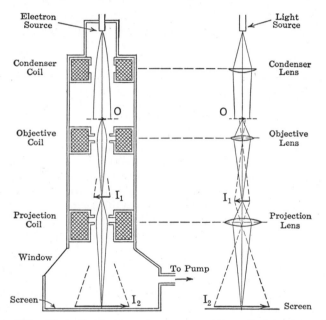

FIG. 438. Magnetic electron microscope and its optical counterpart

motions: the one parallel to the field remains unchanged in direction, while the other crosswise of the field becomes circular, as in the cyclotron, § 275. The combination of these motions causes the electron stream to move along a helical path in such a manner that electrons issuing from a particular object point meet at a corresponding point on a plane to form the image. An electron microscope using magnetic lenses is illustrated in Fig. 438, together with its optical equivalent; the object on a transparent film is shown at O, an intermediate image at I_1, and the final image at I_2. Such an instrument has possibilities of magnifications upwards of 20,000 diameters. The resolving power (§ 450) of any optical instrument is limited by the wavelength of light, and since the equivalent wavelength of an electron (§ 465) is very short, resolution of detail by the electron microscope is very good; in fact, it is much superior to that afforded by the optical microscope.

PROBLEMS

1. Suppose that a near-sighted person cannot see distinctly beyond a distance of 50 cm. from the eye. Apply equations (258) and (263) to determine the focal length in centimeters and focal power in diopters of spectacle lenses to enable this person to see objects at great distances.

2. If a person needs spectacles having a focal power of $+1\frac{1}{2}$ diopters in order to see distinctly an object which is 25 cm. from his eyes, what is the shortest distance at which he could see it distinctly without spectacles?

3. The lens for a certain far-sighted astigmatic eye is to have focal powers of $+\frac{1}{2}$ diopter and $+2\frac{1}{4}$ diopters in mutually perpendicular meridians. The lens is to be ground from glass of refractive index 1.523 and its inner face is to be a spherical concave surface of 16.67 cm. radius. Compute the radii of the outer surface in the two meridians mentioned.

4. The diaphragm for the objective of a small folding camera has four stop positions which provide apertures of the following diameters: 8.9 mm., 6.3 mm., 4.5 mm., and 3.1 mm. Compute the relative exposure times required by these stops, referred to the shortest exposure time as unity.

5. The lens referred to in Problem 4 has a focal length of 12.5 cm. Compute the f-number corresponding to each aperture.

6. It is desired to obtain a 4-in. photograph of a 4-ft. object with a press camera having a lens of $5\frac{1}{4}$-in. focal length. What would be the spacing (*a*) between the lens and the plate, and (*b*) between the lens and the object?

7. The adjustment of a camera is such that when an object 100 ft. away from the lens is photographed the lens is $4\frac{1}{2}$ in. from the film. How far should the lens be moved, and in what direction, in order to photograph an object 10 ft. from the lens?

8. The lens of a camera, adjusted to photograph an object 10 ft. from the objective, has placed next to it a supplementary lens called a portrait attachment. If objects 3 ft. from the lens can then be focused upon the film, what is the focal length of the attachment?

9. In the focal-plane shutter used in many cameras a curtain with a horizontal slit is located directly in front of the film, and is swept rapidly downward during exposure. A picture of a racing car taken with such a camera showed that vertical lines on the car were displaced 15° in the photograph; such distortion is due to the fact that the lower parts were

photographed later than the upper parts. The shutter moved downward 4 in. in 0.032 sec., and the car was 30 ft. from the camera lens of 6-in. focal length. What was the speed of the car?

*10. A combination lens used as a camera objective has six air-glass boundaries. What per cent of the light incident upon the lens will be transmitted through it? Assume normal incidence, neglect loss by absorption, and take the refractive index of glass to be 1.5.

11. A lantern slide is projected upon a screen 30 ft. away from the slide by a projection lens of 8-in. focal length. If the slide is 3 in. wide, how wide will the picture be?

12. A picture taken by a camera is to be projected upon a screen. It is found that the best perspective is obtained when the image on the screen subtends the same angle at the observer's eye that the original scene subtended at the camera lens. Suppose that a photograph 4 in. wide is taken of a distant scene by a camera with a lens of 8-in. focal length and that this picture is projected upon a screen 30 ft. from the projection lens of the projector. In order to provide the desired perspective for observers at the average distance of 20 ft. from the screen, (*a*) how wide should be the picture on the screen, and (*b*) what should be the focal length of the projection lens?

13. An object examined with a jeweler's magnifying glass is held 1 cm. from it and the glass forms a virtual image 25 cm. from the lens. Compute the magnification produced.

14. A certain convex lens yields a magnification of 10 diameters when used as a simple magnifier to produce a virtual image 25 cm. from the lens. What magnification would it yield if it were arranged to produce a real image 25 cm. from the lens?

*15. A spherical glass bulb filled with water acts as a crude magnifier. Consider that the bulb has a diameter of 3 cm. and that the water forms a thick lens. What magnification will it produce when used as a simple magnifier?

16. A compound microscope has an objective lens of 16-mm. focal length and an optical tube length of 18.0 cm.; the eyepiece is used as a simple magnifier and gives a magnification of 10 diameters. The focusing of the instrument is such that the final image is 25 cm. in front of the eyepiece. Compute the total magnification of the microscope, (*a*) approximately, from equation (269), and (*b*) exactly, from the object and image positions.

17. To make a photomicrograph, the position of the microscope eyepiece is changed so that the final image will be real instead of virtual, and this image is recorded on a plate in a light-tight enclosure. Suppose the microscope of Problem 16 to be arranged in this manner and the final image to be 25 cm. behind the eyepiece. Construct an optical diagram of the instrument and compute the total magnification exactly, from the object and image positions.

18. The largest refracting telescope, that at the Yerkes Observatory in Wisconsin, has a diameter of 40 in. and a focal length of 65 ft. Compute its magnification when used with an eyepiece of $1\frac{1}{2}$-in. focal length.

19. All of the light that enters the objective of a telescope is converged by the eyepiece upon a small circle called the "exit pupil." This circle can be determined by finding the image of the objective as formed by the eyepiece. If the focal lengths of objective and eyepiece are respectively 90 cm. and 3 cm., and the instrument is focused for viewing distant objects, (*a*) how far is the exit pupil behind the eyepiece? and (*b*) what is the diameter of the exit pupil if that of the objective is 15 cm.?

20. In the telescope for terrestrial use the image is reinverted by placing a converging lens at twice its focal length behind the image formed by the objective. At an equal distance behind it, this lens forms an erect image which serves as an object for the eyepiece. Suppose such an erecting lens of 10-cm. focal length to be used in the telescope of Problem 19; construct an optical diagram of the instrument and compute the distance between the objective and the eyepiece.

Interference and Diffraction

Chapter XXXVIII

444. Interference of Light.—The wave character of light leads to the consideration of some important interference effects. The superposition of two light waves upon arriving simultaneously at a given point will produce a total illumination that depends upon their wavelengths, amplitudes, and phases. With monochromatic light, waves of equal amplitude will reenforce each other if they arrive in

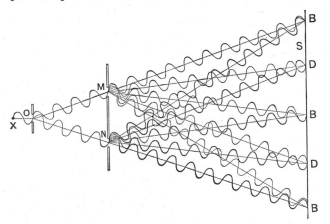

FIG. 439. Reenforcement and annulment of light waves

phase agreement and will annul each other if they arrive in phase opposition. When they annul and produce zero illumination at certain points there will be other points where the illumination is increased, since the total energy of the waves remains unchanged. With white light, in which many colors are blended, the annulment of one color at a particular point still leaves illumination by the other colors.

Interference of light was originally demonstrated and explained by the English physicist, Thomas Young (1773–1829), using an arrangement as shown in Fig. 439. Monochromatic light from a lamp X is directed upon a small opening O in the first shield; this

717

serves as a point source for illuminating two pinholes M and N in the second shield. From these apertures waves spread out in all directions, a few of which are indicated in the plane of the apertures. Waves leaving M and N in phase agreement and proceeding to the screen S reenforce each other and produce brightness at certain places BBB, and annul each other and produce darkness at other places DD. *Reenforcement occurs where the two waves arrive at the screen in phase agreement*, both waves having traveled the same distance or either having traveled one or more complete wavelengths farther than the other. *Annulment occurs where the two waves arrive at the screen in phase opposition*, one wave having traveled an odd number of half wavelengths farther than the other. There results on the screen an interference pattern of lines, called *fringes*, which are alternately bright and dark. The figure shows a sectional view of only the zone containing the interference pattern; this region is very small and is greatly exaggerated for clearness.

The factors which determine the spacing between fringes will be investigated with the aid of Fig. 440, which represents a sectional view of two parallel-sided slits M and N separated by a distance s,

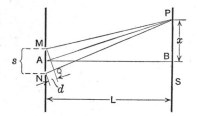

FIG. 440.   Interference produced by two slits

and a screen S which is distant L from the plane of the slits. The line AB is drawn perpendicular to the screen from A, midway between the slits; and rays are shown from the apertures to a point P on the screen at a distance x from point B. Light waves issuing from the slits travel different distances in reaching P. By drawing MQ so as to make $QP = MP$, the difference in path may be expressed as $d = NQ$. A line connecting points P and A will be perpendicular to MQ, and hence the angles NMQ and PAB will be equal. Since these angles are small, d/s, which is approximately the sine of one angle, may be equated to x/L, which is the tangent of the other, giving the simple relation

$$\frac{d}{s} = \frac{x}{L} \tag{271}$$

Let λ represent the wavelength of the light; then the condition for reenforcement or annulment at P may be expressed as $d = \dfrac{n\lambda}{2}$, reenforcement occurring when $n = 0, 2, 4, \cdots$ and annulment occurring when $n = 1, 3, 5 \cdots$. With this value for d in equation (271) a rearrangement of terms gives the expression

$$x = \frac{n\lambda L}{2s} \tag{272}$$

which shows that the spacing of the fringes varies directly as the wavelength λ and the screen distance L, and varies inversely as the distance s between the slits. That the distance between fringes is very small will be evident from a numerical illustration.

Suppose that green light from a mercury vapor lamp ($\lambda = 0.00005461$ cm.) is directed upon two slits 0.1 cm. apart and that the screen is 100 cm. away. The first dark line from the center will be found at a distance of $x = \dfrac{5461 \times 10^{-8} \times 100}{2 \times 0.1} = 0.0273$ cm., the first bright line at 0.0546 cm., the second dark line at 0.0819 cm., and so on.

When white light is used instead of monochromatic light, each color produces its own interference fringes, those for red light being spaced about twice as far apart as those for violet light, and the resulting pattern is due to the combined effect of all colors. Such brilliantly colored designs may also be observed by looking at a distant white-light source through a piece of silk or a fine-mesh screen, the meshes acting as closely spaced sources.

In order to show the interference effects described, the phase relation of the waves must remain unchanged where they emerge from

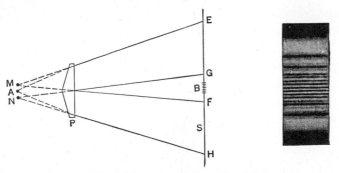

Fig. 441. Fringes produced with a biprism

the slits, and *this requires that the slits receive light from the same point of the source.* Several methods have been devised for accomplishing this result conveniently. In one of these, the pair of apertures is replaced by a thin prism having an angle of almost 180° and known as a *biprism*. Such a prism, shown at P in Fig. 441, refracts the light from a narrow slit A so that it appears to come from two virtual sources M and N. The screen S is illuminated by source M over the region EF and by source N over the region GH. The interference fringes occur near B, at the center of the overlapping region GF; these may be observed with a low-power telescope. They are more distinct than with Young's arrangement because of the greater intensity of the sources M and N.

The photograph at the right shows the interference fringes produced by parallel white light through a biprism. The broader shadings at top and bottom are diffraction bands, § 448.

445. Thin Films.—Colors are frequently observed in films such as soap bubbles, thin layers of oil or water, and coatings of oxide on heated metal. Such films are usually observed by reflection, and the

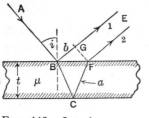

FIG. 442. Interference at thin film

colors are due to interference of light waves reflected at the front and back surfaces. Fig. 442 represents a film of refractive index μ, illuminated by a beam of monochromatic light impinging upon the surface in the direction A. An eye at E receives light reflected partly at B (ray 1) and partly at C (ray 2). In order to compare the optical paths of these rays a line FG is drawn perpendicular to the direction in which they approach the eye. It is seen that the only differences in path occur between the point B and the line FG, and that the second ray travels farther than the first by an amount $2a - b$, where a represents the distance BC or CF and b represents the distance BG. The distance $2a$ within the film is equivalent to an air distance of $2\mu a$, and hence the equivalent light path of ray 2 exceeds that of ray 1 by the amount $2\mu a - b$. For normal incidence, the distance a is the same as the thickness t of the film and the distance b becomes zero, whence the optical path difference is $2\mu t$; in the general case it can be shown to be $2t\sqrt{\mu^2 - \sin^2 i}$, where i is the angle of incidence.

It might be expected that as the film thickness t approaches zero, the two rays would come into phase and reenforce each other, since their optical paths would then approach equality. It is found by experiments with soap bubbles, however, that a black spot appears where the film becomes so thin that it is about to rupture, showing that destructive interference of light rather than reenforcement occurs when the film has negligible thickness. To explain this effect it will be recognized that one reflection takes place within a medium (air) of low refractive index at the boundary of a medium (soap film) of high index, and the other reflection takes place within a medium of high index at the boundary of one of low index. Under these circumstances, there is always a *phase displacement of a half wavelength* between the two reflected waves due to reflection, in addition to the phase displacement due to difference in optical path.

In Fig. 442, the retardation of ray 2 with respect to ray 1 for perpendicular incidence amounts to $2\mu t$ because of path difference, and the phase displacement due to reflection is equivalent to a further retardation of a half wavelength or $\lambda/2$. Consequently, the total retardation of ray 2 with respect to ray 1 is

$$\text{Retardation} = 2\mu t + \frac{\lambda}{2} \qquad (273)$$

When the retardation is an odd number of half wavelengths, there will be destructive interference and darkness; when it is an even number of half wavelengths, there will be a maximum reenforcement and brightness. Thus, for the first reenforcement $2\mu t + \lambda/2 = 2\lambda/2$; whence the minimum thickness of film is $t = \lambda/4\mu$.

Under illumination by white light, the thinnest film to show interference color by reflection is that for which $t = \dfrac{\lambda}{2\mu}$ for violet light; this film will have a residual reddish color. Thick films do not appear colored, because so many wavelengths will satisfy the conditions for reenforcement, namely $t = \dfrac{\lambda}{4\mu}, \dfrac{3\lambda}{4\mu}, \dfrac{5\lambda}{4\mu} \cdots$, that the reenforced waves upon merging will produce the effect of white light.

An interesting experiment on the interference produced by films utilizes a plano-convex lens of large radius and an optically flat plate placed together so that a wedge-shaped film of air is formed between them. When the apparatus is illuminated by monochromatic light and examined by reflection, the observer will see an interference pattern which consists of a series of bright and dark rings concentric around the point of contact. This phenomenon was first described by Newton and the rings are called by his name. The effect is due to the interference of light reflected from both surfaces of the air film between the convex and plane surfaces.

As an illustrative problem on Newton's experiment, show that the bright rings in the interference pattern have radii which are proportional to the square roots of the successive odd integers. At the point of contact O of

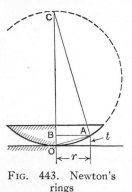

the two glass surfaces, Fig. 443, there will be interference because the air film there has zero thickness and the light waves reflected from its upper and lower boundaries differ in phase by $\lambda/2$, as explained. Reflection which occurs where the film has a thickness $t = \lambda/4$ will result in reenforcement because at these points the light reflected at the lower boundary will be retarded with respect to the other by an amount $\lambda/4 + \lambda/2 + \lambda/4 = \lambda$. Reenforcement will also occur where the thickness is $t = 3\lambda/4,\ 5\lambda/4\ \cdots$, or in general $(2n - 1)\lambda/4$, n being an integer. With the construction lines shown in the figure, the right triangles OAB and ACB are similar, whence $AB:OB = BC:AB$. Let R represent the radius of the lens and r the radius of a bright ring of the interference pattern; it follows that $r:t = (2R - t):r$. Since t is negligibly small compared with $2R$, the radius of the bright ring becomes $r = \sqrt{2Rt} = \sqrt{2R(2n - 1)\lambda/4}$, or

FIG. 443. Newton's rings

$$r \propto \sqrt{2n - 1}$$

where the quantity under the radical represents any odd number.

The interference patterns due to thin films under monochromatic light are used to detect slight surface irregularities in lenses, optical plates, and mirrors.

*446. Non-reflecting Glass.—Lenses and other optical parts are often coated with thin transparent films in order to minimize reflection from the surfaces. The films are designed of such materials and thickness that the light reflected from the film will annul the light reflected from the glass. The two reflected waves should have *equal amplitudes and opposite phase to produce light interference.*

The requirements for meeting the first condition can be determined from equation (251), which gives the intensity of a reflected beam from a boundary surface between two transparent mediums of indices μ_1 and μ_2 when the beams are perpendicular to the surface. It will be remembered that the intensity of a light wave is proportional to the square of its amplitude, and therefore the ratio of the amplitude of the reflected wave to that of the incident wave becomes

$$\frac{A}{A_o} = \frac{\mu_2 - \mu_1}{\mu_2 + \mu_1}$$

Let μ_f and μ_g represent the refractive indices of film and glass respectively; the reflected rays shown in Fig. 444 will have equal amplitudes when

$$\frac{\mu_f - 1}{\mu_f + 1} = \frac{\mu_g - \mu_f}{\mu_g + \mu_f}$$

or

$$\mu_f = \sqrt{\mu_g} \qquad (274)$$

This indicates that the films to be placed on ordinary glass (of index 1.5 to 1.6) should have very low indices of refraction.

The condition for interference of the two reflected rays, with monochromatic incident light of a definite wavelength, requires that the equivalent air thickness of the film should be an odd number of quarter wavelengths, as explained in the previous section. For the minimum thickness t and for a wavelength λ, it follows that

$$\mu_f t = \frac{\lambda}{4}$$

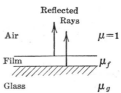

FIG. 444. Annuling reflection of light from glass surface

Ordinary window glass ($\mu_g = 1.52$) can be rendered non-reflecting for yellow light ($\lambda = 0.0000589$ cm.) by placing upon it a film having a refractive index of $\sqrt{1.52} = 1.23$ and a thickness $0.0000589 \div (4 \times 1.23) = 0.000012$ cm. Such thin films can be produced by evaporation, and the index of refraction of the film substance can be lowered to the desired value by decreasing its density through control of the evaporation conditions. Films of the metallic fluorides, such as magnesium fluoride, have been found to stick firmly to the glass and to possess mechanical strength. Glass plates with such films on both sides show very little reflection of white light and they transmit well over 98 per cent of the incident beam. Multilayer films have also been experimented with; they allow a wider choice of film materials and methods of application.

Film coating finds an important application in lenses for cameras, picture projectors, telescopes, and other optical instruments. Most of these are combination lenses having several glass-air surfaces, reflection at which not only reduces the amount of light transmitted but also scatters light over the field of view and thereby lessens the clarity of the image. In addition, so-called ghost images may be caused by internal reflections if there is a bright concentrated light source in front of the lens. Surface coatings on the lenses are largely instrumental in overcoming these objectionable features.

447. The Interferometer.—The *interferometer* makes use of interference in measuring the wavelength of light in terms of a standard of length, or in measuring an unknown length in terms of known wavelengths of light. The essential parts of the instrument devised by Michelson are arranged as in Fig. 445; they comprise two plane mirrors A and B, a glass plate M, of which the upper surface is very

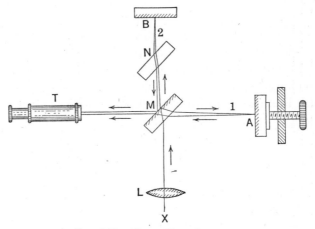

Fig. 445. Plan of interferometer

lightly silvered, and a telescope T. One of the mirrors (A in the figure) is mounted on a fine-pitch screw, and the silvered plate is set at 45° to the axes BX and AT.

Monochromatic light from the source X is formed into a parallel beam by a lens L and projected upon the plate M where it divides into two beams, 1 and 2; these advance to the mirrors A and B respectively and return to M and thence proceed to the telescope. Ray 1 passes through the half-silvered plate M three times, while ray 2 passes through it only once; a second plate N of the same thickness and inclination is introduced to equalize the two paths. If the waves after recombination at M are in phase, the field of the telescope appears bright, and if they are in opposition, the field appears dark.

Suppose that light of wavelength λ is directed upon the half-silvered plate and that the distances to mirrors A and B are such as to cause the field of the telescope to be dark. If the movable mirror is now advanced slowly, a movement of $\lambda/4$ causes a change of path of $\lambda/2$ and the field will appear bright; a further movement of $\lambda/4$

will make it dark again, and so on. An accurate scale is provided for measuring the distance through which this mirror is moved; consequently the wavelength of the incident light can be determined directly from the number of light annulments. Thus, if n successive interferences are observed while the mirror is moved a distance l, the wavelength is found to be

$$\lambda = \frac{2l}{n} \tag{275}$$

On the other hand, if λ is known, the distance l can be measured.

Usually the mirrors are not exactly at right angles to each other, as implied in the foregoing description, but depart slightly from this condition. With this adjustment, the field of the telescope will be crossed by dark interference fringes, separated by bright reenforcement fringes, and the movement of mirror A can be observed by counting the fringes as they sweep past the cross hair of the telescope.

The interferometer can be used to measure extremely small distances, for example, the expansion of crystals under slight temperature changes. Michelson also used this instrument by a doubling process to measure the length of the standard meter in terms of the wavelength of the red line in the cadmium spectrum; this measurement fixes definitely the length of the standard in terms of an unvarying unit. The diameters of a few of the larger stars have been determined by interference methods.

448. Diffraction.—Although it is commonly said that light travels in straight lines, careful observation shows that it bends slightly around the edges of an obstruction. The spreading of a beam of light into the region behind an obstacle is known as *diffraction*. Because of diffraction, a parallel beam of monochromatic light passing through a slit toward a screen will ordinarily produce on it a bright band somewhat wider than the slit, and furthermore this band will be bordered at the edges by a few narrower bands which are alternately dark and bright. This effect can be explained with the aid of Fig. 446, which shows a single slit MN of width s located a distance L from a screen S. The line AB is drawn perpendicular to the screen from the middle of the slit, and P represents any point on the screen distant x from the point B. The line MQ is drawn at right angles to a line connecting A and P to show the difference in path length of the extreme rays NP and MP; this difference NQ is marked d.

If the path difference of the rays from the slit edges is one wave-length of light ($d = \lambda$), P will be a point of darkness rather than brightness. This can be proved by imagining the slit to be composed of a series of much narrower slits extending uniformly from M to N, and investigating their combined effect in producing illumination at the point P. The intensity at P due to the uppermost of these slits can be represented by vector a in part II of the figure; the intensity at the same point due to the next lower slit would be represented by vector b slightly out of phase with a because the light has to travel

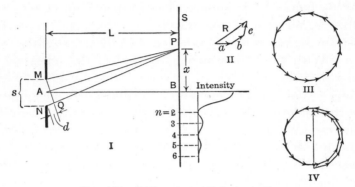

FIG. 446. Diffraction of light by a slit

farther from this slit to reach the point. Similarly, the intensity due to the third slit would be represented by c, and so on. The resultant intensity could be found by placing the individual vectors end to end and drawing the closing line of the figure, as shown at R. If this process were continued from M to N, the extreme vectors would again be in phase, and the resultant of them all would be zero, as shown at III; that is, when $d = \lambda$. This would mark the limit of the central bright band and would show the location of the first dark band above or below the center. Brightness would occur again if the point P were so located that $d = \dfrac{3\lambda}{2}$ (represented at IV in the figure), dark-ness if it were so located that $d = 2\lambda$, and so on. In general, for annulment or reenforcement, the path difference for the extreme rays of the slit will be $d = \dfrac{n\lambda}{2}$; interference occurring for even values of n and reenforcement for the odd values. The locations of the fringes on the screen above and below B are found as in equation (272) to be given by

$$x = \frac{n\lambda L}{2s} \tag{276}$$

annulment occurring when $n = 2, 4, 6 \cdots$ and reenforcement occurring when $n = 3, 5, 7 \cdots$. The diffraction pattern consists of a central band having a width $2x = 2\left(\dfrac{2\lambda L}{2s}\right) = \dfrac{2\lambda L}{s}$, bordered on each side by narrower bands, alternately dark and bright, which become less distinct as the distance from the center is increased. The relative intensities at different points are indicated by the curve in the lower part of the figure. It will be observed that the narrower the slit used, the wider will be the spacing of the bands forming the diffraction pattern. If, however, the width of the slit is reduced to the same order of magnitude as the wavelength of light, it will be apparent from the foregoing construction that no points of annulment will appear on the screen and there will result merely a spreading of light over its surface by diffraction. In Young's experiment, for example, in addition to the interference effects described in § 444, some light will reach all parts of the screen through each slit by diffraction.

The diffraction pattern produced by a circular hole consists of a round patch of light, surrounded by a few rings which are alternately dark and bright. This result may be thought of as a development of that just described. Upon dividing the circle into imaginary strips of equal width it will be apparent that the outermost strips produce little effect because of their small area. Disregarding these outer strips, a circular hole may be considered as equivalent to a slit of reduced width; consequently its diffraction pattern will have a proportionately wider spacing. Mathematical analysis shows that the diffraction bands produced by a round hole of diameter s are spaced 1.22 times as far apart as those for a parallel-sided slit of width s.

449. Diffraction by a Lens.—It has been shown that parallel light passing through a circular hole produces a spot of light somewhat larger than would be indicated by the rectilinear propagation of light. For the same reason, parallel light passing through a lens will produce at the focal plane a small disk of light rather than an ideal point of light such as indicated by the geometrical lens constructions of Chapter XXXVI. It should be observed that this result is not due to any imperfection of the lens but is a consequence of the nature of light itself. The smallness of the disk image determines the ability of the lens to register detail in the object under observation.

Fig. 447 represents a lens of diameter D converging a plane incident wave of wavelength λ upon the principal focus F at a distance AF away; this is the focal length f. By diffraction, the light passing through the lens will spread beyond the region bordered by MF and NF. By analogy with the diffraction at a slit, annulment may be expected at a point such as G, the location of which is determined by rotating the figure MNF to the position MQG, making $NQ = \lambda$. The distance FG will then represent the radius r of the disk image of

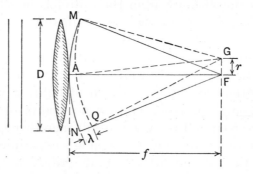

FIG. 447.   Diffraction diagram for lens

an infinitely distant (point) source. The angle between the curves MN and MQ may be taken as equal to that between their radii, and hence, as a close approximation

$$\frac{\lambda}{D} = \frac{r}{f}$$

Because of the correction for the circular shape of the lens, the radius of the disk increases in the ratio 1.22 to 1, consequently the disk image has a diameter

$$d = \frac{2.44f\lambda}{D} \tag{277}$$

and subtends an angle d/f at the lens.

The diffraction pattern produced by a lens of an object point consists of the central bright disk surrounded by alternate dark and bright rings. The registration of minute detail implies a small diffraction pattern, and to accomplish this result, equation (277) indicates that the lens should be of large size compared with its focal length. Aside from the lens constants, the smallness of the disk image involves the wavelength λ and is therefore limited by the wave character of light.

*450. Resolving Power.—The ability of a lens to reveal detail in an image is spoken of as its *resolving power*. If two object points subtend too small an angle at the lens, their image disks will merge and they cannot be resolved. Resolving power is measured by the *smallest angle* between two object points at which these points can be recognized as separate. Users of optical instruments find that they can distinguish two points as separate when their disk images do not overlap by more than the radius of one of the disks. This limit is pictured in Fig. 448, greatly magnified. The angular separation of the object points is clearly the same as that between the disk

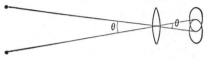

FIG. 448. Overlapping disk images formed by lens

images and, at the limit of resolution, is one-half of the angle subtended by a single disk image at the lens. From the preceding section, this limiting angle of resolution of a lens becomes

$$\theta = \frac{d}{2f} = \frac{1.22\lambda}{D} \qquad (278)$$

The objective lens of the Yerkes telescope has a diameter of about 102 cm.; to illustrate its high resolving power it might be mentioned that with this lens two point sources of light 1 in. apart could be distinguished as separate objects at a distance of over 20 miles.

To verify this statement apply equation (278), in which λ may be taken as 0.00006 cm. for the average wavelength of light; whence the limiting angle of resolution of the lens is $\theta = \dfrac{1.22 \times 0.00006}{102} =$ 7.17×10^{-7} radian or about $\frac{1}{8}$ second of arc. The sources would be separated by 2.54 cm., and this separation would subtend an angle of 7.17×10^{-7} radian at the lens when distant from it by an amount $\dfrac{2.54}{7.17 \times 10^{-7}} = 3.54 \times 10^{6}$ cm. This is equivalent to $\dfrac{3.54 \times 10^{6}}{30.48 \times 5280}$ $= 22.0$ mi.

Two objects 1 in. apart can be resolved by the eye at a distance of about 100 yd., from which the limiting angle of resolution of the eye is found to be about 1 minute of arc. Rays entering the eye with this angular separation fall upon adjacent cones at the central part of the retina.

451. The Diffraction Grating.—The principles of interference and diffraction are applied to the measurement of wavelength in the *diffraction grating*. As constructed for use with transmitted light, the grating is essentially a transparent plate upon which there are a

large number of opaque lines, usually several thousand to the centimeter, all parallel and evenly spaced. A parallel beam of monochromatic light incident upon the grating sets up secondary wavelets
at the slits between the lines, in accordance with Huygens' Principle,
§ 354, and these spread throughout the region beyond the grating.
At points where these wavelets arrive in phase there will be reenforcement and bright lines will result; and where they arrive in opposite phase there will be annulment and the lines will be dark.

In Fig. 449, the arcs in part I show three positions of the wavelets
after advancing distances of λ, 2λ and 3λ beyond the grating, λ being

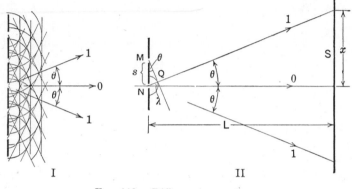

FIG. 449.   Diffracted wave fronts

the wavelength of the incident light. Lines drawn tangent to these
wavelets connect only points which are in phase agreement, and consequently represent wave fronts which advance in the directions of
the arrows. One of these, joining wavelets which have advanced
equal distances, continues along 0 without change of direction. Other
wave fronts, joining wavelets from adjacent slits, one wavelet having
advanced one wavelength farther than the other, are deflected
through rather large angles θ and travel along the directions 1, 1.

Part II of the figure is a plan view showing two of the grating slits,
M and N, separated by a distance s, and a screen S at a distance L
from the grating, toward which the waves advance along the directions indicated. The wavelength λ is the radius of the wavelet at N
and can be evaluated by noting that the angle between the wave
front MQ and the grating is also equal to $θ$, whence

$$\lambda = s \sin \theta = s \frac{x}{\sqrt{L^2 + x^2}} \qquad (279)$$

where x is the distance along the screen from the center bright line to similar lines produced by the diffracted wave fronts along the directions 1, 1. The equation shows that the extent to which a light wave will be diffracted by a grating depends upon the length of the wave and the slit spacing of the grating. The angle of diffraction will be large when the light has a long wavelength (red) and when the slits are close together.

The experimental arrangement of the diffraction grating is represented in Fig. 450. A narrow slit A, illuminated by monochromatic light from the source X, serves as a source, and is placed at the

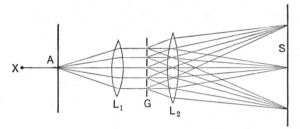

Fig. 450. Formation of images from grating with lens

principal focus of the converging lens L_1, from which a beam of parallel light is directed normally upon the grating G. A second converging lens, L_2, receives the parallel bundles of rays after diffraction and forms images of the illuminated slit upon the screen S, as shown. The upper and lower ones are called the *first order* diffracted images. Images of higher order are formed by wave fronts which join wavelets from adjacent slits, one wavelet having advanced two or more wavelengths farther than the other. With a white light source the central image will be white, but the diffracted images will be continuous spectra because the component colors have different wavelengths and their images on the screen will be spread out. Each diffraction spectrum has the same color sequence as observed with a prism, but the order is reversed, the red light being deflected more than the violet because of its greater wavelength.

Light from magnesium vapor passes through a narrow slit and falls normally upon a diffraction grating that has 5000 lines per cm. The spectrum of magnesium includes three green lines having wavelengths of 5167 Å, 5173 Å, and 5184 Å. Calculate the angular positions of the intermediate of these spectral lines for the various orders as observed on a spectrometer, and also determine the separation of the outer green lines in the second-order spectrum as observed on a straight scale parallel to the grating and distant 80 cm. from it.

The grating space $s = \frac{1}{5000} = 0.0002$ cm. and the angular positions, reckoned from the normal to the grating surface, are found from the following relations: $\sin \theta_1 = \lambda/s = 0.00005173 \times 5000 = 0.2587$ for the first-order spectrum, $\sin \theta_2 = 2\lambda/s = 0.5173$ for the second-order spectrum, and $\sin \theta_3 = 3\lambda/s = 0.7760$ for the third-order spectrum; there are no spectra of higher order under the conditions given because $n\lambda/s$ will be greater than unity for values of n larger than 3. The corresponding angles of diffraction are as follows: $\theta_1 = 15.0°$, $\theta_2 = 31.2°$, and $\theta_3 = 50.9°$.

For the second-order spectrum, $\dfrac{2\lambda}{s} = \dfrac{x}{\sqrt{L^2 + x^2}}$; consequently the departure of the diffracted image from the central one will be $x = \dfrac{2L\lambda}{\sqrt{s^2 - 4\lambda^2}}$.

It follows that the image position for wavelength 0.00005167 cm. will be $\dfrac{2 \times 80 \text{ cm.} \times 0.00005167 \text{ cm.}}{\sqrt{(0.0002)^2 - 4(0.00005167)^2} \text{ cm.}} = 48.28$ cm., and that for wavelength 0.00005184 will be 48.50 cm.; therefore, the separation of these two images in the second-order spectrum becomes 0.22 cm.

Many diffraction gratings operate by reflection rather than by transmission of light. The reflection grating is made by ruling lines with a diamond point on a polished surface, speculum metal (Cu 68%, Sn 32%) often being used for this purpose.

452. Diffraction of X-rays.—To test the wave character of x-rays, the German physicist, Max von Laue, suggested in 1912 that crystals might be used as natural diffraction gratings with such rays, because of the supposedly close and symmetrical spacing of their atoms. The experiment was successful and furnished the key to both the nature of x-rays and the structure of crystals. Today x-ray diffraction techniques provide the experimental means for studying the microstructure of matter in the solid state, and the changes in structure produced by such mechanical processes as hardening, annealing, and rolling of metals.

Fig. 451 shows the effect of directing a narrow beam of x-rays upon a crystal and thence to a photographic plate. The rays fall upon atomic planes inclined in various directions and forming a three-dimensional grating; the result is a symmetrical pattern which indicates that crystals are orderly groupings of atoms into so-called space-lattices.

In most diffraction measurements on crystals it is customary to use monochromatic x-rays, that is, x-rays having a single wavelength, § 463, usually of a value between 0.7 and 2 Å. Suppose a narrow beam of such rays to be incident upon a crystal as shown in Fig. 452. The atoms of the crystal will scatter the incident radiation and send out wavelets as though they themselves were sources of radiation. These wavelets, in general, will not be in phase and therefore will annul one another, but if the angle of incidence is properly chosen,

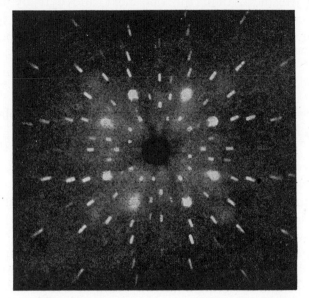

FIG. 451. Crystal diffraction pattern of pentaerythritol (*Photograph by Herman S. Kaufman*)

the wavelets will reenforce and establish a wave front which can proceed to a photographic plate for detection. It is found that reenforcement occurs only for particular values of the glancing angle θ, and that the diffracted ray will emerge at an equal angle. Thus, the diffracted ray appears as a reflected ray from one or another of the several crystal planes.

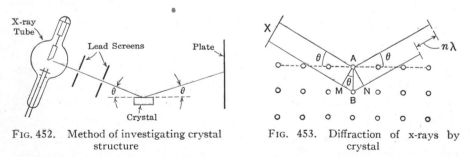

FIG. 452. Method of investigating crystal structure

FIG. 453. Diffraction of x-rays by crystal

The law of crystal diffraction was developed by the British physicist, Sir William H. Bragg (1862–1942), and his son, Sir William L. Bragg. In Fig. 453 the atoms in a crystal are represented by the small circles, and a beam of x-rays from the source X is shown meeting the horizontal atomic planes at the small angle θ. Reflection at an equal angle occurs at innumerable planes, each reflected ray being retarded more than the one next above it by an amount $MB + BN = 2AB \sin \theta$. In order for the reflected rays to reenforce one another, this retardation must be an integral number of wavelengths, and hence Bragg's Law states that

$$2d \sin \theta = n\lambda \qquad (280)$$

where d represents the spacing AB between the atomic planes, and n is an integer giving the order of the diffracted image. From this relation it is seen that reenforcement will occur only when the glancing angle θ is so related to the atomic spacing d that n will be a whole number of wavelengths of the x-rays used. By means of this law, either the atomic spacing of the crystal or the wavelength of the x-rays can be determined by experiment if the other of these quantities is known.

It has recently been found possible to produce x-ray spectra independently of crystals, by using a ruled diffraction grating of the reflection type and directing a narrow beam of x-rays upon it so that they almost graze the surface. The diffracted images are received upon a photographic plate and from this record the wavelengths can be determined accurately.

When x-rays of wavelength $\lambda = 1.542$ Å are diffracted by planes parallel to the cubical lattice faces of a rock salt crystal, the smallest glancing angle for reenforcement ($n = 1$) is found experimentally to be 15.83°. The spacing between the successive planes of atoms in the crystal is given by Bragg's Law as

$$d = \frac{n\lambda}{2 \sin \theta} = \frac{1.542 \times 10^{-8}}{2 \sin 15.83°} = 2.83 \times 10^{-8} \text{ cm.}$$

An independent evaluation of this spacing can be made from the density of NaCl, 2.163 gm/cu. cm., and its molecular weight, 58.45. From Avogadro's number (§ 140), there are 6.02×10^{23} molecules in 58.45 gm. of NaCl; this gives 1.03×10^{22} molecules per gm. or $1.03 \times 10^{22} \times 2.163 = 2.23 \times 10^{22}$ molecules per cu. cm. With 2 atoms to the molecule, there will be 4.46×10^{22} atoms per cu. cm., and if the crystal lattice is a multitude of cubes with atoms at the corners, there will be $\sqrt[3]{4.46 \times 10^{22}} = 3.54 \times 10^7$ atoms in a row

1 cm. long. The spacing between atoms and also between rows is therefore $d = \dfrac{1}{3.54 \times 10^7} = 2.83 \times 10^{-8}$ cm. This result verifies the other value, and indicates that the method using x-rays is correct.

X-ray diffraction may be applied also to crystal specimens in powder form, because the vast number of small crystals which make up the specimen have a random orientation and make every conceivable angle with the incident beam. The powder technique serves for the identification of crystals rather than for the analysis of their structure.

PROBLEMS

1. Light from two narrow slits 1 mm. apart falls upon a screen which is 80 cm. away and is parallel to the plane of the slits. Suppose the light to be monochromatic and to have a wavelength 0.00005 cm., and compute the distance measured along the screen from the center of the interference pattern to the first, second, and third bright fringes on either side.

2. When the slits of Problem 1 are illuminated with white light, violet fringes will appear on the screen at places where there is both reenforcement of violet light of wavelength 3800 Å and annulment of red light of 7600 Å. Compute the distance measured along the screen from the center of the interference pattern to the first and second violet fringe on either side which will be formed in this manner.

3. Light from the slit A in the diagram is directed at a small glancing angle α upon a plane mirror M; the slit and its virtual image I serve as two

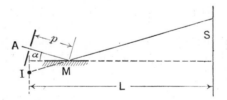

sources and produce an interference pattern on the screen S. In a test using monochromatic light of wavelength 0.00006 cm., the distances p and L are 10 cm. and 50 cm. respectively; what is the value of the angle α if the bright fringes of the interference pattern on the screen are 0.5 mm. apart?

4. The experiment described in Problem 1 is modified by covering one of the slits with a thin piece of glass of refractive index 1.61. If this action causes the center line of the interference pattern to shift along the screen a distance of 9 mm., how thick is the piece of glass?

5. Determine the minimum thickness of a film of gasoline which will cause annulment of violet light of wavelength 4047 Å, when viewed by reflected light. Assume the index of refraction of the gasoline to be 1.46 as measured with this light.

6. Two flat glass plates in contact at one end are separated at the other end by a fiber of unknown diameter. The wedge-shaped air film between the plates is viewed by reflected red light from calcium (wavelength = 6438 Å), and is found to be crossed by 56 dark interference fringes. Calculate the diameter of the fiber.

7. A plano-convex lens is made of glass having a refractive index of 1.62 and its focal length is 10 meters, as determined with light of wavelength 0.00005461 cm. Newton's rings are observed when the lens is placed upon an optically flat surface and illuminated by light of this wavelength. Compute the diameter of the fifth bright ring as observed by reflection.

8. Solve Problem 7 on the assumption that the space between the lens and the flat surface is occupied by water of index 1.333.

*9. A beam of light of wavelength 5893 Å is directed normally upon a plate of extra heavy flint glass, which has a refractive index of 1.917 as measured with this light. What per cent of the incident light is reflected at the surface? If the surface is to be coated to render it non-reflecting, what should be the refractive index and the thickness of the surface film?

10. An interferometer illuminated by green light from mercury (wavelength = 5461 Å) was used to measure the distance between two points. Observations showed that 567 interference fringes swept past a reference point in the field while the interferometer mirror moved from one of the points to the other. Compute the distance.

11. An interferometer is illuminated with monochromatic light and its mirror is moved sufficiently to cause 1000 interference fringes to sweep across the field. If the mirror was moved 0.03219 cm., what is the wavelength of the light used?

12. Monochromatic light of wavelength 0.00006 cm. passes normally through a slit 1 mm. wide and falls upon a screen 100 cm. distant from the slit. Compute the width of the central bright band in the diffraction pattern on the screen.

13. Suppose the slit of Problem 12 to be replaced by a circular hole 1 mm. in diameter. Compute the diameter of the central disk of the diffraction pattern upon the screen, and also the diameter of the first bright ring surrounding it.

14. A distant arc lamp is photographed with a pinhole camera upon a plate 20 cm. away from the pinhole, which has a diameter of 0.5 mm. If the lamp is regarded as a point source and the wavelength of light is taken as 0.00006 cm., what is the diameter of the disk image on the plate?

*15. A camera objective is focused on a distant point source of light. If the objective is rated $f/5.6$ and has a focal length of 4.5 in., what is the diameter of the disk image? Take 0.00006 cm. as an average value for the wavelength of light.

*16. A telescope lens 5 cm. in diameter is pointed at a star and forms a disk image at its focus. What angle does this image subtend at the lens? Take the wavelength of light to be 0.00006 cm.

*17. A newsprint halftone when examined closely is found to be an array of regularly spaced dots. How far apart may they be and still merge into a blended picture when the halftone is held 18 in. from the eye? Consider the limiting angle of resolution of the eye to be 1 min. of arc.

*18. The border of a neon sign consists of several parallel luminous tubes 3 in. apart. Up to what distance from the sign can an observer still see the tubes as separate sources? Take the light emitted to have the median wavelength of 0.0000613 cm. and suppose the pupil of the eye to be dilated to a diameter of 5 mm.

*19. Two stars at a distance of 10 light-years from the earth are viewed through a telescope having a lens 20 cm. in diameter. What is the minimum separation of these stars for which they would still be distinguishable as separate objects?

20. A narrow beam of light from glowing sodium vapor is passed perpendicularly through a diffraction grating having 5000 lines per cm. Spectral lines are produced upon a screen 60 cm. from the grating and parallel to it. Determine the distance along the screen from the center of the pattern to the sodium line (*a*) in the first-order spectrum, and (*b*) in the second-order spectrum.

21. A parallel beam of homogeneous x-rays of unknown wavelength is directed upon a rock salt crystal in the manner shown in Fig. 452. If the first-order diffracted ray appears when the glancing angle is 7.22°, what is the wavelength of the x-rays?

22. Experiments with a beam of helium atoms incident upon a crystal of lithium fluoride showed diffraction effects similar to that produced by light, the smallest glancing angle for reenforcement being 8.65°. Take the spacing between the crystal planes to be 2.0×10^{-8} cm., and compute the wavelength that corresponds to the helium atoms (see Problem 5 of Chapter XL).

Polarized Light — *Chapter XXXIX*

453. Polarization of Light.—The wave character of light is demonstrated by the phenomena of interference and diffraction; the transverse nature of light waves is revealed by *polarization*. This latter phenomenon can be illustrated by a simple test using two thin plates of a mineral called *tourmaline*, the plates having been cut from the crystal in a particular manner. A beam of light is passed through one of these plates and projected upon a screen; except for a slight tinting due to the color of the tourmaline, the beam remains unchanged in appearance. It has, however, been profoundly altered, as a test with the second plate placed in the light path will show. When the plates are parallel the light passes through both, but when one is turned the amount of light transmitted becomes less, and when they are at right angles the light is almost entirely quenched, and the overlapping region appears dark.

A somewhat similar effect can be pictured for a mechanical wave by supposing transverse vibrations in all directions to be set up in a rope stretched horizontally. When the rope is unobstructed the waves travel freely along its entire length, but if the test is repeated with the rope passed through a vertical slit, the horizontal components of the vibrations cannot travel beyond the slit and only the vertical components can proceed. A second slit will produce no further change if it is vertical also, but if it is turned to the horizontal all vibrations beyond will be quenched.

The significance of the test with the tourmaline plates will be considered by the aid of Fig. 454. Light is regarded as a wave in which the vibrations are transverse; that is, in planes at right angles to the line of propagation. When the vibrations constituting natural light are resolved into components, these are found equal in all directions, and a few of them are shown on the incident ray in the figure. Tourmaline transmits only vibrations or their components which are parallel to the crystal axis. Thus, in the light transmitted by the first plate, *P*, the vibrations are restricted to a single plane, as represented by the short vertical lines in the figure. This light is said to be *plane polarized*. The second plate, *A*, when crossed with the first as shown, extinguishes the light because the vibrations incident upon it have no components along the direction in which it is capable of transmit-

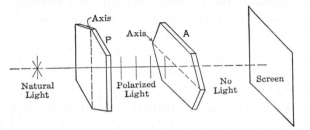

FIG. 454. Polarizing action of tourmaline

ting. Plate *P* is used to polarize the light and is called the *polarizer*, and plate *A* is used to analyze the polarization and is called the *analyzer*.

It is believed that light waves, like radio waves, are due to magnetic and electric fields which continually build up and collapse, and which are at right angles to each other. In specifying the plane of vibration of a light wave in this book, the plane of the electric field is meant.

The term polarization implies a lack of symmetry around the axis of propagation. The fact that a light wave can be polarized is taken as evidence that the wave is transverse, as a longitudinal wave appears to be inherently symmetrical with respect to its direction of travel.

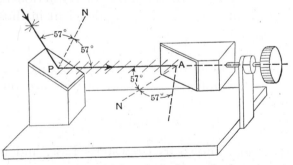

FIG. 455. Light polarized by reflection

454. Polarization by Reflection.—It is found by experiment that when natural light is reflected from the surface of a transparent substance it is partly polarized, the vibrations being parallel to the reflecting surface. This action is indicated at *P* in Fig. 455, which shows a beam of natural light incident upon an unsilvered glass plate. The extent to which the reflected rays are polarized depends upon the direction of the incident light. The angle of incidence for which the polarization is a maximum is called the *polarizing angle*, and is shown in the figure between the incident ray and the normal N; its value for glass is about 57°. Even at this angle, the amount of polarized light produced by a single plate is relatively small, and a pile of six to eight plates is often used to attain sufficient intensity by combining the reflected rays from all the surfaces.

If the polarized beam from the transparent plate P is directed upon a similar plate A that can be turned conveniently, it will be found that when the reflecting surfaces are parallel, reflection takes place from A as with natural light. If, however, the second plate is rotated 90° about ray PA as an axis to the position shown, there will be no reflection. This action explains why a transparent plate can be used to test the polarization of light.

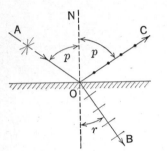

FIG. 456. Polarization of reflected and refracted rays

Fig. 456 shows a ray AO of natural light impinging upon the reflecting surface at the polarizing angle p. The reflected ray OC makes an equal angle with the normal N and is partly polarized, its vibrations being parallel to the surface, as represented by the dots in the figure. Most of the light is transmitted into the transparent medium along the direction OB, the angle of refraction being r. The transmitted light is also polarized, being deficient in those vibrations found in the beam OC.

The Scottish physicist, Sir David Brewster (1781–1868), discovered that when light impinges at the polarizing angle p upon a medium of refractive index μ, these quantities are related by the simple equation

$$\mu = \tan p \tag{281}$$

From this expression, known as Brewster's Law, and from the law of refraction, it follows that $\dfrac{\sin p}{\cos p} = \mu = \dfrac{\sin p}{\sin r}$, whence $\sin r = \cos p$, or $r + p = 90°$. Consequently the angle COB is 90°, showing that the reflected and refracted rays are at right angles for maximum polarization.

455. Double Refraction.—Many crystals possess the property of *double refraction*, a single incident beam being split into two beams within such a crystal. Calcite (Iceland spar, $CaCO_3$), quartz (SiO_2), and mica are doubly refracting substances.

Consider a crystal of calcite, as shown in section in Fig. 457, and a beam of natural light from X incident normally upon the end face. Ray O will pass through without deviation and is called the *ordinary*

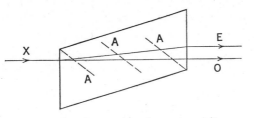

Fig. 457. Separation of rays in calcite

ray because it obeys the law of refraction, while ray E will be deviated despite perpendicular incidence and is called the *extraordinary* ray. The emergent beams will be parallel.

The calcite crystal has six faces forming a rhombohedron, and the three face angles that meet at two opposite corners are 102°. A line through one of these blunt corners which makes equal angles with the three faces meeting there, or any line parallel to it, is called the *optic axis* of the crystal. Lines A in the figure show the optic axis of calcite. A plane containing the optic axis and the normal to any face is called a *principal section*. The view of the calcite crystal in Fig. 457 is a principal section.

The direction of the rays within the crystal will depend upon the direction of the incident beam. The ordinary ray travels with constant velocity regardless of its direction, the refractive index of calcite for this ray having a constant value of 1.658, as measured for the D spectral line. The extraordinary ray travels with different speeds depending upon its direction. If it happens to advance along the optic axis, its velocity will be the same as that of the ordinary ray and the two rays will coincide. If it travels in any other direction its velocity is greater, having a maximum value along a direction at right angles to the optic axis. The refractive index of calcite for the extraordinary ray, as measured for the D spectral line, varies from 1.658 along the optic axis to 1.486 at right angles to that direction.

The wave fronts within the crystal can be found by using secondary wavelets, following Huygens' construction in Fig. 339. For the ordinary beam the wavelets have the familiar spherical shape. For the extraordinary beam they are ellipsoidal, the minor axis of the ellipsoid lying along the optic axis, in which direction the wavelets for the two beams coincide. These conditions are represented in Fig. 458, in which a plane wave *AB* is shown impinging upon the crystal surface *MN*. The wave fronts for the ordinary and extraordinary beams are constructed as shown at *DO* and *DE*, tangent

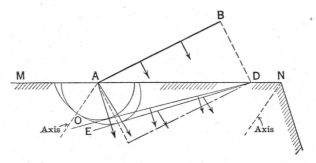

Fig. 458. Wave fronts in calcite

respectively to the spherical and ellipsoidal wavelets, and the corresponding rays are directed from *A* to the points of tangency. It is interesting to observe that for the extraordinary wave, the rays are not perpendicular to the wave front.

The crystals which exhibit double refraction belong to the hexagonal and tetragonal systems. For some of these, such as quartz, the velocity of the extraordinary ray, except along the optic axis, is less than that of the ordinary ray. For these crystals, the ellipse representing the extraordinary wave front has its major axis coincident with the radius of the circular wave front of the ordinary beam, and the extraordinary ray makes a larger angle with the optic axis than the ordinary ray. Some crystals have two optic axes with characteristic angles between them; they are called biaxial crystals.

The ordinary and extraordinary rays in a doubly refracting crystal are found to be polarized.

456. Polarization by Double Refraction.—The polarization produced by a doubly refracting crystal is indicated in Fig. 459, which shows a principal section of a calcite crystal and includes views of the end faces. The vibrations of the incident natural light are resolved into components in the plane of the principal section and at right angles to this plane, and these components are transmitted by the extraordinary and the ordinary rays respectively. Thus, the emergent beams *E* and *O* are polarized at right angles to each other.

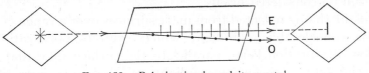

FIG. 459.   Polarization by calcite crystal

The Nicol prism, named for its inventor and used extensively in optical devices utilizing polarized light, is a calcite crystal of the shape shown in Fig. 460. It is prepared by resurfacing the end faces of the crystal at an angle of 68°, sawing the crystal in two diagonally at right angles to these end planes, and cementing the two parts together with Canada balsam. The refractive index of the balsam, as measured for the *D* spectral line, is 1.53, and is intermediate between the refractive indices of calcite for the ordinary and extraordinary rays. The incident ray of natural light is separated as usual into ordinary and extraordinary rays. The ordinary ray is totally reflected at the balsam layer and passes to one side where it is absorbed in suitable covering materials. The extraordinary ray is transmitted as plane polarized light, its vibrations being in the plane of the principal section.

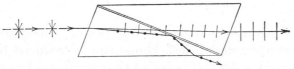

FIG. 460.   Principal section of Nicol prism

Some doubly refracting materials absorb one transmitted ray more than the other, and if the thickness is sufficient one ray will be almost completely absorbed. Such a material is called a *dichroic* substance; the best known example is tourmaline, which transmits only the extraordinary ray and absorbs the other. Sulfate of iodo-quinine is utilized in the new polarizing materials and very thin layers absorb one light component effectively. In *polaroid* the dichroic crystals are distributed densely in a cellulose film mounted between glass plates or bonded between transparent flexible plastic sheets. The individual crystals are needle-shaped and have girth diameters less than a wavelength of light. The average intensity of the transmitted beam is 37 per cent of the incident light over the visible range.

457. Some Applications of Polarized Light.—The introduction of polarizing substances that are relatively inexpensive, like polaroid, has made possible a number of interesting applications, a few of which will be considered briefly.

The light that is reflected from matt surfaces over a range of angles contains considerable glare-light which exhibits polarization, the direction of vibration being parallel to the surface (like that of ray *OC* in Fig. 456. The glare of sunlight reflected from sidewalks and pavements can be reduced by the use of polaroid glasses arranged to

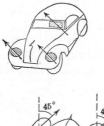

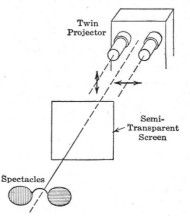

FIG. 461.   Method of eliminating headlight glare

FIG. 462.   Scheme for stereoscopic projection

transmit only vibrations in the vertical plane. The glare from paper observed in reading under desk lamps can be reduced by placing at the lamp opening a sheet of polaroid that is oriented to eliminate the horizontal vibrations.

Fig. 461 shows a method of eliminating the glare of automobile headlights that would require each car to be equipped with polarizing screens on headlamps and windshield. With the direction of polarization at 45° as indicated, each driver can see by the light of his own headlamps, but his windshield screen will reduce greatly the light from cars coming toward him.

Polarized light has also been used to give "depth" to motion pictures, making use of the stereoscopic effect described in § 442. Fig. 462 shows schematically how this may be accomplished, utilizing a twin projector equipped with polarizing screens set at right angles to each other for forming images on a ground-glass surface, and providing each observer with polaroid spectacles so oriented as to give each eye the image intended for it. Such stereoscopic projection is also possible by reflection using surfaces of fine texture preferably coated with aluminum.

458. Optical Rotation.—Certain materials, notably quartz and solutions of sugar, have the property of *rotating the plane of polarization* in transmitting polarized light. This effect may be observed with a *polarimeter*, consisting of a polarizer and an analyzer, together with means for supporting the optically active substance in the light path between them.

Optical rotation is used in determining the percentage of sugar in solutions of unknown concentration. Polarimeters especially designed for testing sugar are known as *saccharimeters*, and are arranged to pass the polarized light through a tube filled with the solution under test. If the polarizer and analyzer are crossed initially, giving a dark field, it will be found upon introducing the sugar solution that the analyzer must be turned to a new position to restore darkness. The difference between these positions is the angle through which the plane of polarization has been rotated, or else differs from it by 180°. The rotation is found to be proportional to the length of the liquid column and to the strength of the solution, and depends also upon the wavelength of light used. With sodium light, an aqueous solution of cane sugar in a tube 10 cm. long produces an optical rotation of 6.65° for a concentration of 0.1 gm. of sugar per cu. cm. of solution. With the same light, quartz causes a rotation of 21.72° per mm. of thickness.

Faraday discovered in 1845 that some materials of high refractive index, such as dense glass, rotate the plane of polarization of light when located in a strong magnetic field. This effect may be observed by placing the specimen between the poles of an electromagnet, the pole pieces being bored so that the polarized light may be passed in the same direction as the magnetic field.

459. Interference Effects.—In order to annul plane polarized light by interference, experiment shows that the interfering waves must originate from a common point of the source and be in phase opposition, as with natural light, and also that *their vibrations must be in the same plane*. Interference is usually demonstrated by placing a doubly refracting substance between a polarizer and an analyzer.

The polarizer and analyzer may be either parallel or crossed; in Fig. 463 they are represented as parallel plates at *P* and *A*, and the doubly refracting crystal *C* is shown between them with its optic axis inclined to the plate axes. White natural light (having transverse vibrations in all directions) entering at w is polarized by the polarizer, giving only vertical vibrations at x. These are resolved by the doubly refracting crystal into two components shown at y, the extraordinary ray having its vibrations in the plane of its optic axis and the ordinary ray having its vibrations at right angles to this plane. These rays are unequally retarded in traversing the crystal, principally because of the difference in refractive index, and the relative retardation will often be an odd number of half wavelengths for some color in the

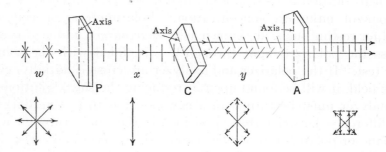

FIG. 463.   Producing interference colors with crystals

incident light. The analyzer passes only the vertical components of these vibrations, and in the region beyond it the colors resulting from the interference can readily be observed. The successive resolutions of the vibrations along the light path are represented in the lower part of the figure. The waves beyond the crystal C overlap almost completely, although the two rays are shown widely separated in the figure for clearness. A colorless crystal when viewed by polarized light shows colors by interference, the colors varying with the thickness and refractive index of the specimen.

The arrangement described is useful in the examination of crystals and in the study of thin rock sections. When viewed with a microscope, they will usually appear colored irregularly and will reveal details and structural differences not readily observed by other means. Such examinations enable the microscopist to determine whether a crystal is uniaxial (like quartz) or biaxial (like mica), whether it is optically active, and the amount of clockwise or counterclockwise rotation of its plane of polarization, and also to measure the numerical values of its refractive indices. Such information permits him to specify to which of the six crystal systems a sample belongs and to effect its identification.

A plate of singly refracting material when substituted for the doubly refracting crystal between polarizer and analyzer would produce no interference effects, since the incident ray would not be separated into two rays. Many singly refracting materials, such as glass or celluloid, become doubly refracting when mechanically strained. Consequently, such substances may be tested with polarized light and the presence of strains, not apparent when viewed in natural light, will be revealed by the appearance of interference fringes. Either white or monochromatic light may be used in such tests.

It was discovered by the Scottish physicist, John Kerr (1824–1907), that a transparent insulator such as glass or turpentine becomes doubly refracting when located in a strong electric field. A specimen of proper thickness placed in a beam of plane polarized light between a polarizer and an analyzer will cut off the light by interference when the field is established. With a rapidly alternating field the arrangement acts as a quick operating shutter, and this action has been used in measuring the velocity of light and for many other purposes.

*460. Elliptical and Circular Polarization.—In the study of Lissajous' figures (§ 373) it was shown that two harmonic vibrations of equal frequency, taking place in perpendicular planes, will give elliptical motion as a resultant when they are combined. The ellipse may have various shapes depending upon the amplitudes and phase relation of the component vibrations. It will be circular if these components are equal and differ in phase by one-quarter cycle.

When plane polarized light is passed through a thin doubly refracting plate, as at *C* in Fig. 463, the components traverse the plate with different velocities, and in general emerge displaced from each other in phase. The issuing light is said to be *elliptically polarized*; it becomes *circularly polarized* if the two components have equal amplitude and if the relative retardation is one-quarter wavelength. A doubly refracting plate designed to produce circular polarization is called a *quarter-wave* plate, and must have proper thickness and appropriate refractive indices for the wavelength of light to be used with it. With circularly polarized light, the field remains equally bright for all positions of the analyzer.

The Dutch physicist, Pieter Zeeman (1865–1943), discovered that if a light source is placed in an intense magnetic field, its spectral lines are broken into two or more components. In the simplest case, when viewed along the direction of the field, a line will be seen as two, the two beams being circularly polarized in opposite directions; and when viewed at right angles to the field three lines appear, the outside beams being plane polarized parallel to the field and the central one being plane polarized at right angles to the field. In many cases, the lines are resolved into four or six components. Such tests have led to important deductions concerning the structure of matter. They have also allowed the ratio of the electronic charge and mass to be evaluated, the results showing close agreement with those obtained by purely electrical methods, § 274.

*461. Photo-elasticity.—The distribution of internal stresses in structural or machine parts may be observed by passing polarized light through models made to scale from sheet celluloid or bakelite,

FIG. 464. Stresses in beam shown by polarized light

which are subjected to external forces simulating those in the actual structures. The method will be illustrated by considering the forces within a loaded beam and the photo-elastic picture of a model of it constructed of sheet bakelite. Such a picture taken by monochromatic circularly polarized light is shown in Fig. 464; the beam supports two loads that are indicated by the shaded arrows.

Throughout the region between the loads the beam fibers are under tension and compression only (see § 107), and under these conditions the relative retardation of the ordinary and extraordinary rays transmitted is directly proportional to the fiber stress. The picture shows 3.5 interference fringes between the neutral axis or "zero-strain" region and the outside fibers, and the model was subjected to a maximum fiber stress of 1570 lb. per sq. in. Consequently for this bakelite sheet, each interference fringe corresponds to a stress of 1570 ÷ 3.5 = 450 lb. per sq. in. This value can be used beyond the region of uniform loading. Thus at points A, where the fringe nearest the neutral axis comes out to the edge of the model, the fiber stress is 450 lb. per sq. in., and at points B, where the next fringe meets the edge, the fiber stress is 2 × 450 = 900 lb. per sq. in.

Fig. 465 shows a section of steel sheet piling such as is driven into the ground to form a wall and permit deep excavation, together with a photo-elastic picture of the interlock between adjacent units. The model of the interlock was made from the same sheet of bakelite referred to in the preceding paragraph, and consequently the same stress values apply to the interference fringes. For example, a zero-stress point appears at C, and the first fringe meets the edge at D;

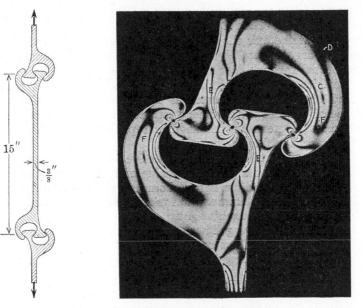

FIG. 465.   Sheet piling and interlock

this shows the fiber stress at D to be 450 lb. per sq. in. The corresponding stresses in the actual structure are determined from such values by taking account of the relative sizes of the structure and model and the relative loads employed. The three points of contact of the interlock exhibit high concentration of stress as indicated by the closeness of the fringes about these points, but this result being due to direct pressure of contact is not regarded as particularly objectionable. The narrow sections E and F are subjected to external forces which cause both tension and bending, and the absence of fringe concentration at these critical places is taken as indicating that the interlock is well designed.

PROBLEMS

1. At what angle of incidence should a beam of sodium light be directed upon the surface of diamond to produce most complete polarization? Construct a diagram showing the directions of the incident, reflected, and refracted beams.

2. With the double-mirror apparatus as shown in Fig. 455, the intensity of the beam reflected from the analyzing mirror is found to vary with the position of this mirror as given by the expression: $I = I_0 \cos^2 \theta$, where I_0 is the intensity when the analyzing mirror is parallel to the polarizing mirror and I is the intensity when it has been rotated from that position through an angle θ about the axis shown. If the intensity is 10 lumens per sq. ft. when the mirrors are parallel, what is its value when the analyzing mirror has been rotated through 30°? 60°? 90°?

3. A calcite crystal has its surfaces reground in such a manner that when a ray of natural light impinges upon the crystal making an angle of incidence of 45°, the extraordinary refracted ray will be perpendicular to the optic axis. Determine the angular separation of the ordinary and extraordinary rays within the crystal.

4. Ice is doubly refracting; its refractive index has a value of 1.3091 for the ordinary ray and a maximum value of 1.3104 for the extraordinary ray, as measured with sodium light. Compute the velocity of the ordinary light wave and also the minimum and maximum velocities of the extraordinary light wave in ice, for this light.

5. In the accompanying figure are shown the sectional views of the Rochon and Wollaston prisms used to produce double images. Each consists of two equal triangular prisms made of calcite and cemented together;

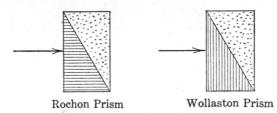

Rochon Prism　　Wollaston Prism

the horizontal and vertical shading lines represent the direction of the optic axes, and the dots represent that axis to be at right angles to the page. A ray of light is shown impinging normally upon the left surface of each prism. Sketch the directions along which the incident ray will be doubly refracted at the interfaces of the prisms.

6. A beam of sodium light is directed upon a Nicol prism. Compute the critical angle for total reflection of the ordinary ray against the layer of Canada balsam.

7. A tube 20 cm. long, filled with an aqueous solution containing 15 gm. of cane sugar per 100 cu. cm. of solution, is placed in the path of plane polarized sodium light. Through what angle will the plane of polarization be rotated?

8. In many saccharimeters, the amount of optical rotation of the sugar solution is determined by compensating it with rotation due to a wedge of quartz. What thickness of quartz would compensate the rotation in a solution of cane sugar containing 0.3 gm. of sugar per cu. cm. of solution?

9. Quartz has a refractive index of 1.544 for the ordinary ray and a maximum index of 1.553 for the extraordinary ray, when measured with sodium light. What minimum thickness of quartz placed between a polarizer and an analyzer will cause annulment of this light?

*10. Compute the thickness that a willemite plate should have for use as a quarter-wave plate for producing circularly polarized sodium light. The refractive index of willemite measured with that light is 1.694 for the ordinary ray and 1.723 (maximum value) for the extraordinary ray.

Radiation and
Atomic Structure

Chapter XL

462. Quantum Relations in Radiation.—An understanding of radiation is made clearer by the application of the quantum theory to the planetary conception of the atom (§ 414). This also provides a theoretical verification of the equations for spectral series. The form of such an equation for hydrogen, due to the Swedish scientist, Johannes R. Rydberg (1854–1919), was given earlier as equation (255), and expresses the wave numbers of the hydrogen spectrum as

$$\nu = 109{,}737 \left(\frac{1}{k_2{}^2} - \frac{1}{k_1{}^2} \right)$$

where k_1 and k_2 are simple integers representing atomic energy levels, and the numerical value is known as the *Rydberg constant*.

Consider the single electron of a hydrogen atom to revolve about the nucleus in a circular path of radius r with angular velocity ω. Because of the charge $-e$ on the electron and $+e$ on the nucleus, the force of attraction between them (§ 209) will be $\dfrac{e \times e}{r^2}$, and will constitute the centripetal force $\omega^2 rm$ acting upon the revolving electron of mass m, by § 51. Under the action of this force, the electron will revolve in a definite orbit of radius r such that

$$\frac{e^2}{r^2} = \omega^2 rm \tag{282}$$

The energy of the electron is made up of potential energy amounting to $\dfrac{-e^2}{r}$, by § 211, and of kinetic energy amounting to $\frac{1}{2}I\omega^2 = \frac{1}{2}mr^2\omega^2$, by § 68, where $I = mr^2$ is the moment of inertia of the electron about the nucleus. Therefore, the total energy of the electron is

$$E = -\frac{e^2}{r} + \frac{1}{2}mr^2\omega^2 = -\frac{e^2}{2r} \tag{283}$$

The two foregoing equations could be satisfied by any value of the radius r and, if no other limitation were imposed, the electron could have any conceivable energy value. Under this supposition, the spectrum of hydrogen would comprise all frequencies in accordance with equation (256); but this conclusion is contrary to fact. In order to secure agreement with experiments on the hydrogen spectrum, Bohr introduced the idea of energy levels described in § 414 and assumed that the *angular momentum* (§ 212) of the electron in its orbit would have to be an exact multiple of $h/2\pi$, where h is Planck's constant. Accordingly, the angular momentum $I\omega$ must equal some integer times $h/2\pi$. Since $I = mr^2$, this restriction means that the electron can have only particular orbits such that the radius r will satisfy the relation

$$mr^2\omega = k\,\frac{h}{2\pi} \tag{284}$$

where the integer k is called the *quantum number*. When the quantizing condition, equation (284), is applied to the relation stated in equation (282), the radius of the orbit will have definite and separated values given by

$$r = \frac{k^2h^2}{4\pi^2me^2} \tag{285}$$

The energy of the electron rotating in the orbit of radius r, as given by this equation, is found by substitution in equation (283) to be

$$E = -\,\frac{2\pi^2me^4}{k^2h^2}$$

and is spoken of as the energy of the atom in the kth stationary state. The energy radiated by the atom in passing from the k_1th to the k_2th stationary state is, therefore

$$E_h - E_l = \frac{2\pi^2me^4}{h^2}\left[\frac{1}{k_2{}^2} - \frac{1}{k_1{}^2}\right]$$

This result may be merged with equation (256), and since the frequency f is equal to the wave number ν times the velocity of light c, the wave number of the spectral line emitted in this energy transfer will be

$$\nu = \frac{2\pi^2me^4}{h^3c}\left[\frac{1}{k_2{}^2} - \frac{1}{k_1{}^2}\right] \tag{286}$$

From the numerical values: $m = 9.11 \times 10^{-28}$ gm., $e = 4.80 \times 10^{-10}$ esu. of charge, $h = 6.62 \times 10^{-27}$ erg-sec., and $c = 3.00 \times 10^{10}$ cm. per sec., it will be found that the coefficient of the bracketed expression agrees with the Rydberg constant given ahead. Its value varies slightly for atoms of different mass numbers, being 109,678 for hydrogen and 109,737 for the heaviest atoms.

The correlation of atomic energy levels that has been shown to exist with the production of the spectral lines of hydrogen also extends to elements having many electrons and producing complicated spectra.

463. X-ray Spectra.—The diffraction of x-rays by reflection from the various atomic planes of crystals (§ 452) has led to an accurate knowledge of the character of x-rays emitted by the elements, and this knowledge has been of great aid in determining the structure of atoms. The radiation from the target of an x-ray tube (§ 323), when investigated by reflection at all angles from a crystal, is found to consist of a continuous spectrum and a superposed bright-line spectrum extending over a range of wavelengths from about 10^{-6} to 10^{-9} cm.

The continuous x-ray spectrum differs in intensity over its range, increasing from very low values at the longer wavelengths to a maximum value and then falling sharply to zero at a particular shorter wavelength. This short-wave limit depends upon the potential difference across the x-ray tube and is independent of the target material. These facts indicate that the continuous spectrum is caused by the rapid retardation and consequent loss of kinetic energy of the electrons from the cathode of the tube as they strike the atoms of the target, or more correctly, as they are deflected by the strong electric fields surrounding the nuclei of the target atoms.

An electron deflected from an atom usually suffers a decrease of energy, and the quantum of energy lost is emitted as radiation and is called a *photon*. The most the electron can lose is the total kinetic energy it had upon arrival at the target, but it may lose less than this amount. Consequently, the highest frequency of the x-rays (i.e., shortest wavelength) will be the frequency of a photon that is emitted when the electron is stopped completely. The maximum kinetic energy of an electron on approach is Ve ergs, where V is the peak value of the potential difference across the tube and e is the charge of the electron (§ 217). This will be the energy of the quantum that corresponds to the highest photon frequency f_m; it is given in § 323 as

$$Ve = hf_m$$

in which Planck's constant $h = 6.62 \times 10^{-27}$ erg-sec., and the electronic charge $e = 4.80 \times 10^{-10}$ esu. Since 300 volts = 1 esu. of potential difference, and the velocity of propagation is $c = 3.00 \times 10^{10}$ cm. per sec., it follows that the minimum wavelength is

$$\lambda_{min} = \frac{c}{f_m} = \frac{3.00 \times 10^{10} \times 6.62 \times 10^{-27} \times 300}{4.80 \times 10^{-10}V} = \frac{12.41}{V} 10^{-5}$$

The wavelength will be in centimeters when the potential difference on the tube is in volts. The wavelength corresponding to the maximum intensity is about $\frac{3}{2}\lambda_{min}$.

Bright-line x-ray spectra are characteristic of the target materials, and the spectrum for any one element consists of several well-defined groups of lines. These groups are conventionally called the K, L, M, $N \cdots$ series in the order of increasing wavelength, or decreasing energy. The wavelengths of the lines are independent of the potential differences across the x-ray tube, but these potentials do determine the intensity of the lines and whether they appear or not. The lighter elements give lines only in the first-mentioned series. The characteristic spectra of all the elements are found to be similar, but the corresponding lines of any series occur at different wavelengths for the different elements. The English physicist, Henry G. J. Moseley (1887–1915), found that the wavelength for a particular line depended upon the atomic number of the element and not upon its atomic weight. The relation between wavelength λ, wave number ν, and atomic number Z, known as Moseley's Law, is given by

$$\frac{1}{\lambda} = \nu = C(Z - \sigma)^2 \tag{287}$$

where C and σ are constants; the value of C depends on the particular line of the series while that of σ is the same for all lines of a series. The higher the atomic number of an element the shorter will be the wavelength for the particular line under consideration. Fig. 466 shows the K-series lines for four metals of atomic numbers 29, 42, 50 and 79, and the L-series lines for the last metal only, because the others fall to the right of the chart.

Analysis and experiment indicate that the emission of characteristic x-rays is due to the inner electrons of the target atoms. In the
planetary picture of the atom, the lines of the *K* series are emitted
when electrons from outer shells fall into the innermost one to fill
vacancies there, those of the *L* series are emitted when electrons fall
similarly to the second shell, and so on. Accordingly, these shells
are referred to as the *K* and *L* shells. Thus, when an impinging electron collides with an atom of the target and ejects one of its electrons
of the *K* shell, the vacancy is filled by an electron from the *L* shell,

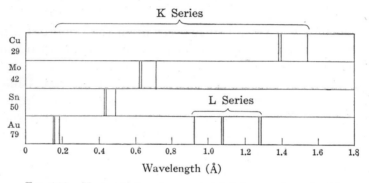

Fig. 466.   X-ray spectra of copper, molybdenum, tin and gold

or one from the *M* shell, and so on. As a result, a line of the *K* series
will be emitted, the energy value depending on the source of the electron. If it comes from the *L* shell the line is called the *K*α line, if
from the *M* shell the *K*β line, and so on. The *K*β line is of higher
frequency than the *K*α line, because the energy difference is greater
between the *M* and *K* shells than that between the *L* and *K* shells.
A vacancy in the *L* shell is made up similarly and spectral lines of
*L*α, *L*β ··· will result.

The fact that x-ray spectra of the elements are similar, except
as to their wavelength scales, indicates that the inner electronic structure of all but the lighter atoms is the same. In contrast, optical
spectra have different characteristics from element to element and
show that the outer structure of atoms differ; their lines are produced
by electrons falling from a number of outer normally unoccupied
levels to inner ones. Studied together with the chemical properties
of atoms, both types of spectra reveal how many electrons can occupy
the several shells; thus, the *K* shell can have 2 electrons, the *L* shell 8,
and so on.

Energy level diagrams like that of Fig. 402 can be constructed to show the origin of x-ray spectral lines of the elements, and equation (255) can be extended to include their wave numbers. The modified expression for the number of waves per centimeter is

$$\nu = R(Z - \sigma)^2 \left[\frac{1}{k_2{}^2} - \frac{1}{k_1{}^2} \right] \qquad (288)$$

In this equation R is the Rydberg constant, Z is the atomic number, k_1 and k_2 are the quantum numbers for the initial and final energy levels, and σ is a constant. For hydrogen $Z = 1$ and $\sigma = 0$, and the equation reduces to (255) for the wave numbers in the infrared, visible and ultraviolet regions. It will be observed that equations (287) and (288) agree in form; the value of C in the former can be evaluated readily.

To find the wavelength of the $K\alpha$ line in the x-ray spectrum of molybdenum, take the atomic number as 42 and $\sigma = 0.5$. This line is produced by an electron falling from shell L of quantum number $k_1 = 2$ to shell K of quantum number $k_2 = 1$. Consequently the wave number is $\nu = 14.1 \times 10^7$ waves per cm., and the wavelength is $10^8/\nu = 0.71$ Å.

Recently attention has been directed to x-ray emission spectra involving the outer parts of the atoms of solids. These studies, together with those on absorption of x-rays, indicate that electrons, once removed from the inner parts of atoms, appear to belong to the solid as a whole instead of to its individual atoms, and that the energies of the electron transitions cover bands rather than specific values. This broadening of the emission lines is ascribed to the interactions of the closely packed atoms of solids, and the falling of the outer or valence electrons into vacancies produced in the inner shells of atoms by electronic bombardment. It is expected that such studies will provide an insight to the structure of solids.

464. Corpuscular Nature of Light.—The effects of interference, diffraction, and polarization, described in the two foregoing chapters, give ample evidence of the *wave character* of light. On the other hand, the photoelectric effect described in § 322 supports the theory that light is *corpuscular* in character. Regarding this effect, it has been stated that: (1) when radiation is incident upon certain substances electrons are emitted, and these are often called photoelectrons to indicate their origin; (2) the velocity of their emission is not influenced by the intensity of the radiation; (3) the velocity of the photoelectrons increases with the frequency of the incident radiation; (4) the fre-

quency must reach a certain critical value depending on the substance before emission occurs at all; (5) the number of photoelectrons
emitted per unit time varies with the intensity of radiation. It has
also been shown that there is no appreciable time lag between the
beginning of illumination and the emission of electrons.

Since the photoelectron receives energy from the incident radiation in order to leave the substance, it is difficult to explain on the
wave theory why the energy (and therefore the velocity) imparted
to the photoelectron will not diminish when the radiation intensity
is reduced, say by moving the source farther from the substance.
The difficulty is removed by assuming that the energy is distributed
discontinuously over the radiation wave front in little packets called
quanta which maintain their identity in traveling from the source.
The quanta or photons have different energy values depending upon
the radiation frequency, the values being given by equation (125),
$E = hf$.

Consequently, the maximum energy of the expelled electrons is
given by Einstein's equation as

$$\tfrac{1}{2}mv_m{}^2 = hf - w$$

where m is the mass of the photoelectron, 9.11×10^{-28} gm., v_m is
its velocity in centimeters per second, h is Planck's constant in erg-
seconds, f is the frequency in vibrations per second, and w is the work
function in ergs. The energy values in this expression may be expressed in electron-volts by using the conversion factor: 1.60×10^{-12}
ergs $= 1$ electron-volt (§ 274). The equation has been verified experimentally with energy values up to a million electron-volts.

The work function represents the energy required to remove one
of the least firmly bound electrons, and its value differs with different
substances. Its presence in the equation explains why the radiation
frequency must have a sufficiently high value before emission can
occur, for the minimum frequency is w/h and the corresponding
maximum wavelength is hc/w, where c is the velocity of light.

In order to have photoelectric emission from potassium, it is found that
the wavelength of the incident radiation must not exceed about 0.00007 cm.;
consequently the work function of this element is

$$w = hc/\lambda = 6.62 \times 10^{-27} \times 3.00 \times 10^{10} \div 7 \times 10^{-5} = 2.84 \times 10^{-12}$$

ergs, or $2.84 \times 10^{-12} \div 1.60 \times 10^{-12} = 1.77$ electron-volts. Thus, the
energy necessary to remove an electron from potassium is equal to the work
done on an electron in falling through a potential difference of 1.77 volts.

The corpuscular theory of light receives further support by an effect discovered by Professor Arthur H. Compton, and now known by his name. He found that when a beam of homogeneous (monochromatic) x-rays of high energy impinged upon one of the lighter elements like carbon, and was scattered by the element, a part of the scattered radiation exhibited an *increase in wavelength*, and this corresponds to a decrease in energy. This effect is explained on the quantum theory by stating that some x-ray photons collide with electrons and in doing so give up some of their energy to the electrons to set them in motion. As a result the photons rebound with diminished energy. Each direction of recoil of a photon is correlated with a certain direction of recoil of the electron, the occurrence of recoil particles in the various directions being governed by laws of probability. The corresponding change in wavelength of the scattered radiation is given by

$$\Delta\lambda = \frac{h}{mc}(1 - \cos\theta) \tag{289}$$

where θ is the angle, with respect to the forward direction, at which the scattered radiation is observed and m is the mass of the electron. The validity of this explanation confirms the belief that all radiation behaves as particles, at least under certain conditions; for example, in its interactions with free or lightly bound electrons.

Thus, light is regarded as a swarm of photons, following each other with the speed c and differing in energy content hf in accordance with the frequency or wavelength. The dual nature of light in acting both as waves and as particles presents a problem which has received the attention of physicists for some time; an account of the progress made is beyond the limits set for this book.

*465. Wave Nature of Particles.—A novel concept of matter was introduced in 1924 by Louis V. de Broglie to the effect that particles of small mass, such as electrons, have a wave character like photons of light energy. By analogy with equation (289), these so-called "matter waves" would have a wavelength of

$$\lambda = \frac{h}{mv} \tag{290}$$

where h is Planck's constant, and m and v are the mass and velocity of the particle respectively. Experiments were conducted by Clinton J. Davisson and Lester H. Germer, physicists of the Bell Telephone Laboratories, to test this hypothesis. They reasoned that if electrons were waves, it should be possible to cause their diffraction with crystals, and in 1927 they succeeded in producing diffraction patterns by projecting electrons upon a nickel crystal.

Measurements of electron diffraction patterns show that Bragg's equation (280) will hold when the wavelength satisfies equation (290). Thus, while tests with the cloud chamber show that electrons are undoubtedly particles, their diffraction shows that they act as light waves. In the same way atoms and molecules have been found to possess a wave character.

Fig. 467 shows a diffraction pattern of high resolution produced with a normally incident beam of electrons passing through a very

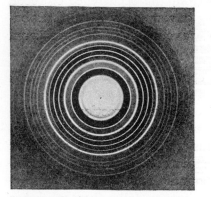

thin film of caesium iodide (Cs I) which is formed upon a suitable supporting foil. The molecules of such inorganic compounds, deposited by evaporation under a high vacuum, are able to move about on the foil surface and agglomerate into crystals; for the pattern shown the mean crystal dimensions were estimated at 200 Å.

It would seem, therefore, that all particles of matter have wave characteristics; the larger their masses, the shorter at a given speed will be the wavelengths according to the de

Fig. 467. Electron diffraction pattern
(*Courtesy of L. H. Germer*)

Broglie equation. The science of Mechanics must take this behavior into account in dealing with particles of electronic and atomic magnitudes, even though the wave effects, like diffraction, are still smaller than in optics. The extension of this science to include such phenomena is called *Wave Mechanics*.

The de Broglie wavelength equation is consistent with the quantum condition introduced by Professor Bohr to fix the energy levels of the normal hydrogen atom (§ 462), namely that the angular momentum of the electron moving in its circular orbit of radius r must be an integral multiple of $h/2\pi$. For the electron to exhibit a wave character, the length of its path in any stable orbit should contain an integral number of wavelengths, just as is the case with vibrating strings (§ 362). Consequently, the wavelength λ should be some integer times $2\pi r$. If the integer is taken as unity

$$\lambda = 2\pi r$$

a result which may be combined with the equation for the angular momentum of the electron, namely

$$mr^2\omega = mrv = \frac{h}{2\pi}$$

to yield equation (290) directly.

The speed of electrons having a kinetic energy of, say, 100 electron-volts or $100 \times 1.6 \times 10^{-12}$ ergs is

$$v = \sqrt{\frac{2}{m} 1.60 \times 10^{-10}} = \sqrt{\frac{3.20 \times 10^{-10}}{9.11 \times 10^{-28}}} = 0.593 \times 10^9 \text{ cm. per sec.}$$

The de Broglie wavelength of such electron waves is, therefore,

$$\lambda = \frac{6.62 \times 10^{-27}}{9.11 \times 10^{-28} \times 0.593 \times 10^9} = 1.23 \times 10^{-8} \text{ cm.} = 1.23 \text{ Å}$$

For 10,000-volt electrons the wavelength is practically 0.123 Å, but for higher energy electrons the change of mass with velocity begins to affect the wavelength.

466. Relativity.—The fact that all motion is relative has been recognized for a long time. A person on a river steamer who looks out and sees only the water near the ship because of fog, cannot tell by observing the water moving past him whether the ship is under way or the tide is passing the ship at anchor, assuming that he is not assisted in this observation by other effects, such as ship vibration caused by its engine. Our own motion in walking along the street is reckoned with respect to the earth as fixed, no consideration being given to the facts that the earth rotates on its axis and travels around the sun. These and other illustrations (§ 29) show that motion in space is ambiguous; it has definite meaning only when expressed relative to something that may be regarded as fixed. Professor Einstein has extended this fundamental idea of relative motion and formulated what is known as the theory of relativity. Much experimental evidence has been accumulated in its support, and the consequences of the theory are of great theoretical importance.

The theory postulates that (1) relative motion is the only motion that has definite meaning, and (2) the velocity of light in free space is independent of the motion of the light source and observer. The first leads to the generalization that the laws of physical phenomena (for example, the laws of Mechanics) are unaffected by uniform rectilinear motion of the system of coordinates to which the physical quantities are referred. The second postulate is a statement resulting from experiment, specifically the failure of an experiment to detect with an interferometer a difference of the velocity of light in the direction of the earth's motion and in a direction at right angles thereto.

A surprising result of the theory of relativity is that it implies *an increase of inertia* (that is, of *mass*) *with velocity*. This variation in mass is insignificant except when the body has velocities approaching that of light. When the mass of a body at rest is represented by m_0, its mass at velocity v will be

$$m = \frac{m_0}{\sqrt{1 - \dfrac{v^2}{c^2}}} \qquad (291)$$

where c is the velocity of light. Thus, an electron having a mass of 9.11×10^{-28} gm. at rest will have a mass when moving with a velocity 0.9 that of light amounting to 20.9×10^{-28} gm.

The theory also indicates *the equivalence of mass and energy*. This equivalence can be obtained by computing the work done on a body, of rest mass m_0, in accelerating it to a velocity v, taking account of the fact that the mass increases to a value m in the transition. The result as obtained by integration shows that the kinetic energy of the body is then

$$E_k = m_0 c^2 \left(\frac{1}{\sqrt{1 - \dfrac{v^2}{c^2}}} - 1 \right) \qquad (292)$$

To find the speed of electrons that have energies of 1 million electron-volts, express this value in ergs and obtain the velocity from equation (292). Thus $E_k = 1.6 \times 10^{-6}$ ergs and $m_0 c^2 = 9.11 \times 10^{-28} \times 9 \times 10^{20} = 0.82 \times 10^{-6}$ ergs. Hence

$$\sqrt{1 - \frac{v^2}{c^2}} = \frac{1}{\dfrac{1.6}{0.82} + 1} = 0.339 \quad \text{and} \quad \frac{v^2}{c^2} = 0.885$$

Consequently $v = c\sqrt{0.885} = 3 \times 10^{10} \times 0.941 = 2.82 \times 10^{10}$ cm. per sec.

The combination of equations (291) and (292) gives a result of great importance. The result shows that the kinetic energy is c^2 times the change in mass, or

$$E_k = (m - m_0)c^2 \qquad (293)$$

If m_0c^2 be thought of as the internal energy of the body at rest, then the total energy equivalent of the body of mass m when moving is $m_0c^2 + E_k$ or

$$E = mc^2 \tag{294}$$

The equation indicates that if a mass m were annihilated in some way, the amount of energy liberated would be mc^2. This relationship implies that the laws of the conservation of mass and of energy are two aspects of a single law of nature.

467. Radioactivity.—Within a year after the discovery of x-rays, the French scientist, Antoine Henri Becquerel (1852–1908), found that uranium in various states of chemical combination emitted spontaneously an invisible radiation that was capable of affecting a photographic plate and producing ionization of the air. This property of uranium was found subsequently to be possessed by a number of the heavy elements, and the name *radioactivity* was applied to it. Remarkable discoveries in this field were made by the French physicist, Pierre Curie (1859–1906) and his wife Marie Curie (1867–1934); among them may be mentioned the isolation of the elements polonium and radium from pitchblende.

It was soon found that radioactive substances emit three kinds of rays called α, β and γ rays, that are widely different in character. They can be differentiated by their power of penetrating matter and of producing ionization.

Alpha rays are particles that carry positive charges, and have been identified as the nuclei of helium atoms. They have a mass 4 times that of the hydrogen atom and a charge equal to that of 2 electrons. Alpha particles have velocities of the order of 2×10^9 cm. per sec. As they move through air they produce ionization by knocking electrons out of its atoms, and naturally their speed is reduced by the successive collisions. In air at atmospheric pressure the α particles are slowed down in traveling 3 to 9 cm. to such an extent that they no longer can produce ionization. Their range is greatly reduced when they are passed through metal foil; for example, a thickness of 0.001 mm. of silver is equivalent to over 2 cm. of air. The alpha particle is believed to be a stable combination of two protons (that is, hydrogen nuclei) and two neutrons.

Beta rays are particles that carry negative charges, and are in reality high-speed electrons. They are ejected from radioactive substances with velocities varying from 0.3 to 0.99 that of light. They are much more penetrating than α particles, but measurement of their ranges in air is difficult because of their irregular paths. The mass of the β particle is much less than that of the α particle and consequently, in colliding with electrons, while the β particle is deviated from its path with each collision, the α particle knocks them out of its way and continues along a fairly straight line. The ratio e/m for β rays is not constant as it is for slow-speed electrons because the mass of the β ray is higher at speeds comparable with the velocity of light, as explained in the previous section.

Gamma rays are electromagnetic radiations of the same character as x-rays but have much shorter wavelengths. Crystal diffraction tests (§ 452) and measurements of velocities of ejected photoelectrons show that γ rays have wavelengths ranging from about 0.005 to 1 Å. The frequencies of gamma radiations are correspondingly high and therefore γ-ray photons have large energy values. The rays can pass through thicknesses of many centimeters of lead.

There is evidence to show that a γ-ray photon can be converted into matter when it impinges upon the nucleus of an atom, producing an electron and a positron by the action. As a result the energy of the photon reappears largely as m_0c^2 in each particle of the electron-positron pair and the rest in the kinetic energy of the particles.

As an illustration, find the minimum frequency of radiation required for the production of an electron-positron pair. The rest mass of electron and positron together is $2 \times 9.11 \times 10^{-28}$ gm. and therefore the minimum energy required for the conversion is $18.22 \times 10^{-28} \times (3 \times 10^{10})^2 = 1.64 \times 10^{-6}$ ergs = 1,025,000 electron-volts. The corresponding radiation frequency is given by equation (125) as $f = \dfrac{E}{h} = \dfrac{1.64 \times 10^{-6}}{6.62 \times 10^{-27}} = 2.48 \times 10^{20}$ per sec.; the wavelength is 1.21×10^{-10} cm. = 0.0121 Å.

468. Ray Tracks and Ray Counters.—Two instruments of importance in the investigation of radioactive rays and other charged particles are the *cloud chamber* and the *ray counter*.

The cloud chamber devised by the British physicist C. T. R. Wilson utilizes the fact that when air saturated with water vapor is expanded suddenly, the cooling effect causes the formation of a cloud of tiny drops. These drops form upon dust or other particles and persist long enough, before they evaporate again, to allow a visual or photographic examination. In using the chamber for the study of charged particles, the air is first rendered dust-free, the particles are then admitted, and immediately thereafter the air is expanded. The charged particle creates a large number of ions along its path, and a track of water drops appears as a white line against a dark background.

Tracks in a cloud chamber can be produced by α particles (helium nuclei), β particles (electrons), protons (hydrogen nuclei), and by other charged particles. Since electrons are much lighter than α particles, a β ray produces fewer ions per unit length of path and its path is easily altered, consequently, the drops forming a β ray track are more widely separated than those forming an α ray track and

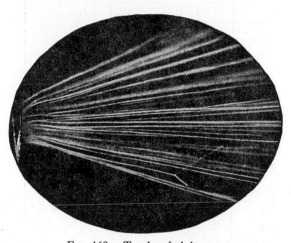

FIG. 468.   Tracks of alpha rays
(*Courtesy of Professor W. D. Harkins*)

frequently they do not lie on a straight line.   The track of a very fast proton might look like that of an electron because of the small probability of ionization.

Fig. 468 illustrates the tracks made by α particles in nitrogen. The forked track shows the rare occurrence when a nitrogen nucleus captured the alpha particle that struck it and emitted a proton (upper branch); the remaining part (lower branch) constitutes the oxygen isotope of atomic mass 17.

The ray counter, devised by the German physicists, H. Geiger and A. Müller, consists of a cylindrical chamber with insulating ends supporting a fine wire arranged axially.   A difference of potential is maintained between wire and cylinder and is adjusted so that the counter is on the verge of discharging. When a charged particle enters the evacuated chamber, it produces a number of ions and the discharge is observed with an electrometer; the discharge is stopped promptly so that the counter may be ready for the next particle. The passage of the particles can be counted automatically with the aid of thermionic amplifiers (§ 327), thyratron tubes (§ 321), and counting mechanisms.

469. Radioactive Transformations.—Experimental study of the disintegration of the radioactive elements by the emission of α and β

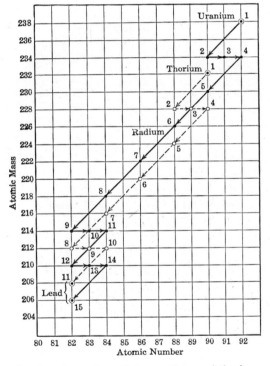

FIG. 469.　Radioactive transformations of the uranium and thorium series. The numbers in the figure refer to the substances listed on the next page

rays has resulted in a definite knowledge of their successive transformations, atomic numbers, atomic masses, and stability. These elements form three groups: the uranium-radium series, the thorium series, and the actinium series. The transformation of the first two series are illustrated graphically in Fig. 469 and the successive products are listed in the following table with corresponding numbers:

Radioactive Disintegration Products

Uranium-Radium Series		No. in Fig. 469	Thorium Series	
Substance	Half-life		Substance	Half-life
Uranium I.....	45×10^8 yr.	1	Thorium........	1.39×10^{10} yr.
" X_1...	24.5 days	2	Mesothorium I..	6.7 yr.
" X_2....	1.14 min.	3	" II.	6.13 hr.
" II....	2.5×10^5 yr.	4	Radiothorium RdTh	1.90 yr.
Ionium........	8.3×10^4 yr.	5	Thorium X......	3.64 days
Radium.......	1590 yr.	6	" Ema-	
" Ema-			nation Tn.....	54.5 sec.
ation Rn....	3.83 days	7	Thorium A......	0.16 sec.
Radium A.....	3.05 min.	8	" B......	10.16 hr.
" B....	26.8 min.	9	" C......	60.5 min.
" C....	19.7 min.	10	" C'.....	3×10^{-7} sec.
" C'.....	1.5×10^{-4} sec.	11	Lead..........	
" D.....	22 yr.	12		
" E.....	5.0 days	13		
Polonium......	140 days	14		
Lead.........		15		

In the figure each inclined line downward to the left signifies the emission of an α particle; such a change causes the atom to be transformed into another having an atomic mass lower by 4 and an atomic number lower by 2, than the values for the parent atom. Each horizontal line toward the right represents the emission of a β particle; such a change is equivalent to increasing the net positive charge on the nucleus, that is, raising the atomic number by 1, without changing the mass number. The end product in both series is lead containing 82 electrons, that from the uranium series having an atomic mass of 206 and that from the thorium series 208. Another isotope of lead having an atomic mass 207 has been found and this comes from the actinium series (see Problem 9). Elements that appear in the same vertical line in the figure are isotopes; thus thorium is an isotope of uranium X_1, and thorium X is an isotope of radium.

It is customary to express the stability of a radioactive element by its *half-life*, that is, the time for half of its atoms to be transformed to something else. Since the number of atoms that disintegrate per unit time is proportional to the number present, the equation of decay becomes

$$M = M_0 \epsilon^{-\delta t} \tag{295}$$

where M_0 is the initial mass, M is the mass at time t, ϵ is the base of natural logarithms, and δ is the decay constant. The half-life is found herefrom by taking $M = M_0/2$ and solving for t. It is determined experimentally with a ray counter by counting the number of particles emitted per unit time at several times.

470. Nuclear Structure.—Before natural radioactivity became known, investigations of the atom were concerned with its outer structure, especially with the electrons in the outer shells. Changes in the arrangement of these electrons served to explain the chemical behavior of most substances, and the atomic nucleus was left out of consideration. The spontaneous liberation of particles from the radioactive elements directed attention to the nucleus and led to the realization that vast amounts of energy could be released in changing its makeup. Research on the atomic nucleus has revealed much information about its composition, has resulted in the artificial transmutation of one element into another, and has shown that nuclear reactions can be controlled and utilized.

It has been pointed out that the nuclei of atoms are believed to be composed of protons and neutrons, the two particles being nearly of the same mass. The proton has a positive electric charge that is equal in magnitude to the charge on the electron but opposite in sign; the neutron has no charge at all. For any electrically neutral atom, the number of electrons outside of the nucleus equals the number of protons in the nucleus. The three fundamental particles mentioned, together with the alpha particle, have the mass values indicated in the table below.

Mass of Basic Particles

Particle	Relative mass with respect to oxygen as 16	Mass in grams (at rest)
Electron	0.000548	9.11×10^{-28}
Proton	1.00758	1.673×10^{-24}
Neutron	1.00893	1.675×10^{-24}
Alpha particle	4.00276	6.644×10^{-24}

The nucleus of the lightest element, hydrogen, consists of a single proton; that of the next element, helium, has two protons and two neutrons; the nuclei of many elements that follow these have equal numbers of protons and neutrons; those of the heavier elements have more neutrons than protons.

The principal characteristic of the nucleus of an atom is its electrical charge, that is, the number of protons which it contains; this is the atomic number Z. Another characteristic of the nucleus is its *mass number*, that is, the sum of the numbers of protons and neutrons which it contains. If N is the number of neutrons in the nucleus, then the mass number is

$$A = Z + N$$

Every element has a number of isotopes; their nuclei have the same number of protons and therefore the same charge, but they have different numbers of neutrons and therefore have different mass numbers. The chemical properties of the isotopes of an element are of the same kind but there are differences in the rate or extent to which reactions with them take place. In a few cases isotopes have been given distinctive names; for example, the isotope of hydrogen having a mass number of 2 is called *deuterium*, and its nucleus, composed of one proton and one neutron, is called a *deuteron*. The usual method of designating an isotope of an element is to use the A-number as a superscript following the abbreviation of the element, and sometimes to use in addition the Z-number as a subscript in front. Thus, the nucleus of ordinary hydrogen is written H^1 or $_1H^1$, and that of deuterium H^2 or $_1H^2$. In this notation the neutron is expressed as $_0n^1$ because its charge is zero and its mass number is one.

The nucleus of oxygen, which serves as the basis of relative mass in the table ahead, is written $_8O^{16}$ and this representation means that there are 8 protons and a total of 16 protons and neutrons in its nucleus; oxygen has the stable isotopes $_8O^{17}$ and $_8O^{18}$, but together they have an abundance of only one-fifth of one per cent that of $_8O^{16}$.

A table of the elements in the Appendix lists the Z-numbers and the A-numbers of over 500 of their isotopes, with their principal or more abundant ones in italics. Many isotopes are stable, but there are also many which have a very short half-life. The table also includes the earlier designations of the radioactive isotopes mentioned in the preceding section as belonging to the uranium, thorium, and

Periodic Table of the Elements

Periods	Group 0	Group I		Group II		Group III		Group IV		Group V		Group VI		Group VII		Group VIII
Type of oxide / Type of hydride	......	R_2O , RH		RO , RH_2		R_2O_3 , RH_3		RO_2 , RH_4		R_2O_5 , RH_3		$R_2O_6(RO_3)$, RH_2		R_2O_7 , RH		RO_4 .....
		A	B	A	B	A	B	A	B	A	B	A	B	A	B	
	He 2 4.0028	H 1 1.0080														
First short period	Ne 10 20.183	Li 3 6.940		Be 4 9.02			B 5 10.82		C 6 12.01		N 7 14.008		O 8 16.00		F 9 19.00	
Second short period	A 18 39.944	Na 11 22.997		Mg 12 24.32			Al 13 26.97		Si 14 28.06		P 15 30.98		S 16 32.06		Cl 17 35.457	
First long period — Even series		K 19 39.10		Ca 20 40.08		Sc 21 45.10		Ti 22 47.90		V 23 50.95		Cr 24 52.01		Mn 25 54.93		Fe 26 55.84, Co 27 58.94, Ni 28 58.69
Odd series	Kr 36 83.7		Cu 29 63.57		Zn 30 65.38		Ga 31 69.72		Ge 32 72.60		As 33 74.91		Se 34 78.96		Br 35 79.916	
Second long period — Even series		Rb 37 85.48		Sr 38 87.63		Y 39 88.92		Zr 40 91.22		Cb 41 92.91		Mo 42 95.95		Ma 43 ?		Ru 44 101.7, Rh 45 102.91, Pd 46 106.7
Odd series	Xe 54 131.3		Ag 47 107.880		Cd 48 112.41		In 49 114.76		Sn 50 118.70		Sb 51 121.76		Te 52 127.61		I 53 126.92	
Third long period — Even series		Cs 55 132.91		Ba 56 137.36		La 57 138.92		Ce 58 140.13 ; Hf 72 178.6		Ta 73 180.88		W 74 183.92		Re 75 186.31		Os 76 190.2, Ir 77 193.1, Pt 78 195.23
Odd series	Rn 86 222		Au 79 197.2		Hg 80 200.61		Tl 81 204.39		Pb 82 207.21		Bi 83 209.0		Po 84		-85	
Fourth long period — Even series		-87		Ra 88 226.05		Ac 89 227		Th 90 232.12		Pa 91		U 92 238.07		Np 93		Pu 94, Am 95, Cm 96
Fifth period																

The Rare Earth Elements — Atomic Numbers 57–71

actinium series.   Also listed are the four new elements made recently
from uranium by nuclear transmutation; these have atomic numbers
93 to 96.

The accompanying chart gives the periodic table of elements arranged in columns and rows.   Those in any one column show similar
chemical behavior, while those in any row exhibit properties changing
from strongly alkaline at the left to strongly acid at the right.   The
symbol R which appears in the upper rows of the table is a general
designation of an element.

The numerals in italics represent the atomic numbers of the elements, and the others indicate their atomic weights based upon their
combining properties in chemical reactions.   If the abundance of the
isotopes of an element are known it is possible to estimate the atomic
weight from the mass numbers.   For example, with boron, the abundance of $_5B^{11}$ is 81.6 per cent and of $_5B^{10}$ is 18.4 per cent; consequently
the atomic weight of this element is $11 \times 0.816 + 10 \times 0.184 =$
10.82.

471. The Mass Spectrograph.—The masses of atoms can be measured by passing positively charged ions of the element through electric
and magnetic fields to deflect them, very much as in the determination
of e/m for electrons (§ 274).   A number of instruments for such
measurements have been devised; they are called mass spectrographs.

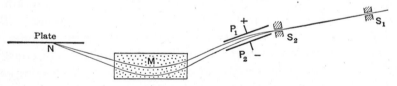

FIG. 470.   Arrangement of the Aston spectrograph

Fig. 470 shows a diagram of the mass spectrograph devised by
Francis W. Aston of Cambridge University.   Positive ions (called
positive rays) enter from a discharge tube through slits S_1 and S_2
and pass through an electric field between plates P_1 and P_2 and a
magnetic field M at right angles to the page.   The electric field deflects the rays downward and the magnetic field upward, in both
cases the ions of higher speed being deflected less than the slower ones.
The field intensities are adjusted so that, no matter what speeds the
ions have, the rays will converge to a common focus N on the photographic plate.   Ions having different masses or charges will, of course,
be deflected differently, and only those having the same e/m ratio

will arrive at a given point on the plate. Various lines will appear on the plate when the ions have various masses, and consequently the atomic masses of the isotopes of an element can be determined accurately.

472. Binding Energy.—It is found that the composite mass of a nucleus is less than the sum of the masses of the protons and neutrons of which it is composed. The difference between the mass of a nucleus and its components is a measure of the energy of cohesion of that nucleus, and indicates the energy required to break up the nucleus into those components. This difference for a given nucleus is called its *binding energy*. When divided by the number of particles in the nucleus it serves as a measure of the stability of the nucleus.

The nucleus of helium, consisting of two protons and two neutrons, would represent on a relative basis an aggregate of $2 \times 1.00758 + 2 \times 1.00893 = 4.03302$ for its components (§ 470), while the nucleus itself has a total mass of 4.00276; hence the binding energy is $4.00276 - 4.03302 = -0.03026$ in atomic mass units.

In grams, the components of the helium nucleus have a mass of $2 \times 1.673 \times 10^{-24} + 2 \times 1.675 \times 10^{-24} = 6.696 \times 10^{-24}$, and the nucleus itself has a mass of 6.644×10^{-24}; hence the loss of mass is 0.052×10^{-24}. The application of equation (294) shows that this loss is equivalent to an energy of $E = 0.052 \times 10^{-24} \times (3.00 \times 10^{10})^2 = 46.8 \times 10^{-6}$ ergs, or $46.8 \times 10^{-6} \div 1.60 \times 10^{-12} = 29 \times 10^6$ electron-volts.

The foregoing illustration shows that relatively large amounts of energy are needed to separate a nucleus into its components. Thus, the alpha particle has a binding energy of -0.03026 atomic mass units, and this is equivalent to 29 million electron-volts of energy. The fact that a nucleus exists at all is evidence that its component particles attract one another, despite the large repulsive forces that must exist between its protons at the very small distances within a nucleus, distances of the order of 10^{-12} cm. Probably the strongest force is the attraction between protons and neutrons, as yet not fully understood. The excess of the forces of attraction over those of repulsion is represented by the binding energy of a nucleus. Thus, in forming a nucleus of particles that have an aggregate mass M when far apart, and a lesser mass M' when together, the total energy of the particles is changed by the amount $(M' - M)c^2$, which is the binding energy. If the binding energy per particle is plotted against the atomic masses of all atomic nuclei it is found that the elements around $A = 65$ have lower values than either the heavier or lighter elements and therefore are more stable. This would indicate that in natural radioactivity the total energy of a nucleus tends toward a minimum.

One of the present theories of the nucleus attributes the large attractive force between the proton and neutron in close proximity to another particle discovered first in the study of cosmic rays, namely the meson. It has a mass from 30 to 300 or more times that of an electron, and its charge may be negative or positive, or perhaps even zero. Just as an electron holds two protons together in the hydrogen molecule ion, so the meson is believed to hold the proton and neutron together in the atomic nucleus. Possibly the neutron changes to a proton and a negative meson, and possibly such a meson unites with a proton to form a neutron. This helps to explain how electrons can issue from the nucleus in the emission of β rays, when no electrons are known to exist in the nucleus.

473. Nuclear Reactions.—The natural disintegration of the radioactive elements considered in § 469 is in fact the transmutation of one element into another. Such transmutation can be effected by artificial means, and the process, termed *artificial radioactivity*, is brought about by bombarding the nuclei of atoms with charged particles or neutrons. The bombardment may cause neutrons, protons, deuterons, or alpha particles to be split from the nucleus, or cause the emission of γ rays, or cause the nucleus to be split in two. Artificial radioactivity was first observed in 1934 by Irene and F. Curie-Joliot with the α-particle bombardment of the lighter elements.

The forked α-ray track shown in Fig. 468 indicates the transmutation of a nitrogen atom into an oxygen isotope. This nuclear change may be expressed in a manner similar to balanced chemical equations (Chapter XXII) by writing

$$_7N^{14} + _2He^4 = _8O^{17} + _1H^1$$

or by abbreviating it to the form

$$N^{14}(\alpha, p)O^{17}$$

where $_7N^{14}$ is the bombarded nucleus, α or $_2He^4$ is the bullet, $_8O^{17}$ is the resulting nucleus, and p or $_1H^1$ is the emitted particle.

The parenthesis in the foregoing abbreviation is used to indicate the type of nuclear reaction; in this case it is an α-particle-proton reaction. Other types of reaction are (n, p), (n, α), (p, n), (p, d), (p, α), (d, n), (d, p), (d, α), (α, n), where n represents a neutron, p a proton, and d a deuteron. When a bombarding particle is captured by a nucleus with no particle expulsion, the reaction may be represented by (n, γ) and (p, γ), where γ represents the emission of a gamma-ray photon to remove the excess energy.

Energy balance must also be considered in expressing nuclear reactions. For example, in a commonly used method for producing neutrons, a beam of deuterons ($_1H^2$) from a cyclotron (§ 275) impinges upon beryllium $_4Be^9$ and changes it to boron $_5B^{10}$, emitting neutrons in the process. The complete equation for this transmutation of beryllium into boron is

$$_4Be^9 + {}_1H^2 = {}_5B^{10} + {}_0n^1 + Q$$

where Q, if positive, is the energy emitted and, if negative, is the energy absorbed in the process. By using deuterons having energy values of several million electron-volts it is possible to produce very high energy neutrons.

The relative mass units of a beryllium nucleus, a deuteron, a boron nucleus, and a neutron are respectively 9.01283, 2.01416, 10.01344 and 1.00893. If these values are substituted in the foregoing transmutation equation, the energy value Q is found to be $+0.00462$ mass units, and this is equivalent to 4.3×10^6 electron-volts. Thus, with an incident deuteron beam of 10 million electron-volts, the energy of the neutrons in the forward direction will be 14.3 million electron-volts.

The nuclear reaction in which the nucleus captures the bombarding particle and causes the emission of a photon can be expressed by an equation of the type

$$_0n^1 + {}_ZR^A = {}_ZR^{A+1} + \gamma$$

wherein an element R of atomic number Z and atomic mass A captures a neutron. The resulting nucleus is an isotope having an atomic mass one unit greater than the target nucleus and is frequently radioactive; the photon emitted is a γ ray. An example of such a reaction is Ag $^{107}(n, \gamma)$Ag ^{108}; the radioactive silver isotope subsequently emits an electron and is transmuted to a stable isotope of cadmium. Such reactions occur only for definite neutron energies, because the frequency of the photon is determined by the transition from one atomic energy level to another.

474. Nuclear Fission.—The bombardment of heavy nuclei by neutrons renders them unstable and often causes a nucleus which captures a neutron to break apart into two fragments of comparable size instead of emitting a small particle. Such fracture is called *nuclear fission*. This effect was first observed in 1938 by Professors Otto

Hahn and Fritz Strassmann of Berlin through the production of barium and krypton from the neutron bombardment of uranium, and the release of energy of the order of 2×10^8 electron-volts per disintegration.

It was later found that the fission of uranium 238, proactinium 231, and thorium 232 required fast neutrons having energies between 1 and 1.5 million electron-volts, and that only the isotope of uranium of atomic mass 235 undergoes fission with slow neutrons. Fission has also been accomplished in elements of lesser atomic numbers than ninety.

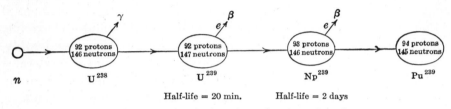

FIG. 471. Transmutation of uranium into plutonium

The creation of several elements that do not exist in nature was accomplished by nuclear bombardment of uranium. The process of making neptunium and plutonium are portrayed graphically in Fig. 471.

475. Chain Reaction and the Pile.—The bombardment of the nucleus of a heavy element by a neutron results not only in the fission of that nucleus but also in the production of several other neutrons. These in turn may split apart other nuclei with similar results, and the process may maintain itself as a *chain reaction*. Should all neutrons be effective in this process, fission would occur at an ever-increasing rate and all of the fissionable material would be disintegrated in a short time; the accompanying release of energy would produce an explosion of catastrophic power. The disintegration in this way of a uranium isotope was utilized in the so-called atomic bomb. Under suitable control the process might be developed into a practical source of energy on a large scale.

The chain reaction process was developed through a governmental project during the war, and a number of complications had to be overcome in a short time. Briefly, these complications were (1) the neutrons given off through fission were fast neutrons in that they had kinetic energies of several million electron-volts, (2) such fast neutrons are not readily caught by uranium nuclei and many of them escape from the material, (3) the uranium 238 nuclei often absorbed such neutrons without producing fission, (4) the uranium isotope 235 which is easily fissionable by slow neutrons forms only $\frac{1}{140}$ part of natural uranium, and (5) it was necessary to develop *moderators* on a large scale for reducing the energy of fast neutrons until they were immune from capture by the uranium 238 nuclei.

The material of the moderator should itself absorb relatively few of the neutrons passing through it, and it should have a low atomic weight so that an impacting neutron may give up a good proportion of its kinetic energy with each collision. For obviously, when a neutron collides elastically with the nucleus of a heavy element it rebounds with little velocity change, but when it collides elastically with a nucleus of comparable mass its velocity falls considerably. Deuterium and graphite (carbon) were found to be good moderator materials. A lattice arrangement of fissionable and moderator materials is called a *pile* or a *nuclear reactor*. Controls were provided by passageways through the pile in which rods, of material (like cadmium) that absorb neutrons strongly, can be inserted or withdrawn by remote action.

Thus, a uranium pile is a controllable machine for fundamental research on nuclei, while an atomic bomb is made of essentially pure uranium 235 and so constructed as to release energy at a colossal rate. The artificially produced element plutonium is another fissionable material which can be used for bombs, and the production of this material was the main purpose of the piles used in the government project. The pile now finds its place as a tool in the production of radioactive isotopes for medical therapy and for tracers in biological investigations, for the study of the chemical and physical aspects of atomic energy, and ultimately for the development of sources of power.

PROBLEMS

1. Compute the wavelength of the $L\alpha$ line of the x-ray spectrum of gold for which $Z = 79$ and $\sigma = 6$.

2. The photoelectric work function of a certain sodium surface is 2.10 electron-volts. What is the maximum velocity with which electrons leave this surface when it is illuminated by light of wavelength 4861 Å?

3. A beam of x-rays having a wavelength of 1.54×10^{-8} cm. is scattered by the free electrons in a graphite block. If one of the x-ray photons is scattered through an angle of 180°, how much energy has the scattering electron received?

4. Calculate the change in wavelength of the scattered radiation of x-rays when observed at angles of 60°, 90°, and 120° from the incident beam.

5. What is the energy and de Broglie wavelength of helium atoms having a velocity of 164,000 cm. per sec.?

6. What would be the mass of an electron relative to its rest mass if it were projected with a speed 99 per cent that of light?

7. What is the percentage decrease in mass of an α particle from radium when its velocity decreases from 1.92×10^9 cm. per sec. to rest?

8. The average daily energy supplied by the Consolidated Edison Company in New York City during the year ending June 1948 is 28,265,000 kw-hr. If this energy could be obtained by the conversion of matter, how much mass would have to be converted?

9. The elements of the Actinium series are believed to have the following atomic masses and atomic numbers in the order in which the disintegration occurs: Actinouranium 235, 92; Uranium Y 231, 90; Proactinium 231, 91; Actinium 227, 89; Radioactinium (RdAc) 227, 90; Actinium X 223, 88; Actinium Emanation (An) 219, 86; Actinium A 215, 84; Actinium B 211, 82; Actinium C 211, 83; Actinium C' 211, 84; Lead 207, 82. Make a chart of these transformations as in Fig. 469, and indicate which changes involve the emission of α rays and which of β rays.

10. A measurement of the decay constant for Thorium 230 (Ionium) by counting the number of α particles emitted yielded a value of 8.35×10^{-6} per year. Determine herefrom the half-life of this element.

11. How much energy in electron-volts would have to be supplied to a helium atom in order to disintegrate it into two hydrogen atoms and two neutrons? Assume the atomic masses of helium, hydrogen, and a neutron to be 4.00386, 1.00813, and 1.00893 respectively.

12. The relative abundance of the stable isotopes of magnesium are $_{12}Mg^{24}$, 77.4 per cent; $_{12}Mg^{25}$, 11.5 per cent; and $_{12}Mg^{26}$, 11.1 per cent. Estimate the atomic weight of magnesium.

13. The nuclear reaction $B^{10}(n, \alpha)Li^7$ indicates the transmutation of boron into lithium, and represents a loss of 0.0032 mass units. Write the full equation for this reaction in electron-volts on the basis that 1 mass unit is equivalent to 930 million electron-volts.

14. Fission in uranium 238 is produced by neutrons that have an energy value of 1.5 electron-volts. What is the speed of such neutrons?

Appendix

Table I.—Constants and Conversion Factors

$$\pi = 3.1416 \qquad \pi^2 = 9.8696 \qquad \frac{1}{\pi} = 0.3183$$

$$\epsilon = 2.7183 \qquad \log_\epsilon 10 = 2.3026$$

1 Ångström unit = Å = 10^{-8} cm.
1 micron = 0.001 mm.
1 centimeter = 0.39370 in.
1 inch = 2.5400 cm.
1 foot = 30.480 cm.
1 radian = 57.2958 degrees

1 gram = 15.432 grains
1 ounce = 28.350 gm.

1 pound (wt.) = 445,000 dynes
1 atmosphere = 14.697 lb. per sq. in.
1 joule = 10,000,000 ergs
1 calorie = 4.186 joules

1 coulomb = 3×10^9 esu. of charge
1 volt = $\frac{1}{300}$ erg per esu. of charge
1 farad = 9×10^{11} esu. of capacitance

1 sq. inch = 6.4516 sq. cm.
1 sq. foot = 929.03 sq. cm.
1 cu. inch = 16.387 cu. cm.
1 liter = 1000 cu. cm.
1 gallon = 3.785 liters
1 gallon = 231 cu. in.

1 pound = 453.59 gm.
1 kilogram = 2.2046 lb.

1 foot-pound = 1.3549 joules
1 Btu. = 252.00 cal.
1 Btu. = 778 ft-lb.
1 horsepower = 746 watts

1 abampere = 10 amp.
1 abvolt = 10^{-8} volts
1 faraday = 96,500 coulombs

Charge of electron = 4.80×10^{-10} esu.
Mass of electron (at rest) = 9.11×10^{-28} gm.
Avogadro's number = 6.02×10^{23}
Planck's constant = 6.62×10^{-27} erg-sec.
Mass of hydrogen atom = 1.6734×10^{-24} gm.
Velocity of light = 299,776 km. per sec. in vacuum

Table II.—Greek Alphabet

A,	α	Alpha	N,	ν	Nu
B,	β	Beta	Ξ,	ξ	Xi
Γ,	γ	Gamma	O,	o	Omicron
Δ,	δ	Delta	Π,	π	Pi
E,	ϵ	Epsilon	P,	ρ	Rho
Z,	ζ	Zeta	Σ,	σ	Sigma
H,	η	Eta	T,	τ	Tau
Θ,	θ	Theta	Υ,	υ	Upsilon
I,	ι	Iota	Φ,	ϕ	Phi
K,	κ	Kappa	X,	χ	Chi
Λ,	λ	Lambda	Ψ,	ψ	Psi
M,	μ	Mu	Ω,	ω	Omega

Table III.—Elements and Their Isotopes

Z	Element	Abbreviation	Isotopes (A-numbers)
1	Hydrogen	H	1, 2, 3
2	Helium	He	3, 4, 6
3	Lithium	Li	6, 7, 8
4	Beryllium	Be	7, 8, 9
5	Boron	B	10, 11
6	Carbon	C	10, 11, 12, 13, 14
7	Nitrogen	N	13, 14, 15, 16
8	Oxygen	O	15, 16, 17, 18, 19
9	Fluorine	F	17, 18, 19, 20
10	Neon	Ne	19, 20, 21, 22, 23
11	Sodium	Na	21, 22, 23, 24, 25
12	Magnesium	Mg	23, 24, 25, 26, 27
13	Aluminum	Al	26, 27, 28, 29
14	Silicon	Si	27, 28, 29, 30, 31
15	Phosphorus	P	29, 30, 31, 32
16	Sulfur	S	31, 32, 33, 34, 36
17	Chlorine	Cl	33, 34, 35, 36, 37, 38
18	Argon	A	35, 36, 37, 38, 39, 40
19	Potassium	K	38, 39, 40, 41
20	Calcium	Ca	39, 40, 41, 42, 43, 44, 45, 46
21	Scandium	Sc	41, 42, 43, 44, 45, 46, 48, 49
22	Titanium	Ti	45, 46, 47, 48, 49, 50, 51
23	Vanadium	V	47, 48, 49, 50, 51
24	Chromium	Cr	49, 50, 51, 52, 53, 54, 55
25	Manganese	Mn	51, 52, 53, 54, 55, 56
26	Iron	Fe	53, 54, 55, 56, 57, 58, 59, 60
27	Cobalt	Co	55, 56, 57, 58, 59, 60
28	Nickel	Ni	57, 58, 59, 60, 61, 62, 63, 64
29	Copper	Cu	58, 60, 61, 62, 63, 64, 65
30	Zinc	Zn	60, 61, 62, 63, 64, 65, 66, 67, 68, 69, 70
31	Gallium	Ga	64, 65, 66, 67, 68, 69, 70, 71, 72, 74
32	Germanium	Ge	69, 70, 71, 72, 73, 74, 75, 76, 77
33	Arsenic	As	71, 72, 73, 74, 75, 76, 77, 78
34	Selenium	Se	74, 75, 76, 77, 78, 79, 80, 81, 82, 83
35	Bromine	Br	78, 79, 80, 81, 82, 83, 84, 85
36	Krypton	Kr	78, 79, 80, 81, 82, 83, 84, 85, 86, 87, 88
37	Rubidium	Rb	82, 84, 85, 86, 87, 88, 89, 90
38	Strontium	Sr	84, 85, 86, 87, 88, 89, 90, 91
39	Yttrium	Y	87, 88, 89, 90, 91
40	Zirconium	Zr	89, 90, 91, 92, 93, 94, 95, 96, 97
41	Columbium	Cb	92, 93, 94, 95, 96, 97, 98
42	Molybdenum	Mo	92, 93, 94, 95, 96, 97, 98, 99, 100, 101
43	Technetium	Tc	96, 99, 101
44	Ruthenium	Ru	95, 96, 98, 99, 100, 101, 102, 103, 104, 105
45	Rhodium	Rh	101, 102, 103, 104, 105, 106, 107, 108, 110
46	Palladium	Pd	102, 104, 105, 106, 107, 108, 109, 110, 111, 112
47	Silver	Ag	102, 104, 105, 106, 107, 108, 109, 110, 111, 112, 115, 116, 117
48	Cadmium	Cd	106, 107, 108, 109, 110, 111, 112, 113, 114, 115, 116, 117

No.	Element	Symbol	Isotopes (mass numbers; radioactive-series names where given)
49	Indium	In	110, 111, 112, 113, 114, 115, 116, 117, 119, 120, 122, 124, 125
50	Tin	Sn	112, 113, 114, 115, 116, 117, 118, 119, 120, 122, 124, 129, 131, 133
51	Antimony	Sb	118, 120, 121, 122, 123, 124, 125, 126, 127, 128, 129, 130, 133
52	Tellurium	Te	120, 121, 122, 123, 124, 125, 126, 127, 128, 129, 130, 131, 133, 135, 137
53	Iodine	I	124, 126, 127, 128, 129, 130, 131, 132, 133, 134, 135, 137, 138
54	Xenon	Xe	124, 127, 128, 129, 130, 131, 132, 133, 134, 135, 139
55	Caesium	Cs	130, 132, 133, 134, 135, 137, 140
56	Barium	Ba	130, 133, 134, 135, 136, 137, 138, 139, 140
57	Lanthanum	La	137, 138, 139, 140
58	Cerium	Ce	136, 138, 139, 140, 142
59	Praseodymium	Pr	140, 141, 142, 143
60	Neodymium	Nd	141, 142, 143, 144, 145, 146, 147
61	(name not decided)		143, 144, 145, 147, 148
62	Samarium	Sm	144, 147, 148, 149, 150, 152, 154
63	Europium	Eu	150, 151, 152, 153, 154
64	Gadolinium	Gd	152, 154, 155, 156, 157, 159
65	Terbium	Tb	159, 160, 161, 162, 163, 164, 165
66	Dysprosium	Dy	158, 160, 161, 162, 163, 164, 165
67	Holmium	Ho	164, 165, 166, 167, 169
68	Erbium	Er	162, 164, 165, 166, 167, 168, 169, 170, 171
69	Thulium	Tm	169, 170, 171, 172, 173, 174, 175, 176
70	Ytterbium	Yb	168, 170, 171, 172, 173, 174, 175, 176, 177
71	Lutecium	Lu	175, 176, 177, 178, 179, 180, 181
72	Hafnium	Hf	174, 176, 177, 178, 179, 180, 181, 182
73	Tantalum	Ta	180, 181, 182, 183, 184, 185, 186
74	Tungsten	W	180, 182, 183, 184, 185, 186, 187, 188
75	Rhenium	Re	184, 185, 186, 187, 188, 189, 190, 191, 192, 193
76	Osmium	Os	184, 186, 187, 188, 189, 190, 191, 192, 193, 194
77	Iridium	Ir	191, 192, 193, 194, 195, 196, 197, 198, 199
78	Platinum	Pt	192, 194, 195, 196, 197, 198, 199, 200, 201
79	Gold	Au	196, 197, 198, 199, 200, 201, 202, 203, 204, 205, 206
80	Mercury	Hg	196, 198, 199, 200, 201, 202, 203, 204, 205, 206, 207, 208
81	Thallium	Tl	200, 202, 203, 204, 205, 206, 207, 208, 210, 211
82	Lead	Pb	203, 204, 205, 206, 207, 208, 209, 210 (RaD), 211 (AcB), 212 (ThB), 214 (RaB)
83	Bismuth	Bi	207, 209, 210 (RaE), 211 (AcC), 212 (ThC), 214 (RaC), 215
84	Polonium	Po	210, 211 (AcC'), 212 (ThC'), 214 (RaC'), 215 (AcA), 216 (ThA), 218 (RaA)
85	(name not decided)		211 (AcC''), 215, 216 (ThC''), 219, 220
86	Radon	Rn	219 (An), 220 (Tn), 222 (Rn), 226
87	(no name)		223 (AcX), 227
88	Radium	Ra	223 (AcX), 224 (ThX), 226, 228 (MsThI)
89	Actinium	Ac	227, 228 (MsThII)
90	Thorium	Th	227 (RdAc), 228 (RdTh), 229, 230 (Io), 231 (UY), 232, 233, 234 (UX₁)
91	Proactinium	Pa	231, 233, 234 (UX₂)
92	Uranium	U	234 (II), 235, 237, 238 (I), 239
93	Neptunium	Np	235, 237, 238, 239
94	Plutonium	Pu	236, 237, 238, 239, 241
95	Americium	Am	241
96	Curium	Cm	241, 242

Table IV.—*Logarithms of Numbers*

N	0	1	2	3	4	5	6	7	8	9	10
1.00	0.0000	.0004	.0009	.0013	.0017	.0022	.0026	.0030	.0035	.0039	.0043
1.01	.0043	.0048	.0052	.0056	.0060	.0065	.0069	.0073	.0077	.0082	.0086
1.02	.0086	.0090	.0095	.0099	.0103	.0107	.0111	.0116	.0120	.0124	.0128
1.03	.0128	.0133	.0137	.0141	.0145	.0149	.0154	.0158	.0162	.0166	.0170
1.04	.0170	.0175	.0179	.0183	.0187	.0191	.0195	.0199	.0204	.0208	.0212
1.05	.0212	.0216	.0220	.0224	.0228	.0233	.0237	.0241	.0245	.0249	.0253
1.06	.0253	.0257	.0261	.0265	.0269	.0273	.0278	.0282	.0286	.0290	.0294
1.07	.0294	.0298	.0302	.0306	.0310	.0314	.0318	.0322	.0326	.0330	.0334
1.08	.0334	.0338	.0342	.0346	.0350	.0354	.0358	.0362	.0366	.0370	.0374
1.09	.0374	.0378	.0382	.0386	.0390	.0394	.0398	.0402	.0406	.0410	.0414
1.10	0.0414	.0418	.0422	.0426	.0430	.0434	.0438	.0441	.0445	.0449	.0453
1.11	.0453	.0457	.0461	.0465	.0469	.0473	.0477	.0481	.0484	.0488	.0492
1.12	.0492	.0496	.0500	.0504	.0508	.0512	.0515	.0519	.0523	.0527	.0531
1.13	.0531	.0535	.0538	.0542	.0546	.0550	.0554	.0558	.0561	.0565	.0569
1.14	.0569	.0573	.0577	.0580	.0584	.0588	.0592	.0596	.0599	.0603	.0607
1.15	.0607	.0611	.0615	.0618	.0622	.0626	.0630	.0633	.0637	.0641	.0645
1.16	.0645	.0648	.0652	.0656	.0660	.0663	.0667	.0671	.0674	.0678	.0682
1.17	.0682	.0686	.0689	.0693	.0697	.0700	.0704	.0708	.0711	.0715	.0719
1.18	.0719	.0722	.0726	.0730	.0734	.0737	.0741	.0745	.0748	.0752	.0755
1.19	.0755	.0759	.0763	.0766	.0770	.0774	.0777	.0781	.0785	.0788	.0792
1.20	0.0792	.0795	.0799	.0803	.0806	.0810	.0813	.0817	.0821	.0824	.0828
1.21	.0828	.0831	.0835	.0839	.0842	.0846	.0849	.0853	.0856	.0860	.0864
1.22	.0864	.0867	.0871	.0874	.0878	.0881	.0885	.0888	.0892	.0896	.0899
1.23	.0899	.0903	.0906	.0910	.0913	.0917	.0920	.0924	.0927	.0931	.0934
1.24	.0934	.0938	.0941	.0945	.0948	.0952	.0955	.0959	.0962	.0966	.0969
1.25	.0969	.0973	.0976	.0980	.0983	.0986	.0990	.0993	.0997	.1000	.1004
1.26	.1004	.1007	.1011	.1014	.1017	.1021	.1024	.1028	.1031	.1035	.1038
1.27	.1038	.1041	.1045	.1048	.1052	.1055	.1059	.1062	.1065	.1069	.1072
1.28	.1072	.1075	.1079	.1082	.1086	.1089	.1092	.1096	.1099	.1103	.1106
1.29	.1106	.1109	.1113	.1116	.1119	.1123	.1126	.1129	.1133	.1136	.1139
1.30	0.1139	.1143	.1146	.1149	.1153	.1156	.1159	.1163	.1166	.1169	.1173
1.31	.1173	.1176	.1179	.1183	.1186	.1189	.1193	.1196	.1199	.1202	.1206
1.32	.1206	.1209	.1212	.1216	.1219	.1222	.1225	.1229	.1232	.1235	.1239
1.33	.1239	.1242	.1245	.1248	.1252	.1255	.1258	.1261	.1265	.1268	.1271
1.34	.1271	.1274	.1278	.1281	.1284	.1287	.1290	.1294	.1297	.1300	.1303
1.35	.1303	.1307	.1310	.1313	.1316	.1319	.1323	.1326	.1329	.1332	.1335
1.36	.1335	.1339	.1342	.1345	.1348	.1351	.1355	.1358	.1361	.1364	.1367
1.37	.1367	.1370	.1374	.1377	.1380	.1383	.1386	.1389	.1392	.1396	.1399
1.38	.1399	.1402	.1405	.1408	.1411	.1414	.1418	.1421	.1424	.1427	.1430
1.39	.1430	.1433	.1436	.1440	.1443	.1446	.1449	.1452	.1455	.1458	.1461
1.40	0.1461	.1464	.1467	.1471	.1474	.1477	.1480	.1483	.1486	.1489	.1492
1.41	.1492	.1495	.1498	.1501	.1504	.1508	.1511	.1514	.1517	.1520	.1523
1.42	.1523	.1526	.1529	.1532	.1535	.1538	.1541	.1544	.1547	.1550	.1553
1.43	.1553	.1556	.1559	.1562	.1565	.1569	.1572	.1575	.1578	.1581	.1584
1.44	.1584	.1587	.1590	.1593	.1596	.1599	.1602	.1605	.1608	.1611	.1614
1.45	.1614	.1617	.1620	.1623	.1626	.1629	.1632	.1635	.1638	.1641	.1644
1.46	.1644	.1647	.1649	.1652	.1655	.1658	.1661	.1664	.1667	.1670	.1673
1.47	.1673	.1676	.1679	.1682	.1685	.1688	.1691	.1694	.1697	.1700	.1703
1.48	.1703	.1706	.1708	.1711	.1714	.1717	.1720	.1723	.1726	.1729	.1732
1.49	.1732	.1735	.1738	.1741	.1744	.1746	.1749	.1752	.1755	.1758	.1761
N	0	1	2	3	4	5	6	7	8	9	10

Table IV.—Logarithms of Numbers (Continued)

N	0	1	2	3	4	5	6	7	8	9	10
1.50	0.1761	.1764	.1767	.1770	.1772	.1775	.1778	.1781	.1784	.1787	.1790
1.51	.1790	.1793	.1796	.1798	.1801	.1804	.1807	.1810	.1813	.1816	.1818
1.52	.1818	.1821	.1824	.1827	.1830	.1833	.1836	.1838	.1841	.1844	.1847
1.53	.1847	.1850	.1853	.1855	.1858	.1861	.1864	.1867	.1870	.1872	.1875
1.54	.1875	.1878	.1881	.1884	.1886	.1889	.1892	.1895	.1898	.1901	.1903
1.55	.1903	.1906	.1909	.1912	.1915	.1917	.1920	.1923	.1926	.1928	.1931
1.56	.1931	.1934	.1937	.1940	.1942	.1945	.1948	.1951	.1953	.1956	.1959
1.57	.1959	.1962	.1965	.1967	.1970	.1973	.1976	.1978	.1981	.1984	.1987
1.58	.1987	.1989	.1992	.1995	.1998	.2000	.2003	.2006	.2009	.2011	.2014
1.59	.2014	.2017	.2019	.2022	.2025	.2028	.2030	.2033	.2036	.2038	.2041
1.60	0.2041	.2044	.2047	.2049	.2052	.2055	.2057	.2060	.2063	.2066	.2068
1.61	.2068	.2071	.2074	.2076	.2079	.2082	.2084	.2087	.2090	.2092	.2095
1.62	.2095	.2098	.2101	.2103	.2106	.2109	.2111	.2114	.2117	.2119	.2122
1.63	.2122	.2125	.2127	.2130	.2133	.2135	.2138	.2140	.2143	.2146	.2148
1.64	.2148	.2151	.2154	.2156	.2159	.2162	.2164	.2167	.2170	.2172	.2175
1.65	.2175	.2177	.2180	.2183	.2185	.2188	.2191	.2193	.2196	.2198	.2201
1.66	.2201	.2204	.2206	.2209	.2212	.2214	.2217	.2219	.2222	.2225	.2227
1.67	.2227	.2230	.2232	.2235	.2238	.2240	.2243	.2245	.2248	.2251	.2253
1.68	.2253	.2256	.2258	.2261	.2263	.2266	.2269	.2271	.2274	.2276	.2279
1.69	.2279	.2281	.2284	.2287	.2289	.2292	.2294	.2297	.2299	.2302	.2304
1.70	0.2304	.2307	.2310	.2312	.2315	.2317	.2320	.2322	.2325	.2327	.2330
1.71	.2330	.2333	.2335	.2338	.2340	.2343	.2345	.2348	.2350	.2353	.2355
1.72	.2355	.2358	.2360	.2363	.2365	.2368	.2370	.2373	.2375	.2378	.2380
1.73	.2380	.2383	.2385	.2388	.2390	.2393	.2395	.2398	.2400	.2403	.2405
1.74	.2405	.2408	.2410	.2413	.2415	.2418	.2420	.2423	.2425	.2428	.2430
1.75	.2430	.2433	.2435	.2438	.2440	.2443	.2445	.2448	.2450	.2453	.2455
1.76	.2455	.2458	.2460	.2463	.2465	.2467	.2470	.2472	.2475	.2477	.2480
1.77	.2480	.2482	.2485	.2487	.2490	.2492	.2494	.2497	.2499	.2502	.2504
1.78	.2504	.2507	.2509	.2512	.2514	.2516	.2519	.2521	.2524	.2526	.2529
1.79	.2529	.2531	.2533	.2536	.2538	.2541	.2543	.2545	.2548	.2550	.2553
1.80	0.2553	.2555	.2558	.2560	.2562	.2565	.2567	.2570	.2572	.2574	.2577
1.81	.2577	.2579	.2582	.2584	.2586	.2589	.2591	.2594	.2596	.2598	.2601
1.82	.2601	.2603	.2605	.2608	.2610	.2613	.2615	.2617	.2620	.2622	.2625
1.83	.2625	.2627	.2629	.2632	.2634	.2636	.2639	.2641	.2643	.2646	.2648
1.84	.2648	.2651	.2653	.2655	.2658	.2660	.2662	.2665	.2667	.2669	.2672
1.85	.2672	.2674	.2676	.2679	.2681	.2683	.2686	.2688	.2690	.2693	.2695
1.86	.2695	.2697	.2700	.2702	.2704	.2707	.2709	.2711	.2714	.2716	.2718
1.87	.2718	.2721	.2723	.2725	.2728	.2730	.2732	.2735	.2737	.2739	.2742
1.88	.2742	.2744	.2746	.2749	.2751	.2753	.2755	.2758	.2760	.2762	.2765
1.89	.2765	.2767	.2769	.2772	.2774	.2776	.2778	.2781	.2783	.2785	.2788
1.90	0.2788	.2790	.2792	.2794	.2797	.2799	.2801	.2804	.2806	.2808	.2810
1.91	.2810	.2813	.2815	.2817	.2819	.2822	.2824	.2826	.2828	.2831	.2833
1.92	.2833	.2835	.2838	.2840	.2842	.2844	.2847	.2849	.2851	.2853	.2856
1.93	.2856	.2858	.2860	.2862	.2865	.2867	.2869	.2871	.2874	.2876	.2878
1.94	.2878	.2880	.2882	.2885	.2887	.2889	.2891	.2894	.2896	.2898	.2900
1.95	.2900	.2903	.2905	.2907	.2909	.2911	.2914	.2916	.2918	.2920	.2923
1.96	.2923	.2925	.2927	.2929	.2931	.2934	.2936	.2938	.2940	.2942	.2945
1.97	.2945	.2947	.2949	.2951	.2953	.2956	.2958	.2960	.2962	.2964	.2967
1.98	.2967	.2969	.2971	.2973	.2975	.2978	.2980	.2982	.2984	.2986	.2989
1.99	.2989	.2991	.2993	.2995	.2997	.2999	.3002	.3004	.3006	.3008	.3010
N	0	1	2	3	4	5	6	7	8	9	10

Table IV.—*Logarithms of Numbers* (*Continued*)

N	0	1	2	3	4	5	6	7	8	9	Proportional Parts								
											1	2	3	4	5	6	7	8	9
1.0	.0000	.0043	.0086	.0128	.0170	.0212	.0253	.0294	.0334	.0374									
1.1	.0414	.0453	.0492	.0531	.0569	.0607	.0645	.0682	.0719	.0755									
1.2	.0792	.0828	.0864	.0899	.0934	.0969	.1004	.1038	.1072	.1106									
1.3	.1139	.1173	.1206	.1239	.1271	.1303	.1335	.1367	.1399	.1430									
1.4	.1461	.1492	.1523	.1553	.1584	.1614	.1644	.1673	.1703	.1732	To avoid interpolation in the first 10 lines use table on preceding page.								
1.5	.1761	.1790	.1818	.1847	.1875	.1903	.1931	.1959	.1987	.2014									
1.6	.2041	.2068	.2095	.2122	.2148	.2175	.2201	.2227	.2253	.2279									
1.7	.2304	.2330	.2355	.2380	.2405	.2430	.2455	.2480	.2504	.2529									
1.8	.2553	.2577	.2601	.2625	.2648	.2672	.2695	.2718	.2742	.2765									
1.9	.2788	.2810	.2833	.2856	.2878	.2900	.2923	.2945	.2967	.2989									
2.0	.3010	.3032	.3054	.3075	.3096	.3118	.3139	.3160	.3181	.3201	2	4	6	8	11	13	15	17	19
2.1	.3222	.3243	.3263	.3284	.3304	.3324	.3345	.3365	.3385	.3404	2	4	6	8	10	12	14	16	18
2.2	.3424	.3444	.3464	.3483	.3502	.3522	.3541	.3560	.3579	.3598	2	4	6	8	10	12	14	15	17
2.3	.3617	.3636	.3655	.3674	.3692	.3711	.3729	.3747	.3766	.3784	2	4	6	7	9	11	13	15	17
2.4	.3802	.3820	.3838	.3856	.3874	.3892	.3909	.3927	.3945	.3962	2	4	5	7	9	11	12	14	16
2.5	.3979	.3997	.4014	.4031	.4048	.4065	.4082	.4099	.4116	.4133	2	3	5	7	9	10	12	14	15
2.6	.4150	.4166	.4183	.4200	.4216	.4232	.4249	.4265	.4281	.4298	2	3	5	7	8	10	11	13	15
2.7	.4314	.4330	.4346	.4362	.4378	.4393	.4409	.4425	.4440	.4456	2	3	5	6	8	9	11	13	14
2.8	.4472	.4487	.4502	.4518	.4533	.4548	.4564	.4579	.4594	.4609	2	3	5	6	8	9	11	12	14
2.9	.4624	.4639	.4654	.4669	.4683	.4698	.4713	.4728	.4742	.4757	1	3	4	6	7	9	10	12	13
3.0	.4771	.4786	.4800	.4814	.4829	.4843	.4857	.4871	.4886	.4900	1	3	4	6	7	9	10	11	13
3.1	.4914	.4928	.4942	.4955	.4969	.4983	.4997	.5011	.5024	.5038	1	3	4	6	7	8	10	11	12
3.2	.5051	.5065	.5079	.5092	.5105	.5119	.5132	.5145	.5159	.5172	1	3	4	5	7	8	9	11	12
3.3	.5185	.5198	.5211	.5224	.5237	.5250	.5263	.5276	.5289	.5302	1	3	4	5	6	8	9	10	12
3.4	.5315	.5328	.5340	.5353	.5366	.5378	.5391	.5403	.5416	.5428	1	3	4	5	6	8	9	10	11
3.5	.5441	.5453	.5465	.5478	.5490	.5502	.5514	.5527	.5539	.5551	1	2	4	5	6	7	9	10	11
3.6	.5563	.5575	.5587	.5599	.5611	.5623	.5635	.5647	.5658	.5670	1	2	4	5	6	7	8	10	11
3.7	.5682	.5694	.5705	.5717	.5729	.5740	.5752	.5763	.5775	.5786	1	2	3	5	6	7	8	9	10
3.8	.5798	.5809	.5821	.5832	.5843	.5855	.5866	.5877	.5888	.5899	1	2	3	5	6	7	8	9	10
3.9	.5911	.5922	.5933	.5944	.5955	.5966	.5977	.5988	.5999	.6010	1	2	3	4	5	7	8	9	10
4.0	.6021	.6031	.6042	.6053	.6064	.6075	.6085	.6096	.6107	.6117	1	2	3	4	5	6	8	9	10
4.1	.6128	.6138	.6149	.6160	.6170	.6180	.6191	.6201	.6212	.6222	1	2	3	4	5	6	7	8	9
4.2	.6232	.6243	.6253	.6263	.6274	.6284	.6294	.6304	.6314	.6325	1	2	3	4	5	6	7	8	9
4.3	.6335	.6345	.6355	.6365	.6375	.6385	.6395	.6405	.6415	.6425	1	2	3	4	5	6	7	8	9
4.4	.6435	.6444	.6454	.6464	.6474	.6484	.6493	.6503	.6513	.6522	1	2	3	4	5	6	7	8	9
4.5	.6532	.6542	.6551	.6561	.6571	.6580	.6590	.6599	.6609	.6618	1	2	3	4	5	6	7	8	9
4.6	.6628	.6637	.6646	.6656	.6665	.6675	.6684	.6693	.6702	.6712	1	2	3	4	5	6	7	7	8
4.7	.6721	.6730	.6739	.6749	.6758	.6767	.6776	.6785	.6794	.6803	1	2	3	4	5	5	6	7	8
4.8	.6812	.6821	.6830	.6839	.6848	.6857	.6866	.6875	.6884	.6893	1	2	3	4	4	5	6	7	8
4.9	.6902	.6911	.6920	.6928	.6937	.6946	.6955	.6964	.6972	.6981	1	2	3	4	4	5	6	7	8
5.0	.6990	.6998	.7007	.7016	.7024	.7033	.7042	.7050	.7059	.7067	1	2	3	3	4	5	6	7	8
5.1	.7076	.7084	.7093	.7101	.7110	.7118	.7126	.7135	.7143	.7152	1	2	3	3	4	5	6	7	8
5.2	.7160	.7168	.7177	.7185	.7193	.7202	.7210	.7218	.7226	.7235	1	2	2	3	4	5	6	7	7
5.3	.7243	.7251	.7259	.7267	.7275	.7284	.7292	.7300	.7308	.7316	1	2	2	3	4	5	6	6	7
5.4	.7324	.7332	.7340	.7348	.7356	.7364	.7372	.7380	.7388	.7396	1	2	2	3	4	5	6	6	7
N	**0**	**1**	**2**	**3**	**4**	**5**	**6**	**7**	**8**	**9**	1	2	3	4	5	6	7	8	9

Table IV.—Logarithms of Numbers (Continued)

N	0	1	2	3	4	5	6	7	8	9	Proportional Parts								
											1	2	3	4	5	6	7	8	9
5.5	.7404	.7412	.7419	.7427	.7435	.7443	.7451	.7459	.7466	.7474	1 2 2			3 4 5			5 6 7		
5.6	.7482	.7490	.7497	.7505	.7513	.7520	.7528	.7536	.7543	.7551	1 2 2			3 4 5			5 6 7		
5.7	.7559	.7566	.7574	.7582	.7589	.7597	.7604	.7612	.7619	.7627	1 2 2			3 4 5			5 6 7		
5.8	.7634	.7642	.7649	.7657	.7664	.7672	.7679	.7686	.7694	.7701	1 1 2			3 4 4			5 6 7		
5.9	.7709	.7716	.7723	.7731	.7738	.7745	.7752	.7760	.7767	.7774	1 1 2			3 4 4			5 6 7		
6.0	.7782	.7789	.7796	.7803	.7810	.7818	.7825	.7832	.7839	.7846	1 1 2			3 4 4			5 6 6		
6.1	.7853	.7860	.7868	.7875	.7882	.7889	.7896	.7903	.7910	.7917	1 1 2			3 4 4			5 6 6		
6.2	.7924	.7931	.7938	.7945	.7952	.7959	.7966	.7973	.7980	.7987	1 1 2			3 3 4			5 6 6		
6.3	.7993	.8000	.8007	.8014	.8021	.8028	.8035	.8041	.8048	.8055	1 1 2			3 3 4			5 5 6		
6.4	.8062	.8069	.8075	.8082	.8089	.8096	.8102	.8109	.8116	.8122	1 1 2			3 3 4			5 5 6		
6.5	.8129	.8136	.8142	.8149	.8156	.8162	.8169	.8176	.8182	.8189	1 1 2			3 3 4			5 5 6		
6.6	.8195	.8202	.8209	.8215	.8222	.8228	.8235	.8241	.8248	.8254	1 1 2			3 3 4			5 5 6		
6.7	.8261	.8267	.8274	.8280	.8287	.8293	.8299	.8306	.8312	.8319	1 1 2			3 3 4			5 5 6		
6.8	.8325	.8331	.8338	.8344	.8351	.8357	.8363	.8370	.8376	.8382	1 1 2			3 3 4			4 5 6		
6.9	.8388	.8395	.8401	.8407	.8414	.8420	.8426	.8432	.8439	.8445	1 1 2			2 3 4			4 5 6		
7.0	.8451	.8457	.8463	.8470	.8476	.8482	.8488	.8494	.8500	.8506	1 1 2			2 3 4			4 5 6		
7.1	.8513	.8519	.8525	.8531	.8537	.8543	.8549	.8555	.8561	.8567	1 1 2			2 3 4			4 5 5		
7.2	.8573	.8579	.8585	.8591	.8597	.8603	.8609	.8615	.8621	.8627	1 1 2			2 3 4			4 5 5		
7.3	.8633	.8639	.8645	.8651	.8657	.8663	.8669	.8675	.8681	.8686	1 1 2			2 3 4			4 5 5		
7.4	.8692	.8698	.8704	.8710	.8716	.8722	.8727	.8733	.8739	.8745	1 1 2			2 3 4			4 5 5		
7.5	.8751	.8756	.8762	.8768	.8774	.8779	.8785	.8791	.8797	.8802	1 1 2			2 3 3			4 5 5		
7.6	.8808	.8814	.8820	.8825	.8831	.8837	.8842	.8848	.8854	.8859	1 1 2			2 3 3			4 5 5		
7.7	.8865	.8871	.8876	.8882	.8887	.8893	.8899	.8904	.8910	.8915	1 1 2			2 3 3			4 4 5		
7.8	.8921	.8927	.8932	.8938	.8943	.8949	.8954	.8960	.8965	.8971	1 1 2			2 3 3			4 4 5		
7.9	.8976	.8982	.8987	.8993	.8998	.9004	.9009	.9015	.9020	.9025	1 1 2			2 3 3			4 4 5		
8.0	.9031	.9036	.9042	.9047	.9053	.9058	.9063	.9069	.9074	.9079	1 1 2			2 3 3			4 4 5		
8.1	.9085	.9090	.9096	.9101	.9106	.9112	.9117	.9122	.9128	.9133	1 1 2			2 3 3			4 4 5		
8.2	.9138	.9143	.9149	.9154	.9159	.9165	.9170	.9175	.9180	.9186	1 1 2			2 3 3			4 4 5		
8.3	.9191	.9196	.9201	.9206	.9212	.9217	.9222	.9227	.9232	.9238	1 1 2			2 3 3			4 4 5		
8.4	.9243	.9248	.9253	.9258	.9263	.9269	.9274	.9279	.9284	.9289	1 1 2			2 3 3			4 4 5		
8.5	.9294	.9299	.9304	.9309	.9315	.9320	.9325	.9330	.9335	.9340	1 1 2			2 3 3			4 4 5		
8.6	.9345	.9350	.9355	.9360	.9365	.9370	.9375	.9380	.9385	.9390	1 1 1			2 3 3			4 4 5		
8.7	.9395	.9400	.9405	.9410	.9415	.9420	.9425	.9430	.9435	.9440	0 1 1			2 2 3			3 4 4		
8.8	.9445	.9450	.9455	.9460	.9465	.9469	.9474	.9479	.9484	.9489	0 1 1			2 2 3			3 4 4		
8.9	.9494	.9499	.9504	.9509	.9513	.9518	.9523	.9528	.9533	.9538	0 1 1			2 2 3			3 4 4		
9.0	.9542	.9547	.9552	.9557	.9562	.9566	.9571	.9576	.9581	.9586	0 1 1			2 2 3			3 4 4		
9.1	.9590	.9595	.9600	.9605	.9609	.9614	.9619	.9624	.9628	.9633	0 1 1			2 2 3			3 4 4		
9.2	.9638	.9643	.9647	.9652	.9657	.9661	.9666	.9671	.9675	.9680	0 1 1			2 2 3			3 4 4		
9.3	.9685	.9689	.9694	.9699	.9703	.9708	.9713	.9717	.9722	.9727	0 1 1			2 2 3			3 4 4		
9.4	.9731	.9736	.9741	.9745	.9750	.9754	.9759	.9763	.9768	.9773	0 1 1			2 2 3			3 4 4		
9.5	.9777	.9782	.9786	.9791	.9795	.9800	.9805	.9809	.9814	.9818	0 1 1			2 2 3			3 4 4		
9.6	.9823	.9827	.9832	.9836	.9841	.9845	.9850	.9854	.9859	.9863	0 1 1			2 2 3			3 4 4		
9.7	.9868	.9872	.9877	.9881	.9886	.9890	.9894	.9899	.9903	.9908	0 1 1			2 2 3			3 4 4		
9.8	.9912	.9917	.9921	.9926	.9930	.9934	.9939	.9943	.9948	.9952	0 1 1			2 2 3			3 4 4		
9.9	.9956	.9961	.9965	.9969	.9974	.9978	.9983	.9987	.9991	.9996	0 1 1			2 2 3			3 3 4		
N	0	1	2	3	4	5	6	7	8	9	1 2 3			4 5 6			7 8 9		

Table V.—*Trigonometric Functions* (*Natural*)

Angle	Sine	Cosine	Tangent	Angle	Sine	Cosine	Tangent
0°	0.000	1.000	0.000				
1°	.018	1.000	.018	46°	0.719	0.695	1.036
2°	.035	0.999	.035	47°	.731	.682	1.072
3°	.052	.999	.052	48°	.743	.669	1.111
4°	.070	.998	.070	49°	.755	.656	1.150
5°	.087	.996	.088	50°	.766	.643	1.192
6°	.105	.995	.105	51°	.777	.629	1.235
7°	.122	.993	.123	52°	.788	.616	1.280
8°	.139	.990	.141	53°	.799	.602	1.327
9°	.156	.988	.158	54°	.809	.588	1.376
10°	.174	.985	.176	55°	.819	.574	1.428
11°	.191	.982	.194	56°	.829	.559	1.483
12°	.208	.978	.213	57°	.839	.545	1.540
13°	.225	.974	.231	58°	.848	.530	1.600
14°	.242	.970	.249	59°	.857	.515	1.664
15°	.259	.966	.268	60°	.866	.500	1.732
16°	.276	.961	.287	61°	.875	.485	1.804
17°	.292	.956	.306	62°	.883	.470	1.881
18°	.309	.951	.325	63°	.891	.454	1.963
19°	.326	.946	.344	64°	.899	.438	2.050
20°	.342	.940	.364	65°	.906	.423	2.145
21°	.358	.934	.384	66°	.914	.407	2.246
22°	.375	.927	.404	67°	.921	.391	2.356
23°	.391	.921	.425	68°	.927	.375	2.475
24°	.407	.914	.445	69°	.934	.358	2.605
25°	.423	.906	.466	70°	.940	.342	2.747
26°	.438	.899	.488	71°	.946	.326	2.904
27°	.454	.891	.510	72°	.951	.309	3.078
28°	.470	.883	.532	73°	.956	.292	3.271
29°	.485	.875	.554	74°	.961	.276	3.487
30°	.500	.866	.577	75°	.966	.259	3.732
31°	.515	.857	.601	76°	.970	.242	4.011
32°	.530	.848	.625	77°	.974	.225	4.331
33°	.545	.839	.649	78°	.978	.208	4.705
34°	.559	.829	.675	79°	.982	.191	5.145
35°	.574	.819	.700	80°	.985	.174	5.671
36°	.588	.809	.727	81°	.988	.156	6.314
37°	.602	.799	.754	82°	.990	.139	7.115
38°	.616	.788	.781	83°	.993	.122	8.144
39°	.629	.777	.810	84°	.995	.105	9.514
40°	.643	.766	.839	85°	.996	.087	11.43
41°	.656	.755	.869	86°	.998	.070	14.30
42°	.669	.743	.900	87°	.999	.052	19.08
43°	.682	.731	.933	88°	.999	.035	28.64
44°	.695	.719	.966	89°	1.000	.018	57.29
45°	.707	.707	1.000	90°	1.000	.000	∞

Trigonometric Functions for Angles Larger than 90 Degrees

When the angle lies beyond the first quadrant, the accompanying table of trigonometric functions of any angle θ can be used by applying the following:

Second Quadrant............$\begin{cases} \sin\ (\ 90 + \theta) = \ \cos\theta \\ \cos\ (\ 90 + \theta) = -\sin\theta \\ \tan\ (\ 90 + \theta) = -\cot\theta \end{cases}$

Third Quadrant............$\begin{cases} \sin\ (180 + \theta) = -\sin\theta \\ \cos\ (180 + \theta) = -\cos\theta \\ \tan\ (180 + \theta) = \ \tan\theta \end{cases}$

Fourth Quadrant............$\begin{cases} \sin\ (270 + \theta) = -\cos\theta \\ \cos\ (270 + \theta) = \ \sin\theta \\ \tan\ (270 + \theta) = -\cot\theta \end{cases}$

ANSWERS TO PROBLEMS
HAVING ODD NUMBERS

MECHANICS

Chapter I

1. 9219 meters. **3.** (Proof). **5.** 2125 mi. **7.** 0.307 parsec. **9.** 41.4°. **11.** 173 ft. **13.** 153 mi. from A; 191 mi. from B. **15.** 38,700,000 gal. **17.** 3.196 acres. **19.** 0.200 sq. in. **21.** \$35.00. **23.** 81.4 lb. per cu. ft. **25.** (Explanation).

Chapter II

1. 109.6 mi.; 24.2° north of west. **3.** 17.7 mi.; 28.7° south of east. **5.** 404 cm. each. **7.** 3.64 mi. **9.** 4.20 lb. **11.** Vertical 130 lb.; other 150 lb. **13.** 8.66 ft. **15.** (*a*) 180 lb-in., (*b*) 0, (*c*) 103.2 lb-in.

Chapter III

1. 8.24 min. **3.** A; 7.27 sec. **5.** 19.2 km. per hr.; 55.6° east of north. **7.** 1548 ft. per sec. **9.** 6.00 rev. per min. **11.** 47.1 ft. per min. **13.** 6.67 meters per sec. **15.** 28.1 ft. per sec. **17.** 36.8 mi. per hr. to Richmond; 51.5 mi. per hr. beyond. **19.** 45.6 ft. per sec. **21.** 56.9° east of north; 2.47 hr. **23.** 12.72 knots; from a direction 19.4° west of south.

Chapter IV

1. 4.00 km. per hr. per sec. **3.** 77.0 ft. **5.** 41.8 ft. per sec. per sec.; 4.03 sec. **7.** 1210 ft. **9.** 14.0 meters per sec. **11.** 4.95 sec. **13.** 9.77 ft. **15.** 514 meters. **17.** 0.465 sec.; 3.47 ft. **19.** 17.3 meters per sec. **21.** 2.55°. **23.** 1231 ft. **25.** −6.28 radians per sec. per sec.; 200 rev. **27.** 1.75 ft. per sec. per sec.

Chapter V

1. 75.0 cm. per sec. per sec. **3.** 1,500,000 dynes. **5.** 939,000 lb-ft. per sec. **7.** 5.96×10^{24} kg. **9.** 57.1 ft. **11.** 9850 lb. **13.** 3.20 ft. per sec. per sec.; 3.06 sec. **15.** (*a*) 175 lb., (*b*) 145 lb. **17.** 8.00 ft. per sec. per sec. **19.** 1.157 ft. per sec. per sec. **21.** 74.2 lb. **23.** 760 lb. **25.** 2020 lb. **27.** 7.25 lb. **29.** 262,000 times as large. **31.** 15.7°.

Chapter VI

1. −20.0 radians per sec. per sec. **3.** 467,000 gm-cm.² **5.** 12.03 lb-ft.² **7.** (*a*) 120 lb-in.², (*b*) 420 lb-in.² **9.** $I = \dfrac{M}{2}(r_2^2 + r_1^2)$. **11.** 9.80 radians per sec. per sec. **13.** 28.9 cm. **15.** 5.57 rev. **17.** 19.3 lb-ft. **19.** 33.1 rev. per min.

Chapter VII

1. 8400 kg-meters or 82,300 joules. **3.** 159,000 ft-lb. **5.** 2500 ft-lb. **7.** 12,730 ft-lb. **9.** 13.8 lb-ft.; 6500 ft-lb. **11.** 8530 ft-lb. **13.** (*a*) 886,000 ergs, (*b*) 154 cm. per sec. **15.** 7.56 hp. **17.** 2290 lb. **19.** 46.7 hp. **21.** 11.14 hp. **23.** \$2.06. **25.** (*a*) 8.00, (*b*) 5.33, (*c*) 66.7 per cent

Chapter VIII

1. 50.0 lb. **3.** 833 lb. **5.** (Derivation). **7.** 10.0 kg.; 22.0 cm. from D. **9.** (a) 189 lb., (b) 333 lb-ft. **11.** 12.40 in. **13.** Left, 3.80 tons; right, 4.20 tons. **15.** 2.00 in. **17.** 0.000524 degrees per milligram. **19.** Window, 25.5 lb. perpendicularly; ground, 190 lb. vertically downward and 25.5 lb. horizontally away from window. **21.** Tension, 136.8 lb.; thrust, 125.3 lb., 22.3° down from horizontal. **23.** 121.4 lb. **25.** 36.1 lb.

Chapter IX

1. 58.8 sec. **3.** 5.09 vibrations per sec. **5.** (a) 1.248 vibrations per sec., (b) 1.307 ft. per sec. **7.** 12.41 kg. **9.** 3.85 sec. **11.** 35.7 cm. **13.** 1.53 sec. **15.** 9.00 lb. each. **17.** 0.245 dyne-cm.

Chapter X

1. 250,000 lb. per sq. in. **3.** Yes; 0.1250 cm. per meter. **5.** 0.0960 in. **7.** 4190 lb. **9.** 476 kg. per sq. mm.; 0.00210. **11.** 0.183 cu. cm. **13.** Breadth $\times$ depth^2 = 157.5 in.^{3} **15.** 1.201°. **17.** 181 lb-ft. per radian; 0.877 in. **19.** 15.63 lb-ft. per sec.; 7320 lb. **21.** 172 cm. per sec.; after impact, first ball 0 cm. per sec., second ball 172 cm. per sec.

Chapter XI

1. (a) 0.433 lb. per sq. in., (b) 0.100 kg. per sq. cm. **3.** 1345 lb. per sq. in.; 5330 lb. per sq. in. **5.** 185 ft. **7.** 1997 lb. **9.** At the 65.0-cm. mark; 550 gm. **11.** 42,200 lb-ft. **13.** (a) 374,000 lb-ft., (b) 1,800,000 lb-ft. **15.** 57.0 cu. cm.; 8.09. **17.** 17,800 lb. **19.** 0.889; 1,008,300 dynes per sq. cm. **21.** (Derivation). **23.** 1.001 ft. **25.** (a) 7.20 lb., (b) 92.8 lb. **27.** 1.57 cm.

Chapter XII

1. 626 cm. per sec.; 443 cm. per sec.; 313 cm. per sec. **3.** 0.265 cu. ft. per sec. **5.** 54.2 lb. per sq. in. **7.** 319 hp. **9.** 8.65 meters per sec. **11.** 103.5 cm. per sec. **13.** 6.02 poises.

Chapter XIII

1. 8.79 per cent. **3.** 1033 gm. per sq. cm. **5.** 40.3 meters. **7.** $p_1d_2 = p_2d_1$. **9.** 8.65 in. **11.** Gage 46.0 cm. of mercury, absolute 122.0 cm. of mercury. **13.** 8.00 km. **15.** (a) 2.95 lb., (b) 39.0 cu. ft. **17.** 156 lb. **19.** 792 lb.; 4.83 ft. per sec. per sec., taking density of hydrogen as 0.0056 lb. per cu. ft.

HEAT

Chapter XIV

1. 37.0° C. **3.** 19.0° F.; 137.8° F. **5.** −40.0. **7.** 0.0220 per cent. **9.** 0.001144 in. **11.** 32.0 lb. **13.** 59.2 cu. in. **15.** 0.729 gal. **17.** 99.34° C.

Chapter XV

1. 4590 Btu. **3.** 120.1° F. **5.** 4660 Btu. **7.** 20,000 Btu. per hr. **9.** 38.5° C. **11.** 126 cal. **13.** 225 Btu. **15.** 0.0287 in. **17.** 26.7 gm. **19.** 252° C.; 57 per cent tin and 43 per cent lead. **21.** 540 cal. per gm. **23.** 4000 Btu. per hr. **25.** 51.3 gm. of ice and the rest water, all at 0°C. **27.** 7.70 lb.

Chapter XVI

1. 112.0 cu. ft. **3.** 10.06 in. **5.** 160° C. **7.** 46.9 kg. per sq. cm. gage pressure. **9.** 17.5 liters. **11.** 158.25 cm. of mercury. **13.** 0.201 lb. **15.** 129.5 lb. per sq. in. **17.** 0.200 cal. per gm. per centigrade degree at constant pressure; 0.129 cal. per gm. per centigrade degree at constant volume. **19.** (*a*) 152 cm. of mercury, (*b*) 201 cm. of mercury. **21.** 97.6 per cent.

Chapter XVII

1. (*a*) 335 joules, (*b*) 112,000 ft-lb. **3.** 0.0273 watt-hr. **5.** 23,900 Btu. **7.** 0.811 cal. **9.** 0.703 centigrade degree. **11.** 25.4 per cent. **13.** 38.0 per cent. **15.** 2200 ft-lb.; 16.0 hp. **17.** 19.6 per cent. **19.** 0.492 hp.

Chapter XVIII

1. 1,313,000 cal. per hr. **3.** 328 Btu. per hr. **5.** (*a*) 912,000 Btu. per day, (*b*) $219.60. **7.** 241 gal. per min. **9.** 1.55 hp. **11.** 25.8 cal. per sec. **13.** 0.0169 cal. per sec. per sq. cm. **15.** 76.3° F.

ELECTRICITY AND MAGNETISM

Chapter XIX

1. 120 dynes attraction. **3.** 1,012,000 tons repulsion. **5.** +1.307 esu. of charge. **7.** 2.49 cm. from smaller charge. **9.** (Derivation). **11.** 38.5 cm. from larger charge. **13.** (*a*) 100.0 ergs per esu. of charge, (*b*) 29.6 ergs per esu. of charge. **15.** 10.58 dynes per esu. of charge, toward AB and 40.9° from BC; −100 ergs per esu. of charge. **17.** 0.472 erg per esu. of charge. **19.** 2.25×10^8 cm. per sec. **21.** 178.

Chapter XX

1. 2500 dynes attraction. **3.** 2050 dynes repulsion. **5.** 1000 dyne-cm. **7.** 25.0 oersteds, away from N pole. **9.** Either 45.5 oersteds or zero. **11.** (Derivation). **13.** 0.570 oersted; 71.4° from horizontal. **15.** 0.185 oersted.

Chapter XXI

1. 87.6 per cent. **3.** 93.8 cents. **5.** 0.313 volt. **7.** 275,000 ohms. **9.** 0.930 cent. **11.** 69.8 sec. **13.** 100.0 dynes per esu. of charge. **15.** 0.0597 ohm. **17.** 20.5 ft. **19.** (*a*) 14.95 ohms, (*b*) 15.25 ohms. **21.** No. 2 Awg. **23.** 5.40 volts; 2.25 ohms. **25.** 4.00 volts; 44.4 watts. **27.** Singly 720 and 480 watts; in series 288 watts; in parallel 1200 watts. **29.** 0.190 ohm. **31.** First 96.0 volts; second 144.0 volts. **33.** In E_1 0.0983 amp.; in E_2 0.0103 amp.

Chapter XXII

1. 0.0829 gm. **3.** 48.3 gm. **5.** 413,000 joules. **7.** Silver 0.001118; gold 0.000681. **9.** 10,710 coulombs. **11.** 5.00; 5.30. **13.** 4.99 lb. **15.** 1245 watts. **17.** (*a*) Parallel, (*b*) series. **19.** 1.000 amp. **21.** In E_1 0.688 amp.; in E_2 0.156 amp.; in load 0.531 amp.

Chapter XXIII

1. 11.78 oersteds downward. **3.** 201 dynes. **5.** 0.0348 amp. **7.** 0.0984 oersted. **9.** 424,000 maxwells. **11.** 754 dynes. **13.** 70.0 dynes. **15.** 4.36×10^{-8} amp. **17.** (*a*) 0.01001 ohm, (*b*) 29,990 ohms. **19.** 2.00 volts. **21.** 14,900 maxwells per sq. cm. **23.** (*a*) 0.0500 volt, (*b*) decrease. **25.** (*a*) 0.00375 coulomb, (*b*) 0.00375 coulomb. **27.** (Derivation). **29.** 9780 maxwells per sq. cm.

Chapter XXIV

1. 0.00625 henry. **3.** 0.327. **5.** 9.05 henries. **7.** 8.00 millihenries. **9.** First 100.0 amp. per sec.; second 50.0 amp. per sec. **11.** 5.87 joules. **13.** 323 watts. **15.** 15.75 oersteds; 366,000 maxwells. **17.** 0.1130 amp. **19.** 4.06 mf. **21.** 2.83. **23.** Three; two in series and this group in parallel with the third. **25.** Initial state—first condenser, charge 24 microcoulombs, potential difference 24 volts, stored energy 2880 ergs; second condenser, no charge, no potential difference, no stored energy. Final state— each condenser, charge 12 microcoulombs, potential difference 12 volts, stored energy 720 ergs. Heat and radiation.

Chapter XXV

1. 0.0600 sec.; 33.3 times. **3.** 14.14 amp. **5.** 43.0 centigrade degrees. **7.** (*a*) 160 volts, (*b*) 60.0 volts, (*c*) 120.8 volts. **9.** 120.0 volts; lags *B* by 120°. **11.** 1131 ohms. **13.** (*a*) 4780 ohms, (*b*) 79.6 ohms. **15.** (*a*) 75.4 ohms, (*b*) 78.0 ohms, (*c*) 2.82 amp., (*d*) 75.1°. **17.** 100 volts across resistor; 100 volts across coil; 200 volts across condenser. **19.** 2.21 henries. **21.** 159 watts; 25.7 per cent. **23.** 69.6 per cent.

Chapter XXVI

1. Like lower curve in part II of Fig. 292; each lobe is 0.300 sec. on base and peak value is 0.0209 volt. **3.** 2300 rev. per min. **5.** 12,210 maxwells per sq. cm. **7.** (*a*) 117.0 volts, (*b*) 1.17 amp. **9.** 3,600,000 dyne-cm. **11.** 16.4 amp. **13.** 85.5 per cent. **15.** (*a*) 500 rev. per min., (*b*) 60. **17.** 16.3 amp. **19.** 4.55 amp.

Chapter XXVII

1. 4.45 millivolts. **3.** 82° C. **5.** 6. **7.** 4.52 electron-volts. **9.** 78,000 ohms. **11.** 0.250 to 0.750 microamp. **13.** 12.09×10^{18} cycles per sec.

Chapter XXVIII

1. 32.0 ohms per mi. **3.** (*a*) 0.1096 amp., (*b*) 4.11 per cent. **5.** 54.0 db. **7.** 0.000253 mf. **9.** 907,000 cycles per sec. **11.** 4.13 megacycles per sec. **13.** (*a*) 70.0, (*b*) 3000.

Chapter XXIX

1. 3070 newtons. **3.** 34.0 kw. **5.** 287 joules per kg. per kelvin degree. **7.** (Proof). **9.** 2.50 millivolts. **11.** 6.00×10^6 newtons per coulomb toward negative charge.

SOUND

Chapter XXX

1. (*a*) 0.00250 sec.; 86.3 cm., (*b*) 0.00250 sec.; 368 cm. **3.** 392 ft. per sec. **5.** 60.0 vibrations per sec. **7.** Advancing and reflected waves in light rope, velocity 640 ft. per sec., wavelength 160 ft.; transmitted wave in heavy rope, velocity 320 ft. per sec., wavelength 80 ft.; all waves, frequency 4.00 vibrations per sec. **9.** 4420 ft. **11.** 0.1181 sec. **13.** 10.1 centigrade degrees. **15.** 3,000,000 kilocycles per sec. **17.** 3.83 ft. per sec. **19.** 1.163 cm. **21.** 367 ft. **23.** 19.6 ft.

Chapter XXXI

1. 225 units. **3.** (Equation). **5.** 6.00 ft.; 3.00 ft.; 2.00 ft. **7.** 250, 500, and 750 vibrations per sec. **9.** 8.00 ft.; 2.67 ft.; 1.60 ft. **11.** 1.042 ft. **13.** 266 and 508 vibrations per sec. **15.** 1096 ft. per sec. **17.** 2.20 ft. **19.** (*a*) 310 vibrations per sec., (*b*) 254 vibrations per sec. **21.** The *G* above the lowest *C*.

Chapter XXXII

1. 0.0100 microwatt per sq. cm. **3.** 1000 microwatts. **5.** 4:1; 6.02 db. **7.** 11.25 in. **9.** In rod, 3370 meters per sec.; in gas, 334 meters per sec. **11.** 368,000,000 vibrations per sec. **13.** 0.365.

LIGHT

Chapter XXXIII

1. 29.3 lumens per sq. ft. **3.** 50.7:1. **5.** 1.325:1. **7.** 31.5 ft-candles. **9.** (a) 4.65 ft-candles, (b) 65.0 cp. **11.** 1432 microamp. per lumen. **13.** 221,000 astronomical units. **15.** 240 rev. per sec.

Chapter XXXIV

1. 1 ft. and 7 ft. behind one mirror; 3 ft. and 5 ft. behind the other. **3.** Three images; object and images are at the corners of a rectangle measuring 6 x 8 cm. with mirror intersection as center. **5.** 0.229°. **7.** 13.33 in. and 6.67 in. in front of mirror. **9.** Linear 12.7; surface 161. **11.** 1.55. **13.** 0.717 cm. **15.** (a) 0.889, (b) 1.125. **17.** 36.2°. **19.** (a) 46.0°, (b) 1.60. **21.** 1.54. **23.** $\frac{2}{3}$ full. **25.** 1.414. **27.** 0.980:1.000.

Chapter XXXV

1. (Explanation). **3.** 0.20°. **5.** 10.53°; 5.45°. **7.** 14.32°. **9.** 1.631; 7.57°. **11.** 0.331 mm. **13.** Lyman—82,300, 97,540 and 102,880 waves per cm.; Balmer—15,240, 20,580 and 23,050 waves per cm.; Paschen—5330, 7800 and 9150 waves per cm. **15.** (Diagram). **17.** (Explanation).

Chapter XXXVI

1. 2.81 ft. **3.** 1.640. **5.** 11.68 in. **7.** Respective image distances: 30, 60, 90, ∞, −60, and −15 cm. **9.** 7.14 cm. from lens. **11.** ±13.33 and ±40.0 cm. **13.** (Derivation). **15.** 30 cm. from lens. **17.** 11.30 diameters; 10.00 diameters; 113.0 diameters. **19.** (a) 60.0 cm. beyond second lens, (b) 30.0 cm. ahead of this lens. **21.** 5.26 and 100.4 in. **23.** −7.63 cm. **25.** 7.36 cm.

Chapter XXXVII

1. −50 cm.; −2 diopters. **3.** 14.38 and 9.71 cm. **5.** $f/14.1; f/19.8; f/27.8; f/40.3.$ **7.** 0.16 in. away from film. **9.** 113 mi. per hr. **11.** 10.74 ft. **13.** 25 diameters. **15.** 9.33 diameters. **17.** 88.2 diameters. **19.** 3.10 cm.; 5.00 mm.

Chapter XXXVIII

1. 0.040 cm.; 0.080 cm.; 0.120 cm. **3.** 0.172°. **5.** 0.0000139 cm. **7.** 7.80 mm. **9.** 9.88; 1.385; 0.0000106 cm. **11.** 6438 Å. **13.** 0.1464 cm., 0.2196 cm. **15.** 0.000820 cm. **17.** 0.00524 in. **19.** 3.46 × 10⁸ km. **21.** 0.711 Å.

Chapter XXXIX

1. 67.5°. **3.** 3.2°. **5.** (Sketch). **7.** 19.95°. **9.** 0.00327 cm.

Chapter XL

1. 1.23 Å. **3.** 4.0 × 10⁻¹⁰ erg. **5.** 8.94 × 10⁻¹⁴ erg; 0.607 Å. **7.** 0.21 per cent. **9.** (Chart). **11.** 28.3 × 10⁶ electron-volts. **13.** (Equation).

INDEX

i